A PATRON FOR PURE SCIENCE

The National Science Foundation's Formative Years, 1945-57

By J. Merton England

National Science Foundation
Washington, D.C.

Library of Congress Cataloging in Publication Data

England, J. Merton (James Merton), 1915-
 A patron for pure science.

 Bibliography: p. 423
 Includes index.
 1. National Science Foundation (U.S.)—History.
I. Title.
Q11 .N2949673E5   1982   353.0085'5   82-14368

NSF 82-24

A Patron for Pure Science

Contents

Preface and Acknowledgments   vii

PART I—*The Long Debate, 1945-50*

Introduction   3

1. Dr. Bush Writes a Report   9
2. Compromise Achieved   25
3. Division and Defeat   45
4. Veto   61
5. New Frontiers—Endless or Finite?   83

Looking Backward, 1950-1945   107

PART II—*Beginning, 1950-54*

6. Board and Director   113
7. "Welcome Aboard!"   129
8. Defining a Program—the 1952 Budget   141
9. Ways and Means of Administration   161
10. Evaluation and Policy   181

End of the Beginning   203

PART III—*Cold War Growth, 1954-57*

11. Men and Means   211
12. Quality and Quantity in Science Education   227
13. Little Science   255
14. Bigger Science   279
15. Policy for Science   311

How Firm a Foundation?   347

Appendixes
  1 Executive Order (10521) Concerning Government
    Scientific Research   353
  2 Peer Review in the Earth Sciences Program   357
  3 NSF Organizational Structure, 1950-57   363
Notes   367
Glossary of Abbreviations   421
Note on Unpublished Source Materials   423
Index   425

Preface and Acknowledgments

"Science seems so much simpler than its Machinery!" wrote a scientist worrying about taking an administrative position in the National Science Foundation in its early days. It is the way that machinery was built and worked in an independent federal agency that I have attempted to narrate and describe in this history. A legislative and administrative history of a federal institution during its formative years, this book does not discuss that institution's important achievement—the advancement of science—but I hope it will contribute to greater understanding of how the achievement was made.

When I began this work I expected to write a single-volume history of the National Science Foundation covering the thirty-year span from the time it was first proposed to the mid-1970s. Perhaps I should have stuck to that aim. Yet, many ideas and decisions that I first thought could be treated summarily—and perhaps could have been if I had been writing only for old NSF hands—later seemed to demand fuller explanation. Even so, I regret elisions of several matters that seem important to me.

I should say why I have included what many readers will consider excessive detail. As one who had spent years on a university campus before taking a government job, I was fascinated to learn something of how a federal agency works, how its dominant ideas and characteristics are formed, how its battles—internal and external—are won, lost, drawn, or put off till another year. Bureaucrats ceased being "faceless," and few of those who were my associates were drones. I am convinced that the society they serve should know more about their work. Also, my years at the Foundation, and especially the great turnover of the agency's staff and the new directions NSF has taken, have made me acutely conscious of its lack of an institutional memory. Although I have not intended this study as one for the edification of my colleagues, I hope they will find it instructive and useful.

About the organization of the book: Part I, "The Long Debate, 1945-50," narrates the legislative history of the Foundation's creation. Part II, "Beginning, 1950-54," discusses the appointment of NSF's first board, director, and staff; their early decisions on research and fellowship programs and means of administering them; and conflict over the agency's policy responsibility, culminating in a presidential order of March 17, 1954. Part III, "Cold War Growth, 1954-57," beginning approximately with the executive order and ending—again approximately—with the orbiting of the first Soviet Sputnik in October 1957, discusses NSF's expanding educational and research programs, including ventures into international cooperation, and the continuing effort to determine the Foundation's role in the making of national science policy.

Historians are too prone to detect "watersheds" as they scan the past's jumbled topography, but surely Sputnik I marks a divide between complacency and concern in Americans' attitudes toward their scientific and educational institutions. The Soviet feat furnished a convenient stopping place for this volume and a point of departure for a second volume, which I now expect to cover the years from Sputnik to June 30, 1969.

If the chronological divisions in this volume are fairly precise, some of the frequently used words are not. If pressed to define basic research, I would fall back on the brief description in Vannevar Bush's *Science—The Endless Frontier*: "Basic research is performed without thought of practical ends." I apologize for the use of other terms, such as "liberal" and "conservative," whose meaning has become increasingly dubious, and for my occasional references to a perhaps imaginary scientific "community" or scientific "establishment."

While in an apologetic mood, I also express regret to friends and colleagues, past and present, for not writing the kind of book many of them hoped for. Many fine NSF staff members and their important programs go unmentioned. I hope they understand that while they were not the intended audience for this book, their good works made NSF an institution worth explaining to a wider public.

Busy colleagues, most of them much more interested in the future than in the past, have generously helped me in the research and writing that have gone into this study. But they have never tried to control its content or interpretations. If the book bears marks of "court history," the fault is mine alone.

I cannot name all of the people who have assisted my research and writing, but a few deserve special thanks. First, three women, whose importance in the Foundation's work is not revealed in my narrative but who made my account possible: Doris McCarn, secretary to the first director (and all of his successors to 1980), who with a southern woman's sense of history vigilantly saved and carefully organized the records of his office and helped me in countless ways; Vernice Anderson, executive secretary of the National Science Board, who performed a similar service for history and for me with the records of the board; and Mildred C. Allen, a colleague with a keen understanding of what has enduring value, who when she retired gave me her thoughtfully culled collection of policy documents and publications, many of them the products of her own meticulous work.

I am indebted to a large number of readers of sections or chapters of the study in its early drafts. I wish to thank especially Dael Wolfle, who read all my chapters and gave me valuable advice and much needed encouragement. The late Louis Levin, whose critical ability I had come to admire and apprehend when he was my boss, read Parts II and III, as did my friend and colleague Nathan Kassack. Others who have given me helpful suggestions and saved me from embarrassing errors include: William E. Benson, Lee Anna Blick, Charles F. Brown, William D. Carey, Lyman Chalkley, Bowen C. Dees, Frank K. Edmondson, Estella K. Engel, Jerome H. Fregeau, William T. Golden, William J. Hoff, Gerald Holton, Walton M. Hudson, Daniel J. Kevles, Paul E. Klopsteg, Robert F. Maddox, Patrick M. Olmert, Don K. Price, Bertha W. Rubinstein, Oscar M. Ruebhausen, Irvin Stewart, C. E. Sunderlin, Barbara J. Tufty, Bethuel M. Webster, Carroll L. Wilson, John T. Wilson, and Albert T. Young.

Milton Lomask and I served each other as research assistants, in a sense, while he was working on his informal history of NSF, *A Minor Miracle*, and I was starting research on this volume. He was delightful company, and I am grateful for his continuing interest in my project.

My warm thanks go to my colleague Joyce E. Latham. Although she shares, to some extent, my distrust of modern technology—and did share my ignorance too—she bravely learned enough of the mystery of electronic printing to transform a much-revised typescript into a printed book. It would have been a better book if she had had an opportunity to edit the manuscript. Thanks also to the printing and reproduction staff of the Foundation who shepherded this work from manuscript to bound book, especially typesetter Edna James and designer Rizalino Jacob.

Finally, my greatest debt is to my secretary, Justine Burton, who carefully transcribed my notes and tape recordings, typed and read copy on many revisions of what must have seemed an endless task, checked quotations and citations, and most important, organized and indexed our historical files so that they should be a ready store of information for NSF staff members seeking precedents and a permanent resource for historians aiming to do a better job than I have done.

J. Merton England
NSF Historian

Part I:
The Long Debate, 1945-50

"Men only debate and question of the branch, not of the tree."
Montaigne

Introduction

The National Science Foundation honors Vannevar Bush as its Founding Father. His famous report, *Science—The Endless Frontier*, the result of a request from President Franklin Roosevelt, is the seminal document from which NSF traces its origin. This story of the agency's genesis largely follows the official hagiography. But in doing so it perhaps slights harbingers, now nearly forgotten at NSF, who held ideas quite different from Bush's about the purposes of a federal science agency.

Harley M. Kilgore, a liberal Democratic senator from West Virginia, first proposed the creation of a new science agency during World War II and first suggested the name National Science Foundation. His bills owed much to a physicist on the staff of his subcommittee on War Mobilization, Herbert Schimmel, whose beliefs about government and the economy had been shaped by personal hardships during the Great Depression and by what he saw, while war came, as the continuing failure of American industry to subordinate private profit-taking to the national interest. Kilgore and Schimmel wanted to draft science and technology into wartime public service. Meeting strong resistance from opponents of federal interference with business or science, they modified the coercive features of their legislation, gradually changing its primary intent from scientific and technical mobilization for prosecution of the war to the support, through a central coordinating agency, of science and technology for peacetime use by government and society.[1]

Especially in its later stages Kilgore's plan promised to ease the transition from war to peace, stimulate small business and industrial enterprises, and provide research money for pure science as well as applied. The huge wartime outlays for research and development would of course drop, but academic scientists need not worry about a return to their prewar penury.

The growing appeal to scientists of Kilgore's evolving legislation helped call forth Bush's conservative response.

The son of a Universalist minister, Bush had grown up near Boston, done his undergraduate work at Tufts College, and earned a doctorate in engineering given jointly by Harvard University and the Massachusetts Institute of Technology. After twenty years of teaching and administration at MIT, he accepted the presidency of the Carnegie Institution of Washington and moved to the national capital in 1939. He continued to hold that position while giving "part-time" service to the federal government throughout World War II from the Institution's administrative offices at 1530 P Street in Northwest Washington.

By 1939 the government was beginning to make faltering preparations for war. Bush, as chairman of the National Advisory Committee for Aeronautics, was soon drawn into the arrangements for national defense. He greatly admired NACA's organization, but its scope was too narrow to deal with the many defense needs that worried him and his associates. Over lunch at the Century Club in New York in May 1940, Bush and other members of the Committee on Scientific Aids to Learning—a small group created by the Carnegie Corporation but attached to the National Research Council—discussed the need to organize science for war. NACA's effective structure and the luncheon conversation of Bush and his fellows—James B. Conant, president of Harvard University, Frank B. Jewett, president of the National Academy of Sciences and chairman of the board of the Bell Telephone Laboratories, Bethuel M. Webster, a New York lawyer, and Irvin Stewart, the director of the committee—are credited with crystallizing an idea that Bush soon proposed to President Roosevelt.[2]

Through what seems an unlikely friendship with Harry Hopkins—the prince of New Dealers, whose social-reform notions were abhorrent to Bush, an idolater of Herbert Hoover—Bush managed to see the President and quickly got his approval for the establishment of the National Defense Research Committee (NDRC) in June 1940. Bush was named chairman of the new organization, which was directed to supplement the research of the army and navy on military weapons. Among those joining Bush as original members of NDRC were Karl T. Compton, president of MIT, and two of Bush's fellows on the Committee on Scientific Aids to Learning, Conant and Jewett. They are usually considered the "big four" of American civilian-controlled science during World War II. The committee that held its last meeting at the Century Club also furnished NDRC and its wartime successor with an able executive secretary, the political scientist Irvin Stewart.[3]

A year later NDRC became part of an organization of wider authority, the Office of Scientific Research and Development (OSRD). Headed by Bush, while Conant succeeded him in NDRC, the new agency was empowered not only to sponsor research on weapons of war, but also to fill the gap between research and procurement through the development of prototypes ready for production. The executive order establishing OSRD also brought under Bush's direction another important war resource by creating a Committee on Medical Research. As OSRD director, Bush had access to the President, becoming in effect his science adviser, and OSRD's placement in the Executive Office of the President added to the power which he showed no reluctance to wield.[4]

That kind of authority was necessary. Some generals and admirals resented civilian meddling in what they regarded as their affairs, but despite their occasional resistance, OSRD had outstanding success in bringing science, engineering, and medicine to bear on the conduct of the war. Many of the ablest academic scientists, whose lecture rooms and laboratories were depleted by the draft, found employment in military research, shifting from pursuit of knowledge for its own sake to means of applying it to defeat their country's enemies.[5]

While the war lasted, the feeling that they were serving a noble cause sustained pure scientists working for OSRD, but as its end came in sight most of them eagerly looked forward to getting back to teaching and *real* research. Bush knew that there was no possibility of keeping OSRD intact after the war, though he did want to devise some means of continuing long-range military research under civilian control.[6] And whether he planted the idea of a postwar agency of wider scope than one for military research or simply seized an opportunity suggested by a proposed letter from the President, his wartime experience convinced him that the integrity of science would not inevitably be compromised by federal subsidies for university research and that they would be needed to meet the nation's requirements for new knowledge.

The President's request and the report resulting from it set the stage for the long debate that ended with the creation of the National Science Foundation in 1950. Yet "ended" may not be the right word, since the issues around which the debate centered have continued to stir controversy. They relate to strongly held beliefs about the nature of knowledge and the means of applying it to social use, and to the authority and purposes of government. A brief preliminary examination of the polarizing issues may serve to clarify the chronological account of the five-year debate. The main issues were: patents, the social sciences, geographical distribution of federal research funds, basic research versus applied, and—most important—control of the foundation.

Kilgore's view was that patents resulting from government-supported research should become the property of the United States, freely available for use by all taxpayers, not the property of individuals or corporations who could exploit publicly paid-for discoveries for private gain. This conviction had been deepened by his service on Senator Harry S. Truman's special investigating committee, which revealed that patents held by international cartels had blocked preparations for war by American industry. The National Association of Manufacturers and various trade associations argued that Kilgore's patent policy would destroy individual initiative and socialize American industry. Bush disliked Kilgore's patent proposals, but his ideas also differed from those of representatives of big business. Bush hoped to develop a uniform government patent policy that would encourage and protect innovative small industries, and thus he opposed both the public ownership that Kilgore advocated and a policy that would allow monopolies to squeeze out emerging new competitors.[7] During the course of the long debate the issue lost its original intensity as proponents of the legislation pointed out that basic research was unlikely to generate patentable inventions. In the event, the act of 1950 sought to safeguard the rights of the inventor and of the public.

Kilgore's legislation provided support for the social sciences as well as the natural. The Bureau of the Budget and President Truman also favored inclusion of the social sciences. Bush deliberately omitted them (and the humanities) from the recommendations in his report, explaining their exclusion by saying that the President's letter had requested a report only on the medical and natural sciences; what his explanation ignored was that he had in effect written the letter. But Bush, much less rigid than some of his disciples, was willing to compromise on the issue, and the act of 1950, while not specifically naming the social sciences, provided for their possible inclusion in the Foundation's program.

Unlike his stand on patents and the social sciences, Bush enjoyed the backing of the Budget Bureau on the issue of geographic distribution of federal research money. Although justifying the extreme concentration of OSRD funds in a few universities and technical institutes on the ground of wartime exigency—the need to procure the best science from the best scientists quickly—he recognized the desirability of stimulating the building of new centers of scientific strength. Still, Bush's rather frugal estimates of appropriate postwar subsidies for basic research left little opportunity for institutional development. Again, however, he was willing to yield a little ground. Continuing to resist the pressure from land-grant and state university presidents and their congressional spokesmen to spread the wealth through formula distribution of research funds, he nevertheless acceded to the insertion in the legislation of words calling for the avoidance of "undue concentration." How much concentration was "undue" would remain an open question.

The most striking feature of the legislation based on Bush's report was that it created an agency dedicated to basic research—research "performed without thought of practical ends," in the words of the report. Despite the modification of Kilgore's bills to include assistance for fundamental science, a strong element of practicality remained in them, a purpose of applying science and technology to the solution of the nation's pressing problems. Members of Congress, generally ignorant of the subtle distinctions between basic (or fundamental or pure) research and applied research, understandably felt that expenditures of tax revenues must be for a clear purpose, to achieve some tangible result. This feeling lent some support to the move to include the social sciences in the agency's program, since however "unscientific" they might be, they were thought to be practical in purpose. Hearings and debates on foundation bills over five years did inform many senators about the nature of the agency they were creating, but probably only a few representatives ever understood it. If they had, the foundation's birth might have been even longer delayed. The belief that the agency did have a supremely practical purpose—the supplying of scientific and technical personnel and weaponry for national defense—probably did more than anything else to muster the votes needed for passage of the act of 1950.

The biggest issue of all concerned control of the foundation. Bush held that the agency's policies should be made by an authoritative board, appointed by the President but not connected with the government, whose members should name a full-time director responsible to them. Kilgore's legislation provided instead for an advisory board, and the Administration insisted that the foundation's director should be appointed by the President and be directly responsible to him. As those supporting the Bush report saw the matter, it was a question of who should direct science, scientists or politicians and bureaucrats? Their antagonists believed just as strongly that private persons should not control a public agency. Partisan conflict made the problem even more difficult to solve. The effort to resolve the issue of control is the principal burden of the following chapters on the National Science Foundation's legislative origin.

1
Dr. Bush Writes a Report

Writing on Pearl Harbor Day 1944, Palmer Putnam, who as a wartime scientist had turned his talents as engineer and yachtsman to developing amphibious vehicles, asked his friend Carroll Wilson a series of questions: "Please tell me what I may know about the background of the President's letter to Bush. Did Bush write it? Did Bush ask for it? . . . Is it welcome to Bush? Will he carry out the requested studies? Are they under way? By whom?"[1]

Wilson sent a prompt reply: "As to the President's letter to Bush, Bush did not write it nor did he ask for it, but he had the opportunity to see it before it was sent and made some suggestions which were incorporated. . . . Bush welcomes the letter and is now organizing studies to enable him to reply on the four numbered items." Wilson expected all four studies to be completed within two months.[2]

The letter they referred to was one from President Franklin D. Roosevelt to Vannevar Bush, director of the Office of Scientific Research and Development. After expressing his belief that OSRD's wartime experience might "be used in the days of peace ahead for the improvement of the national health, the creation of new enterprises bringing new jobs, and the betterment of the national standard of living," FDR asked for Bush's recommendations on four questions: (1) How can scientific knowledge developed during the war be released to the world quickly? (2) How can a program of medical research be organized to continue the attack on disease? (3) How can the government assist research by public and private organizations? (4) Can a program be suggested to develop the scientific talent of American youth to ensure high-quality research in the future?[3] As Wilson, who was Bush's executive assistant, said in his reply to Putnam, Bush quickly organized groups to help him make recommendations on these four matters.

Wilson's letter contradicts the general assumption that Bush originated the President's request. Perhaps Bush had suggested the idea and Wilson did not know, but worries about a possible return of the bread lines of the Great Depression may have had more to do with the letter's genesis than did concern for postwar support of science. At least there is evidence that the idea came from outside OSRD, and very likely from Oscar S. Cox, general counsel of the Foreign Economic Administration. Cox, who had worked closely with Bush in establishing the National Defense Research Committee and OSRD, reached agreement with Harry Hopkins several weeks before the November election that the President should call on Bush for a report. Cox's rough draft of the proposed letter, dated October 18, shows a concern simply "to utilize our war-time discoveries, research and development to create fuller peace-time employment." Bush was to "prepare and submit . . . a list of those discoveries which to your knowledge and judgment are likely to have ready peace-time application." This "inventory of ideas" would "stimulate thinking by enterprising business" and suggest the creation of new industries.[4]

The full-employment emphasis of Cox's draft was soon substantially broadened. After a meeting on October 24 of Bush, Cox, and Oscar M. Ruebhausen, OSRD's general counsel, Ruebhausen drafted another presidential request, which reflected ideas gleaned from talks he had with other OSRD officials—James B. Conant, Irvin Stewart, and Wilson. Several people helped shape and cut this version, and Hopkins adopted Bush and Conant's suggestion of a postelection release, but the letter signed by FDR on November 17 contained the substance of Ruebhausen's draft, including the four points which furnished the agenda for Bush's study.[5]

One reason for Bush's readiness to undertake the report was his worry about legislation sponsored by Senator Harley M. Kilgore. Since 1942 Kilgore had introduced and held hearings on bills to mobilize science and technology for more effective prosecution of the war and for application of science to national problems when peace came.[6] Bush had strongly opposed these bills, but he had also tried to guide Kilgore toward more acceptable measures.[7] Besides wanting to avoid antagonizing Kilgore to the point of not being asked for advice, Bush thought the senator was "honestly trying to get at the root of matters." Although "some of the people about him steer him into strange paths," Bush said, ". . . he himself may yet grasp the subject in a way that will be helpful rather than the reverse. He has certainly made some progress in the last two years, and I hope he makes a great deal more."[8]

Evidence of Kilgore's movement toward "a much more rational approach" came to Bush from New York scientists who attended a luncheon with the senator and his aide, Herbert Schimmel.[9] At the luncheon, Kilgore impressed William J. Robbins, director of the New York Botanical Garden, as "an earnest man" who needed "guidance and education." George B. Pegram, a Columbia University physicist, regretted the senator's obsession with patents, which got a lot of attention in the discussion, but said that Kilgore "seemed to agree most heartily . . . that the government should give support to research on fundamental scientific subjects in which questions of application were not involved." Pegram noted, however, that the senator's examples of research were invariably of the sort leading "to some directly useful results"—e.g., as Robbins mentioned, "the use of radio phones on passenger and freight trains . . . , the development of plants for obtaining magnesium, and so on."[10]

By the late spring of 1944 Kilgore had indeed made a good deal of progress in the eyes of several of Bush's associates. A new draft of his bill showed "a metamorphosis," according to Lyman Chalkley, an assistant to Bush. Karl T. Compton, chief of OSRD's Office of Field Service, found the bill "enormously better" and said he had a "decidedly favorable" reaction. Wilson, who said that Compton's letter "would make the Senator's heart glow," saw several objectionable features in the bill but also "enough alluring parts" to give it a chance of passage. The pressures following D-Day and the introduction of new German weapons kept Bush too busy to study the bill closely, but he did ask Chalkley to relay to the senator some preliminary observations. One of these dealt with the bill's patent clauses. Another expressed Bush's view that OSRD should not be perpetuated in peacetime. ("It is not democratic enough in organization for peacetime—the Director has too much autocratic power.")[11]

But if OSRD should not be perpetuated, Bush had come to favor some kind of postwar federal aid for university science. When he and Cox met on October 24, they agreed that an alternative to Kilgore's bill should be developed and that the proposed letter from the President offered an opportunity.[12] The fact that Kilgore and his staff continued to modify his legislation, which by this time provided for the creation of a "National Science Foundation" to sponsor basic research as well as applied research and development, must have given a sense of urgency to the generation of an alternative proposal, especially since Kilgore was actively seeking support from the science and engineering communities. A prompt, well-considered response to the President's letter would enable Bush to capture the initiative and shape a postwar organization more acceptable to leading scientists than the liberal senator was likely to devise.[13]

* * *

Bush believed that the first and fourth of the President's questions—those relating to release of new scientific knowledge and the education of future scientists—could be answered quickly. He realized it would be difficult to reach agreement on a postwar program for biomedical sciences, and much harder still to reconcile differences over government aid of research by public and private agencies.[14] If he shared Wilson's view that the four studies could be done in a couple of months, he was too optimistic. The problem of getting men who were deeply committed to the traditions of independence of scientific research to concede that some measure of public control must accompany public subsidy proved to be complicated and time consuming. Much of this resistance was still unresolved when Bush submitted his completed report to President Truman in June 1945. The aversion to public control shown by some of the scientists and medical men foreshadowed the dispute which held up the establishment of the National Science Foundation until five years after the submission of the report.

One of Bush's problems was his relation to the internal work of the committees. The report to the President was to be a personal one, yet its persuasiveness would depend largely on its general harmony with the backup studies. After clearing the committees' membership with Judge Samuel I. Rosenman, special counsel to the President, and getting Bureau of the Budget acknowledgment that the final report did not require the Bureau's approval, Bush expected to stay out of the study groups' deliberations. He knew that if he attended committee sessions, he would not be able to keep quiet; and since he wanted to "remain in the detached position of possible umpire," he should not be one of the players. He did believe, however, that he should bring to the attention of the chairmen important topics that their groups should address, and he did not hesitate to use this prerogative.[15]

The first question caused no difficulty. The committee, headed by Irvin Stewart, consisted entirely of OSRD officials. Early in January they submitted a report recommending, as Bush had already proposed, that a board be established in the National Academy of Sciences "to control the release and promote publication of certain scientific information." The board, to be made up of army, navy, and civilian members, should permit release of information as soon as it could not be used against the United States in the war. Scientists should be encouraged to publish promptly when the Academy board cleared the release of their research results, and government agencies should assist publication. The President's letter had emphasized the need to publish war-generated knowledge in order to encourage new enterprises and create jobs for returning veterans. Stewart's committee also pointed out that some servicemen would want to resume interrupted college training in science or engineering. That training should reflect the scientific and technological knowledge of 1945, not 1940.[16]

The Stewart group's brief suggestions about education were amplified in the report of the Committee on Discovery and Development of Scientific Talent.[17] Headed by Henry Allen Moe, secretary general of the John Simon Guggenheim Memorial Foundation, the committee that dealt with FDR's fourth question reached its decisions without much trouble, though after a good deal of correspondence and consultation. To ensure an adequate supply of scientists and engineers in the long-term future, but without robbing society of talent required for other needs, the committee proposed the annual award of 6,000 four-year undergraduate scholarships and 300 three-year graduate fellowships, the scholars to be chosen by state committees and the fellows through national competition. In both instances selection should be based solely on merit. Upon completing their education, scholars and fellows were to be enrolled in a National Science Reserve, subject to call into federal service during a national emergency.[18]

Moe's committee estimated that it would take a decade to fill the depleted ranks of scientists and engineers. Selective Service policies had largely caused the problem, but it was too late to remedy the actions of local draft boards. However, highly talented young men who had ended up in the armed services instead of college might be identified and ordered to enter scientific or engineering education in the United States while still in uniform. Since their number would probably be fewer than 100,000, their loss to the services following V-E Day would not matter greatly. For many other servicemen the plans of the U.S. Armed Forces Institute to establish overseas "universities" offered an opportunity for up-to-date technical training of a different sort.[19] Extension of the provisions of the recently enacted GI Bill of Rights would also help fill the manpower gap. The prospect of tough war veterans moving from battlefronts to college campuses caused the committee to issue a warning to institutions of higher learning: Forget academic rigidities. "It is a condition, not a theory, that confronts us and our judgment is that the Nation will lose much if our educational institutions do not recognize that many veterans will feel the need for making up for lost time, and help them make it up."[20]

* * *

The Committee on Science and the Public Welfare, formed to study government aid of research, was headed by Isaiah Bowman, president of Johns Hopkins University. Since Bowman was confined to his home with the grippe for several weeks and missed some of the committee's early sessions, much of the work of directing and coordinating its work fell on the vice-chairman, John T. Tate, research professor of physics at the

University of Minnesota, and the secretary, W. Rupert Maclaurin, an MIT economics professor. Bowman's illness may have led to more direct intervention by Bush in this panel's business than in that of the other committees, but Bush's intense interest in the subject matter would undoubtedly have caused lapses from his umpire role in any event.

Bush hoped that the research panel could open the way for applications of science by new industries. He wrote to Bowman that he would forward any constructive ideas he had on patent policy and that he hoped the committee would adopt a broad view of research that would encompass its crude beginnings in "pioneering effort of a technical sort," like that of the Wright brothers, which might bring "the advent of new, vigorous, small industrial units of all sorts."[21] Bush's temper flared when the committee ignored this suggestion. Since they did not think a "couple of bicycle mechanics working on a flying machine would . . . be doing research," maybe, he suggested, the panel should be enlarged to include members representing "the rugged type of thing that the Wright brothers exemplified."[22]

Bush's worries about the research panel were soon eased when it settled down to work and parceled out assignments to subcommittees. But patent policies continued to occupy his thoughts. He believed there should be a thorough legislative modernization of the patent system, one which would especially stimulate "the young struggling concern." Bush decided that he would assist Bowman's committee by attempting "to focus for them the relationship of the patent system to research."[23] Soon he determined to make patent recommendations on his own, separate from the committee report, but then President Truman directed Secretary of Commerce Henry A. Wallace to study the patent laws. Bush wrote to a friend: ". . . this quite effectively stops me from sending a separate patent report directly to the President . . . ."[24]

While studying the patent question, Bush also had to deal with an impatient Senator Kilgore on the one hand and perturbed members of the National Academy of Sciences on the other about the activities of the research committee. Kilgore was preparing to introduce the latest version of his bill and proposed to meet with representatives of OSRD and other government agencies for joint consideration of desirable revisions, though he first wanted an informal meeting with Bush. They met at a luncheon, and later members of Kilgore's staff talked with Bowman. All seemed harmonious, and the senator's men agreed that his bill should not be introduced for several weeks at least, by which time Bowman expected his committee members to reach agreement on their statement of purpose and social philosophy. Bush concluded that Kilgore was in a cooperative mood and would probably withhold his bill until after the report to the President had been released.[25]

If rumors of these friendly dealings reached the science establishment, they surely added to anxieties about the Bowman group's activities. Several members of the National Academy of Sciences, Frank B. Jewett wrote, had asked if there would be reports at the April meeting on the work of Bush's committees. Jewett complained: "I am so completely uninformed as to who the Committees are or what you have in mind that I do not know whether anything can or should be said." Bush replied that it would be inappropriate to discuss the report before its release by the White House, but he sought to reassure the Academy president. "I shall, of course," Bush wrote, "wish to have your own comments and reactions to the final document as it begins to take shape...."[26]

From Robert A. Millikan, Nobel laureate in physics of the California Institute of Technology, came a complaint about a "very unfortunate letter" from Maclaurin which raised the issue of federal subsidies to institutions of higher education. Millikan asked Bush whether the Policies Committee of the Academy should discuss this matter. "Knowing the position that you have taken on the Kilgore bill," Millikan said, "and on other movements toward collectivism, I could not understand how the Maclaurin letter could have been formulated by yourself or any of the other outstanding scientists to whom the President's inquiry was directed as to the need of federal subsidies for our most outstanding institutions, whether heretofore financed by private sources or from state funds."[27]

Bush replied that the committees would resolve questions for themselves without his interference, though he would not submit a report to the President with which he disagreed on a fundamental issue. He did not expect a dilemma of that sort to occur. Since Millikan had referred to his stand on Kilgore's bill, Bush said that "I have at no time opposed his main thesis," and he claimed credit for revisions that made the bill "much less objectionable." If research were subsidized by government after the war, there must not be any "stifling controls." Bush said that he had "not gone on record either for or against federal subsidy," but the government was already giving some support to higher education, and this seemed likely to increase. He was "not inclined to attempt to reverse the trend," he said. "However, if the strong committee which I have set up should take some other point of view, I am . . . still open-minded on the entire matter." Finally, Bush saw no objection to discussion of this issue by the Academy's Policies Committee, but the committee's agenda was already rather full.[28]

Bowman thought Bush's reply was "admirable." He did not intend to write the Caltech physicist himself but thought Millikan would calm down if he saw the research panel's statement of social philosophy.

This statement was very carefully drafted. It contains the best judgment of the committee. It is a deliberate judgment following wide differences of opinion at the beginning. It is a unanimous judgment. Without these few pages on social philosophy about half of the committee would be unwilling to sign our report. I would be among that half. We must express our fears regarding Federal control and we must state explicitly how we would avoid such control. Having done so, we are ready to present our recommendations regarding the scale of support and the method of distribution.[29]

The statement of "social philosophy" is the introductory chapter in the committee's report to Bush. It argues that since the nation's defense and welfare depend on the continued advance of science, the federal government must encourage scientific progress, not simply in its own laboratories but also in universities and other nonprofit institutions. It claims that America's remarkable achievements in applied science in the past depended on the importation of fundamental knowledge from Europe but that now Europe's "intellectual banks" have been ruined by war. In addition, a new direct relation between pure science and technological progress has developed. "In the next generation, technological advance and basic scientific discovery will be inseparable; a nation which borrows its basic knowledge will be hopelessly handicapped in the race for innovation." Despite dangers of centralized control, safeguards can be devised to keep science free—"free from the influence of pressure groups, free from the necessity of producing immediate practical results, free from dictation by any central board."[30]

The committee's main recommendation was that Congress establish an independent federal agency, a National Research Foundation, to promote scientific research and its applications. A board of part-time trustees, appointed by the President from nominees submitted by the National Academy of Sciences, was to control the Foundation and appoint its executive director.[31]

A board chosen from an Academy panel of names could he relied on to foster pure science and guard against the kinds of social uses and federal direction that conservatives feared would result from Kilgore's proposals. Bowman's group hoped that the transit of knowledge from the laboratory to products and services could be speeded up, but not through central planning and guidance of science.

* * *

The fear of government control was even greater among the members of Walter W. Palmer's Medical Advisory Committee. Palmer was a professor of medicine at Columbia University, and all his committee's members except Linus Pauling, a Caltech chemist, were medical school professors. Perhaps the normal desire of medical school faculties for free-standing autonomy within their university structures helps explain another of the committee's fixations—the need for a National Foundation for Medical Research that would be independent of the National Research Foundation recommended by Bowman's committee. The medical panel's persistent adherence to this notion caused headaches for Bush and his OSRD staff.

When the chairmen and secretaries of the four committees met in Bush's office early in March, it was revealed that Palmer's group wanted an independent foundation and that it had not even discussed its ideas with officials of the U.S. Public Health Service and the Surgeon Generals' offices of the army and navy.[32] The medical men wanted to avoid entanglement in science legislation which involved revision of patent and tax laws or "aid to small industry or alleviation of depressions," Homer W. Smith, the panel's secretary, wrote Carroll Wilson. "Medicine can not cure all the ills," he added. Smith asked for advice on nominating procedures. (The committee wanted to create an essentially self-perpetuating organization.) "Should we deprive the President of choice, by-pass the Academy entirely, or place the Academy simply in a screening position?" he asked.[33]

Wilson reminded Smith that other government agencies had important roles in medical research, and the committee's plan should be related to the existing structure. Wilson thought it was "unrealistic to expect the creation of another independent agency." With regard to appointments, the committee seemed to be attempting to contrive "a rubber stamp role" for the President and the Academy. "Certainly the President . . . cannot discharge his responsibility if he has no choice or selection in naming those to whom he delegates his authority, nor the power of removal," Wilson continued. In a note to Bush transmitting a copy of his letter, Wilson wrote: "This is my fatherly lecture. I trust I've not been too paternal." "Right on the button!" Bush responded.[34]

The "fatherly lecture" did not persuade the Medical Advisory Committee to abandon hope for an independent agency. Palmer admitted, however, that the idea might "be too idealistic and impracticable" and professed a willingness to have his committee consider an alternative plan which would protect "the independence so cherished by the Committee and the profession in general."[35] The secretary of another committee told Wilson that a foundation executive concerned with medical research "urges that Dr. Bush tell Palmer et al that their proposal for a separate agency is not acceptable and do so with considerable firmness."[36] Bush seems to have followed this advice, and he wrote Jewett that he had heard from Palmer "that the mechanism I propose is preferable to the one proposed by his committee."[37] A week later, after Bush had discussed his completed (but still in manuscript form) report with President Truman, Wilson wrote Palmer about the possibility of adding a footnote in page proof to the medical committee report, indicating that the committee accepted Bush's recommendation of a unitary research foundation rather than a separate agency for medicine. "Dr. Bush hopes that your committee will see fit to express such a view," Wilson said, "because I think it is important that the opposition which will undoubtedly arise in certain quarters is not given the opportunity of driving a wedge between your committee and Dr. Bush on this matter of mechanism."[38]

Prompted by this eleventh-hour plea, Palmer's group agreed to the insertion of a footnote in their recommendations. The footnote said that in proposing an independent medical foundation they had been unaware of the recommendations of the Bowman and Moe committees; they now recognized "the practical desirability of a single agency" and proposed a medical division as one of its components, "provided the Division is left free to carry out its program."[39] The footnote does not appear in the published report. Perhaps the proviso made it seem useless to Bush. In any event, in his own report Bush repeatedly said that all committees concurred in the recommendation of a single new agency.[40]

Whatever the degree of concurrence in a single agency for the natural and medical sciences, the published recommendation in the Palmer committee report shows the panel's desire for an autonomous and self-perpetuating medical research foundation. The foundation was to consist of a policy-making board of trustees, a technical board, and an executive secretary and administrative staff. The five trustees were to be "eminent scientists" appointed by the President; vacancies were to be filled, also by presidential appointment, from lists of candidates submitted by the chairman of the board after consultation with the president of the National Academy of Sciences. The trustees were then to appoint the twelve scientists of the technical board, who were to recommend the awarding of general research funds (block grants whose use could be determined by the recipient institutions), research fellowships, and special grants-in-aid of important research projects. The foundation was to have no direct links to the specialized medical services of other government agencies, which in turn were to exercise no control over the foundation. Although it was not to engage in research itself, the foundation "would initiate and coordinate research in existing institutions."[41]

* * *

Roosevelt's letter had asked Bush to give his answers to the four questions "as soon as convenient—reporting on each when you are ready, rather than waiting for completion of your studies in all."[42] Nevertheless, Bush decided to present a single report, with the four committee reports appended to it.

The job of overseeing the preparation of the general report and relating it to the recommendations of the committees fell mainly on Carroll Wilson and Oscar Ruebhausen. Bethuel M. Webster worked with the committee chairmen and secretaries in guiding their work toward a common goal, and with Wilson and Ruebhausen in writing drafts of the overall report.

Richardson Wood, who had been recommended to Bush by Eric Hodgins of Time, Inc., helped to apply polish and emphasis in the final stages. Another contributor to the final version was a Coast Guard lieutenant on loan from the Bureau of the Budget, Don K. Price, a political scientist, who collaborated with Wilson and Ruebhausen.[43] Finally of course it was Bush himself who made the hard choices, and it was his own report that went to President Truman. Much more aware of political realities and more flexible than were most of the members of his committees, Bush seems to have agreed, late in the drafting stage of the report, to a critical change that provided for presidential appointment of the foundation's director. But he then reverted in order to avoid a conflict with committee recommendations.

The critical point was public control. The Bowman committee proposals would have ensured a board dominated by scientists and a foundation director dominated by the board. Moreover, the committee, looking to the example of the British University Grants Committee, proposed that the foundation be given a half-billion dollar capitalization for a long-term expenditure without detailed Budget Bureau or congressional oversight.[44] Similarly, the medical committee wanted an agency that was immunized from presidential authority and political pressures.

Bush and his associates knew that the Administration would balk at accepting these recommendations. Carroll Wilson, after reading a May 20 draft report, suggested five fundamental principles that should characterize the proposed federal research agency. Although the final report contains a "Five Fundamentals" section, the degree of public control that it calls for is much less than in Wilson's statement, which emphasized that the agency "should adequately represent public interest"; its board "should be truly representative . . . and not composed primarily . . . from those groups which will be the recipients of support"; and while "Stability of support is essential, . . . this should come about through the sympathetic understanding and support of Congress and not through devices to lessen the full responsibility to Congress for the use of public funds."[45]

Bush endorsed most of Wilson's views and suggested adding that the agency "should be responsible to will of Congress." Apparently in response to the Bowman group's desire for freedom from budgetary and expenditure controls, he wrote: "No use to avoid the review of the Budget [Bureau]. In fact Budget & Congress must balance needs of this agency against those of Depts for their own research programs," with the assistance of an independent science advisory board. But Bush thought the draft showed that "we are getting pretty close to a finished job."[46]

A week later a near-final version of the overall report was sent to the committee members for their criticisms. Bush's covering letter said that a single agency was required, and in devising this "mechanism" he had drawn upon the best suggestions made by the four committees. Bush repeated verbatim the five principles that Wilson had said should characterize the agency. He asked that criticisms and comments be returned by June 6, the day before copy was due at the printer's.[47]

Most comments praised the report. The three New York members of the medical committee, for example, agreed on its excellence. Maclaurin liked Bush's suggestions on the foundation better than those made by Bowman's committee, of which he had been secretary. The Harvard astronomer Harlow Shapley, a member of the education panel, thought it was a "remarkably fine report"; as for the medical group's proposal of an independent agency for medical science, "we all knew all along that a unit mechanism would be inevitable and highly to be recommended. . . . we do not want to indicate dissension." But Shapley did not like the "abject kowtowing" to Congress and the Budget Bureau that appeared in the "Five Fundamentals" section. This was "undignifiedly subordinating scientists to politicians. The *will* of Congress sounds to me like the *whim* of Congress. You know, this sounds to me as if it were 'writ sarcastic' a bit. Some Congressmen could spot bootlicking, perhaps."[48] Bush and his colleagues accepted many of the suggestions for changes in a swift scissors-and-clip revision of the report.[49]

Bush also asked Jewett for a quick comment on the next-to-final draft. The Academy president wrote back that he had thought all along that Roosevelt's letter would start a "violent controversy," and after his hasty reading he still thought so. He was troubled in part by the report's format and style. Not only did Bush "hand down conclusions as those of final authority," but he did so with too much emphasis. "I think you weaken your case by italicized over-statement," Jewett wrote, "rather than by adopting the powerful English method, viz., that of the sweet reasonableness of understatement." Basically, though, Jewett objected to the report's assertion that federal funding of science was necessary. Why not try to revive the "fruitful stream" of private patronage "before plunging into the uncertain waters of the Federal tax pool"?[50]

Bush replied that he was essentially summarizing the recommendations of his capable committees and that he concurred with their conclusions. The fact that the Bowman panel had deliberated earnestly over the danger of federal control of university research and had finally come to a unanimous conclusion had resolved his own doubts. Since sending out his report, Bush wrote, "I have had no dissension on this particular point from anyone. . . . I have come to the conclusion that we are bound to go down this path . . . ."[51]

A few days later Jewett sent Bush three more observations: (1) Both the army and navy would oppose the mixing of peacetime military research and civil science. (Bush had recommended a civilian-controlled division for military research within the foundation.) (2) "Kilgore would be both delighted and disappointed in the report. Delighted that you subscribe in part at least to his philosophy. Disappointed that you fall far short of his ideas in the application of that philosophy." (3) Members of Congress would probably oppose the establishment of "any more new independent agencies." One congressman had told Jewett "We've got too damned many of them now."[52]

The document sent out for comment and suggestions specified that "The chief administrative officer of the Foundation should be a Director chosen by the Members and responsible to them." After the report had been mailed to committee members, however, an important change was entered on the "Master Copy" on which the modifications made as a result of the mailing were incorporated. The words "chosen by the Members and responsible to them" were stricken and "appointed by the President" was inserted in their stead.[53] Bush approved this change,[54] but it was fundamentally at odds with the recommendations of Bowman's and Palmer's committees. Since Bush wished to stress that he was summarizing the recommendations of his study groups and that he endorsed them, he must have decided to abandon the principle of presidential appointment of the director, after agreeing to it, because of its incompatibility with the committees' stand. Or he may have decided that the committees were right after all and that the change should be rescinded. At any rate he became committed to the idea of board control and held to it steadfastly thereafter.

* * *

On June 14 Bush met with President Truman for about fifteen minutes. The President had read and liked the report, Bush recorded, and gave his permission for its release. Judge Rosenman, with whom Bush talked about arrangements for releasing the report, said that the President would probably send a message to Congress with a recommendation after there had been some public reaction to the report.[55] The expected release of the report before the end of June ran into a snag in the Government Printing Office where appropriations printing took priority over everything else. It was not until July 19 that the White House made a public release of *Science— The Endless Frontier*.[56]

In a letter transmitting the report to the President, Bush said that he had interpreted FDR's questions as applying only to the natural sciences and medicine. His recommendation of a "single mechanism" was his only departure from the committees' proposals, but this now met their full approval.[57]

The report was carefully designed to build a case for a new federal agency which was to supplement the basic research resources of colleges, universities, and research institutes, support long-range research for the armed services, and administer a national program of science scholarships and fellowships. In addition, the proposed National Research Foundation "should develop and promote a national policy for scientific research and scientific education." The foundation

> should be composed of persons of broad interest and experience, having an understanding of the peculiarities of scientific research and scientific education. It should have stability of funds so that long-range programs may be undertaken. It should recognize that freedom of inquiry must be preserved and should leave internal control of policy, personnel, and the method and scope of research to the institutions in which it is carried on. It should be fully responsible to the President and through him to the Congress for its program.[58]

The policy-making body of the foundation—essentially a board, though not so called in the report—was to consist of a group of perhaps nine members, appointed by the President. They should not hold any other government positions, receive compensation other than expenses for their part-time services, or be eligible for immediate reappointment on the expiration of their four-year terms. They were to elect their own chairman and choose the foundation's director, who would administer the agency's business under their supervision.[59]

The members were to establish professional divisions and appoint their part-time members, aided by recommendations from the National Academy of Sciences. Five divisions—medical research, natural sciences, national defense, scientific personnel and education, and publications and scientific collaboration—were to be established at the outset. Each division was to have at least five members; on the division of national defense, in addition to the civilian members, there were to be two representatives designated by the secretaries of War and the Navy. Responsible to the members of the foundation, the divisions were to formulate their particular policies and programs, present budgets, assess the quality of the research they sponsored, and make recommendations on the allocation of research programs and other pertinent matters.[60]

Although Bush's effort to make an independent recommendation on patent policy had been frustrated, he did include a paragraph giving his views on patents. Obviously intending to counter Kilgore's aims, Bush said that the foundation should be allowed "discretion as to its patent policy in order that patent arrangements may be adjusted as circumstances and the public interest require."[61]

Not only were the members of the foundation and its divisions to be free to have private employment, but legislation was also to provide for special authority for the agency in other respects. Its research contracts or grants should not require competitive bidding, and the recipients of research contracts should not have to submit the detailed itemized vouchers normally required by the General Accounting Office.[62]

Rough budget estimates submitted by the committees furnished the basis for a table showing growth "in a healthy manner from modest beginnings." After five years, Bush expected, the foundation's operations should reach "a fairly stable level."[63]

	Millions of dollars	
Activity	First year	Fifth year
Division of Medical Research	$ 5.0	$ 20.0
Division of Natural Sciences	10.0	50.0
Division of National Defense	10.0	20.0
Division of Scientific Personnel and Education	7.0	29.0
Division of Publications and Scientific Collaboration	.5	1.0
Administration	1.0	2.5
Total	33.5	122.5

Finally, *Science—The Endless Frontier* urged congressional action:

"Legislation is necessary. It should be drafted with great care. Early action is imperative, however, if this nation is to meet the challenge of science and fully utilize the potentialities of science. On the wisdom with which we bring science to bear against the problems of the coming years depends in large measure our future as a nation."[64]

Bush had, in fact, already arranged for the drafting of legislation, and it was introduced in the House and Senate the very day his report was released.

2
Compromise Achieved

A week before the release of the Bush report Carroll Wilson talked with Congressman Wilbur D. Mills about a bill to establish a National Research Foundation. The draft measure, prepared under the guidance of Wilson and Oscar Ruebhausen, meshed perfectly with Bush's recommendations. The Democratic congressman suggested a few changes and, though he was going home to Arkansas to fish and relax for a while, arranged to have the bill introduced in the House on July 19, 1945. Warren G. Magnuson (D., Washington) planned to introduce the bill in the Senate the same day.[1]

Magnuson's introduction of the bill (S. 1285) angered Senator Kilgore, who thought he and Bush were still collaborating. Although Magnuson had told Kilgore two days before that he might introduce a science bill, Kilgore seems to have thought it would deal only with scholarships and fellowships. After weeks of pressing OSRD for drafting assistance, the surprised West Virginia senator now tried to get in touch with Bush, only to find that he was away from Washington and unreachable. "Consequently," Don Price informed a Budget Bureau associate, "Senator Kilgore considers himself doublecrossed and is mad as anything."[2] Four days later Kilgore introduced his own bill (S. 1297) to establish a National Science Foundation. Kilgore's anger was probably warranted. Presumably Bush had decided that the recommendations emerging from the committees working on his report differed too basically from Kilgore's ideas to make a compromise bill possible, and since he had decided to endorse those recommendations, independent legislative action was necessary.[3]

Actually the two bills were much alike. Both provided for the support of research in the natural sciences, medicine, and national defense matters, for science scholarships and fellowships, and for the publication of scientific information. Both were intended to assist the coordination of federal research and development activities and the making of national science policy. They differed mainly—and significantly—on organization and control of the foundation and on patent policy. Following Bush's recommendations S. 1285 provided for a controlling board of nine presidentially appointed members who would choose the agency's executive director and supervise his work. Kilgore's bill gave the President the right to appoint the director; an advisory board was to consist of the director as chairman, eight other government officials, and eight public members. Magnuson's bill left the control of patent policy to the foundation's governing board; Kilgore's provided that important discoveries resulting from all federally supported research would be United States property, to be patented by the government and licensed for nonexclusive use. Magnuson's bill was referred to a subcommittee, which he headed, of the Commerce Committee; Kilgore's to his subcommittee on War Mobilization of the Military Affairs Committee. During the summer arrangements were made for joint hearings on the two foundation bills and on S. 1248, legislation introduced by J. William Fulbright (D., Arkansas) to establish a Bureau of Scientific Research in the Department of Commerce.

On September 6 Truman included in a long message of legislative proposals a section on research in which he urged Congress to establish an agency to carry out the functions mentioned in the Magnuson and Kilgore bills.[4] Some of the President's suggestions disturbed backers of the Bush report, especially his advocacy of research support for the social sciences, which the Magnuson bill did not mention. The Kilgore bill's reference to "related economic and industrial studies" would have opened the door to some social science fields.[5] The President also said that the agency should "Coordinate and control diverse scientific activities now conducted by the several departments and agencies of the Federal Government." The Magnuson bill, besides directing the agency "to develop and promote a national policy for scientific research and scientific education," said that the foundation should "correlate" its programs with those of other government and private research organizations.

The joint hearings scheduled for October required a clearer statement of Administration views than the generalities of Truman's message to Congress. Although Bush had been able to bypass Director of the Budget Harold D. Smith in making his report to the President, now Smith and his Executive Office associates could interpose their objections to provisions of Magnuson's bill (and Kilgore's) that did not meet their standards of proper public policy. Smith outlined the Administration's position in a letter to Bush on October 1.[6]

Several weeks earlier Bush, as required by his position in the Administration, had asked for the Bureau's advice on his response to congressional requests for his views, but he urged preference for Magnuson's bill. He argued that the rigid patent provisions of Kilgore's bill would deny small industries the protection they needed. Though Magnuson's bill would ensure civilian control over military research, Kilgore's would put the military in a dominant position. Magnuson's bill met the test of the "Five Fundamentals" of *Science—The Endless Frontier*; Kilgore's did not. Early action on S. 1285 would permit a smooth transfer of OSRD functions to the new foundation and would make unnecessary the continuance of the Research Board for National Security (RBNS) in the National Academy of Sciences or its establishment as an independent agency, as proposed in legislation sponsored by Senator Harry F. Byrd (D., Virginia).[7]

Smith's response to Bush was drafted by Price in collaboration with James R. Newman of the Office of War Mobilization and Reconversion (OWMR), a lawyer, a brilliant popularizer of science and mathematics, and a principal author of the McMahon atomic energy bill. In interpreting Truman's message Smith laid down "the principle that science is fundamentally unitary, and must not be separated into tight compartments." Thus the President would not favor an independent agency charged only with military research (Byrd's proposed RBNS) or autonomous divisions or committees within the foundation (Kilgore's defense and medical committees) which would have final control over some segment of the agency's total program. A presidentially appointed director possessing "full administrative responsibility for the operation of the Foundation and its several divisions" was essential "to make the agency effectively responsible to the President and the Congress." The uncertainties resulting from Truman's remark about coordination of federal science programs were clarified—and the ominous word "control" interpreted away—by Smith's statement that the Kilgore bill's provisions met the President's needs; the foundation should have "the duty of maintaining a comprehensive survey of federally financed research and development activities, the authority to call on Federal agencies for whatever data and reports may be needed, and the responsibility for making to the President and to the agencies concerned recommendations with respect to such research and development activities." The foundation's coordinating role would not relieve other federal agencies of their research responsibilities. While Magnuson's bill provided various exemptions for the foundation from normal federal controls, Kilgore's allowed only freedom from advertising for bids on research contracts and some relaxation of Civil Service rules for the appointment of technical and professional employees. Smith insisted that any exemptions beyond those in Kilgore's bill required clear justification. With respect to the patent issue, Smith said Congress should ensure that the results of federally funded research would be made "fully, freely, and publicly available to commerce, industry, agriculture, and academic institutions."[8]

While helping to define the Administration position, Price and Newman also participated informally in an effort, organized by Herbert Schimmel, to write a "compromise" bill.[9] This move seems to have excluded Magnuson's aides. Now, according to an advocate of his bill, it was the Washington senator's turn to be surprised by the breakdown in cooperation:

> On October 4th, Senator Magnuson was summoned to the White House for a conference. On arriving, he found the President, Senator Kilgore, and Mr. [John W.] Snyder [head of OWMR] in possession of a new draft of a science bill, in regard to which the President expressed pleasure that the two senators had been able to find common ground for "compromise". Despite his political proximity to Senator Kilgore and despite continued friendly conferences between his staff and Senator Kilgore's, Senator Magnuson had not heard of any impending compromise. In astonishment, he replied that he concurred in the desire for a compromise and felt that one could be attained with further study, but that he would like an opportunity to examine the "compromise" before committing himself further.[10]

Nonetheless, the President told Harold Smith the following day that he thought the senators "were now in agreement and were going to develop a joint bill." Truman assured Smith that in his conversation with them "he had supported a director and an advisory committee, rather than a board, to administer the Research Foundation."[11]

* * *

Hearings on the legislation opened at 10 a.m., October 8, in Room 357 of the Senate Office Building.[12] Besides Kilgore, who presided, Magnuson and Fulbright were present at the opening session. They were flanked by two individuals whose rivalry and conflicting social and political ideas helped build personal antagonism between the groups they represented and made accommodation difficult. These two were Schimmel and John H. Teeter, an aide to Bush in OSRD who was now on loan to Senator Magnuson.

Senator Kilgore's opening statement described the differences between his and Magnuson's original measures and inserted in the record a "working draft" of an improved bill, that is, a new S. 1297. After discussing this revised bill and its differences from the earlier measures, Kilgore announced that Isaiah Bowman would be the first witness. Magnuson then interrupted and asked to make a statement. Magnuson said that the witnesses were not restricted in their testimony to the new S. 1297 but were free to refer to the earlier bills. The revision inserted in the record by Senator Kilgore was merely "work sheets." Magnuson said that he had not had an opportunity to see the committee print until a few days before, and there were some things in it that he might want to change.[13]

Bowman made it plain that he opposed central control of scientific research. He wished it were not necessary to have federal support of science at all, but wartime developments had shown that such support was essential. By no means, though, should the proposed National Research Foundation be formed along the lines of other government bureaus. "Do not," he pleaded, "open doors for untrained and worse than worthless employees who may creep into positions of control and attempt to pass themselves off as wise administrators who understand better than so-called fuzzy scientists how the job should be done."[14]

Bowman's lecture on bureaucrats and the danger of political control drew a stinging rebuke later in the hearings from Maury Maverick, head of the Smaller War Plants Corporation. A Texan who disliked academic pomposity as much as he did government "gobbledygook" (a word he brought into popular usage), Maverick said Bowman should "not be so smug." The American government was a political institution and public servants were just as pure as scientists. "I get a little tired of these hired hands of the monopolies and some of the professors, some of these bulldozing scientists, piously arrogating to themselves all the patriotism . . . . I get tired of their superior attitude," Maverick said. It was high time they began "to develop some social consciousness." He urged the senators to "get busy. Pass this bill. There is no time to waste." But it was Kilgore's bill, not Magnuson's, that he wanted.[15]

If Bowman represented the view of conservative academic scientists, the next witness, Nobel prizewinner Irving Langmuir of the General Electric Company, represented the industrial establishment. Langmuir emphasized the importance of privately owned patents and free enterprise to American industrial progress. He lamented the decline of the pioneering spirit in the United States just as Russia was beginning to incorporate many of the incentives of capitalism into its system. He attacked the patent provisions of the original Kilgore bill. Strongly objecting to a presidentially appointed director, Langmuir insisted that scientists needed to be in control.[16]

On the second day of the hearings Harlow Shapley suggested a return to Kilgore's earlier title for the new organization, National Science Foundation, rather than National Research Foundation, because science education in high schools badly needed updating and a broader title would encompass this objective. Also, smaller colleges and universities throughout the country needed to be encouraged. Although concentration of research grants in a few institutions was justified during the war, it would not be in peacetime. Shapley inclined to agree with other scientists that the board should appoint the director, but experts on administration—perhaps his son in the Budget Bureau—had told him "the other method would be better." The important thing was to "get competent men in this job." Shapley favored including the social sciences in the scope of the foundation but suggested that they be dropped if inclusion would prevent quick action on the legislation. At any rate, scholarships in the social sciences could be included from the start.[17]

Following Shapley, Howard A. Meyerhoff, executive secretary of the American Association for the Advancement of Science (AAAS), reported on a questionnaire which had been circulated to members of the AAAS council. The 163 replies, he said, represented the opinions of about 400 people. The respondents overwhelmingly favored federal support of the natural sciences, medicine and public health, and military research, and two-thirds favored support of the social sciences. Two out of three also believed that coordination of government research activities should be a primary function of the agency. Most indicated a fear of political control and expressed a strong preference for a board composed of scientists.[18]

Budget Director Smith was the first to present the Administration's views. He told the committee, "I feel it is my duty to keep the scientists from making a mistake in the field of public administration."[19] He insisted that "the most important principle involved in these bills is that an agency which is to control the spending of public funds in a great national program must be a part of the regular machinery of government. If the Government is to support scientific research, it should do so through its own responsible agency, not by delegating the control of the program and turning over the funds to any non-governmental organization."[20] The board should be advisory, not controlling, and there should he a single administrator, appointed and removable by the President. "On questions of judgment and policy," Smith said, "the only effective means of enforcing responsibility is the President's power of appointment and removal." Since board members were apt to be from institutions benefiting from the foundation's support, there would inevitably be suspicions, even if unwarranted, if they had administrative responsibility over the agency.[21]

The foundation could play a key role in federal science activities, Smith held, not in competition with other agencies but by encouraging exploration of the frontiers of knowledge and by coordinating government science programs. Expressing an idea that the Budget office would cling to with increasing frustration for years, Smith said:

The President, and the Bureau of the Budget in his Executive Office, need scientific advice on the balance of various research programs and their technical quality. The proposed foundation can fulfill a valuable function in supplying such advice. It will need to be given, either by statute or Executive order, authority to call on the scientific bureaus of the Government for information, and the duty of making recommendations to the department heads and the President on their programs. It should not be given coercive powers, for its function of coordination can be most effective if its authority does not conflict with that of the department heads, or encroach on that of the President himself.[22]

Though the foundation should allow substantial freedom of research, Smith told the senators, its support of research should be extended through specific contracts rather than general-purpose grants. He suggested that the agency be exempt from advertising for competitive bids for contracts but be otherwise subject to the normal procedures of government.[23] On patents he inclined toward the Kilgore view "that if Federal funds are to be used for the support of research, the results of such research should be devoted to the general public interest, and not to the exclusive profit of any individual or corporation."[24]

The Cabinet member best qualified to speak as a scientist, Henry A. Wallace, Secretary of Commerce, supported Kilgore in his testimony. Wallace favored including the social sciences in the scope of the foundation and the support of technological development as well as pure science. Inventions resulting from federal support should be secured to the public. There should be free exchange internationally of scientific information. "No nation," he said, "can hope to achieve or maintain a position of scientific leadership working in the isolation of security regulations and secrecy provisions."[25]

Discord within the executive branch soon became obvious. Vannevar Bush testified on October 15, two days after he had tried unsuccessfully to persuade the President to accept his version of the proposed science foundation. But Truman had given Bush a free hand to express his own views despite their variance from Administration policy.[26] Before the committee Bush argued for the Magnuson bill. OSRD's "autocratic form of organization was vital in a war emergency" but would be inappropriate for the sponsoring of "truly free and fundamental scientific research." The foundation's controlling board should not be made up only of scientists but should also contain eminent persons who understood the importance of science in public affairs. Bush would not object to the President's appointing federal officials to the board, but they should be appointed for their qualifications, not as spokesmen for their departments or agencies. He thought the foundation could in the long run provide an effective means of partnership between the natural and social sciences, but this should evolve as a "result of careful study by the foundation after its establishment."[27] He did not think the foundation should be asked to control the research programs of other agencies. Since the foundation would be supporting basic research rather than applied, it would seldom have to deal with patent questions; at any event, Bush contended, legislation dealing broadly with patent problems did not belong in the bill but should be a matter for separate consideration by House and Senate patent committees.[28]

Representatives of the War and Navy departments who followed Bush emphasized that they would have preferred a separate agency for military research—that is, the Research Board for National Security which had been wiped out by presidential order—but believed they could work effectively with the foundation. Since Secretary of War Robert P. Patterson indicated that he would take the advice of Bush, Karl Compton, and other scientists about the foundation's form of organization, Kilgore asked him if he disagreed with the President. Patterson said no. Kilgore then cited Smith's testimony. After some quibbling over whether Smith was quoting the President or stating his own opinion, Kilgore said he would find out later what the President's view was in order to remove any doubt on this point.[29] The following day, when spokesmen for the Navy department gave views similar to Patterson's, Kilgore entered in the record that he had got in touch with Smith after yesterday's session, and the Budget Director had confirmed that he was speaking for the President in his letter of October 1 to Bush. ". . . in this particular case," Kilgore said, "he cleared every phase of the letter with the President before he issued it, and particularly the phase on the President's opinion as to the director."[30]

The differences between Kilgore and Magnuson, reflective of those within the Administration, became obvious a few minutes later in an exchange between Kilgore and another witness, who said there seemed to be some question as to whether the substitute measure (the revised S. 1297) was a "joint" bill—that is, one representing the views of both Kilgore and Magnuson. Kilgore replied: "It was supposed to be when it was brought in here, but it has become evident that the joinder was not complete. It seems that one spouse wants a divorce."[31] Executive branch dissonance brought an unequivocal statement from Snyder of OWMR. "To clarify possible misunderstanding," since President Truman was concerned about "ambiguity" in the Administration's position, Snyder wrote to Kilgore and Magnuson reaffirming the views expressed in Smith's letters to Bush and other officials and endorsing the principles of the revised S. 1297.[32]

At times the intense interest in atomic energy legislation and the increasing dismay among some nuclear scientists that the May-Johnson bill was going to be rammed through Congress almost threw the Kilgore-Magnuson hearings off the track. Denied a hearing in the House, the nuclear scientists were given a forum by Kilgore at the suggestion of Schimmel and Barry Commoner, a biologist on detail from the navy to Kilgore's subcommittee. Before a large crowd in the Senate committee room they expressed their ideas on the control of atomic energy, and occasionally on a science foundation.[33] The leadoff witness—a vacillating endorser of the May-Johnson bill—was J. Robert Oppenheimer, who had brilliantly directed the work of atomic scientists at Los Alamos during the war. After reading a statement from Nobel prizewinner Enrico Fermi urging the abandonment of wartime regimentation and secrecy,[34] Oppenheimer similarly warned against letting the war's tight controls set a pattern for a peacetime science foundation. The work of academic scientists should not be overorganized; their judgment of what was worth doing should be trusted. He wanted to be sure that the committee knew that the purpose of the proposed foundation could not be interpreted as attacking the problems of peace just as OSRD had attacked the problems of war. "The trouble is that they are not the same problems," he said.[35] Representatives of the Association of Oak Ridge Scientists and the Association of Los Alamos Scientists also opposed secrecy and emphasized the difference between programmatic or directed research and fundamental research.[36] Later in the hearings Harry Grundfest, secretary of the American Association of Scientific Workers, deplored the "star-chamber regulations" that had featured the Manhattan Project.[37]

The third week of hearings began with a procession of men of medicine, all in favor of Magnuson's bill. Homer W. Smith's testimony included a tabulation of a poll of consultants to the Palmer committee, which he had served as secretary, showing overwhelming preference for S. 1285. Schimmel exposed the poll's lack of objectivity, since contrasting statements were specifically identified as Kilgore's views and Magnuson's, making their names a guide to the response.[38]

After the medical scientists came the biologists. They advocated a separation of their fields from the applied science of medicine. Detlev W. Bronk of the University of Pennsylvania suggested a single division of basic sciences, including biology, which would discover new knowledge and provide new ideas; other divisions—medicine, national defense, and natural resources—"directed to specific practical ends of national importance ... would translate the findings of the workers under the Division of Basic Sciences into practical usefulness."[39] Philip R. White of the Rockefeller Institute for Medical Research also wanted a basic sciences division but including medicine as a branch, even though medicine was a technology rather than a science. White did not believe it administratively feasible to have in the same organization a national defense division, with its inevitable secrecy requirements, and a basic sciences division, in which freedom from controls was essential. There should be "two entirely separate foundations."[40]

Social scientists had their day on October 29. A panel made up of two economists, a political scientist, a psychobiologist, a sociologist, and an anthropologist sought to convince the senators that research in their disciplines contributed to military strength and the health of social institutions. Thus Edwin G. Nourse of the Brookings Institution argued that an adequate defense hinges on the strength of the industrial system, for which an understanding of economic principles and practices is fundamental. William F. Ogburn, a University of Chicago sociologist who was a close student of technological innovations, testified that all important mechanical inventions inevitably precipitate social change and social problems. Consequently, a government that supports invention or discovery has a responsibility to support social science research to solve the resulting problems. A statement by Herbert Emmerich of the Public Administration Clearing House pointed to the dangers of "instruments" (the atomic bomb?) resulting from heavy emphasis on physical research without a counterbalance of "knowledge and skill in their proper control and utilization for the benefit of mankind." Private universities, he said, found it even more difficult to finance research in the social sciences than in the physical and medical.[41]

Support for the social scientists' cause came occasionally from other witnesses. Henry Allen Moe, for example, expressed his pleasure that President Truman's message of September 6 had asked for the inclusion of the social sciences, although they had been left out of the calculations of the Bush report panel which Moe had headed.[42] And although other engineers wanted to exclude the social sciences,[43] Abel Wolman, a sanitary engineer from Johns Hopkins, argued that they were needed to apply science to such practical problems as water and atmospheric pollution and disposal of solid waste.[44]

Although there had been frequent criticisms of the concentration of OSRD contracts in a few universities and technical institutes, neither Magnuson's bill nor Kilgore's contained any provision for wider institutional or geographic distribution of the foundation's research support. Scientists and administrators from the leading academic institutions generally wanted to avoid a prescription for disbursement according to formula, as had long been the practice of the Department of Agriculture in providing research funds to land-grant colleges. Karl Compton of MIT, arguing for Magnuson's bill, warned against any such arrangement in the science foundation; rather than distribute money indiscriminately among institutions, the foundation should adopt a strategy of "pin-point bombing" on selected objectives.[45] But Edmund E. Day, president of Cornell University, testifying for the Association of Land-Grant Colleges and Universities and the National Association of State Universities, urged that 30 percent of the foundation's funds be allocated among the states according to population and then disbursed by land-grant and other tax-supported institutions.[46] Reflecting on his testimony a week later, he thought that his remarks had not particularly moved the committee members.[47] Nonetheless, Kilgore's revised bill introduced later in the year (S. 1720) provided for formula distribution of one-fourth of the foundation's research funds.

The hearings finally droned to an end the afternoon of November 2, with no senators present but with Teeter chairing the session. Throughout the twenty days of hearings the senators had been buffeted by conflicting and repetitious testimony, much of it designed to promote or protect some special interest. Thus an engineering spokesman complained that "neither of the bills even deigns to mention engineering science,"[48] and guardians of the Office of Education tried to limit the foundation's responsibilities in education.[49] Yet, despite arguments over these matters and the more controversial ones of organization and control, patent policy, and inclusion of the social sciences, the distinguished cast of witnesses overwhelmingly endorsed the establishment of a science foundation. Discounting several spear carriers who came to back up their chiefs, about one hundred persons testified—all of them male and, one suspects, all white. Their enthusiasm for a science foundation and their views of what it should do differed greatly, but the record indicates that ninety-nine of the hundred were in the fold.

One remained defiantly astray. The unregenerate was Bush's friend and wartime associate Frank Jewett. Jewett admitted that OSRD had been necessary, and he was proud of his part in its success. But, he said, "Any program of science for the future . . . patterned on OSRD is doomed to essential failure." Though scientists during the war had patriotically developed weapons and abandoned the quest for new knowledge, now they wanted to do fundamental science again.[50] Private initiative should furnish the means for their important work. Jewett continued:

Every direct or indirect subvention by Government is not only coupled inevitably with bureaucratic types of control, but likewise with political control and with the urge to create pressure groups seeking to advance special interests. I feel strongly, therefore, that every proposal to inject Government into the operational affairs of our daily lives should be examined most carefully and adopted only when it is clear that it is the only way the desired objective can be attained.

The enactment of either Kilgore's bill or Magnuson's would "be a radical departure from the normal American way." Perhaps, Jewett acknowledged, "conditions have so changed permanently that we must abandon the old way which depended on the voluntary action of free men operating in the thousand and one ways that men choose and turn to the State for a large part of the support of science, through a politically controlled agency." Perhaps, but he did not believe it.[51]

If Jewett's words were resonant of the conflicts between rugged individualism and the New Deal of the 1930s, those of the following witness forecast the struggles of the Cold War. The Reverend J. Hugh O'Donnell, president of the University of Notre Dame, told the senators that only the military phase of World War II was over. Now would come the war of opposing philosophies—American freedom versus communism. A science foundation was essential for maintaining national strength in this polarized world.[52]

Jewett's opposition to a foundation may have been unique, but many shared his dread of political interference with scientists' freedom. For some of the atomic scientists, who, in Oppenheimer's words, had "known sin,"[53] the fear was of military domination of science with accompanying requirements of compartmentalization and secrecy that had been so irksome during the war. Others, of conservative political and economic views, were haunted by the specter of a revived New Deal in which science would become a tool for federal planners. They saw Kilgore and his assistants as the American counterparts of the Marxist J. D. Bernal, whose book *The Social Function of Science* (1939) had caused British scientists to fear that he wanted "to dragoon [them] into work which they would not necessarily want to undertake, in the pursuit of ends of which they would not approve."[54] Their anxiety rose when they heard testimony like that of an elderly former New Deal official, Morris L. Cooke, representing the Independent Citizens Committee of the Arts, Sciences, and Professions: "We favor the coordination of all Government-financed research whether in private or public institutions by a National Science Foundation in order to further efficient planning and the most comprehensive use of facilities."[55] Substitute "business" for "science" and the statements of conservative scientists would have been almost interchangeable with those issuing from manufacturing and trade associations demanding the end of price controls and the return of a "free market." And probably in part because they linked planning and government controls with social science, the natural scientists and engineers who testified were generally reluctant to include the social disciplines in the foundation.

Opening the final day of hearings, James B. Conant said: "If the proposals before you become law and Congress appropriates the money, we will see a flowering of scientific work in this country the like of which the world has never seen before."[56] The nearly twelve hundred pages of testimony and statements built a strong case for a national science foundation to make Conant's dream of a springtime for science a reality. But owing to the climate of politics the dream was to be long deferred.

* * *

The strong line taken by the Administration in favor of a presidentially appointed administrator for the foundation alarmed some of the scientists who had been supporting the Magnuson bill. On November 14, shortly after the hearings ended, Isaiah Bowman issued a call to a number of persons to discuss ways of supporting the Bush proposal. The meeting brought into existence a Committee Supporting the Bush Report, which sent a stiff letter to the President:

We are in favor of a responsible board composed of laymen and scientists appointed by the President on the basis of interest and capacity, with a full time administrator appointed by and responsible to the board. We are opposed to mandatory provision for *ex-officio* members either of the board or of the professional divisions. The board should not be empowered to control or coordinate other Government scientific agencies, although effective liaison should be established and maintained. This legislation should contain no provision respecting patents or the social sciences.

The forty-three men who signed this letter, headed by Bowman as chairman of the committee, insisted that they spoke for "the great majority of American scientists."[57]

To ensure that the letter would be "properly interpreted" by the President, Bowman sent a telegram to Truman's press secretary, Charles Ross:

A tidal wave of protest by American scientists against the Kilgore bill has been recognized by a large and representative group which will report by open letter to President Truman tomorrow. I have been requested to inform the President that the letter is addressed to him because we believe that the initiative respecting legislation to implement the Bush report should be put back into his hands.

On the whole the Magnuson bill expresses the indispensable principles emphasized in the Bush report. The Kilgore bill makes possible political control and thereby endangers the future of scientific research so important to national security.[58]

In a phone conversation Bowman told Ross that the steering committee of the Committee Supporting the Bush Report thought "that it was very much better to channel the protest of scientific men and associations than to let screams arise from all quarters which could only create confusion in the minds of the public, of Congress, and the President. Unless the protests were coordinated, put into reasoned form and attached to practical suggestions, we were not likely to find our way out of the present deplorable situation." Bowman had heard that Kilgore was going to call on Truman, and the committee wanted the President to direct the legislative effort rather than let it be controlled by the West Virginia senator. According to Bowman's wishful interpretation of the conversation, "Mr. Ross listened to all this and commented upon it sympathetically. . . . I gained the impression that he was genuinely grateful on his own behalf and on behalf of the President for the orderly and timely presentation of the country-wide protest that we have tried to express."[59]

The full text of the letter and the list of signers appeared in the New York *Times* November 27, 1945. The following day Budget Director Smith saw the President and recorded in his diary: "I brought to the attention of the President the current propaganda of the scientists against his position in favor of a single administrator for the research foundation and I inquired as to whether he had altered his views in any way. The President replied in most positive language that he had not and that he did not propose to do so."[60]

Truman replied to Bowman's letter on December 20. He stated bluntly that his views on science legislation had been given by Harold Smith and John Snyder, and he was confident that the Bowman committee's "basic objectives of freedom of research, and non-partisan administration of a program of aid to scientific research and education, will be attained under such an organization as I have recommended."[61]

Jewett had predicted that the Bowman committee would stir up a "Kilkenny cat fight."[62] That prediction seemed warranted in view of the uncompromising language of the Bowman group's letter and Truman's unequivocal reply. Bowman's committee soon collected many more endorsements as scientific groups met and, like the New York section of the American Chemical Society, "approved without reservations the principles expressed" in the letter.[63] Other scientists, more concerned about getting a national science foundation under way without necessarily sticking to the exact terms of the Bush report, organized a Committee for a National Science Foundation late in December. Leaders in this move were Shapley and Nobel laureate Harold C. Urey, both of whom were regarded suspiciously by conservatives because of their participation in the Independent Citizens Committee of the Arts, Sciences, and Professions, a liberal group heavily sprinkled with Communists.[64]

But if there were increasing signs of polarization, there were also important movements toward compromise under way late in 1945. Kilgore himself, in preparing a revised bill, broached the subject of a possible compromise by which the foundation's administrator would be appointed by the President only after nomination by the members of the advisory board. Price told Schimmel that he thought this would be the same as a board "appointment of the Administrator . . . and would be contrary to the interests of the President and our whole constitutional practice." Harold Smith told Price to let Kilgore know that there was no need to compromise; besides, "such a provision may be unconstitutional as a restriction on [the President's] appointing power."[65]

Other voices urging compromise and suggesting new ideas for a science foundation were also beginning to be raised toward the end of the year. President Day of Cornell phoned Bowman to suggest that a board different from that proposed by the Kilgore bill but still somewhat in line with the ideas of the Administration might be desirable. As he had in his testimony, Day urged that a percentage of the foundation's research funds be earmarked for geographical distribution. Perhaps because of the rigid terms of the Bowman committee's letter, Day sought to convince the Johns Hopkins president "that scientists alone cannot put this thing across. We need the help of men in Congress who see the problem." Proponents of a foundation "should work for a reasonable set-up with reasonable safeguards against Federal control and with reasonable compromise or modification in the direction . . . of a Board of laymen authorized to make an independent report to the President." Day warned that there might be "a counter movement stimulated possibly by Schimmel and spearheaded by Urey and Shapley and a group of social scientists."[66]

Bowman was obviously worried about Shapley's loyalty to the cause. A few days after Day's call he wrote the Harvard astronomer expressing regret that Shapley had not been able to attend a meeting of the Committee Supporting the Bush Report. The group hoped to achieve "unanimous action so as not to weaken the case by divided opinions that offer the politician a golden opportunity to do his stuff. There is wire pulling and confusion as well as partisanship in the Washington end of this business. We should not stimulate these tendencies by divisions among ourselves." The now three hundred signers of the letter, Bowman wrote, represented "many thousand more scientists." Undoubtedly their influence on senators would be great. Bowman reported that Kilgore had accepted the view of the Committee Supporting the Bush Report "except on one important matter, that of one-man control to which he adheres and which we resist. We believe that our movement is irresistible and that only negligence or division on the part of scientists will halt this legislation or set it up in an undesirable way."[67]

* * *

While the Bowman committee continued to garner signatures, Kilgore and his aides completed their drafting of a revised bill, introduced on December 21 as S. 1720. The measure incorporated a number of suggestions proposed in the hearings and made some concessions to the opposing camp. Nonetheless, the administrator was to be appointed by the President and was to be advised by a board of nine members, also appointed by the President; besides these nine, the board would include the chairmen of the several divisional scientific committees of the foundation. Eight divisions were specified in the legislation: mathematical and physical sciences, biological sciences, social sciences, health and medical sciences, national defense, engineering and technology, scientific personnel and education, and publications and information. In addition, the administrator was authorized to create as many as three other divisions. The campaign of state universities and land-grant colleges for geographic distribution had succeeded: a quarter of the foundation's research funds was to be distributed by a formula—two-fifths to be divided among the states equally, the remainder in accordance with population; only tax-supported institutions were to be entitled to these funds. Another 25 percent of the research funds would be restricted to nonprofit institutions, including private colleges and universities, but not subject to state quotas. At least 15 percent of the foundation's research money should be spent for research for national defense and 15 percent for research in health and medical sciences. (These minimum percentages had been set at 20 in Kilgore's earlier bills.)

Kilgore's bill again sought to establish a government-wide patent policy but was less rigorous on public ownership of patents. An escape clause carefully prescribed conditions under which patents might be held by the contractor or inventor; the most important condition was that the patent had "been developed substantially as the result of earlier research or development activities of the contractor which were not federally financed." Joining Kilgore in sponsoring the bill were Senators Fulbright, Leverett Saltonstall (R., Massachusetts), Edwin C. Johnson (D., Colorado), and Claude D. Pepper (D., Florida). Magnuson had not committed himself to the measure.

Describing the bill in *Science*, Howard Meyerhoff said that it was "a serious endeavor to meet the demand of the majority of the scientists by setting up a board of qualified men and by making this board a check and balance to the administrator, without nullifying the latter's responsibility to the President and the Congress."[68] The same issue of *Science* printed a statement issued on December 28 by the Committee for a National Science Foundation, which had been formed by Urey and Shapley, saying that although there was serious disagreement over the question of a governing board or a single administrator, "it should be possible to devise a plan of organization which will meet the major objections to either alternative." Among the signers were such luminaries as Einstein, Fermi, and Oppenheimer.[69]

The Bowman committee meanwhile sought ways to bring the legislation more in line with the Bush proposals. Since Bush was preparing to have a bargaining session with Kilgore, he wanted a clear expression of the committee's views. Homer Smith sent all committee members an "Emergency Memorandum of Utmost Importance," which said that Bush and Magnuson had agreed that they would present four propositions to Kilgore: (1) the board "would have the right to submit a panel of nominations to the President for the office of administrator"; (2) the patent provisions now in S. 1720 would be further modified; (3) the provision for distribution of 25 percent of the foundation's research funds to tax-supported colleges and universities "would be replaced by a statement of principle intended to insure geographical distribution"; (4) support for the social sciences, at least in the beginning, "would be limited to scholarships and fellowships." Smith understood that Bush would support the bill if Kilgore accepted these provisions. Smith said that the committee's Washington office did not believe it possible to pass a bill giving policy-making powers to a part-time board, and that Magnuson "is not prepared to fight against the President's desire for a full-time administrator and a straight-line organization." Members of the Bowman committee would have to decide whether to go along with these modifications of the original Magnuson bill if Kilgore agreed to them, or work "to defeat the bill on the ground that it is dangerous and unsatisfactory."[70]

Bowman received his copy of Smith's memorandum on January 15. The next day he went to Washington to talk with Bush before their meeting with Senators Kilgore, Magnuson, and Elbert D. Thomas (D., Utah), chairman of the Committee on Military Affairs. Smith was also present at the preliminary meeting with Bush. Bush "dressed down Smith" for some of his statements in the "Emergency Memorandum" and indicated that it "was a stupid thing" to make them—a harsh but accurate assessment as shown a little later in the afternoon.

Following their conference Bush and Bowman went to Senator Thomas's office. Bowman describes what occurred: "Presently Kilgore and Magnuson came in. Kilgore had been accompanied to the door of Thomas' room by his office staff and evidently they told him to come in with both fists flying. He made a holy show of himself. Mad as a wet hen, he attacked Magnuson in particular, then Bush, then Homer Smith, and so on." Kilgore had obtained that morning a copy of the "Emergency Memorandum." He was especially irritated by a statement that it might be necessary to "bring further pressure" on him. "He imputed bad faith and behind-the-back actions to Magnuson and Bush. Thomas tried to break in but failed. Nothing could stop him. I tried several times and gave up. He had to throw himself around and work off his anger before we could get down to business." At length, though, he did agree to some of the views expressed by Bush and Bowman and suggested that Magnuson be a cosponsor of a revised bill. The group agreed to meet a week later. Bowman recorded that "as we left the room Thomas spoke to Bush and myself and said, 'You fellows may not know it but you have won a victory.' The point was that Kilgore was himself defeated and by a great show of anger recovered his face."[71]

Riding on the train back to Baltimore with Smith and Bethuel Webster, Bowman told them about the conference with Bush and the senators. They agreed that the letter to President Truman should be publicized again the next day and that the news lead should emphasize that there were now five thousand signers. "Kilgore will not like this," Bowman wrote, "but we must keep the pressure on him." Bowman cautioned Smith against sending out any more memoranda that might fall into Kilgore's hands. "He should make no more revelations of tactics and make no mention of Kilgore. He agreed to this." Bowman also recorded that Bush was very satisfied with the result of the meeting with the senators.[72]

A week later Bush and Bowman met again with Kilgore, Magnuson, and Thomas. Senators Fulbright and Saltonstall were also present, as was Schimmel. This time Kilgore kept his temper, and the group made significant progress toward compromise on the questions of patents, the social sciences, and the administrator's relation to the board. On the key problem of administration, Bowman wrote, "Kilgore held out until the last..., his arguments growing weaker and Schimmel obviously nervous," but Bush warned that there would be no bill without a change. Then Saltonstall suggested a modification and "Kilgore surrendered."[73] A quite different interpretation was that "the individual concessions by Senator Kilgore were minor ones designed to save the faces of the opposite parties." Even so, Price thought they might result in giving the board too much control, and he prevailed on Schimmel to make some revisions in drafting the compromise bill. Although Price did not think the matter serious "enough to justify holding up legislation," he did "not want to see Senator Kilgore give in on it if he can be persuaded not to."[74]

But Bowman and Bush thought they had accomplished more than they had reason to hope for. As Bush assessed the conference, "things went pretty well.... If we get a decent patent clause I think the job is done. We will have to have a mild geographical distribution clause, and on the whole I think it is just as well if it is held in reason—as a rock the Board can lean on under pressure. Also I think we have to let the social sciences get a nose under the tent—to the extent we agreed on." Bush asked his secretary to tell Bradley Dewey, an industrial chemist who was president of the American Chemical Society, "that while he and his group need to remain in a position to squawk or block, I think we are going to get all we can expect ...." To this optimistic estimate Bush added a prophetic reflection: since he had not given assurances that scientific groups would approve the compromise decisions, "they will still be in a position to push things further in our direction in the House."[75]

* * *

Despite Bush's satisfaction, he had not succeeded in arranging for board control of the foundation's administrator and program. Meyerhoff—soon to replace Schimmel as the *bête noire* of Bowman and company—wrote in *Science* that the Committee Supporting the Bush Report had "recognized that the President cannot be restricted in his appointive powers and is satisfied that a strong board which may submit nominations for the post of Administrator, and which can check or balance the Administrator at crucial times, will adequately protect scientists from possible political control or domination."[76] A week later he reported that Saltonstall had presided over a meeting where "Complete accord was effected on every issue." Meyerhoff praised the revised S. 1720 (shortly to be introduced as S. 1850) as "a document which combines sound scientific thinking with sagacious political realism and to which scientists can unhesitatingly lend their support."[77] Although Senator Raymond E. Willis

(R., Indiana) had muddied the waters by introducing a bill (S. 1777), instigated by Jewett, providing for "a self-perpetuating committee of 50" to administer a limited research program under National Academy of Sciences guidance, Meyerhoff thought prospects for Senate passage of the compromise bill were fairly good. The economy-minded House, however, uninformed and uninterested in science legislation, needed to be educated by letters, telegrams, and personal calls from scientists.[78]

The compromise bill, S. 1850, sponsored by Kilgore, Magnuson, and other senators from both parties, was introduced on February 21 and referred to the Committee on Military Affairs. On the central issue of control, the bill provided for a presidentially appointed administrator and an advisory board; the President was to "consult with and receive recommendations" from the board before making the appointment. No term of office was specified for the administrator, and he would be removable by the President. The President was also to appoint nine board members, and joining them on the advisory body would be the chairmen of the foundation's divisional scientific committees. Although the administrator was to appoint the members of divisional committees, with the board's advice and approval, the committees, like the board itself, were to choose their own chairmen. Eight divisions were named in the bill, but the administrator was authorized to establish as many as three more.

One of the named divisions was Social Sciences. Here the Bush-Bowman conferees gained a concession, since the division was to be limited at first "to studies of the impact of scientific discovery on the general welfare and studies required in connection with other projects supported by the Foundation." Similarly they managed to ease some restrictions in the patents and inventions section, though it still provided for a government-wide policy of dedicating to public use any patents resulting from federally financed research. Other modifications were designed to bolster the independence of the board and give it direct access to Congress and the President. But instead of the "mild geographical distribution clause" that Bush had anticipated, the 25 percent formula backed by the land-grant and state universities associations remained. The ultimate bill, which had seemingly won general assent, was fundamentally the same as the one Kilgore had introduced in December following the hearings.

VANNEVAR BUSH
(Courtesy Massachusetts Institute of Technology)

ISAIAH BOWMAN
(Courtesy Johns Hopkins University)

BETHUEL M. WEBSTER

CARROLL L. WILSON
(Courtesy U.S. Department of Energy)

SHAPERS OF *Science—The Endless Frontier*

HARLEY M. KILGORE

WARREN G. MAGNUSON

H. ALEXANDER SMITH

SENATE ADVOCATES
(all Courtesy Senate Historical Office)

FRANK B. JEWETT
(Courtesy National Academy of Sciences)

HERBERT SCHIMMEL

HOWARD A. MEYERHOFF

JOHN H. TEETER
(photo by Underwood and Underwood, Washington, D.C.)

KINDLERS OF CONTROVERSY

EDMUND E. DAY
(Courtesy Cornell University News Bureau)

HARLOW SHAPLEY
(Courtesy American Association for the Advancement of Science)

RUSSELL I. THACKREY

DAEL WOLFLE

INTER-SOCIETY AND LAND-GRANT ADVOCATES

3
Division and Defeat

With the introduction of the joint Kilgore-Magnuson bill (S. 1850) in February 1946 the rift between the two groups of scientists and their cohorts had apparently been closed. The task before them now was to persuade Congress to take action before its mild interest in a science foundation evaporated in the heat of re-election campaigns. In the Senate the bill had to compete with much more exciting legislative matters—atomic energy, restrictions on labor unions, price controls, draft extension, and a loan to Britain. The House was expected to mark time until the Senate passed the compromise bill. Unless the Senate approved it in the spring there was little likelihood of favorable House action in the Seventy-Ninth Congress, and certainly not unless the scientists' united front remained intact. But Senate passage came late, and by then scientists were squabbling again.

Even as Howard Meyerhoff hailed the accord on a joint bill, his words annoyed some thin-skinned adversaries. He called the Committee Supporting the Bush Report a "rather miscellaneous group,"[1] a characterization that immediately irritated Isaiah Bowman and continued to.[2] And not only Bowman's correspondence showed the persistence of distrust and animosity. Frank Jewett of course had never liked the compromise bill—or any bill except the one that Senator Raymond E. Willis had introduced for him—and he continued his efforts to wreck it. Writing to Bush he quoted a letter he had received from a friend on Capitol Hill:

> Senator Kilgore's left-wing staff is already making plans to take over and "guide" the work of the Foundation. They have launched a study to "plan a science program for the United States."

If the scientists don't awaken to their danger, this group will be able to have their way. S. 1850 is the perfect vehicle to socialize and nationalize a large and independent section of our economy.[3]

In another letter Jewett complained about Harlow Shapley's sending a telegram to all chapters of Sigma Xi, an honorary science society of which Shapley was president, asking them to push for enactment of S. 1850 without amendments. This was an abuse of office, Jewett thought, but he took a sardonic relish in observing scientists venturing into politics: "... I can't help but be a bit amused after all the yelling that the scientists have done about allowing politics to play any part in the matter of Government support of science. Heaven knows that so far at least as the Kilgore crowd is concerned, there has been little else than politics from the beginning."[4] Bush agreed that "Shapley has very little judgment" and commented on his and Harold Urey's participation in the Independent Citizens Committee of the Arts, Sciences, and Professions, which reportedly had "some very left-wing individuals pulling strings in it."[5]

Of the allegation that Kilgore's staff planned to "guide" the foundation's work, Bush said that he knew about the problem—in this instance an effort to get a large appropriation for Kilgore's subcommittee to investigate science. Since "Kilgore has about him a group that have strange ideas," Bush wrote, "he hardly gets ... a fair cross-section of scientific opinion."[6] Bush at this time (early April) still thought Congress was likely to pass a bill in the current session, and that amendments would move it "in the right direction. As the compromise bill now stands it is not a good bill or a bad one; I would prefer it to no bill at all, but by no outstanding margin." Bush hoped that when it came time for board appointments, President Truman would "have sound advice. He will have mine, whether he asks for it it or not, but whether he pays any attention to it is another matter."[7]

Soon after the introduction of S. 1850 Kilgore, speaking for the Military Affairs subcommittee considering science legislation, presented a detailed report recommending early action on the bill. On the same day Magnuson, on behalf of his Commerce subcommittee, concurred in that report. On April 9 the Committee on Military Affairs favorably reported the bill.[8] The majority leader, Alben W. Barkley (D., Kentucky), promised a "Science Week" on the floor, and Magnuson expected debate sometime during the first two weeks of May, passage by the Senate "without controversy," and enactment by June 30.[9] But controversial legislation on labor and price controls, which backers of the science foundation had hoped would be deferred until after their bill had passed, commanded priority and intensified partisan politics. Not until July 1 did S. 1850 come before the Senate. Much had happened in the meantime to jeopardize its chances.

Although name-calling in personal letters indicated that relations among scientists were less than amiable, during the spring both groups continued publicly to support the compromise bill. The AAAS council voted 230-10 in its favor, and Meyerhoff reported that "the only known organized opposition" was that of the National Association of Manufacturers (NAM). The Committee Supporting the Bush Report also appealed for enactment of the bill, though mentioning the objections of many scientists to inclusion of the social sciences, changes in patent policy, and distribution of research funds by formula. "While many would be better satisfied if these provisions were dropped," the committee stated, "protracted delay or failure to enact this legislation would be far more prejudicial to the public interest than the inclusion of the provisions objected to."[10]

On the Hill Jack Teeter maneuvered for the bill's passage with the zest of a born operator. In personally typed memos with idiosyncratic spelling, he kept Bush up to the minute on developments and rumors. Though Teeter considered Homer Smith and his New York University colleague and collaborator W. Parker Anslow, Jr. "heavy handed" and likely to "do more harm than good to the cause of science and S1850 in particular," Teeter "felt that if they had any money to spend on the legislation . . . I could show them how to use it more intelligently"—as, for example, in the informal buffet dinners at his "club" at 2900 Cleveland Avenue where he brought legislators together with Bush. Teeter thought that congressional interest in science might soon wane, but he found hope in reports that the President wanted legislation before the summer recess and did "not wish to sustain any more setbacks . . . on controversial bills."[11] Before long this kind of reasoning led some of the Bush-Bowman group to believe that Truman would accept a bill similar to the original Magnuson proposal rather than let Democratic congressmen face their constituents in the fall elections with only an atomic energy act to their credit—and perhaps not even that, since the McMahon bill faced a tough fight in the House.

Bush concluded early in May that Congress probably would not pass S. 1850 in 1946. This did not bother him, except that he wanted to hand over the wind-up tasks of OSRD to the science foundation. He wrote Jewett: "Looking back to the early days of the Kilgore bill, we have come quite a distance, and the situation is no longer dangerous. Hence I am inclined to believe that legislation enacted at the next session might be even better than we can expect today, although I believe S. 1850 as it stands is not at all bad considering where we started from."[12]

Conservative scientists' misgivings about S. 1850 were mild compared to those of Republican members of the committee which reported the bill. On May 24, a month and a half after it had been reported favorably, six of the seven minority members of the full committee issued their contrary views. In their opinion S. 1850, despite some modification from its earlier form, still exemplified "a clear exposition of the philosophy of centralization and control of science with its attendant bureaucratic autocracy." It would make the foundation's administrator a science czar, "one of the most powerful men in the Government and in the country." It would create one more big agency which would bring yet another "large sector of our national economy . . . under the centralization, control, and supervision of Washington," shift state responsibility for education to the federal capital, and add huge expenditures "to our already dangerously unbalanced budget." It would abrogate the private patent system, impair existing contracts, and endanger national security. In short, it was "a link in the chain to bind us into the totalitarian society of the planned state."[13]

The one Republican who did not sign the minority report was H. Alexander Smith of New Jersey. A former executive secretary and lecturer in politics at Princeton University, Smith wanted a federal agency to sponsor research in universities, but one along the lines of Bush's original proposal. He led the effort to revise S. 1850 in the debate that began July 1, and he continued to be the principal Republican advocate in Congress of a science foundation until its eventual establishment.

* * *

A few days before the Republican senators issued their report, the scientists' united front had split wide apart. The occasion for the open break was the introduction in the House by Wilbur Mills on May 15 of H.R. 6448, a modified version of the proposal he and Magnuson had first introduced in July 1945. The bill was referred to the generally conservative subcommittee on Public Health of the House Interstate and Foreign Commerce Committee.[14]

Some of the backers of S. 1850 were surprised and furious. Writing in *Science*, Meyerhoff blamed Teeter, without naming him ("an ardent and unreconstructed proponent of the old—and abandoned—Magnuson bill"), who not only "handed" the reworked measure to Mills but also quickly arranged for two days of hearings featuring friendly witnesses. Meyerhoff was sure that members of the AAAS council and most of the association itself still backed S. 1850, and he urged them to "become more vocal with their congressmen than the willful individuals or the reactionary organizations who may yet lobby objectionable and obstructive legislation onto the statute books and who are evidently determined to do it!"[15] In the same issue Watson Davis, director of Science Service, deplored the division among scientists and commented on the "hurriedly called hearings" at which Bush, Homer Smith, and George E. Folk of the National Association of Manufacturers had testified for a bill continuing commercial patent rights, failing to provide for geographic distribution of research funds or support for the social sciences, and vesting control in a part-time board.[16]

Teeter was in fact largely responsible for the unexpected move in the House. He wanted action and fretted over the Senate delay. Personal rivalry with Schimmel and a fear that Kilgore's staff would dominate the foundation seem to have stimulated him. Evidently he believed, or at least told Bowman, that the House would bring the Mills bill to the floor promptly but that S. 1850 would either be amended "to death" or fail to pass the Senate. Teeter played on conservatives' fears by mentioning Kilgore's ties to the Congress of Industrial Organizations (CIO). Obviously relaying Teeter's views, Bowman wrote to Day of Cornell:

Kilgore's connection with labor and his inclinations with respect to it are well known. Given a supervisory role and a wide open door for his version of the "social sciences" and the opportunity would be created for doctrinal guidance of so-called social studies supported by millions obtained through Congressional appropriation. I believe these to be the facts but I do not assert them as such. They had the force of facts in the gradual formulation of Senate opinion that Kilgore's influence was bad and that the compromises we had made with him, as embodied in S. 1850, were not wise.[17]

Since there were strong objections to S. 1850 in the House, Bowman continued, and since Magnuson's original bill had a good calendar position in the Senate and would be taken up promptly if the House passed the Mills bill, Magnuson "told the House leaders to go ahead." Besides, the guessing was that Truman would sign the Mills bill since "the Democrats need to come before the country at election time having accomplished something concrete with respect to science legislation." If he disapproved the foundation bill, the Republicans would exploit the veto and reap partisan benefit.[18]

The two-day House hearings, presided over by J. Percy Priest (D., Tennessee), were stacked to favor the Mills bill, though Commerce Secretary Henry A. Wallace managed to get his opposing views on the record. Wallace's statement, given by Edward U. Condon, director of the National Bureau of Standards, contended that H.R. 6448 would "lead to an increasing monopolization of science by a small clique and operate to the detriment of small and independent business."[19] But Bush said that the Mills bill would "fulfill the needs of the country better than any other piece of legislation" he had seen.[20] Detlev W. Bronk testified that he would be satisfied with either H.R. 6448 or S. 1850 or some combination of the two.[21] A statement submitted by the Reverend J. Hugh O'Donnell of Notre Dame warned of the dangers of totalitarianism and a "slavish policy of government direction and control."[22] And a minority member of the committee, Clarence J. Brown of Ohio, when questioning Bowman revealed his and likely many of his colleagues' opinion about the social sciences:

> ... the average American just does not want some expert running around prying into his life and his personal affairs and deciding for him how he should live, and if the impression becomes prevalent in the Congress that this legislation is to establish some sort of an organization in which there would be a lot of short-haired women and long-haired men messing into everybody's personal affairs and lives, inquiring whether they love their wives or do not love them and so forth, you are not going to get your legislation. It is my thought that we should be very, very practical in this hour of need.[23]

The attacks in *Science* on those who had "jeopardized" the compromise bill predictably angered the Bowman-Bush group. Still smarting from seeing his committee labeled a "rather miscellaneous group," Bowman wrote Homer Smith that Meyerhoff and Davis "argue and think like New Dealers of the original brand," and he urged Bush to talk with AAAS officials about the "deplorable misuse" of the magazine.[24] Instead, Bush wrote to James Conant criticizing the reports in *Science* and defending the introduction of the Mills bill and his testimony on it. ". . . this is very decidedly Jim Conant's affair since he is President of AAAS," Bush told Bowman.[25]

"We are at least getting some action," Teeter wrote, responding to criticisms of his role in the affair.[26] Peter Edson, a newspaper columnist, had charged that "the shenanigans behind the Mills bill" revealed that "Magnuson was willing to sabotage the compromise" in the interest of his original bill. Edson thought that a blast from the National Association of Manufacturers against the compromise bill's patent provisions might be related to the "end run" the Bush forces were trying to pull in the House. At any rate, Edson wrote, private universities in the East joined big business in opposing government ownership of patents, and their jealousy of western state universities explained their resistance to the geographic-distribution formula in S. 1850. And the Mills bill dropped research support for the social sciences because the "physical sciences have no use for the social sciences." The Bush group's tactical move, Edson said, was designed to get quick House approval of the Mills bill and thereby force the Senate to consider that instead of the compromise measure.[27]

Certainly Teeter was working hard for the Mills bill. He and Father O'Donnell called at Mills's office on June 3 and were confronted there by Edson, who asked Teeter about his "shenanigans." At lunch, where they were guests of the congressman from South Bend, Father O'Donnell "made a hit," Teeter wrote Bush. "The entrance into the House dining room was like high mass. Every man we needed to see came to the table including Mr. MacCormack [John W. McCormack (D., Massachusetts), the majority leader]. We saw at least a dozen representatives and Father

O'Donnell sold each one on the bill and on a militant attitude towards communism." Teeter reported too that Priest, who was getting a lot of pressure from the Administration "to flop" to the compromise bill, hoped to see the President and find out directly whether he would veto a bill giving control of the foundation to a part-time board.[28]

Yet, despite the bickering, the desire for a science foundation, even an imperfect one, remained strong among persons of differing views and spurred renewed efforts for passage of a bill of some kind. Even as Teeter lobbied for the Mills bill he also suggested to Homer Smith that the Bowman committee's letter asking for action on S. 1850 be sent to members of the Senate. The Edson column caused a warning from Magnuson that no legislation was likely if there should be a split over the compromise measure.[29] After Bush issued a statement saying that legislation was needed now and that it was up to Congress to decide on its form, Teeter proposed that Conant, Bowman, Urey, and Shapley join Bush in a press release to the same effect.[30]

It soon developed that S. 1850's prospects in the Senate were brighter than Teeter had painted them. Bowman learned in conversations with Schimmel, Teeter, and Senator Wallace White (R., Maine) that there was a "disposition on both sides . . . to make concessions"—even including Kilgore's willingness to drop government ownership of patents—and that the bill would probably get through the Senate. Bowman told Schimmel that he supported S. 1850, though he again qualified the endorsement by saying that he recognized the necessity for compromises on some of its provisions. If only Kilgore's name were not on the bill, Bowman thought, it "would have much easier sailing."[31]

The bill would "face a tough fight," Magnuson heard from his Republican colleague Leverett Saltonstall, but the Washington senator, belying the charge that he had sabotaged the joint measure, prepared for the effort. He suggested that Teeter arrange appointments for Bush with several key senators—Harry Byrd and White being designated "urgent"— and that Bowman see the two senators from Maryland. If there were any chance for enactment, Magnuson thought, the bill ought to clear the Senate hurdle before the Fourth of July. Teeter advised that he be prepared to jettison some of the bill's most controversial provisions.[32]

* * *

On July 1 Senator Barkley called up S. 1850 for debate. Kilgore first carried the burden of argument for the bill, then Magnuson. Fulbright gave important assists, especially on the social sciences. The attack was led by Smith and Thomas C. Hart (R., Connecticut), who together with four others submitted an amendment which would have substituted an entirely new bill, establishing an agency over which the President would have no effective control but would be dominated instead by scientists nominated by the National Academy of Sciences. The substitute also revived the old Byrd proposal for a separate defense research organization.[33]

Most of the argument during the three days of debate revolved around familar issues—control, patents, social sciences, and geographic distribution of research funds. The intensity of senators' partisanship and the firmness of their social and economic creeds influenced their votes on these specific questions, but so too did their varying degrees of pragmatism and desire for a science foundation. Smith, for example, while leading the opposition and characterizing the shaky compromise as a surrender, in the end voted for the bill as did three other sponsors of his substitute measure. His belief in the need for federal support of research—and perhaps a feeling like Bush's that the House would correct the bill's flaws—enabled him to resolve his "quandary" when the final vote came. But for Willis, who accepted Jewett's notions about the stifling effects of bureaucracy, or Kenneth D. McKellar (D., Tennessee), who thought federal research expenditures already constituted "the grossest extravagance," or Robert A. Taft (R., Ohio), who wanted to withhold power and patronage from a Democratic President, there was no quandary to resolve.[34]

Of the two chief proponents of the bill, Kilgore's task was simpler than Magnuson's. Remote as the joint bill was from his original conception, it was much closer to the bill he had introduced the year before than to Magnuson's. Kilgore was blunt and combative in the debate, attacking as readily as defending, while Magnuson had to answer charges that he had deserted the great Dr. Bush and that the "compromise" was a sellout. Kilgore called the National Academy of Sciences "a scientific oligarchy" and compared scientists' control of the foundation board to the "public be damned" arrogance of a nineteenth-century railroad baron. Magnuson, on the other hand, had to play down essential features of his first bill and portray Bush, Bowman, and its other supporters as now fully converted to the compromise.[35]

Magnuson's task was especially difficult because of Smith's exploitation of the Bowman committee's letter of November 24 to President Truman, which the New Jersey senator skillfully used to show the defects of Kilgore's earlier bill that were still present in the so-called compromise. Admittedly, the Bowman committee had recently asked for the passage of S. 1850, but with "a sort of despairing note," Smith said, quoting their words: "While we stick to our former views, we think that this is a compromise which had better be taken than nothing." Good reason to despair: the joint bill "was a complete concession . . . to the Kilgore position."[36] When Smith and Hart brought up the House hearing on the Mills bill, Kilgore characterized it as "merely a quiet little hearing . . . for propaganda purposes" and compared Bush's going "back on an agreement" to that of a West Virginian who sold some property but then had his wife refuse to sign the deed when he saw a chance to get a better price. Magnuson was less forthright in trying to explain Bush's testimony.[37] The House hearing, particularly Bush's testimony, was embarrassing to backers of S. 1850, but Kilgore could cite one piece of more recent evidence of unity behind the joint bill—a statement of June 24 signed by ten officials of educational and scientific organizations, among them Conant, Bowman, and Shapley. Kilgore said he resented the implication that he had "blackjacked into an agreement" such men as Bush and Bowman.[38]

In presenting the case for his substitute measure, and simultaneously laying the groundwork for specific amendments after its defeat, Smith ticked off the flaws he saw in S. 1850. Several of these he tied directly to the statements of the Bowman committee's letter to the President. The first and most serious defect, in Smith's view, was presidential appointment of a director who would be independent of the foundation's board. Next he objected to distribution of funds by states and by population—the "porkbarrel feature" as Hart called it. After deploring mistakes about patents and inclusion of the social sciences, he opposed assistance to undergraduate students through scholarships. (Smith did not object to graduate fellowships.) What he termed "the national security issue" was the inclusion of military and civilian research in the same agency; hence a separate title in his bill for defense research. One reason for this separation was that the science foundation should support only basic research, not applied. What Smith called a "planning issue" was closely related to that of control: scientists rather than the foundation administrator should have responsibility for planning research activities. Similarly, the joint bill threatened to destroy the country's existing science structure centered in universities and private foundations. All of these objections, Smith said, were met by his substitute measure.[39]

Kilgore responded that Smith's substitute "would set up a virtual scientific autocracy which would not be responsible either to the President, to the Congress, or to the people." To allow dictation of national science policy by the Academy—whose president was "the only outspoken opponent of a public foundation"—would be analogous to letting Baptists choose some of their denomination to represent all American Christians.[40] Magnuson replied to other items in Smith's bill of particulars, and Robert M. La Follette, Jr. defended the formula for geographic distribution of funds by citing the successful research of land-grant colleges. Smith's substitute, the Wisconsin Progressive said, would "inevitably result in the concentration in a handful of institutions" of federal research funds and fellowships.[41] When the vote came on Smith's substitute, it went down 39-24.[42]

Following the defeat of the substitute Smith submitted specific amendments to S. 1850, and these and other proposed changes were taken up on the final day of debate. Smith's first amendments provided for the substitution of "Board" for "Administrator" throughout S. 1850 and other textual changes to ensure board control. Appealing to authority—*Science—The Endless Frontier*—Smith argued again that Bush had not changed his opinion on this matter and quoted his recent testimony on the Mills bill. Replying, Magnuson loyally defended the "compromise." On this critical issue Smith nearly won, but a tie vote (34-34) meant the rejection of board control.[43]

Next Smith tried to eliminate the complicated patent provisions of S. 1850 and to leave the foundation free to decide on the disposition of inventions. To Kilgore this simply meant signing "a blank check" allowing patents developed with public funds to be converted to private profit. Strongly influenced by his discovery, as a member of the wartime Truman Committee, of the machinations of international cartels, and perhaps begrudging the ground he had already relinquished on an issue he considered vital, Kilgore slugged away at the opposing views presented by the Republican senator from his state, W. Chapman Revercomb, who argued that the bill's provisions represented "a new theory and philosophy which is being advanced to do away with the patent system."[44] Smith's amendment was rejected, 41-31.[45]

The amendment to exclude the social sciences was offered by Hart. In the bargaining sessions with Bush and Bowman, Kilgore had already agreed that the foundation's support of social science research would be restricted at first, but S. 1850 still provided for a division of social sciences. Hart's amendment would remove it. Not only had the Bush report omitted the social sciences, Hart said, but "no agreement has been reached with reference to what social science really means. It may include philosophy, anthropology, all the racial questions, all kinds of economics, including political economics, literature, perhaps religion, and various kinds of ideology."[46] If this catalogue of subjects did not stir enough uneasiness, some senators may have recalled Taft's words of the day before that social science research "means a political board. It means someone concerned with promoting all the health legislation which someone may want, all the housing legislation . . . and all the other matters which come in under the all-inclusive term of 'social sciences.' . . . Social sciences are politics."[47] And Smith, while reminding his colleagues that he had been a faculty member at Princeton and professing his interest in the social sciences, contended that the bill before the Senate was "for research in pure science, not in applied science." Elbert Thomas, a former professor of political science in the University of Utah, pointed out the irony of Republicans' opposing social science while the only important achievement of their revered Herbert Hoover's presidency was the series of studies he instituted of recent social trends. Yet Thomas's plea too tended to emphasize the practical, problem-solving aspects of the social disciplines, and the success of Hart's amendment (46-26) probably reflected a general feeling that there were fundamental differences between the natural and social sciences, and perhaps something ominous about research that might upset senators' cherished values.[48]

Next Hart tried to remove the foundation's authority to award undergraduate scholarships and thus "narrow the field in which the Federal Government would be subsidizing education" to the graduate level. Magnuson, citing the wartime mistakes of drafting young scientists, the manpower shortages documented by the Bush report, and the encouragement given to scientifically talented youth by other countries, answered that the "development and training of young scientists is as essential to our military defense and to our peacetime welfare in the future as could be any thing else which the Congress might consider." Hart's amendment was rejected, 42-27.[49]

The final attempt to amend S. 1850 was Smith's move to strike the provision allocating 25 percent of the foundation's research funds to tax-supported colleges and universities. His calculations showed "some curious results" deriving from the formula. If, for example, the foundation had a research budget of $40 million, one-fourth of which would be divided among the states in accordance with the bill's provisions, the territory of Alaska would get an allocation of $4,800 for each of the 17 teachers in the public university; Delaware would receive only $876 for each of the 103 teachers in its university. Research money should go to institutions capable of performing research, Smith argued, but if there must be a formula, it should be devised scientifically, not in this faulty manner.[50] Magnuson pointed out that the foundation would not be required to distribute funds automatically; there must first be a satisfactory institutional research plan.[51]

The main rebuttal came from La Follette, who claimed authorship of the distribution plan. Referring to the ignorance of some of his colleagues of the strong universities beyond the Alleghenies and of the valuable research done with federal money by land-grant colleges, he said he resented the implications that this was a "pork-barrel scheme." True, research in the land-grant colleges had largely been applied rather than basic, but it had brought "great scientific achievements, without the withering hand of bureaucracy" that Republican senators harped on in their attacks on the bill. The land-grant experience demonstrated not only the validity of the proposed method of allocation, but also "that there can be an economical use of the money and at the same time the greatest possible freedom for scientific research." Reminding his colleagues that during the war the ablest scientists in lesser known institutions were attracted to faculty positions in the few universities receiving the bulk of government research contracts, he said he wanted to redress the balance. Continued concentration of research funds would result in a similar concentration of scholars and fellows. La Follette then struck a chord appealing to western pride and prejudice: "I say it is just as likely that a great future scientist may be living somewhere west of the Mississippi as it is that he is living east of the Alleghenies." Wayne L. Morse (R., Oregon), who like La Follette had grown up in Madison, Wisconsin and absorbed the spirit of Progressivism there, echoed his colleague's arguments.[52]

Senator Smith recognized the certain defeat of his amendment and did not call for the yeas and nays, but he said he was pleased to have on the record an acknowledgment that research funds should not be distributed automatically to institutions lacking scientific competence. Then he confessed to his "difficult quandary." He was unhappy that his colleagues had rejected his amendments, and he would not appeal to those who had supported his efforts to improve the bill to vote as he intended to, but he would vote for its passage. (In other words, like the Bowman committee statement he had ridiculed the day before: "... this is a compromise which had better be taken than nothing.")[53] Eighteen senators (15 Republicans and 3 southern Democrats) did not agree. Those for passage numbered 48; 30 senators were recorded as not voting.[54]

* * *

There was still time enough for the House to act on foundation legislation, and perhaps it would have if the Mills bill had not brought the dissension among scientists into the open. In the Senate debates Smith had laid bare the half-hearted support for S. 1850 in the Bush-Bowman forces, despite Magnuson's stalwart effort to show their commitment to the compromise. Yet both sides tried to prod the House committee handling the legislation to move quickly.

At the White House, Byron S. Miller, co-author of the McMahon atomic energy measure, recognized that it would "be an uphill task" to pass a satisfactory foundation bill but learned from Percy Priest that it might be possible if the President intervened personally. Miller recommended that Truman meet with Clarence F. Lea, the chairman of the Commerce Committee, or with Lea and Priest, or with all the subcommittee members. Since Senate amendments had eliminated the social sciences and authority to establish new divisions, Miller hoped that the House would correct these changes, at least by permitting the creation later of a social sciences division.[55] On the opposition front, Teeter sent out memoranda listing the committee members and other congressmen to whom "a word of guidance" might be addressed in order to bring S. 1850 into harmony with the Mills bill. Teeter believed that the hairbreadth margin of the Senate defeat of board control made it likely that the House would reverse that arrangement, and the thumping rejection of the social sciences ensured their elimination. He thought that patent provisions could be made "less onerous," and he listed the members of the House Patents Committee who might be persuaded that "their prerogatives are being invaded." Teeter expected the House to vote for a science foundation bill within ten days.[56]

In *Science* Meyerhoff exhorted scientists to push for passage of one of the three foundation bills before the House. His choice was plainly S. 1850. Meyerhoff reminded his readers of the overwhelming endorsement of the compromise bill by the AAAS council and explained that favorable committee and floor action on the bill already approved by the Senate would avoid the hazards of going to conference. Without "the conviction that the legislation is both sound and urgent," Priest's subcommittee, Lea's full committee, and then the House Rules Committee would not "act with the dispatch which is essential. *And it is up to the scientists to give the members of these committees that conviction.*" He continued:

> This is, again, a time for action! No individual scientist can allow summer teaching, research, or relaxation to interfere with his duty to let his congressman know his position on these bills. It makes no difference if he has written sometime before this. He must write again, or better, telegraph, or even use the telephone, but in some manner, he must communicate with the following key people in the House![57]

The flurry of appeals and pressure—apparently including a personal request from the President to Lea "to expedite action on some bill"[58]—went for naught. Although the subcommittee approved a bill, the full committee on July 19 decided to pass it over. Schimmel told a Budget Bureau official that Lea's committee felt it did not have enough time to consider the controversial issues, or as *Science* put it, "the issues were 'too involved and too important' to be acted on in the few final days of the 79th Congress." *Science* also reported that "Legislative observers said that 'by failing to present a united front scientists themselves caused the legislators to doubt the wisdom of any of the competing measures.'"[59]

In the Executive Office of the President, Byron Miller, who had just seen the McMahon bill pass the House and go to conference, still thought there should be an attempt to get the science foundation legislation—bad as the subcommittee draft probably was—out of committee and onto the floor. He told his boss, John R. Steelman: "There has been tremendous pressure for the creation of a National Science Foundation from scientists, educators, industrialists, and people from all walks of life." The agency could provide "in a very real sense the first line of national defense." A last-ditch effort to pass a bill was justified, even though its provisions might require a veto. If enactment should fail, Miller thought the executive branch should take other steps "to provide for coordination of government scientific efforts to achieve as many objectives of the legislation as possible."[60]

* * *

If anyone made the effort Miller suggested, it brought no result. Isaiah Bowman, irritated by comments in *Science* about scientists' lack of unity, suggested that Teeter write an article setting forth their side of the story. *Science* had promised "a final and authoritative analysis of the legislative picture," and Bowman knew he would not like it.[61]

Howard Meyerhoff's "Obituary: National Science Foundation, 1946" met Bowman's worst anticipations:

> At noon, 19 July 1946, The National Science Foundation was pronounced dead by the surgical staff of the House Committee on Interstate and Foreign Commerce. The death was a homicide!
> Readers of *Science* are familiar with the promising career of the deceased, and many will mourn this untimely and unnatural passing, for the killing was done, not by politicians, but by scientists.[62]

Not that congressmen were without fault. Priest had "decamped" to Tennessee to run for re-election, leaving Alfred L. Bulwinkle (D., North Carolina) to guide the legislation through the subcommittee, and it reported out a slightly revised Mills bill. Before the full committee, Meyerhoff wrote, the subcommittee could neither "make a case" for this bill nor explain its rejection of S. 1850. Hence the parent committee had no recourse but to table both.[63]

But the real blame did not belong to the congressmen. "It must be placed upon the shoulders of those who drafted and introduced the Mills Bill . . . into the House," Meyerhoff said. "Let no one be so naive as to suppose that this was Representative Mills." It was Bush's "own representative"—that is, John Teeter—who had pulled the strings, persuading some who had been committed to the compromise bill that it would not pass the Senate and that the only way to salvage a science foundation was to introduce a new bill in the House. Even Bush may have been misled, Meyerhoff suggested, but "he must personally assume the burden of responsibility" for the action of his agent. Not only was the introduction of the Mills bill "unilateral action betraying the democratic principles upon which the compromises in S. 1850 were worked out in conference," Meyerhoff asserted, but it was also

> a political blunder which has cost science at least a year of life for the National Science Foundation. Every scientist has the right to his convictions, but no scientist—no group of scientists, whether a majority or minority—has the right to impose its convictions at this cost. The moral of 19 July is simple: *Only in a reasonable show of unity, achieved by some compromise, can scientists expect political results.*[64]

The elderly rugged individualist Frank Jewett could hardly mourn the burial of foundation bills, of whatever variety, but he did have some advice for his old friend Van Bush. Writing from Martha's Vineyard, where he was "cooped up . . . by a howling nor'easter," Jewett said that Bowman had phoned him about Meyerhoff's "vicious attack on you." Instead of replying, as Bowman advised, Bush should stay out of the "hog wallow."

My observation [Jewett continued] has been that when one tackles a pole cat both he and the general neighborhood are likely to take on a musky odor.

Since Meyerhoff is Jim Conant's particular skunk I'd be inclined to let him deal with the varmint. . . .

Altogether I fear that scientists haven't raised themselves in the opinion of thoughtful men by their performances these past few months.[65]

During the Kilgore-Magnuson hearings in October 1945 Raymond Swing had commented in a radio broadcast on the remarkable effectiveness of young atomic scientists—"as impressive a group of men as ever came to modern Washington"—in press conferences and before congressional committees.[66] In the battles over atomic energy legislation they had been persuasive and successful. But the summer of '46 showed that the scientists advocating a national science foundation had not yet mastered the art of politics.

4
Veto

When scientists split over the Mills bill they ensured the defeat of science foundation legislation in 1946. Nearly all of them recognized that fact and concluded that future success would depend on agreeing to disagree without breaking ranks. But their originally nonpartisan cause had become entangled with broad political issues that led to failure in the Seventy-Ninth Congress and foreshadowed more difficulties in the Republican-controlled Eightieth.

A Harvard sociologist, Talcott Parsons, offered a thoughtful interpretation of the rift among scientists and its political implications. An "inner group" who had controlled OSRD and were associated with a few major universities and industrial laboratories, organizers of the Bowman committee, at first showed no special concern for national issues other than defense and the general welfare, nor overt opposition to the social sciences; but during the legislative struggle their position "tended to become identified both with political conservatism, and with a desire to exclude the social sciences." Another "much broader group of scientists," organized by Urey and Shapley into the Committee for a National Science Foundation, "tended to be suspicious of too great a monopoly in the hands of a 'scientific oligarchy' and of a privileged group of research institutions, both academic and industrial." The wartime development of close relations between industry and research, and industrialists' fear of federal encroachment, not only helped explain the kind of opposition to a science foundation exemplified by Jewett, but also the insistence, among those favorable to the continuance of a government research agency, on "the most elaborate safeguards against 'political' influence." The lobbying by the National Association of Manufacturers for the Mills bill and the partisan character of the Senate votes on S. 1850 showed the coincidence of interests of the OSRD inner group and of "prominent elements of politically influential 'big business.' "[1]

Most scientist participants in the recent effort to influence Congress, discouraged by their failure and irritated by the actions of their opponents, made more personal and less abstract assessments than that by Parsons. Edmund E. Day wrote Bowman that because of the introduction of the Mills bill "we got pretty much what was coming to us, namely, nothing at all." Next time there would have to be "a compromise agreement that will stick."[2]

The Hopkins president disagreed with Day's analysis. Meyerhoff was the culprit. He had "belittled" the Bowman committee as a "rather miscellaneous group," used "amateurish and harmful" tactics, and "indulged in personalities and showed other deficiencies too numerous to mention." But then, putting on his statesman's cloak, Bowman concluded: "It would be wasteful of time to answer him. Our public responsibility requires us to make a choice on a high plane. It requires us to make an extraordinary effort. It does not require us to engage in name-calling."[3] He advised against replying to Meyerhoff, who would be leaving his AAAS position soon anyway, and Teeter, who had drafted a reply, discussed the matter with Bush and agreed.[4]

Bowman proposed that Conant, as president of the AAAS, take the lead in organizing a new, unified effort in which scientists would debate the issues but not allow their differences to be turned into discord. A conversation with President Truman raised Bowman's optimism about the prospects for science foundation legislation in the next session of Congress.[5] That conversation, however, occurred in September, before the elections brought economy-minded Republicans into control in both houses. If a coalition of Republicans and conservative southern Democrats had shown little enthusiasm for the proposed research agency the year before, the new Congress which would convene in January 1947 would have even less interest in legislation in accord with the Democratic President's prescription.

Other novel circumstances raised possible obstacles along the course to enactment of a law. The establishment of the Office of Naval Research (ONR) in 1946 provided a channel for the flow of federal money to university laboratories for the support of basic research, thus lessening or, in the view of some congressmen, obviating the need for a science foundation. Truman added a confusing element in October by signing an executive order establishing the President's Scientific Research Board (PSRB), under the chairmanship of Reconversion Director John R. Steelman. Bush, as director of OSRD, was named as one of the members, but he told a colleague that he had not been consulted.[6] Nor had the secretaries of War and Navy, and they, like Bush, were apprehensive about the aims of the reputed author of the order, James R. Newman, and suspected that he intended to block further growth of army and navy control over scientific research.[7] Bush had become accustomed to his role as informal science adviser to the President, but here was a strong signal that he was being displaced by Steelman.

The creation of the Steelman board injected a disruptive element of partisanship into the endeavor to get a foundation. A Budget Bureau official, who came to regret that he had not attempted to block the order establishing the PSRB, said that "its inspiration was political in the sense that its primary mission was to promote the right type of Science Foundation."[8] To Jack Teeter the board was obviously "a tool of the Snyder, Steelman, Kilgore, Newman, Byron Miller, Schimmel group." But he believed Congress would frustrate those adversaries of Bush's. Anticipating the Republican victory in November, Teeter expected the revival of the Mills bill. To achieve harmony among scientific groups, the National Academy of Sciences should offer a forum at which a leader from the House of Representatives would tell the scientists plainly what kind of legislation was possible. Teeter agreed with Bush that the Academy had not shown much capacity for leadership, but the only hope of passage of science legislation in the Eightieth Congress hinged on its sponsorship by a conservative body.[9]

Bush no more than Teeter liked the idea of AAAS leadership, but he was hardly in a position to try to block the renewed effort for unity, formally proposed by Bowman to Conant and by the latter to the AAAS council. In an informal request for Bush's views, Conant wrote that he had talked with Leverett Saltonstall, who had helped achieve the compromise with Kilgore leading to S. 1850, and they thought "a united front on the general objectives would be very useful." Bush agreed, but he expressed his annoyance at the AAAS and *Science*, which he said had suppressed communications from Magnuson and Mills. The likelihood of Republican control of the Senate caused Bush to expect Congress to "enact a good bill," but it would not hurt if scientists were organized to exert pressure on general matters. As for the risk that increased support of basic research by the army and navy would diminish congressional interest in the foundation, Bush thought fears of that result were groundless. He had helped get the navy program under way, and helped guide it now as chairman of a new Joint Research and Development Board, but he considered it "a temporary measure to fill the gap before the Foundation appears.... in the long run I believe it would be very troublesome to have federal subsidy of university research of a fundamental nature flowing through the military services." Since the Budget Bureau and Congress also looked on ONR as a surrogate for a science agency, its creation could really be used to support the argument for the foundation.[10]

Unlike Bush, scientists in the Urey-Shapley-Condon group worried a good deal about possible military domination of research, in the social sciences as well as the natural, and they worried about the November election results. Even if scientists should again unite behind the compromise provisions of S. 1850, the Republican leadership in the House and Senate was likely to disregard their pleas. Yet they were reluctant to give ground. Following a meeting at the Science Service offices in Washington, Shapley wrote Bowman that he hoped the AAAS council would lead a new effort and take as its starting point the "jointly signed document of last summer" supporting S. 1850. A small steering committee—perhaps Bowman, Urey, Day, and Shapley—with an able executive officer, might serve to direct the campaign. Shapley found strong supporters for a foundation in Presidents Edwin B. Fred of the University of Wisconsin and Day of Cornell. "Both of them," he wrote, "are acutely aware, as too many of us at Harvard are not aware, of the great need for assistance throughout the Middle West, if we are to maintain scientific scholarship and scientific research on a broad basis." But he found widespread doubt about Bush's position.[11]

Bowman answered brusquely that the legislative situation required objective appraisal, not propagandist activities for "a pet program." As for Shapley's argument for including the social sciences, Bowman thought that would "endanger if not wreck the whole business." National defense was the prime need. Slinging a barb at Shapley and his associates in the Independent Citizens Committee, Bowman wrote: "The flagellants among us seem to think that we can convert the Soviets and secure One World by merely whipping ourselves." Though Bowman approved the idea of a steering committee, he would not have time to serve on it.[12] Two months later, writing to Day, Bowman professed wry amusement at Shapley's effort for unity since he "was one of those who beautifully gummed the game last year." It was unfortunate, Bowman thought, that Conant had not acted more decisively to lead the AAAS, especially since Shapley was now the president-elect of the association.[13]

Actually Conant had acted promptly and properly. After Bowman's request in September he had arranged to bring the matter of the AAAS role before the council. At the association's annual meeting in Boston in December an informal gathering of eighteen men representing both sides of the foundation issues suggested the formation of an intersociety committee to prevent a repetition of their split, and on December 29 the council adopted a resolution calling for the appointment of two representatives from each affiliated society to an Inter-Society Committee for a National Science Foundation. Conant extended this invitation to a few unaffiliated scientific and educational associations as well and asked Kirtley F. Mather, a Harvard geology professor, to call the committee together for its first meeting. Representatives of about seventy-five organizations met in Washington on February 23, 1947 and elected a nine-member executive committee, of which Day was chairman, Shapley the vice-chairman, and Dael Wolfle, the executive secretary of the American Psychological Association, the secretary-treasurer. Bowman was chosen as one of the members at large but declined to serve, on the ground that his presidential duties at Johns Hopkins were heavy.[14]

By the time of the Inter-Society Committee's first meeting—to which several senators and representatives were invited but only Elbert Thomas came—a number of foundation bills had been introduced in the House and Senate. A Princeton physicist, John Q. Stewart, who attended the meeting as an observer, had helped Alexander Smith draft his new bill (S. 526), and he described the differences between Smith's measure and Thomas's S. 525. In what was supposed to be "an off-the-record straw vote" the representatives indicated the kind of administration they preferred for the foundation. This perhaps unfortunate sounding of opinion—reported in the Washington *Post* the next day—resulted in 41 ballots for a single, presidentially appointed administrator; 22 for control by a large board as specified in Smith's bill; 32 for a small board similar to the Atomic Energy Commission; and 18 showing no preference for any of these alternatives. (Later the executive committee mailed a questionnaire to all representatives asking their views on this and three other issues.) Although eighteen members opposed provision for undergraduate scholarships, there was unanimity for graduate fellowships. Only four members opposed research support for the social sciences.[15] Stewart thought that the social sciences were overrepresented in the meeting and regretted that the "more conservative members" were generally "very poorly informed." His comments confirmed Smith's view, which coincided with Bush's, that the Inter-Society Committee did not really represent the science community.[16]

"In closing the meeting," Wolfle's annual report said, "Chairman Day summarized the consensus of the group: Despite their differing opinions on individual features of the bills before Congress, scientists—all of them—had to get together to support the kind of National Science Foundation favored by a majority, for if they failed to agree and failed to make their support unanimous, there might be no Foundation."[17]

* * *

Although Bush did not try to block the formation of the Inter-Society Committee, he kept apart from it and sought independently to steer the new legislative effort. In December Alexander Smith, who would chair the Senate subcommittee considering foundation legislation in the new

Congress, asked Bush's advice on the bill he had prepared. Bush promised to send specific suggestions, but his immediate impression was that the recent arrangements for military research would make possible a "simpler structure" than the draft measure provided. He believed the armed services would transfer most of their basic research to the foundation once it was under way.[18]

Since he was still a member of the Administration, Bush knew that his personal counsel to members of Congress transgressed normal procedure and would infuriate the President's close advisers. Unwilling to be fenced in, he composed a long letter to Director of the Budget James E. Webb. Bush wrote that while he and President Truman had differed over the form of the earlier legislation, the President "told me to proceed to give to Congress my exact opinions on the matter, and assured me that this would in no way embarrass him." Bush assumed that this arrangement still stood and that the President "wishes the Congress to have the benefit of the various shades of opinion as it proceeds toward legislation." The presentation of differing views from the executive branch seemed to Bush to be

> an entirely appropriate thing. On very important issues the President should have a clear-cut policy, and this should be thoroughly supported by his official family. However, on an important issue this should follow a consideration at which each individual who is called upon to render support should have the opportunity to present his views before the President takes a strong position. Moreover, it would be absurd to attempt to carry this principle into effect on every matter that comes up in legislation, and it would be generally unwise that it should be carried to the point of insisting on uniformity of advocacy in regard to the details of legislation. I feel confident, therefore, that the President feels that the Congress if it proceeds toward detailed legislation on this matter should have the benefit of diverse points of view, as it makes up its mind as to the exact form. In fact, I believe that Congress on this particular matter has already made up its mind to a very large extent.[19]

In this argument designed to establish an independent role for himself Bush was saying in effect that the President, at the time of their early conversation, "did not have strong opinions concerning the form" of foundation legislation, and moreover that he had still not taken "a strong position" on the issues. But Congress had largely "made up its mind" on the main issues—control, patents, and the social sciences. Bush thought Congress would now insist on board control, simple patent provisions, and elimination of the social sciences. As he wanted to give Senator Smith and other members of Congress his personal ideas on these matters, which his letter tried to transmute into "details of legislation," Bush concluded:

> Unless you see some reason to the contrary I will proceed along the lines indicated in this letter. This will involve my rendering personal aid to committees of Congress as they call for it, and will also involve consideration with the Armed Services of the aspects of the subject in which they are primarily interested, either

directly or through the Joint Research and Development Board. I feel confident that in so doing I will be carrying out the wishes of the President, but I will appreciate it if you find that this is not the case if you will advise me very promptly, as I am exceedingly anxious that the small time that I have yet to remain within the official family as the head of a governmental agency shall be as harmonious as it has been throughout my past association.[20]

Bush was a supremely self-confident person. Despite his irritation over his diminished influence in the White House, he still believed he could bring the President around to his way of thinking. Perhaps because in their first conversation about his report Bush had formed the opinion that Truman had no strong feelings about the way the foundation should be organized, he persisted in believing that the President was malleable, or at least would be satisfied with the trappings of presidential authority though a board held the substance. While Bush overestimated his influence with the President and underestimated Truman's firmness, he was at least more realistic than partisan congressmen who in the Eightieth Congress would try to withhold even the appearance of the Chief Executive's control over the foundation.

After sending his letter to Webb, Bush wasted no time in beginning to act as he had proposed to do. Four days later he wrote again to Smith, suggesting the elimination of a special title for defense research and commenting favorably on the bill's elaborate but "somewhat cumbersome" method of choosing the foundation's controlling board.[21] At the White House, meanwhile, the political scientist J. Donald Kingsley, who was serving as executive secretary of PSRB, informed Steelman of the difference between the Bush "inner" group of scientists and the Urey-Shapley-Condon group, in an analysis like that of Talcott Parsons.[22] And at the Budget Bureau staff members briefed Webb on foundation legislative history to prepare him for discussions with Steelman and Kingsley on an appropriate response to Bush's letter. The resulting recommendations, which Webb carried to the White House late in January, concurred in Bush's view on the social sciences (i.e., exclude, but handle in separate legislation), did not object to his suggestion to eliminate the patent provisions contained in S. 1850, but disagreed with his proposal to give control to a part-time board. Webb's memorandum recommended to the President "that Dr. Bush be advised, either directly by yourself or through me, that you do not favor such an administrative part-time board.... I strongly favor a single administrator; and would like to see Dr. Bush advised that you were of that opinion." A possible compromise would be a full-time board like the Atomic Energy Commission.[23]

It is doubtful that Bush ever received the definite statement of Administration policy on control that the Bureau recommended. On January 27 Bush and Webb had a long talk and then went to the White House to see

Steelman. Following their conference Bush expressed optimism that "things will move merrily at this session on science legislation."[24] Only on the question of control did Webb and Steelman disagree with him, Bush said, since

> they still adhere to the idea of an administrator holding the authority. Mr. Webb is entirely reasonable on this matter and makes out an interesting case based on the difficulty that obtains in Washington when commissions carry on executive and administrative activities. I quite agree that a commission should not administer, but point out that the commission setting policy is what is looked for here and is quite a different thing. I would not be at all surprised if Mr. Webb and I finally agree in our approach to this aspect of the subject, and certainly he does not feel like pressing his ideas with the President, for he agrees with me that the President should leave this matter to Congress this time.[25]

Bush wrote Conant in similar vein:

> We had a most interesting conference and no fireworks. Steelman and Webb, I believe, will urge the President simply to endorse sound science legislation, which he has already done in his message, but not to urge any particular form or become active as the matter is considered. I spoke very strongly on this point and think made quite an impression on Steelman, who agreed with me that the thing had been handled very poorly in the last session. The chances are that Steelman, Webb, and I will see the President shortly.[26]

Bush's comments on policy-setting by commissions sound as if there may have been some confusion of the part-time board idea he espoused and one of a full-time commission, similar to the recently established AEC, that the Budget Bureau memo had suggested as a possible compromise solution of the issue of control. Possibly Bush's arguments favorable to a "commission" were intended as a defense of a part-time policy-setting group. Possibly too the Budget Director did not follow up the recommendation to the President that Bush be firmly informed of Administration policy against board control because Webb concluded that Bush was likely to accept a small, full-time commission as a substitute. At any rate Bush came away from the meeting feeling that the essential element of board control was likely to emerge in legislation which would be acceptable to the President. Two weeks later Bush wrote Bernard M. Baruch that while he still differed with Webb and Steelman, "I believe that the President this time will not place his influence behind Kilgore."[27]

* * *

While the President's science advisers debated policy, legislative artisans and tinkers worked away on Capitol Hill. On leave from a new job with a company manufacturing shovel handles, Teeter was back on the scene, assisting Senate Republicans at first and then the majority members of the House committee handling foundation legislation as well. Besides helping to revise Smith's bill—introduced on February 7 as S. 526—Teeter arranged two days of hearings on the several bills before the House Committee on Interstate and Foreign Commerce. His old antagonist, Herbert Schimmel, caused him some concern for a while but soon left Kilgore's office for private life—"thank God," Homer Smith wrote. Kilgore himself, Homer Smith reported to Bowman, seemed to be "in a state of depression," and added, "I hope he stays that way."[28]

Senator Smith's S. 526—sponsored also by his fellow Republicans Saltonstall, Revercomb, and Guy Cordon and by Democratic Senators Magnuson and Fulbright—provided for a foundation of forty-eight members. This large group, to be appointed by the President for eight-year terms, was to select the real controlling board—an executive committee of nine of the members. The executive committee was to meet at least six times a year to "exercise the powers and duties of the Foundation," among which was the appointment of a full-time director, or chief executive officer, whom they were to supervise. A majority of the foundation's members would have to approve the choice of the director. In other respects S. 526 was much like the original foundation bills introduced by Magnuson and Mills in 1945. Senator Thomas's S. 525, introduced on the same day, was a duplicate of S. 1850 as passed by the Senate the year before. On the principal matters at issue other than control, Smith's bill reflected the advice he had received from Bush and friends at Princeton. The restrictive patent provisions urged by Kilgore had of course been eliminated. There was no mention of the social sciences, but the use of the term "other sciences" opened a way for their inclusion at the discretion of the foundation. Although Smith opposed the granting of undergraduate scholarships by the foundation, his bill permitted them as well as graduate fellowships. Conant's arguments, backed up by those of George W. Merck, president of an important pharmaceutical company with offices in New Jersey, persuaded Smith to make this concession, though the senator did so "with great trepidation." Both Conant and Bush worried that the navy's "enormous" program of undergraduate scholarships would lure "too many bright boys" who were potential scientists into the naval reserves.[29]

Scholarships and fellowships were to be awarded on the basis of ability, but the bill did encourage their wide geographic distribution. In making research contracts the foundation should aim at selecting the most competent performers, but also seek to strengthen research staffs throughout the country. Perhaps the most important recognition of the principle of spreading support widely was the provision for a foundation of forty-eight members who were to represent "the views of scientific leaders in all areas of the Nation." But to presidents of state universities and land-grant colleges, who had succeeded in getting a distribution formula through the

Senate before, these polite bows in their direction seemed meaningless.

Unlike the scientists on their faculties, most heads of public universities knew their way in political corridors, on Capitol Hill as well as the local statehouse. In Washington they had a hard-working and able servant in Russell I. Thackrey, a former newspaperman and professor of journalism who came to the newly established office of the Association of Land-Grant Colleges and Universities as executive secretary early in 1947. He sent them detailed, up-to-the-minute information on matters relating to foundation legislation and moved quickly to counter actions likely to hurt the association's institutions. Though he was scrupulous in following the instructions of the association's executive committee, Thackrey's energy and initiative made him an effective coordinator of a renewed effort to get a distribution formula written into foundation legislation.

But the chances of getting a formula written into Smith's bill seemed slight. The New Jersey senator disregarded both the Inter-Society Committee, which did not take a position on the issue, and the spokesmen of public institutions.[30] His only concession was to add, in committee, the names of the associations of land-grant colleges and state universities and, during floor debate, the Association of American Colleges to that of the National Academy of Sciences as organizations whose recommendations of foundation members should be considered by the President. Nor were most other senators willing to fight for special provisions on geographic distribution. Their replies to letters from university presidents were generally noncommittal or claimed that a broadly representative board would ensure equity for all regions.[31] Since the Bureau of the Budget also opposed the inclusion of a distribution formula,[32] Democratic members of Congress did not get pressure from the Administration to help the state institutions. Moreover, private colleges and universities generally opposed a special provision favoring tax-supported institutions. In view of all these obstacles, it is a testimony to the effectiveness of the campaign of the land-grant and state universities that Smith's bill was amended during the Senate debate to include a geographical distribution formula.[33]

Until floor debate in the Senate began in mid-May, Smith was in complete command there of foundation legislation. The Committee on Labor and Public Welfare held no hearings but unanimously gave a favorable report to S. 526 on March 26, and Senator Thomas, the sponsor of the rival S. 525, joined Smith in signing the report.[34]

Without a minority report arguing for the Administration stand on control of the foundation, the Steelman group in PSRB and Budget Bureau officials felt increasingly uneasy about defending their earlier firm position. Kingsley thought S. 526 was highly objectionable both because the foundation (now cut in half to twenty-four members) and its executive committee and director were "almost completely removed from responsibility either to the President or the Congress" and because the director would have authority to initiate national defense research and to coordinate federal research programs even despite his insulation from presidential control. Possibly a substitute bill could be introduced, though that did not offer much hope and might alienate Democratic senators who had endorsed S. 526; or an amendment might be supported providing for presidential appointment of a full-time foundation chairman who would be the agency's director. Kingsley urged that Steelman or the President tell Bush, "who is really in control of the situation," that the bill as reported to the Senate was not acceptable.[35]

At the Bureau William D. Carey argued that "the real objective is to get a workable Science Foundation, even at the price of some administrative faults," and he suggested the acceptance of "a middle ground compromise" which provided for nomination of a director by a part-time board but appointment by the President.[36] Bureau staff members had no reason to hope that the House Commerce Committee would alter the administrative provisions of S. 526, and Teeter tartly reminded them that "there was an election last fall." Like Kingsley, they began to cast around for acceptable alternatives. One of these, approved by the President and suggested by Webb to Bush, was a science agency patterned after the proposed International Broadcasting Foundation, consisting of a twenty-four member board, appointed by the President and confirmed by the Senate, of which the chairman, selected by the President, would be the only full-time member. The board would formulate policy, determine standards for awarding research contracts and fellowships, approve annual budget estimates before their submission to the Bureau, and prepare an annual report to the President and Congress on the foundation's activities. The chairman of the board would manage the foundation.[37]

This suggested arrangement, remarkably like the one established three years later by the National Science Foundation act, sank without stirring a ripple of interest. Bush reportedly discussed it with Senator Smith, but it conceded too much to executive authority to suit the senator.[38] After conferring with Webb, Smith did agree to accept an amendment granting presidential appointment of the foundation's director, but restricting him to internal administration under the control of the board and subject to its removal. If Webb and Steelman objected to this, Smith thought he could reach the President over their heads.[39]

Webb wrote Bush on May 9 that he could not understand Smith's "insistent demand for exemption from the normal Presidential and other governmental controls." Administrative standards required that "persons with responsibility for the disbursement of public funds should not be actively associated with the beneficiaries of those funds. . . . Only an official with undivided allegiance and fully supported by a responsible relation to the President can safely make such determinations." Private citizens could of course give advice and "might even be given certain broad policy functions," but there must be someone whom the President could hold accountable if he was to carry out his constitutional duty of seeing to the faithful execution of the laws. The failure of Smith's bill to meet this requirement was compounded by the provision that the director was to chair an interdepartmental committee on science and thus have a key role in coordinating federal science programs—"peculiarly a matter of Presidential responsibility and concern." Webb said that the Bureau's views were not "doctrinaire" but grew out of government experience in the operation of research and scholarship programs and the use of advisory committees. Finally, he could cite the advice of scientists themselves, proffered by the Inter-Society Committee, for changes in S. 526 to ensure greater presidential authority. "While I see a great need for the creation of a National Science Foundation," Webb told Bush, "you can appreciate in the light of these circumstances the real difficulty I will encounter in reconciling these matters with a recommendation to the President that he sign a bill with administrative arrangements similar to those in S. 526."[40]

Webb's four-page letter elicited a seven-page response, carefully worded to overcome the Bureau's objections to Smith's bill. Admitting that committees should not engage in "day-by-day executive operations," Bush argued that the foundation would be an unusual government agency requiring special care with respect to "where the ultimate authority shall rest for the policies and over-all performance of the organization." It would be unfair to give full authority to one person, since he needed "protection against unfair accusations of favoritism," and so did the President. A representative board would provide this protection. American business furnished the appropriate model: a general board to set policies and an administrator, responsible to the board, to execute them. Because of the "range and complexity" of science, Congress could not fill the role of board of directors.

Webb's conflict-of-interest argument Bush turned around. It applied more to an individual than to a group. Though public service might not lead men to shed their private interests, the "merged judgments" of a representative group would prevent an individual's interests from determining outcomes. Taken literally, Webb's argument would end in absurdity: Only persons ignorant of research and education could serve on the board, because otherwise they would have a private interest. Presidential appointment and Senate confirmation guaranteed essential safeguards. And able persons would not accept appointment without "authority commensurate with the responsibility which is being carried."

As for coordination of federal science programs, Bush said that authority would still remain with the Budget Bureau and the President. The foundation would not interfere with budgetary control, but it would make available to the Bureau good advice on science programs. Coordination as provided in Smith's bill was voluntary, not compulsory, and not an essential feature of the measure. Someday "more authoritative and regular ways in which to correlate the entire research effort of the federal government" would probably be needed, but not yet.

Bush concluded that it would be most unfortunate "if this important move should now come to an impasse.... it reaches close to the prosperity and security of the nation." Industry could be depended upon to apply science, and specialized federal agencies to foster research in their fields.

But we cannot place fundamental research in this country, the basic research upon which we will ultimately depend, upon a secure foundation for the future unless the federal government moves effectively and intelligently to its support. Our whole future may well revolve around the question of whether or not we do this thing well. I feel that we will either do it soon, or not at all. It would be extraordinarily unfortunate if, having moved a long distance in this direction, the whole affair should now become bogged down on the basis of what seems to me, after all, merely an incident in a great movement.[41]

A Budget Bureau official told a White House aide that Bush's letter "obviously is written for the benefit of the men on the Hill rather than Mr. Webb. He has been very resourceful in making a fallacious argument sound plausible."[42]

Senator Smith did receive copies of the Webb-Bush correspondence, and he continued to hold fast to the idea of board control. Letters from his home state helped keep his spine stiff. From industrial and academic correspondents in New Jersey he heard complaints that modifications of his bill in committee gave the President far too much freedom in the appointment of foundation members. Was there not some way to *require* the President to nominate the right kind of members—that is, those recommended by the National Academy of Sciences? Smith answered that "the very great pressure" from land-grant colleges had compelled the addition of their association as one from which suggested nominees were to be solicited, in order to counter the complaint "that we were trying to keep the control of science within the four corners of the so-called Ivy League of colleges and scientific institutions." After discussions with Bush and others he had concluded that "we will have to trust President Truman or any other President who succeeds him to understand the importance of leaving the control of this enterprise in the hands of pure scientists. I agree with you," he told Princeton physicist Henry D. Smyth, "that if the movement ever becomes political it will die of its own weight."[43]

Some of his more partisan Republican colleagues likewise counseled against any further yielding. If Saltonstall supported Conant's views on the administration of the foundation, the stand of the dominant Taft wing was probably reflected in a letter, clearly inspired by Teeter, from the staff director of the Senate's Republican policy committee urging Smith "to stand firm against the attempt to shift" control from the board to a "politically-appointed administrator." "You have made concession after concession to those who pushed the left-wing 1850 last year," the staff director wrote. "Practically all their pet ideas, except the patents provision, now have a place in your bill. ["No!" Smith wrote in the margin.] The President will never veto your bill as now written. The left-wingers around him are using him as a pressure instrument to get you to make the supreme concession"—to abandon the scientists and give control to politicians. The writer warned that Republican leaders in the House would surely oppose "any compromise on the board principle." As Smith's bill now stood it was "an eminently fair compromise," had Democratic sponsors, and no dissent from the committee. "If you stand on that platform and vigorously resist any further encroachment," the letter concluded, "you can easily win in the Senate and impress the House with your performance."[44]

Yet the warnings from the opposite end of Pennsylvania Avenue were strong enough to wring one more concession from Smith. Together with Webb and Saltonstall, he met with the President about control of the foundation, and if Truman's recollections are accurate, Smith heard some pretty tough talk.[45] Following that conference the Budget Director discussed the issue further with Bush, Conant, and Smith. As a result Smith drew up a substitute section for his bill that granted presidential authority to remove as well as appoint the foundation director, but kept him under the supervision of the executive committee. Although Webb was inclined to accept this arrangement, others in the Bureau had "serious questions," and they sought an opinion from the White House.[46] A draft Bureau memorandum for the President suggested that the proposal be rejected. But if Smith would agree to delete a few words from his substitute section, "it might possibly be viewed as giving the bare minimum of Presidential representation in the Foundation . . . ." Smith's substitute section, with the Bureau official's suggested deletions italicized, read:

> There shall be a Director of the Foundation who, *subject to the supervision and control of the Executive Committee*, shall execute the policies of the Foundation and perform such additional duties as may be prescribed *by the Foundation*. The Director shall be appointed by the President by and with the advice and consent of the Senate after receiving the recommendations of the Executive Committee, and he shall serve at the pleasure of the President. The Director shall receive compensation at the rate of $15,000 per year.[47]

Apparently the draft memorandum was never put in final form and placed before the President for a decision. Senate debate began on the date of its composition, and Senator Smith's comments on his consultations with Webb and the President indicated, since Congress received no contrary evidence from the White House, that Truman would probably accept the organizational arrangements Smith had agreed to, though Smith was careful to state that he did not know whether the President and his advisers would approve them.[48] It seems likely that the President would have accepted Smith's bill, as amended, if it had come to him in the form passed by the Senate. However, he never had to make that decision. As the staff director of the GOP policy committee had warned, Republican leaders in the House strongly opposed any further concessions, and that body restored the original Smith bill provisions on the director's selection and role and did not back down in conference committee.

* * *

The Senate debated the Smith bill five days, beginning May 14. Kilgore's efforts to return to the provisions of S. 1850 were soundly defeated, as was Fulbright's amendment to add a social sciences division.[49] Smith's opponents won a notable victory, however, in passing an amendment providing for distribution of 25 percent of the foundation's funds (two-fifths in equal shares to the states and three-fifths in proportion to states' population) to be spent on foundation-approved research projects by tax-supported colleges and universities. A similar Kilgore amendment had failed (49-30), but the maverick Republican Wayne Morse, in a tour de force of debating tactics, delayed a vote over a weekend, allowing the land-grant and state universities associations time to bring their influence to bear, and succeeded in reversing the earlier decision, 42-40 (32 Democrats and 10 Republicans voting for Morse's amendment, 35 Republicans and 5 Democrats opposing it).[50]

The debate over geographical distribution revealed two different conceptions of the foundation: on the one hand, an agency to support fundamental research in institutions of demonstrated strength; on the other, an agency to foster the development of new centers of scientific education and research throughout the nation. From the land-grant association office Thackrey effectively outlined to the heads of his institutions the argument for institutional development. He pointed to wartime pirating by elite institutions with OSRD contracts of able scientists from colleges like his own Kansas State; quoted Bush's testimony about the need to develop new centers; and highlighted Smith's misconception that land-grant universities did only applied research.[51]

The vote approving the amendment, offered by Magnuson, providing for presidential appointment of the director was even closer (42-41). Although Taft had argued that compromise on the issue was impossible, 5 Republicans, including Smith and Saltonstall, joined 37 Democrats in voting for approval; only one Democrat (W. Lee O'Daniel of Texas) voted for rejection.[52] The outcome was confused, however, because Magnuson had sent two versions of the amendment to the desk, one granting to the foundation as well as the President the power to remove the director, the other restricting removal, before the expiration of the director's four-year term, to the President. The vote was on the amendment giving removal authority only to the President, but during the discussion the clerk had also read the version containing the words "or the Foundation," and Smith thought he was voting for that; he would have voted in the negative otherwise, thus defeating the amendment. Others may have been similarly confused. But by the time the Senate realized what had happened it had voted to approve the bill as a whole. A motion to reconsider the director amendment would have required first a vote to reconsider the vote for passage of the bill. Smith entered such a motion, but on the following day he withdrew it in order to get the bill before the House of Representatives.[53]

Another amendment adopted during the Senate debate signified a rising concern in Congress for federal action to conquer major diseases—a concern that was leading to the creation of "categorical" institutes in the Public Health Service and a phenomenal growth in the budget of the National Institutes of Health.[54] Two senators usually on the opposite ends of the political spectrum—Taft of Ohio and Pepper of Florida—joined by Magnuson, proposed to direct the foundation to establish special commissions on cancer research, heart and intervascular diseases, and any others that might be deemed necessary. (To these the House added a special commission on poliomyelitis and other degenerative diseases.)[55]

Despite the closeness of the votes on some amendments, final passage of S. 526 in the Senate came easily and with bipartisan support. Only 6 Republicans and 2 Democrats voted no, while 79 senators voted yes.[56] Yet it might have been thought ominous that the Senate's paramount Republican, Taft, cast one of the eight negative votes. He had taken a no-compromise position on presidential appointment of the foundation's director, and when his stand on this issue lost, he chose to vote against the bill as a whole and let it be known that he would urge the House to restore board domination.[57] Many House Republicans proved similarly unwilling to make a concession on which the fate of the bill might depend.

* * *

Hearings in March before the House Commerce Committee had already shown the tendency of those handling science legislation there to limit presidential authority. Indeed, the committee's long and friendly colloquy with Jewett, who argued for change in tax laws to encourage private support of science instead of public, suggested that his once lonely stand was now backed by other conservatives. He and Bush exchanged amicable letters about their conflicting testimony.[58] Bush noted that Under Secretary of Commerce William C. Foster "presented the old line Kilgore ideas quite completely"—and with unusual clarity and force—and a spokesman for the Social Science Research Council called Foster's statement "perfectly splendid."[59] Day testified for the Inter-Society Committee and later submitted for the hearings record the results of a poll of the member organizations, in which nearly two-thirds favored a single administrator for the foundation rather than control by a large foundation or a small commission; half favored specific inclusion of the social sciences, and nearly all the rest permissive inclusion; 86 percent favored the granting of undergraduate scholarships by the foundation; and 94 percent thought the legislation should not make specific requirements about patents. The poll revealed that desire for a foundation made the respondents rather flexible on these issues, since 95 percent were willing to accept a commission, 88 percent a single administrator, and 86 percent a large foundation; 99 percent would accept permissive inclusion of the social sciences, 94 percent specific inclusion, and 37 percent would accept exclusion.[60]

After the two days of hearings the House committee, under the chairmanship of Charles A. Wolverton of New Jersey, took no action before the Senate passage of S. 526 in May. And then the committee seemed indifferent or even hostile to the establishment of a new science agency. Budget Bureau officials learned in conversations with members of the House committee staff that Wolverton thought the real need was a mechanism to coordinate federal research, and he wanted to wait and see what the PSRB report would have to say on this matter.[61] The interdepartmental committee on science provided for in S. 526 did not require legislation; it could be established by executive order and given responsibility for coordinating federal research activities.[62] "Coordination" had a special appeal to economy-minded legislators who suspected that there was a lot of expensive overlap and duplication in government-supported research.

Carey of the Budget Bureau reported that Kurt Borchardt of the committee staff told him that "we might as well forget our fine theoretical arguments about responsibility of the President, because the plain facts are that the present Congress views the problem in a political context, and that it will not concede anything further to Presidential leadership."[63] Yet, surprisingly, Borchardt and Teeter devised additions to the Senate-passed amendment on the foundation director that would have strengthened his independence and given him the power to veto budget estimates and spending actions proposed by the executive committee. Teeter's role in this indicated that Bush approved the arrangement and thus made the bill's chances somewhat rosier.[64] But this was a short-lived aberration. On second thought the committee knocked out the new language, and presidential appointment of the director too.

The committee's dawdling disturbed some of Bush's associates, and they sought ways of building a fire under the slow-moving group. Charles F. Brown, OSRD's general counsel in its closing days, reported to Bush in mid-June that the committee had "been haggling over the bill for nearly two weeks with very low attendance." Five or six members seemed to have accepted Jewett's ideas, and "they apparently fear that the bill represents an attempt by the big, rich and strong laboratories, coupled with State and Land Grant people to get a gob of federal funds without the nuisance of contractual obligations which they must fulfill in getting funds from the Services."[65] Since they felt that the military establishment was providing ample research money, it might be a good idea to get the service secretaries to tell congressmen that only a science foundation could handle some matters vital to national defense.[66] Bush heard from his assistant at the Carnegie Institution of Washington, Paul A. Scherer, that when Oscar Cox heard about the situation, "Oscar picked up the ball in the role of a Free American Citizen and, with Oscar Ruebhausen and Jack [John T.] Connor, is getting active as the devil. They are getting in touch with all the members of the Committee through channels which seem to be best and, I think, will lift this thing out of apathy!" Unfortunately, though, Scherer reported, "Jewett continues to have lunch on the Hill, and I am afraid is not very helpful."[67] In his syndicated column Marquis Childs also blamed Jewett's "one-man crusade" for the stalling of the bill in committee.[68]

Not until July 10 did Wolverton's committee issue a report on its bill (H.R. 4102),[69] which contained important differences from the one approved by the Senate. The foundation, not the President, was to appoint the director, whose term was not fixed and whose salary was reduced; no scientific or educational organizations were named from which the President should solicit names of prospective foundation members; the provision of specific allocation of funds for distribution among the states was replaced by a general injunction against "undue concentration" of research and educational support; the foundation was "to formulate, develop, and establish a national policy for the promotion of fundamental research and education in the sciences" rather than simply "to develop, and to encourage the pursuit of, a national policy for scientific research and scientific education"; and the correlation function of the interdepartmental committee on science was expanded to the making of recommendations for "preventing and eliminating unnecessary duplication" in federal science activities.

The brief floor debate in the House revealed that Jewett's testimony and his lunches with representatives had persuaded several of them that the legislation threatened to bureaucratize American science and revive New Deal planning. Hugh D. Scott, Jr., a Pennsylvania Republican, tried to substitute Jewett's tax-credit plan for the bill, but his amendment was ruled not germane.[70] Others expressed concern about invasion of the spheres of private organizations, such as the National Foundation for Infantile Paralysis, or of other government agencies, such as the U.S. Public Health Service.[71] The discussion of special commissions on particular diseases showed that next to the foundation's importance for national defense many congressmen viewed it as a potential stimulus for medical research. Emanuel Celler (D., New York) made a touching reference to his daughter, who was confined to a wheelchair with spastic paralysis. "I hope and I pray," Celler said, "that this National Science Foundation will yield a cure for her as well as those afflicted with poliomyelitis... and the other dreadful diseases that bring so much misery and suffering to the people of this land."[72] A guardian of the Public Health Service, however, was assured that the foundation would not supplant that agency's research activities, but rather assist and "correlate" them.[73]

The committee's rejection of responsibility of the director to the President, embodied in the Senate amendment of S. 526, produced no argument in the House. The only criticism of control by a part-time executive committee came from a Jewett convert, Alfred Bulwinkle, who opposed the establishment of a science foundation and feared that it would be extremely costly.[74] Wolverton, in explaining his committee's decision on organization and control of this untypical federal agency, repeated Bush's arguments; and a Democratic spokesman for the bill, J. Percy Priest, also echoed Bush's frequent citation of the National Advisory Committee for Aeronautics as an appropriate model, an organization free from political influence, some of whose members were nongovernmental part-timers.[75]

The committee's rejection of Morse's amendment did raise some complaints. Wolverton and Priest answered by calling attention to the provisions of H.R. 4102 enjoining "undue concentration" of the agency's funds. Charles R. Robertson (R., North Dakota) offered an amendment to restore the Senate provision. In replying to an Idaho Republican, Abe McGregor Goff, who supported the amendment and objected to allowing federal subsidy of "a few colleges in New England," Wolverton said that his bill did not give preference to any group of institutions but that the amendment did—to about two hundred tax-supported colleges and universities over fifteen hundred private. The amendment was defeated, 81-33.[76]

The lopsided vote on an issue which had brought so many telegrams and letters from the campuses of public institutions manifested the strength of House resistance to amendments that had gained a place in the Senate bill. When the bill—carrying the Senate number, S. 526—went to conference, the House managers were in a strong position to insist on the omission of the main Senate changes, and they met little opposition from their Senate counterparts. The principal concession to the Senate version of the bill was the restoration of names of organizations from which the President should request recommendations of foundation members.[77]

The House readily accepted the conference report, but in the Senate it met spirited resistance from Wayne Morse. He urged postponing action till next year to let senators check with educators in their states. Taft, who had been one of the managers in the conference committee, warned that unless the Senate accepted the report now, advocates of a science foundation should give up hope of its establishment for the duration of the Eightieth Congress—that is, for at least two years. When put to a vote Morse's motion to postpone further consideration of the report until January 1948 was defeated, 46-38.[78]

* * *

Approved by both houses on July 22, S. 526 went to the White House for President Truman's consideration. Even among well-informed persons there was doubt about his decision, and in varying ways they sought to influence it. The land-grant and state universities associations, despite their disappointment at the rejection of Morse's amendment, recommended approval, and so did the Inter-Society Committee.[79] Frank P. Graham, president of the University of North Carolina and a staunch supporter of the President, congratulated Truman on his vetoes of a labor bill (Taft-Hartley), a tax bill, a wool bill, and (Graham hoped) a railroad bill, but he wanted him to sign the science bill even with its flaws.[80] A great number of letters and telegrams, many from other university and college administrators and many from academic scientists, came to the White House asking approval.[81]

Others hoped for a veto. Senator Morse told the President that his opposition was based not simply on "the failure of the Senate conferees to make a fight for the Morse amendment" but especially on "the failure of the bill to protect the American people against the development of a science research monopoly."[82] In a longhand note to Truman's aide for congressional affairs, Charles Murphy, the president of the National Foundation for Infantile Paralysis, FDR's former law partner and close associate Basil O'Connor, said that the provisions for special commissions—"pushed by the cancer people unwisely from their own point of view"—might ruin private medical research.[83] And Condon of the Bureau of Standards wrote Steelman that the bill deserved a veto "because of the bad administrative structure it provides"; he suggested that Steelman's PSRB could then recommend "a constructive program," which should "include establishment of a science unit in the White House, by executive order."[84]

Whatever influence Steelman and presidential assistants may have had on Truman's decision, the advice of the Budget Bureau was probably decisive. On August 1 Webb sent a proposed memorandum of disapproval. Although only the departments of Commerce and Interior had recommended a veto and seven other executive agencies had either favored a signature or offered no objection, Webb stated:

> In the opinion of the Bureau of the Budget, the provisions of this bill regarding the vesting of part-time officials with full administrative and political responsibility, the virtual nullification of the President's appointment power, and the interference with the President's authority to coordinate and correlate governmental programs, are at such variance with established notions of responsible government in a democracy, that the President should withhold his approval....
> Because of the importance of this issue, I have given the bill the most careful deliberation, and it is my firm belief that the enactment of this legislation would be injurious to the whole tradition of Presidential responsibility for the administration of the executive branch, and would also serve as a bad precedent for possible future enactments.[85]

Webb's statement gave no hint of dissent inside the Bureau. Several days earlier, however, Carey had drafted a veto message—and then written a memorandum arguing vigorously against using it. He pointed out that the President had asked Congress to establish a science foundation, emphasizing its importance for national security; the bill was well designed to meet this need despite its administrative defects. Not only would a veto "suggest political retaliation" for suspected through "hard to prove" partisan motives in Congress, but it would also be difficult to explain, since most citizens, including scientists, would not understand the administrative concepts on which it was based. "At no time," Carey contended, "did the President indicate to Congress that this form of legislation is unacceptable to him"; his expressions of dissatisfaction in conversations with Smith did not amount to clear disapproval, as Smith's remarks in the Senate debate showed. Perhaps the most important function of the foundation would be its program of scholarships and fellowships, an authority not likely to be extended to other agencies. Nor did Carey accept the argument that the bill "seriously undermined" the President's position; funds could not be transferred to the foundation from other agencies without the consent of their heads, who were subject to the President's control, and the interagency committee established by the bill would not change the fact that final powers of coordination rested with him. On "the issue of part-time government," the President should wait until it came up more clearly and when he would have "widespread public support and political reinforcement." A veto would likely bring to a close the outstanding service on federal boards and advisory committees of such eminent scientists as Conant and Karl Compton, since it would imply that the President "cannot trust them to serve the public interest first." Finally, Carey argued, "The President should sign the bill, but sound a warning" expressing his fears and his determination "to resist any legislative movement to commit the care of important public interests to selfish groups which are not responsible to the representatives of the people."[86]

Carey guessed that the veto "message will be used, and the memo thrown away," but he "had fun writing it." Elmer Staats thought that "Bill has a little the better argument. His points should be considered carefully."[87] No doubt they were, but over a long period the Bureau had been pressing the other arguments contained in Webb's letter of August 1. So too had Steelman's group. The President accepted them.

President Truman could have let the bill die without comment, since Congress had adjourned in fewer than ten days after it reached his desk, but he chose to give the reasons for his pocket veto in a memorandum of disapproval on August 6.[88] Senator Smith's office immediately issued a press release denouncing the President for making "a 'political football' out of what undoubtedly would have been the greatest contribution made to this country by any Congress since the turn of the century."[89] The following day Truman wrote to Smith: "As I told you, when you discussed the matter with me, if you sent me an unworkable bill I could not sign it." Not saying whether he would have signed the bill as it emerged from the Senate, Truman concluded: "I regret very much that you couldn't see your way clear to discuss the matter further with me before it came to the stage where I had to disapprove it."[90]

The veto made many scientists gloomy, but Bush took the long view and remained optimistic. Ultimately, he was sure, a good science bill would pass and win presidential approval. "If the matter had died in any way in the last session of Congress," he wrote a friend, "that would probably have been the end, but where it blew up with a magnificent bang I am sure the show is not over." It was too bad, he thought, that Congress refused the "courteous gesture" of allowing the President to appoint the director, and certainly there was little reason to believe that the present Congress would back down very far, but there would be another election in 1948. Meantime "the Navy will continue to fill the gap," with an assist from the Atomic Energy Commission. As for Truman, Bush would not join the crowd heaping abuse on him: ". . . on the whole I think he has proven to be a pretty good President even if he does not catch the nuances of some . . . things and even if he leans on a weak group in scientific matters and the like. He may change, and in any case the way to correct any such matter is not to howl about it but to try to give him the service he needs or rather to try to get him to call for it, which may even yet occur."[91]

Bush was right in his assessment of the congressional temper. And Taft's estimate that it would be at least two years before another science foundation bill passed proved conservative. Hope revived among the foundation's backers, but they would have to endure another long wait.

5
New Frontiers— Endless or Finite?

O n balance, it seems fair to say that the President has somewhat the better of the argument with Senator Taft," the editors of the Washington *Star* commented after Truman's veto. Even so, their editorial continued, "the case against the bill as enacted is not strong enough to justify a veto, with the accompanying risk that a Republican Congress, having been rebuffed by the President, will refuse to adopt any new legislation setting up a Science Foundation."[1] The San Francisco *Chronicle*, defending the veto, saw "no merit" in Taft's opposition to presidential appointment of the foundation's director and thought it unfortunate "that partisanship was allowed to get in the way of an essentially good piece of legislation."[2] An aide told Bush: "Rumor has it that Taft said after learning of the veto 'That's the end of such legislation until we have a president who will approve proper bills.' " And Jack Teeter advised Bush to "hold your fire until Senator Taft and Senator Smith have agreed on their plan of action. It is now a political issue. You no doubt saw Senator Taft's statement about no health, welfare or education bills in 1948."[3] Not surprisingly, the effort to establish a new federal science agency had come to be viewed in partisan terms, with Taft, the chairman of the Senate's Republican policy committee, in a position to control any new legislative action.

Since Kilgore's first bill in 1942, proponents of a science foundation had looked hopefully to the Senate. Kilgore, Magnuson, Thomas, Smith, Fulbright, Saltonstall, Morse—these senators had been the chief actors in the sometimes tedious, sometimes spirited drama. Well versed themselves, they had also instructed their colleagues on the matters at issue. By contrast, the brief debate in the House of Representatives on July 16, 1947 displayed general ignorance of the aims of the legislation and an overriding concern for economy. The House had also shown a stubborn spirit of independence from the other chamber. Taft may have stimulated resistance to compromise among Republican (and some Democratic) representatives, but their opposition needed little encouragement, either in 1947 or during the next three years. From the 1947 veto until the spring of 1950, scientists' attention focused mainly on the House, where, to the rising frustration of the proposal's backers, parliamentary bottlenecks and indifference prevented any forward movement.

The veto angered Bush's followers, even though some of them deplored the House refusal to concede appointment of the director to the President.[4] Their gorges rose when their old foe Howard Meyerhoff reappeared in *Science* approving the veto. "Is it not reasonable, now," Meyerhoff asked, "to urge that those who have tried to get a particular type of legislation passed and have twice failed, relinquish the task to disinterested . . . scientists [i.e., the Inter-Society Committee], who will view the problem more broadly and dispassionately?"[5] These were hardly words of sweet reason to those cherishing the vision of Bush's "endless frontier." Yet one of their number, the New York lawyer Bethuel Webster, who had worked for harmony before, sought "to help keep the crowd together and thinking constructively rather than sulking over the obstinate and ignorant attitude expressed in the [President's] memorandum" disapproving the foundation bill. A few days after the veto a letter from Webster appeared in the New York *Times* urging the formation of a "committee representing the President, the Congress and science to prepare a bill which can be passed and put into effect soon after the first of the year." Webster told Bush that one of his aims was "to head off intemperate statements which might have done some harm. I had to take a large sedative before I wrote with such restraint; the men I have been in touch with were discouraged and indignant."[6]

Pleased with the response to his letter in the *Times*, Webster followed it up with an extended comment in *Science*, pointing out essential matters of agreement on the foundation among scientists, Congress, and the President and features of conflict on which concessions must be made.[7] The calm, clear statement helped revive a compromise spirit. Meyerhoff regretted that the magazine's space limits had forced Webster to cut his comment by half but assured him that the letter had caught the attention of many readers.[8] Among them were political leaders to whom Webster sent reprints. Congressman Clifford P. Case (R., New Jersey), for example, took a copy to Senator Smith's office, where he learned that the senator planned "to look into the possibility of an agreement with the President."[9]

Meanwhile the President and Bush had already discussed the possibility of another legislative effort. They argued over whether the board should be controlling or only advisory, and Bush thought he managed to convince the President "that both he and the director needed the protection of a board having authority, for otherwise there would not be adequate defense against political pressure for inappropriate grants to various universities." To Truman's worry about the board becoming "simply a log-rolling affair to make grants to things that its members were interested in," Bush responded that this would not happen if the board contained, along with university scientists, "a strong group of representative citizens interested only in furthering the public welfare." Perhaps Bush was merely displaying his usual self-confidence when he wrote in his memorandum of the conversation, "I think he felt satisfied on this matter," but the outcome was that he, Budget Director Webb, and Secretary of Defense James Forrestal should try to devise a new bill, "and if it looks favorable we will place it before the President. Thereafter we will see whether it appears feasible to urge action on it in Congress. On this latter point we felt that we should go ahead with the matter if there was a reasonable chance of a bill being enacted that would be acceptable to the President, but, on the other hand, we felt that if it was likely to become a political football we should not open the matter."[10]

Among Bush's opponents too there was an obvious willingness to compromise. Harlow Shapley as vice-chairman of the Inter-Society Committee had prompted a good many telegrams asking the President to sign the recently passed bill.[11] Now Shapley energetically went to work to determine exactly how the vetoed measure might be revised, or a new one drawn up, to suit both the Republican Congress and the Democratic President. He talked with Conant and Karl Compton in Cambridge and then went to Princeton to confer with Alexander Smith and Luther P. Eisenhart, Princeton University's president. Next came visits to Washington, where his son Willis in the Budget Bureau helped arrange meetings with Webb and other Bureau officials who would have a voice in deciding Administration policy, and where he also met with Oscar R. Ewing, the Federal Security Administrator, who was interested in locating the science agency in a proposed new Department of Health, Education and Security as suggested in a report issued late in August by the President's Scientific Research Board.[12] In discussions with land-grant college officials Shapley asked that if they continued to push the Morse amendment, they drop the provision limiting formula funds to tax-supported institutions.[13] Then came visits to Capitol Hill, where in some offices Shapley's association with left-wing political action groups caused him to be regarded with intense suspicion, though the simplicity and earnestness so evident in his autobiography must often have thawed initial hostility.[14] At the end of the year, in

Chicago, he reported on his activities at a meeting of the Inter-Society Committee, which authorized its executive committee to support legislation it deemed satisfactory.[15]

Not only was Shapley doggedly attentive to matters of detail that might prove sticky in Congress or executive offices; he was also diligent in keeping all parties at interest informed of his findings. Bush, after lunching with Senator Smith, wrote Shapley: "It looks to me as though you have done a fine job on your excursions about here recently, and I am quite optimistic that we will have good sound legislation under way in the next session."[16] Even before his meeting with the President in September, Bush had asked Charles Brown to draft a bill which would meet the main objections set forth in the veto memorandum. Brown's several drafts from September to December reflected not only Bush's ideas but those forged and tempered in Shapley's many conferences as well.[17]

The process of accommodation was often complicated and many-sided. For instance, Smith, in order to satisfy Taft, wanted the director to be appointed by the President "from the membership of the Foundation." Shapley was willing to accept this but the Bureau was not. It pointed out awkward situations that might arise, as, for example, the continuing presence on the board of a director who had resigned or been removed from his position. The Bureau proposed instead that the director must meet the qualifications prescribed for foundation members. For a while Wolverton insisted on retaining a division of national defense despite the objections of most scientists; ultimately he acquiesced in its elimination, but foundation-supported research related to national defense would require prior consultation with the military establishment. Wolverton's earlier insistence on an interdepartmental committee to coordinate federal research activities, a provision of the vetoed bill, was answered by the creation of such a committee by executive order. The Federal Security Agency (FSA), knowing that the President's Commission on Higher Education would recommend a college scholarship program to be administered by the Office of Education, wanted to strike the foundation's authority to grant undergraduate scholarships—the most important function of the foundation in Conant's view. Scholarships remained in the bill and a Budget officer commented that the Bureau might be able to maintain a consistent federal policy through budgetary control.[18]

Ideas clashed and so did personalities. Pride and prejudice continued to threaten to break through the surface of harmony that men like Webster and Shapley were promoting. Bush's friends were alarmed when the widely published Washington Merry-Go-Round column said that Truman had spoken "very critically" of Bush's work in OSRD, largely blamed him for the passage of a "hodgepodge science foundation bill," and was "very much undecided" about appointing him to head the new Research and

Development Board.[19] Although Truman did make the appointment and assured Bush that he remained in good standing in the White House, the column increased Bush's animosity toward the *de facto* science adviser. In private correspondence Bush and his close associates wrote scathing comments about Steelman's *Science and Public Policy* report.[20]

The Steelman report introduced a confusing element into the plans to make only slight revisions of Smith's bill for a science foundation. Government planners began to consider drawing up an entirely new bill, and drafters in the Federal Security Agency went to work on such a measure. An informal meeting of staff members from PSRB, FSA, the Bureau of Standards, and the Budget Bureau, called by a member of Steelman's group, discussed drafting an Administration bill "for the support of education, including support for the social sciences and for basic scientific research," but they decided that they "ought to plug for the same kind of a foundation as had been considered heretofore." One of the group, Edward Condon, "spoke bitterly" about Bush's empire and his Research and Development Board's munificent budget for military research.[21] Although the Budget Bureau considered the possibility of a completely new tack, placing the foundation in FSA, it settled on Shapley's strategy of revisions in Smith's bill.[22]

Another threat to consensus came from a study group of the Washington Association of Scientists, under the chairmanship of Clifford Grobstein, a biologist at the National Cancer Institute. Their paper "Toward a National Science Policy?", which appeared both in *Science* and the *Bulletin of the Atomic Scientists*, argued that there was a fundamental difference in the philosophy of science-government relations between the "Kilgore-Administration school" and the "Magnuson-Smith school." "The basic issue," the group held, "is none other than the proper role of the Federal Government in regulating those areas of our national life which are intimately related to the public welfare and security, in this instance the shape and scope of science." Unless a foundation subject to public control and interested in developing strong science centers throughout the country came into being soon, the military establishment would increasingly dominate science policy. The group even resurrected the Kilgore stand on patent policies.[23] Presumably Shapley agreed with most of their premises and conclusions, but in the interest of achieving a foundation, he reportedly tried to stop their publication of any more such divisive articles.[24] Conant was so annoyed by what he considered the article's misrepresentation of Administration views that he wrote to Secretary of Commerce Averell Harriman asking him or one of his Cabinet colleagues—anyone but Steelman!—"to bring the matter to the President's attention" in the hope of keeping revived foundation legislation from becoming a partisan issue.[25]

The potentially greatest disturber of the peace was John Teeter. Now with the American Cancer Society, Teeter was evidently itching to get back on Capitol Hill to steer foundation legislation. He saw the Steelman report as "a move by the administration to recapture scientific leadership" and to regiment research; advised Bush against compromise moves that would drift away from the views of Taft's Senate GOP policy committee; attended the annual meeting of the land-grant colleges association to hear the discussion of renewing the fight for the Morse amendment; worried about Shapley's becoming a spokesman for the *real* leaders of science but professed to welcome his aid in bringing "the left wing elements and liberals along"; and got permission from his boss "to give any effort to the Foundation."[26]

To most advocates of a foundation who wanted to avoid another partisan battle, Teeter had become an intolerable mischief-maker. Early in December Bethuel Webster sent Bush, Homer Smith, and Oscar Ruebhausen copies of a letter he had just received from Meyerhoff. The Smith College geology professor told Webster that he had been pleased to see renewed legislative efforts

> going along quite smoothly and promisingly. This is still the case, but during the past ten days there has been one development which prompts me to write to you rather frankly. This is no time to mince words, and I am writing you because of your close connection with the Bush group.
>
> Although there has been a great deal of optimism regarding the possibilities of a compromise among such people as Harlow Shapley, James Conant, and many others, this optimism received a serious setback two weeks or more ago when John Teeter appeared once again on the Washington scene. Teeter has aroused so much wrath among scientists that it is absolutely essential for Dr. Bush to keep him out [of] current developments. He may, if he wishes, insist upon his right to lend any member of his staff to Senate or House committees, but in this instance even the rudiments of diplomacy demand that Teeter be eliminated. Since I seem to be the only one who has guts or gall enough to speak out, I have been asked to get this message across, and I am using you for my medium. I think you know why the reaction against Teeter exists, but if there is any doubt in your mind, I can document these facts to any degree you may wish. But I was so thoroughly gratified with the initiative you took in bringing forth a compromise, that I do not want to see anything happen to negotiations which are under way. Because of my status with the Bush group, I am keeping carefully out of them; and it is for this reason that I feel privileged to ask in the name of many people on the other side that Teeter be kept out, too. He very obviously lacks the good sense or the independence to stay out on his own accord.

This was not an expression of personal prejudice, Meyerhoff said. "Present negotiations are much too important . . . to be jeopardized by personalities, and unfortunately, John Teeter has become a personality which will jeopardize the spirit of compromise which happily exists." His own activities with respect to foundation legislation, Meyerhoff continued, had not sprung from "any personal motive or prejudices.... I have merely tried to reflect the opinions of a very large but inarticulate group of scientists. I felt that both your article and your letter to me were written in the same spirit, and I want to assure you of my whole-hearted cooperation in thinking out a happy denouement of this entire problem."[27]

Homer Smith confirmed the animus toward Teeter and told Bush "it might be well to pull Jack off." Bush replied that he was puzzled about what to do, especially since he no longer had any official connection with Teeter.[28] But he obviously did suggest to Teeter that he not upset the negotiations for a bill that would meet Administration approval. In a long letter to his former OSRD chief, Teeter analyzed the conflict between congressional majority policy and Administration stands and concluded: "It all adds up to this: If you could put yourself in Senator Taft's shoes would you let the bill come out of Committee and become an achievement of President Truman in 1948?" But then he added: "I respect your advice and will stay out of the project, but I would be less than honest if I failed to pass on my belief that the bill has a less promising future than it had in 1947. I hope I am wrong."[29]

The irrepressible Teeter would bob up again, annoying land-grant association officers among others, but he did not upset negotiations between Congress and the executive branch.[30] After Shapley's exploratory visits, a series of conferences between Smith and Wolverton and White House officials, including the President, and between staff members of the Senate Committee on Labor and Public Welfare and the Budget Bureau, brought agreement on a bill which was introduced in both houses on March 25, 1948. Kilgore joined Smith, Magnuson, and others in sponsoring the Senate measure (S. 2385).[31]

Smith told the Senate that he believed the bill met most of the objections raised in the veto memorandum and would receive presidential approval. In executive offices, however, amendments in committee following the slowly reached agreement were viewed as stripping power from the foundation's director, and Webb suggested that they might cause another veto. Smith replied that the committee did not intend to reduce the director's executive authority, and his explanation satisfied both his colleagues and the Bureau. On May 5 the Senate passed the bill, as amended in committee, without a record vote.[32]

Although the bill sailed easily through the Senate, its sponsors had anxiously watched Wayne Morse to see if he would renew the fight for mandated geographic distribution of research funds. While the land-grant and state universities associations wanted such a provision in the law, they concluded that it would probably cause another defeat. But they hesitated to tell Morse, and after they did they feared that he might openly oppose the compromise bill. Morse did not oppose it, but he told the president of the University of Minnesota of his disappointment that the land-grant association had taken a "runout powder." " 'This compromise was completely unnecessary,' he said, 'and we could easily have won the principle.' He indicated that he had rather lost interest in the bill and in our cause."[33]

* * *

Now attention shifted to the House, where Wolverton's committee had before it the Senate-approved bill and H.R. 6007, identical to the original S. 2385. The members showed little sense of urgency, and foundation backers' high hopes began to fall when the committee decided to hold a day of hearings on June 1. Delay always opened the door to discord, and the political battles of an unusual presidential election year ensured that almost no issue could avoid partisanship. As the Cold War deepened, fears of Russia and of home-grown radicals like those in Henry Wallace's Progressive party made security and national defense obsessive concerns of many congressmen. What point was there in a science foundation whose most important division—National Defense—had been excised, especially since the armed services were now providing ample support for military research and Bush's Research and Development Board was coordinating their efforts?

Another big worry in the House was government spending. At the June 1 hearings Hugh Scott pressed Lawrence R. Hafstad of the Research and Development Board, appearing in Bush's stead, for estimates of the annual cost of the foundation and of the number of scholarships and fellowships it would award. Several other committee members were similarly skeptical about the need for a new science agency.[34]

In comments to the Budget Bureau some executive agencies also expressed sharp criticisms of the House bill. These may have been bureaucratic in spirit but were not always so in style. To Condon of the Bureau of Standards,

the Foundation would be simply a polite group of university officials who would give the requisite stuffed-shirt backing to their stooge, the Director, in the operation of log-rolling grants of Federal aid to colleges, while giving no support to the agencies of the Federal government which are struggling to do a conscientious job of public service, against the great handicap of various arbitrary out-dated limitations on salary, contract arrangments, etc.[35]

J. Donald Kingsley, formerly with Steelman's group and now Ewing's deputy in FSA, questioned allowing the foundation to conduct a scholarship and fellowship program, wanted specific arrangements for the assumption of the foundation by another agency if a broad program of federal aid to higher education should be enacted, and urged stronger provision for the social sciences. The final paragraph of the letter Kingsley proposed to send to Wolverton was, according to Carey, "a ringing denunciation of the part-time board as the primary government of NSF." This had been the Bureau's position in the past, but, Carey commented, "we are a party now to the administrative arrangements called for in the legislation, and our criticism ought to be pretty temperate."[36] The NACA letter was even worse, in Carey's opinion—"a rather ill-tempered harangue" containing "not one favorable word for an NSF."[37]

Budget Bureau screening kept executive offices' grumbles from reaching Wolverton's committee through direct channels. In any event the committee reported out H.R. 6007, with several changes, on June 4 and recommended its prompt passage.[38] But it was clear by then that the legislation was in trouble. Day said it was "threatened with pernicious anemia," and he appealed to heads of land-grant institutions to push their representatives to act quickly.[39] A delegation from the Engineers Joint Council visited Steelman at the White House and then went to the Capitol. While they found "no organized opposition in either House," they did see "the urge for economy" as a danger to passage of a bill. More threatening was lack of time, since "a glut of unpassed legislation" might prevent getting a foundation measure on the House calendar.[40]

Neither the House bill nor the Senate's raised a question of a veto, in Carey's estimate, and he thought that whatever emerged from a conference committee was likely to be better than the legislation disapproved by the President in 1947.[41] Yet, unless the House acted, there could be no conference, and the House could not consider a bill until it was placed on the calendar. With Congress scheduled to adjourn on June 19, the pressure of time required that H.R. 6007 gain a position on the "consent calendar." An objection prevented this, however, and the bill went back to the Rules Committee. The only remaining way to consideration was the granting of a rule by that committee. But the majority leader, Charles A. Halleck (R., Indiana), did not consider the bill "must" legislation, and two outside sources of opposition also frustrated those seeking a rule: a former Democratic congressman from Texas, Fritz G. Lanham, who claimed that the bill gave the foundation the right to acquire patents and thus "stifle the small inventor," and the National Infantile Paralysis Foundation, which objected to the House bill's provision for a special commission on poliomyelitis—part of a " 'Communistic', un-American . . . scheme contrived by Dr. Harlow Shapley and others."[42]

Shapley, Day, and Wolfle of the Inter-Society Committee talked selectively with members of the Rules Committee but failed to get action. Wolfle also talked with a member of Senator Smith's staff who thought "the bills are totally lost unless [Speaker Joseph W.] Martin [R., Massachusetts] and Halleck can be persuaded to bring them to a vote." The longtime enmity between Martin and Shapley made this slim chance even less likely. Charles Brown agreed to talk to Bush in the hope that he might influence James W. Wadsworth (R., New York) and Christian A. Herter (R., Massachusetts), both members of Rules; but this too seemed like grasping at a straw, especially since "Bush has taken the line this year that he is not going out of his way to push this legislation unless he is urged to do so."[43] In a telephone call to Bush's office Brown left word that because of the "smear campaign" by Lanham and the polio people, "the only hope now is to apply direct and vigorous pressure to Speaker Martin, Leo Allen [R., Illinois], Chairman of the Rules Committee and/or Majority Leader Halleck." The Defense Department could not approach them directly, Brown said, "but the more outside pressure the better, except from Harlow Shapley. I am seeking to reach Bethuel Webster. Jack Connor is unavailable. I suggest that you stir up Mr. Conant or political figures in Massachusetts, Illinois, and Indiana."[44]

All the desperate efforts were unavailing. The legislation never came to debate in the House before adjournment or in the brief special session following the presidential nominating conventions.

* * *

The third time had not been the charm. Frustrated again, discouraged and baffled by the ways of politicians, scientists were said to have lost hope of achieving a foundation and had no plans to lobby for it.[45] Still, the latest effort had come so close to success that some leaders of the campaign resolved to keep pushing. One of these was President Edmund Day of Cornell University. Day had worked hard for the legislation in both the Inter-Society Committee and the land-grant association. In the summer and fall of 1948 he began to prepare for a fourth try.

Like most other persons Day expected a Republican victory over the divided Democrats in the November elections. So he wrote Senator Smith, whom he thought likely to be in the driver's seat again with Republicans in control of Congress and the presidency, asking what the Inter-Society Committee could do to help pass legislation in the next Congress. Despite the past "discouraging experiences," Day said, "I think the Foundation can be had and had in an essentially sound form."[46] And shortly after the surprising outcome of the presidential contest Day wrote Steelman to find out whether Truman intended to give the foundation a "high priority" in his legislative proposals. Steelman replied that he expected the President to urge the Congress to act speedily.[47]

Truman did not mention the foundation in his State of the Union address, but in his budget message a few days later he again asked for its creation.[48] The Budget Bureau had already learned that the House Commerce Committee would probably assign preferred status to science legislation.[49] Early in January the Bureau began intensive discussions with informed and concerned persons in and out of government to determine whether to revive the latest compromise measure or try a new tack.

The Democratic control of both houses of the Eighty-First Congress encouraged some individuals and groups to argue for a return to Kilgore principles of 1945, but they failed to recognize that the coalition of Republicans and conservative southern Democrats could still throttle the kind of legislation they wanted. The safest course, the Bureau decided, was slightly to revise the compromise bill of the Eightieth Congress. Even this cautious endeavor met obstacles. Old-fashioned conservatism was being displaced by chimeras. The growing virulence of the crusade against "un-American" or "subversive" activities became manifest in attacks on backers of the legislation so that it acquired, through association with them, a taint of suspicion. Bolstered by the continuing strength of Jewett's warnings of the stifling effects of bureaucracy on research, the attack on subversion and the urge to economize long served to delay action on a science bill.

In talking with federal agency officials members of the Budget Bureau found the usual kind of territorial protectiveness. Kingsley of FSA had come to doubt "the merits of a Foundation under almost any circumstances" but thought unrestricted research grants to universities might be a good idea. He did not believe an independent agency could coordinate federal research programs, and Carey's mention of the Interdepartmental Committee for Scientific Research and Development (ICSRD), which had been established by executive order but some thought should be incorporated in the science foundation, drew "a cry of dismay from Kingsley," who considered it a hopeless failure.[50] Condon denounced federal "fat cats"—the military establishment and the Atomic Energy Commission—and, in Carey's paraphrase, "sees NSF as another rival for research appropriations, and visualizes educators crowding into Washington with their briefcases to lobby for NSF grants and raising a rumpus if money is granted to old line Government-operated laboratories like his own. He predicts increasing tension and rivalry among Federal research agencies if NSF is set up." But a foundation having only policy-making functions—not grant-making authority, which would make it another "fat cat"—did meet Condon's approval. He wanted better management and coordination of federal science programs but believed that any agency charged with these functions would require "the protection and prestige of the Executive Office." Like Kingsley, he considered the ICSRD "a total failure" owing to lack of leadership and of White House support.[51] Smithsonian Institution officials suggested that the Administration seek only minor changes in the bill passed by the Senate in May since they wanted quick enactment. Agreeing with Condon on the danger of the "withering away of activity in Federal laboratories," they feared that the foundation would overemphasize support of university research. They opposed vesting coordinating authority in the agency.[52]

In a meeting arranged at Day's request, he and Don Price told the Bureau that "nothing should be done at this time to rock the boat"—there should be no attempt "to get an ideal bill." Day cautioned that a change in the board's role from policy-making to a more advisory one would raise a protest from Bush's followers. Although all of those in the meeting agreed on the desirability of keeping mandated special commissions, as for cancer and polio, out of the bill, Day and Wolfle reported that there was strong feeling in the House committee that they should be restored. Day said that the land-grant institutions' effort to achieve a formula for distribution of research funds had been designed not to dole out "pork" but as "a safeguard against Federal domination of research in the state universities." Carey concluded, however, that Day would advise against reviving this divisive issue. Day opposed saddling the new agency with a coordination function, and he thought that "stronger language requiring the Foundation to formulate a national research policy," as advocated by the Federation of American Scientists (FAS), "would inevitably arouse suspicions as to the real purposes of the Government."[53]

The Washington Study Group of the FAS advocated quite different ideas in their meeting with Budget Bureau officials:

> The basic charter of the Foundation should be broadened to give it the power actually to *implement* a national policy for the promotion of research rather than merely to develop and encourage the pursuit of such a policy. FAS feels very strongly that the NSF should be *the top Federal scientific agency* rather than merely another agency for the distribution of funds for the support of research and training in the sciences. The Foundation's charter should require it to survey continuously world science and continuously to adjust our own policy to the total situation.

While the foundation's grants should be restricted to basic research, its policy role should extend to applied research as well.[54]

Grobstein and his associates thought that the recent Democratic electoral victory made the time "opportune for the Administration's pushing an ideal bill rather than picking up where the Congress left off last spring." They presented detailed suggestions for improvement of the bill (S. 247) which Senator Elbert Thomas had recently introduced. These included: specific extension to the social sciences; a policy-making director with "a fairly long statutory term"; emphasis on development of centers of scientific strength and "wide geographic distribution of scholarships and fellowships"; stronger "public interest language" in the patent provisions; more freedom from State Department restrictions on international cooperation; and transfer of classified research to the Defense Department. To get away from the confusing identification of the presidentially appointed board as the "Foundation," the FAS representatives proposed that the bill's first sentence read: "The Foundation shall consist of a 24-member board and an Executive Director." The board should be strictly advisory. In sum, the group proposed a return to Kilgore principles and provisions similar to those of the compromise bill (S. 1850) of early 1946.[55]

The FAS study group's effort to rally the Administration from weariness persuaded Carey that "we . . . can and should put a little more muscle into the Foundation. As it now shapes up, our Foundation is a rather puny creature." He recommended giving it genuine responsibility for policy formulation and for "broadening the research base of the Nation instead of feeding the 'fat cats,'" though quality and efficiency of research should also be sought. Other proposed changes in Thomas's bill would strengthen the director's role. Thus, in accepting the FAS suggestion that the foundation be defined as consisting of "a National Science Board of 24 members, and a Director," Carey said that this "would serve to clarify . . . internal relationships" and "make the Director a partner in the formulation of policies." Some of Carey's colleagues strongly dissented from his view that the foundation should formulate policy. They thought that the most important change to propose to Senator Thomas was "specific inclusion of the social sciences."[56]

Carey lost the argument on a strong policy responsibility for the foundation. The Bureau suggested several drafting revisions to Senator Thomas, largely directed toward administrative tidiness, and proposed dropping names of divisions since the board could disestablish them anyway and determine the agency's internal organization. To clear up the confusion of the word "Foundation," the Bureau adopted the idea of defining the agency as a board and a director, but said that this was not intended to reduce the board's authority nor to increase the director's.[57]

After a month with no response from Senator Thomas, persons at the Bureau began to wonder why nothing was happening. Carey inquired and learned that while Thomas's committee had not taken exception to any of the Bureau's points, it had made a strategic decision to make no changes in S. 247. The committee wanted to avoid hearings and floor debate; by "passing the buck to the House of Representatives" it hoped to shift fights with special-interest groups to that body. If the House passed a bill, the Senate could try to make changes desired by both the committee and the Bureau through negotiations in conference.[58] Consequently, the Senate Committee on Labor and Public Welfare reported S. 247 without amendment, and it passed the Senate without discussion on March 18.[59]

* * *

During the five days of hearings before J. Percy Priest's House subcommittee in March and April most of the witnesses followed well-worn paths. Never before, however, had the far Right been so zealous in throwing suspicion on the motives of foundation backers—especially Shapley and members of the FAS—and raising the specter of government dictation of research policy. Fritz Lanham went far beyond Jewett's orthodox rugged individualism. Quoting the Chicago *Tribune* and the House Committee on Un-American Activities on Shapley's links to Communist causes, Lanham argued that

> even the disclosed facts [concerning Shapley's advocacy of the foundation] are enough to arouse suspicions and put us on notice that in the original conception of the suggestion may have lurked a desire of other than American origin to lead us to abandon our time-honored principles and systems....
>
> Of one thing we may be very sure. The American pre-eminence we have attained has not been based upon the centralization of arbitrary power in government. That's a doctrine of certain foreign regimes, and it is becoming increasingly evident that they wish us to adopt it to their own totalitarian advantage. Our progress has come from that rugged individual upon whose freedom of action our governmental philosophy has been predicated, an individual laboring under the incentives of our Constitution and laws to give full expression to his God-given ingenuity in creative accomplishments for our progress. And, oh, how well the achievements of that unhampered individual have proved the wisdom of our policy. From the cellars and garrets of these humble, but independent, folk have emanated the forces of American greatness. Let us be sure to remember that. Surely no such legislation as this is necessary to inspire loyal American scientists to do their duty, and isn't it equally clear that no step should be taken which could diminish the ardor or the effort of those who have taken us to the forefront?

Lanham ended by quoting first Scripture and then Kipling: "Lord, God of Hosts, be with us yet; lest we forget! Lest we forget!"[60]

John W. Anderson, president of the National Patent Council, said that his organization was "much alarmed by persistent efforts of . . . coldly fanatical men, alien-inspired, believed to have as their objective the stifling of that incentive to invent and produce which has given to America its phenomenal industrial growth." He reminded Priest's subcommittee of the almost daily shocks of "new revelations of the depth of penetration by this vast fifth column of underground operatives set upon us by the Kremlin." These exposures seemed "to warn that the proposed legislation for a National Science Foundation dovetails significantly into this general subversive pattern." Anderson suggested that Kilgore's first bill may "have been spawned somewhere within the long leftist shadow of Henry Wallace," elaborated on Shapley's suspicious activities, and gave an account of a visit to the office of the Federation of American Scientists (on the second floor above a cigar store) that made it seem like a dingy conspiratorial den. ". . . should we not make certain," Anderson asked, "that we have proved our ability to identify and clear all subversives out of other agencies of government before we set up this one, so skillfully tailored to subversive purposes?"[61]

Although rejecting these jeremiads and the notion that private fortunes and lonely inventors in cellars could provide the research needed for industrial progress, Priest and his colleagues and then their parent committee proceeded with great deliberation. The five days of hearings stretched out over almost four weeks, and nearly another month passed before Priest introduced a "clean bill" (H.R. 4846) on May 24. Meantime the Bureau and the President had encouraged the committee and the House leaders to make a few modifications in the legislation and move it along.[62] Finally, on June 14, the Commerce Committee favorably reported a bill which reflected some of the Bureau's suggestions but also, in one respect, the growing fear of communism. Every recipient of a scholarship or fellowship was to file an affidavit "that he does not believe in, and is not a member of and does not support any organization that believes in or teaches, the overthrow of the United States Government by force or violence or by any illegal or unconstitutional methods."[63] Another important committee amendment directed the foundation "to evaluate scientific research programs," both public and private.

Despite the delays, which some attributed to the lobbying of the National Patent Council, there was still ample time for the House to pass a science bill and to reach agreement with the Senate before the end of the session. But once more the coalition of Republicans and southern Democrats on the House Rules Committee blocked action. Wadsworth, who some believed was influenced by Jewett, did not want to create a new drain on the treasury. Nor did the chairman of Rules, Adolph J. Sabath (D., Illinois), who was presumably subject to pressure from the President and the House leadership.

Beginning in June and throughout the summer the White House, the Budget Bureau, and Bush's cohorts all tried unsuccessfully to budge the committee. Charles Murphy wrote Sabath that the President considered H.R. 4846 "an important part of the Administration program, and he will appreciate it if you can get a rule reported so that the bill may be considered in the House." Bush wrote Wadsworth that the bill was "much needed" and "should not increase expenditures in fiscal 1950." Day and Conant also urged Wadsworth to get the bill passed. Charles Brown enlisted another of Bush's Washington lawyer friends, Lloyd N. Cutler, to try his hand. Cutler learned that Wadsworth had shaken even Christian Herter by producing two letters, one from Conant and one from Bush, which "were contradictory as to the basic purposes of the Bill." Unless Bush could persuade Wadsworth or Herter, or both, the bill would probably stay in Rules until Congress adjourned.[64] Carey suggested that either the President or Steelman make another effort with Sabath. In a phone conversation Sabath reportedly told Steelman that he hoped to arrange a trade which would clear "a rivers and harbors bill on condition that the science bill also be cleared." Besides pressing the Democratic chairman, the President invited Wadsworth to the Oval Office and tried to persuade him that the foundation was needed.[65]

Since the chief objection to the foundation seemed to be its possible expense, Priest suggested that this might be overcome if the Administration submitted a budget estimate. The President agreed to this procedure and said that Sabath had indicated that Rules would release the bill.[66] Nevertheless, the New York *Times* reported on September 29 that the Administration "suffered a major setback" two days before when the Rules Committee, by a one-vote margin, refused to clear the bill. Only one chance remained, Sabath told the reporter: new House rules provided that after twenty-one days in Rules a bill might be called up by the chairman of a standing committee—in this instance, Robert Crosser (D., Ohio)—on either the second or fourth Monday of the month. This meant either October 10 or 24, but Crosser was in Europe and not expected to return for four weeks. The bill remained buried in Rules when the first session of the Eighty-First Congress came to an end.

Still, the setback might not mean final failure. The Senate-passed bill continued on the House agenda and the twenty-one day rule could still be used in the second session beginning in January 1950. Perhaps Wadsworth had this in mind when he suggested to Bush, shortly before the first session ended, including in the bill a statement denying any intent to increase the amount of federal expenditures for research. If Bush would draft such a provision, Wadsworth would discuss it with members of Crosser's committee and his own colleagues on Rules, with a view to proceeding with the legislation when Congress reassembled. Bush said he agreed that the federal budget should not continue to grow, but he thought the science foundation would enable the Budget Bureau to give Congress a better understanding of research expenditures and actually help reduce them. He told Wadsworth he would discuss the matter with the Bureau.[67]

In transmitting Wadsworth's proposal to the Bureau, Bush wondered whether it might not be appropriate to say in the bill's preamble "that this is not merely a drive for further funds." The substantial increase in government support of science since the war had led him to conclude that federal money for research in universities had reached "just about the right amount. . . . I feel that the danger of wasting funds or encouraging mediocre work by over-support is just as great as failure to support worthwhile things . . . ."[68] Later Bush had lunch with Director of the Budget Frank Pace, and they decided that the Bureau should reply directly to the New York congressman.[69]

The issue troubled Bureau officials. Carey feared that acceptance of the suggestion would "be buying a cat in a bag." Recalling the estimates of the foundation's budget in *Science—The Endless Frontier*, Carey found it puzzling that Bush now thought basic research expenditures were about right. To adopt this view would change the idea of the foundation from one to promote basic research and education to a management agency concerned

> with the re-ordering of existing basic research programs and the redefining of emphasis according to concepts of balance of program.... there would be no room for social science research if we should now set our brakes on basic research. A fundamental query, I think, is whether the President could find 24 men, good and true, to come to Washington even on a part-time basis to guide a Foundation whose frontiers have suddenly become not endless but abruptly finite, and preside over the dreary task of preparing a cold snack out of everybody's leftovers.

Other government agencies, some of them already leery about the foundation, would "make powerful medicine" if they concluded that the new agency "is to become a holding company for all Federal basic research and training."[70]

Carey admitted that Bush was "probably right" that federal subsidies for basic research had reached proper limits. Yet National Research Council panels had been "recommending sky-high expenditures in various fields of basic research. Who, then," Carey wondered, "is to speak with authority on the question of whether we ought to shut off the spigot?" Wadsworth would not be satisfied by a reminder that the Bureau and Congress controlled expenditures; but a promise of frugality written into the foundation's charter would cause "a very bad reaction both from the highbrow press and from the scientific organizations."[71]

Another Bureau official, perhaps too concerned about getting Rules to release the science bill voluntarily, argued for a counterproposal that would require the foundation to spend a year or two in deciding what it should do and how to do it. He suggested withholding program funds from the agency until it had appraised and evaluated the nation's research activities and, using this background information, formulated for itself a policy, program, and standards acceptable to the President. Only then would the President be authorized to transfer other agencies' research programs to the foundation or recommend a budget for its support of research and education.[72]

Pace's response to Wadsworth rejected the idea of pledging a limit on spending but tried to assure the congressman that he need not worry. Several months earlier the Bureau had estimated that the foundation would add only about $15 million to the federal budget in 1950, perhaps add another $10 million the next year, and then level off. The Bureau believed that the foundation should provide direct support of basic research on important matters. "Equally important," however, was its responsibility to evaluate the national research effort and to assist the President and the Bureau "in improving the management of research and development programs." The Bureau had attempted to analyze and coordinate these programs, but the task required a range of specialized knowledge that only an agency like the foundation could provide.[73]

Wadsworth called the Bureau's response "most disappointing." He told Bush that the science bill went further than Pace realized, "not only in the field of expenditure but in the exercise of power." Perhaps the question could be taken up again when Congress returned.[74]

In the past Bush had taken a long-range, serene attitude toward congressional delays. The trend had been in the right direction. But he decided that the endeavor had now reached "a critical state." He had written Wadsworth earlier of their similar worry about "the trend toward the welfare state." In seeking to explain the Bureau's position to the congressman, Bush reaffirmed his own conservative views, but he artfully turned them into an argument bolstering Pace's.[75]

The trouble with the numerous existing programs of federal support of university research, Bush said, was that they were

being administered by individual bureaucrats. There is nothing opprobrious in the term bureaucrat; they have their place; but when they are handing out large amounts of federal money essentially as gifts the effect on the bureaucrat and also on the recipients is such as to make one pause and wonder what may come in another decade. The recipients of these grants are quite happy, they have several sources of funds and can trade about, but they are likely to become adept at that sort of political maneuvering at the sacrifice of more virile characteristics.

This interesting forecast refurbished Bush's old argument for a responsible, policy-making board and against unchecked decisions by single persons.[76]

The establishment of the foundation would not, Bush said, immediately lead to the shifting of other agencies' basic research to the new agency, and thus create "a unitary program" enabling the President and Congress to see a single sum for fundamental science. The Public Health Service would resist transferring its medical research, but AEC and ONR would gladly give up some of their functions. Even if the foundation had no new money but simply assumed other federal programs, its board-supervised administration "would set an example" which would spread to other agencies or, if they failed to profit by it, cause transfers of their funds.[77]

Bush's final argument sought to force Wadsworth to reconsider his consistent opposition to federal aid to higher education:

We are at a time when federal money in rather large amounts has got to be used for scientific research in this country if the universities are to maintain their position in comparison with industrial research and research in the government laboratories, and it is very much to our interest, from the national security angle and from the standpoint of the general prosperity of the country, that the universities should be thus maintained with a strong program of pure research. If the matter is handled wisely it can be of enormous benefit. But the system now being used ... is a dangerous situation for the long pull. I trust that the Congress with the full matter before it will have the wisdom to correct that system before it is too late.[78]

Wadsworth remained unconvinced, and others in the conservative coalition on the Rules Committee also continued their opposition to discharging the bill. Some of them tried to repeal the twenty-one day rule, and thus block Truman's Fair Deal program, but this effort failed. Late in February Crosser resorted to the rule to get the science bill to the House floor.[79] Meanwhile, in his State of the Union and budget messages the President had again asked Congress to establish the foundation.[80] The Budget Bureau and the White House kept closely in touch with the legislation and expected the bill to pass, but as Staats told Steelman, "it would be unwise to relax our efforts."[81]

Dael Wolfle, who was taking an increasingly important role in working with Bureau officials and members of Congress and their committee staffs, informed the readers of *Science* of the precise status of the legislation and suggested that individual scientists let their representatives know how important it was. Through the columns of that journal too, the Inter-Society Committee answered a pamphlet published by the National Patent Council which ranted that the foundation would be "empowered to invade all research and development activities of industry and individuals, and to confiscate and pool patents, for purposes of harassment of industry in perpetuation of political power." Since the council asserted that the legislation was "so adroitly drafted" that it had deceived even such persons as Bush, the Inter-Society Committee reply showed the absurdity of the indictment by listing hundreds of eminent spokesmen for the agency who scarcely fitted the council's description, "naive and non-legalistic."[82]

The House debate revealed the strength of the budget-cutting mood, exemplified in Wadsworth's arguments, and the fear, stimulated in part by the National Patent Council but much more by the public anxiety which followed Senator Joseph R. McCarthy's accusations, that Communists and fellow travelers would subvert American free enterprise and give away scientific secrets vital to national security.

An amendment offered by Oren Harris (D., Arkansas) showed the tight fiscal temper. He proposed a ceiling of $15 million on the foundation's annual appropriation. This need not be permanent, Harris said; after a few years the foundation might persuade Congress to remove it. A Budget Bureau observer of the debate concluded that the bill would not pass without some kind of dollar limitation. Priest, who handled the bill on the floor, accepted Harris's amendment and so did the House.[83]

To the committee amendment calling for a loyalty oath (affidavit) by holders of fellowships and scholarships, Dwight L. Rogers (D., Florida) proposed to attach additional requirements. The affidavit should be "accompanied by such supporting evidence as the foundation may by regulations require," and the director and a majority of the executive committee must be satisfied as to the truth of the affidavit. Priest objected that these requirements were unnecessary and burdensome. Rogers's amendment was defeated, 73-63, and the committee amendment was accepted.[84] But this was only a preliminary skirmish. The power of the drive for security would become manifest the following day.

Before that denouement the House approved a substitute for another committee amendment—on the foundation's evaluation function—and a substantial "legislative history" was written into the record to keep the agency from poaching on the research programs of the National Institutes of Health (NIH).

The change in the committee's provision on evaluation was offered by John W. Heselton (R., Massachusetts). It dropped the requirement that the foundation evaluate private research but retained evaluation of federal science programs. The committee version was obviously vulnerable to the old arguments about government invasion of private activities, and Priest accepted Heselton's substitute without comment.[85]

Some representatives were disturbed that the committee had excised a provision that the foundation's activities would supplement but not supersede those of other federal research agencies. Frank B. Keefe (R., Wisconsin) asked whether the deletion meant that the foundation would take over other federal programs, specifically those of NIH. Priest answered that the committee had considered the provision unnecessary; it had no intention of transferring NIH research to the foundation. Carl Hinshaw (R., California) opposed restoration of the language since it might "rob this agency of any right to criticize or to point out that there is duplication going on in the various Government agencies." The committee's deletion stood, but Keefe, in his long colloquy with Priest, had established a "record" that might be cited later by defenders of NIH or other preserves.[86]

On the second day of debate, after seeing the orderly progress of the bill toward enactment, proponents who had been keeping their fingers crossed must have begun to relax. Then came a shock. Howard W. Smith, a conservative Virginia Democrat, offered an amendment to add a paragraph to the bill:

No person shall be employed by the Foundation and no scholarship shall be awarded to any person by the Foundation unless and until the Federal Bureau of Investigation shall have investigated the loyalty of such person and reported to the Foundation such person is loyal to the United States, believes in our system of government, and is not and has not at any time been a member of any organization considered subversive by the Attorney General or any organization that teaches or advocates the overthrow of our Government by force and violence.

Since persons in the foundation, according to Smith, "will have access to the most vital secrets of this Government," he wanted "to lock the door against Communists, against fellow-travelers, and against foreign agents, and against anybody who does not believe in our form of government before the horse even gets a chance to be stolen." He could not imagine any "possible objection anybody can have to this amendment." James G. Fulton (R., Pennsylvania) and John E. Rankin (D., Mississippi) supported the amendment, and Fulton thought it should be extended to include "all . . . organizations and institutions and individuals in the United States or foreign countries" who participated in the foundation's research program.[87]

Priest went into a quick huddle with Speaker Sam Rayburn, Majority Leader McCormack, and Wolverton. They "concluded that in view of the lateness of the hour the Smith amendment would be overwhelmingly approved by the House." The best strategy, therefore, was to accept it and "water it down in conference."[88]

Despite Priest's acceptance of the Smith amendment, Chet Holifield (D., California) assailed the addition to the bill. He pointed out that never before had the FBI been charged with going beyond its investigative function to certify an individual's loyalty or disloyalty. By giving the FBI this "function of Hitler's Gestapo and Stalin's OGPU and MKVD," his "jittery" colleagues were embracing the kind of totalitarian practices they professed to deplore. Holifield warned that if the amendment remained in the bill after conference with the Senate, he would vote against the legislation. Barratt O'Hara (D., Illinois) endorsed Holifield's remarks and said that the "amendment would go further in the establishment of a police state than anything that has been suggested up to this time by the most rabid advocate of police statism."[89]

Nonetheless, the House quickly tacked on another security amendment, offered by Daniel J. Flood (D., Pennsylvania), which stipulated that no foreign national could be associated with the foundation unless he had been cleared by the FBI. Flood reminded the House that Klaus Fuchs, a British scientist recently arrested for espionage, had been cleared by his government to work at Los Alamos but not by the FBI. The amendment was adopted without debate.[90]

On March 1, following an unsuccessful effort to recommit H.R. 4846, it was passed by the House, 247-126. The Senate number was then attached to the bill, paving the way for a conference to resolve the differences between the two versions of S. 247.[91]

* * *

The Smith and Flood amendments angered and dismayed scientists. The Budget Bureau heard that Wolfle thought he had "a mandate from his group to attempt to kill the bill rather than accept the Smith amendment." Carey counseled patience and concentration on the conferees, but he thought Wolfle was "afraid to poll his membership lest he get an instruction to fight the bill rather than seek to compromise it."[92] Samuel A. Goudsmit, a physicist at the Brookhaven National Laboratory, asked Bush what scientists could do to kill the amendment. "Pretty soon bachelor's degrees will be awarded by the F.B.I.," Goudsmit predicted. Bush thought letters to members of the conference committee would be the best form of pressure, but they had not been appointed, and Bush seemed worried "that the Senate may accept the House version without conference."[93] The council of the National Academy of Sciences told the President and members of Congress that the Smith amendment would "work serious damage to the development of science in the United States and to those persons upon whom that development depends." The foundation did not need FBI investigations to determine the "character, loyalty and competence" of applicants for its assistance. Indeed, FBI investigations and reports would lead to an excess of caution inimical to the advancement of science and start a "deplorable trend to conformity and a deterioration in the intellectual climate."[94] All sixteen senior members of the Harvard physics department signed a telegram to Priest and Senator Thomas attacking the amendment, and the department chairman wrote Bush that they believed "there can and should be no compromise on the basic issue, the requirement of loyalty clearance for non-secret work in educational institutions. It will be tragic if such a procedure, however administered, becomes established as a national policy."[95]

The Harvard telegram reflected the alarm of academic scholars about the hysterical anti-intellectualism welling up from McCarthy's accusations. The cries of outrage from the nation's campuses were echoed in government offices, but at lower decibels of panic. At the White House, Steelman suggested that Smith's "vicious provision," which "lets the police determine loyalty" and "covers *past* as well as *present* membership in proscribed organizations however innocent," called for a talk with Priest or McCormack to get it out of the bill. "This would leave regular loyalty procedures for employees of the Foundation and a loyalty affidavit requirement for the scholarship recipients—a sensible arrangement," Steelman believed.[96] Carey advised that Wolfle "hold his fire" and that Charles Brown draft substitute language which the President might suggest to Democratic leaders in Congress. Carey thought the Justice Department could deliver a knockout blow by "repudiating the extraordinary power given . . . to the FBI," and Brown arranged for a conference between the general counsel of the Research and Development Board and FBI officials, who it turned out were "very unhappy" about Smith's mandate to them.[97]

McCormack asked Bush for a letter giving reasons for eliminating the unfortunate amendments, and Brown and Lloyd Cutler furnished arguments and substitute provisions. The majority leader found the letter "splendid," gave a copy to Priest, and urged Bush to send copies to all the conferees. Bush did a similar service for Alexander Smith at his request.[98] Perhaps more important in influencing the conference committee was a strong letter, stimulated by Brown, from the Justice Department. Peyton Ford, assistant to the Attorney General, told the committee that giving the FBI the job of determining loyalty would "lay a foundation for criticism of the Bureau as a state police organization"; with respect to Flood's amendment, the FBI did not have the capability of carrying out investigations in other countries. Furthermore, the Defense Department endorsed a draft substitute for the two amendments, eliminating their most objectionable features but retaining the requirement of a loyalty affidavit by scholarship and fellowship holders.

The new security provisions, worked out in conference with the assistance of the Budget Bureau, stipulated that the AEC would have to approve foundation support of research on nuclear energy, and the provisions of the Atomic Energy Act would apply to the control of "restricted data" under that act and security clearance of individuals having access to the data; the Secretary of Defense should establish security requirements for national defense research supported by funds transferred from Defense, and on other defense-related research the foundation should establish necessary safeguards; and no foundation employee should have access to restricted information until the agency had given him clearance after investigation under the regular government loyalty program.[99]

Only in the irrational political climate of 1950 could anyone claim that these security requirements were in any respect loose. Indeed, they revealed the effect of Cold War anxieties on the minds of moderate men. Probably any attempt to eliminate a loyalty oath for fellowship holders, if one had been made, would have been rejected in conference. As Bush wrote to a Harvard physicist: "We have to realize . . . that the bill as it comes out of conference has to pass the House, and there is a lot of immature sentiment there in regard to security which takes strange forms."[100]

Nearly two months after the House passage of the science bill the conference committee reported out an amended S. 247. The House accepted the report and passed the amended bill on April 27 and the Senate on April 28.[101] As the Budget Bureau had hoped they would, the conferees mainly followed the House version. Only one provision really disturbed Bureau officials: the board had to approve every award of a grant, contract, scholarship, or fellowship. But the Bureau staff members thought that ways might be found to get around detailed review of every action, perhaps through later amendment of the agency's charter. Somewhat bothersome to them too was the language of the conference report erecting no-trespassing signs around other agencies' research programs, especially those of NIH. "Our flash reaction to this," two Budget officials commented, "is that the Division of Medical Research probably should not be activated and that biological research should perhaps not be emphasized." In general, though, they found the bill satisfactory. A few days later the Bureau recommended that the President sign the bill.[102]

At six in the morning on May 10, early-rising Harry Truman announced from the rear platform of a train in Pocatello, Idaho that he had just signed the National Science Foundation Act of 1950. In a statement issued the same day he recalled the report he had received from Vannevar Bush five years before, *Science—The Endless Frontier*.[103] It was somehow fitting that the man from Independence, Missouri, once a jumping-off place for the Far West, should make the announcement at the spot where a century before the trails to Oregon farm lands and California gold fields diverged. The new frontiers represented by the foundation had been conceived by men concerned about opening new opportunities to replace those lost by the closing of the frontier of western land. Would the foundation open endless "new frontiers of the mind . . . and a fuller and more fruitful life" as its originators had hoped, or had five years of change drawn finite limits?

Looking Backward,
1950-1945

Although the National Science Foundation was an outgrowth of a new relationship between government and science established in World War II, it also had origins in the Great Depression and in America's dominant myth—the frontier. These origins may be detected in the title of Bush's report, *Science—The Endless Frontier,* and a sentence from Roosevelt's letter which appears as an epigraph to the published document: "New frontiers of the mind are before us, and if they are pioneered with the same vision, boldness, and drive with which we have waged this war we can create a fuller and more fruitful employment and a fuller and more fruitful life."

To a natural scientist "The Endless Frontier" may connote the mysteries of an expanding universe, or the continual revelation of new questions as research knowledge unfolds. But to government officials in 1944, like those outside OSRD who suggested the preparation of the report, the word "frontier" was more likely to stir memories of New Deal efforts to fight the depression. By the 1930s Frederick Jackson Turner's "frontier thesis," announced by the young Wisconsin historian in 1893, had become a pervasive idea in American thought and a persuasive explanation of the nation's economic and social ills. It was a popular doctrine that the end of the frontier of cheap western land had shut off a safety valve for industrial America and helped bring on at last the financial collapse of 1929 and the years of desperation that followed. Thus the depression-ridden nation needed, in a cliché of the times, "new frontiers." The use of those words in FDR's letter, and especially in the original draft with its emphasis on the creation of new industries and new jobs, suggests that the seminal "frontier" was Turner's, not Einstein's, though transmuted of course when it became a part of the title of Bush's report. During the closing stages of World War II government leaders and American intellectuals generally expected a postwar depression. Its failure to occur was an important non-event.

Animated by similar worries and by a belief in the efficacy of science and technology, properly directed, to solve national social and economic problems, Senator Kilgore developed plans for a science foundation and won increasing support for the idea. But to leaders of business and industry the prospect of a revived New Deal was abhorrent, and to conservative scientists government planning of science was rank Jacobinism.

Bush's report represented a conservative reaction to Kilgore's challenge. The report proposed a new federal agency founded on quite different principles. In oversimplified terms: The new agency should be controlled and directed by scientists; it should emphasize basic research, not applied, and the natural sciences, not the social; it should protect the government's interest but allow the patenting of discoveries by private individuals; and its support should flow to a small group of strong institutions. This last feature was implicit in Bush's plan, despite his expressed wish to encourage the growth of new science centers. He did not envision a large budget for basic research, which would have been necessary to develop other institutions, and he could not accept the notion that his opponents in the Inter-Society Committee, the Federation of American Scientists, or the associations of public universities might also represent the interest of science.

These ideas, especially when espoused by men more doctrinaire than Bush, provoked vigorous dissent from some government officials and from scientists who believed that the agency must be under public control, should help solve national problems (and hence include the social sciences as well as the natural), should ensure that discoveries resulting from federal support became public property, and should encourage research and education in a large number of universities and colleges throughout the nation.

Although the necessity of compromising these opposing views was soon recognized, agreement took an inordinately long time. Real fears and convictions hindered efforts to achieve compromise, and so did changing political circumstances that sometimes seemed to give one group or the other the upper hand. Yet differences over issues and party electoral victories may have been less consequential than differences in personalities and individual rivalries. Some persons automatically touched off hostility in others, and they were slow to learn the political skills of working together for a broad purpose that most of them shared. Ultimately scientists from both camps and congressional and Administration backers of the foundation gained success through teamwork, but only after some of the most abrasive individuals were on the sidelines.

Perhaps the most substantial reason for the long delay in creating the foundation was the agency's restriction to basic research. Kilgore's bills aroused interest in Congress because they promised to mobilize science and technology to solve recognized national problems. But basic research was an act of faith which practical, cost-conscious congressmen found both difficult to understand and a dubious investment for scarce federal dollars. Twenty years later Bush still marveled that the scientists' campaign had succeeded: "To persuade the Congress of these pragmatically inclined United States to establish a strong organization to support fundamental research would seem to be one of the minor miracles."[1]

The act signed by President Truman in 1950 was recognizably related to Magnuson's 1945 bill, but the legislation picked up a good deal of clutter in five years as various groups succeeded in inserting provisions to protect or advance their interests. Important features of Bush's plan were lost. Thus the Division of National Defense, which would have provided for civilian control of military research, was lopped off, though it was probably true that many congressmen voted for the bill anyway because they thought its main benefit would be the strengthening of national security. Another loss, not in the act itself but in the legislative history accompanying its passage, was a viable Division of Medical Research. The rise of the NIH research empire forestalled an opportunity for the science foundation to cultivate a field that many congressmen considered second only to national defense in importance. The most significant change of all was the provision for a presidentially appointed director of the foundation—a provision that Bush had briefly accepted during the drafting of his report.

In matters relating to national science policy the act of 1950 showed both accretions and losses since Magnuson's bill. Instead of Bush's charge to the foundation "to develop and promote a national policy for scientific research and scientific education," the act limited this authority to *basic* research and science education—potentially a serious limitation, or in another sense, a protection from powerful departments with large applied research and development programs. The act, unlike the 1945 bill, directed the agency "to appraise the impact of research upon industrial development and upon the general welfare" and "to evaluate scientific research programs undertaken by agencies of the Federal Government"—possibly a significant coordinating role, or a source of trouble with the agencies whose programs were being evaluated.

The need to coordinate federal science programs was becoming increasingly evident by 1950. During the five-year debate other science agencies came into being and grew apace. Not only did they sponsor basic research projects originally contemplated for the science foundation, but their missions to develop atomic energy, devise new weapons, and conquer dread diseases drew strength and dollars from the nation's anxieties. As their budgets grew, so did congressional concern about the national debt. Little wonder, then, that when Congress finally created a basic research agency with no specially popular mission it also imposed a low ceiling on annual appropriations. In short, prove that fundamental science is worth while.

Part II: Beginning, 1950-54

"Things are always best in their beginning."

Pascal

6
Board and Director

The long-drawn-out effort to reconcile the freedom of science with responsibility to its public patron resulted in a compromise embodied in the statutory definition of the new independent agency: "The Foundation shall consist of a National Science Board . . . and a Director." Before the Foundation could begin the work set out at the head of its charter—"To promote the progress of science; to advance the national health, prosperity, and welfare; to secure the national defense; and for other purposes"—a twenty-four member board and a director had to be nominated by the President and confirmed by the Senate.

The board had to come first. Those fearful of political or bureaucratic domination of the agency had not succeeded in arranging for the director's appointment by the policy-making group, nor in requiring that the director meet the qualifications for board nominees, but they did get written into the act the board's right to recommend to the President persons for his consideration for director. Just as important, the act forbade the appointment of a director before the board "had an opportunity to make such recommendations." After his appointment the director would become a nonvoting ex officio board member.

Old fears and suspicions similarly shaped the statement of qualifications of board members. The nominees, the act provided, "(1) shall be eminent in the fields of the basic sciences, medical science, engineering, agriculture, education, or public affairs; (2) shall be selected solely on the basis of established records of distinguished service; and (3) shall be so selected as to provide representation of the views of scientific leaders in all areas of the Nation." These criteria were intended to ensure representation of diverse fields of science, including the utilitarian, of generalists as well as specialists, and of all regions of the country. A further attempt to balance the often conflicting ideas of laboratory scientists and university administrators, and of public and private institutions of higher education, was incorporated in the request that the President consider recommendations from the National Academy of Sciences, the associations representing land-grant institutions, state universities, and liberal arts colleges, and "other scientific or educational institutions."

Board members were to serve for six years, although the terms of the first group were to be staggered so that one-third of the members would be appointed every two years. A member could serve two consecutive full terms but would then become ineligible for reappointment until two years later. The director's term was also six years, but he was subject to removal by the President before his term expired. As a full-time employee he was to receive an annual salary of $15,000; the part-time board members were to be compensated only for the days when they were engaged in the agency's business. The act left unclear whether federal officeholders might be board members, though it did provide that executive branch officials might serve as members of divisional committees and special commissions.

* * *

Long before passage of the act interested groups began to compile lists of names for the President's consideration. In 1947, when the chances for passage of Alexander Smith's bill looked good, Bush and Oscar Ruebhausen urged the president of the National Academy of Sciences—first Frank Jewett and then A. Newton Richards—to prepare to submit nominations. Bush warned Jewett that the land-grant college people would "act vigorously" and quickly. As effective lobbyists, they might cause an unbalanced board which scientists would resent. Jewett, in his last month as Academy president, still found the whole idea of the new agency distasteful, and a land-grant slate, he thought, would make "advice from the Academy or any other scientific organization largely pleasant window dressing . . . since they are the only group in position to exert real political pressure. It would take a stronger more ardent supporter of science than Truman to disregard advice from that source." Jewett told Ruebhausen, "I have no present reason to think that the President is particularly solicitous to have advice on this matter from the Academy—he has not sought its advice in connection with the formulation of science legislation." Still, Jewett would talk with his successor, Richards, and Detlev W. Bronk, chairman of the National Research Council. Perhaps the Academy might be able "to present a panel of names so distinguished, with such unanimity of backing and with such publicity that [the President] would have to take cognizance of it even though the sponsors had no direct political power he need respect." Jewett continued to grumble, but he did begin the process by which the Academy solicited and screened names.[1]

Bush also prepared to make a canvass of his own, and while he thought Truman would probably call on someone at hand, John Steelman or Clark Clifford perhaps, he sent his travel schedule to the White House in case the President should want him to assemble a list of candidates. Receiving no indication that his advice would be asked, Bush wrote Richards that "it will be rather up to the Academy, whether called on or not, to be sure that the President has some sound suggestions in his hands." Most of the two hundred names first submitted to the Academy were, naturally, those of scientists, though Bush believed those "of non-scientists with particular interest in science and great public understanding are fully as important."[2]

Truman's veto removed the short-lived sense of urgency, and the Academy and other groups could proceed to winnow nominees in careful fashion. By April 1949 the council of the Academy had agreed on thirty-one men, five eminent in "public affairs," the others in science. Reviewing this list, Bush suggested the deletion of his name and those of Karl Compton, Richards, and Reuben G. Gustavson, a chemist who was chancellor of the University of Nebraska and an advocate of geographic distribution of research funds; he proposed the addition of eight other scientists, four engineers, six educational administrators, and six men of public affairs.[3]

Early in 1950 when signs appeared of a break in the long legislative deadlock, the nominating game began to attract new attention. Still trying to influence selections where they would finally be made, in the Oval Office, Bush told the President that while he did not want an appointment and thought there should be "new faces" on the Washington science scene,

> When you come to consider appointments on the Foundation I would be gratified if you allowed me to aid you in selection. You will have many nominations before you. Since I wish you to leave me out personally I could comment on these without embarrassment, and of course quite confidentially. I do know many of the scientists and quite a lot about some of them, and my comments added to those of others might conceivably help. Or I will be happy to aid on the matter of selection in any other way you might prefer.[4]

The President replied that he hoped "the people on the Board will have a scientific slant instead of a political one" and said he would be glad to talk to Bush about the matter.[5]

The White House requested suggestions for board and director even before the passage of the NSF act. At the Budget Bureau, Elmer Staats advised staff members to concentrate on "finding the best possible person" for director since the Bureau expected to rely heavily on his advice about federal science programs.[6] They did focus on this position, but the composition of the board was a more interesting intellectual puzzle. As William Carey viewed the problem: "It should not be an all-male cast; recognition should be given to women where possible. We should make an effort to have one or more Catholics included. One or more Negroes should also be included. In the area of public affairs, we should recognize labor's interests as well as industry's. One or more Federal research men should be included. Geographic dispersion is, of course, necessary." On distribution by profession, Carey allocated two members to "public affairs," three each to education, the social sciences, engineering, and medicine and biology, and ten to the physical sciences and mathematics. Of his forty-one suggestions, five were appointed to the first board.[7]

Another Bureau official, C. Spencer Platt, advised selecting only a few representatives of private eastern universities, institutions that were likely to be principal applicants for research funds; and unlike Carey he opposed having any members from federal agencies. Edward Condon of the Bureau of Standards, on the other hand, thought it "extremely important" that the government be adequately represented on the board to ease the job of coordinating federal programs. But an inquiry by the Budget Bureau into the legality of appointing federal officials to the board raised enough doubt to suggest a caveat to the White House.[8]

Condon's colleagues on the Interdepartmental Committee on Scientific Research and Development (ICSRD) also thought there should be several federal scientists on the board, although they refrained from listing any because of the legal question. Otherwise their panel of twenty-four nominees and an equal number of alternates was carefully constructed to provide about a third of the membership to the natural sciences and engineering; another third (including an economist and three or four university presidents) to education and public affairs; and several members having first-hand understanding of industry, military research, and the relations of science and government. The interagency committee considered a "diversity of viewpoints and ... the breadth and maturity of the individuals" more important than full representation of the fields of science. Six of the ICSRD nominees and alternates were appointed to the first board, and one other, a black industrial chemist, was offered but declined an appointment.[9]

Most federal agency recommendations reached the White House before the end of April.[10] The Budget Bureau sent a preliminary list on May 8 but continued work on the project, and as late as June a White House staff member noted that Staats intended to make some personal recommendations.[11] Outsiders who worried that political appointees or the wrong sort of scientists or educators might dominate the board got reassurance from Bush, even though his frequent offers of advice were disregarded, for which he blamed "the group immediately about the President." When Alexander Smith expressed a hope that Truman would rely on Bush's advice, Bush replied that the lists before the President were good ones. Similarly he wrote Bethuel Webster that the "excellent men" in the Budget Bureau, in whom he had "great confidence," were "making a careful study of the whole affair" and he expected good results. Webster was glad to learn that there seemed to be slight "basis for my fear that the Inter Society Committee, the Federation of [American] Scientists, et al., would be overly influential."[12]

Recommendations from individuals and from professional societies and groups continued to stream into the White House during the spring and summer.[13] Before long Bush's confidence that the "excellent men" in the Bureau were in control began to wane. "I do hope that you have been guiding the matter," Warren Weaver of the Rockefeller Foundation wrote Bush. "To see, as I did yesterday in a paper, that *Congressmen* are backing certain candidates makes me apprehensive." Bush replied that he would not worry if the men at the Bureau "are allowed to make the suggestions to the President," but "all sorts of things can happen." By October Bush showed signs of alarm. He asked a Budget officer what was happening about the board appointments. "Much to my dismay, I found that the list had gotten out of their hands and is now being handled somewhere in the White House. . . . I am a little apprehensive that it may not be as good a list as I had hoped. Apparently the appointments are to be made rather soon."[14]

Members of the White House staff scrutinized the array of candidates with an attention to political and personal considerations that had been overlooked or slighted in most recommendations, even from the Budget Bureau. Lists submitted by the Bureau and the Civil Service Commission together contained the names of 75 persons, of whom 16 were offered appointments and 14 accepted. Ten of the 14 were on the Bureau's panel, 10 on the Commission's; 6 of the 14 had been recommended by both agencies. Yet a surprising aspect of the selection process is that 10 of the first board appointments appeared on neither the Bureau's list nor the Commission's—indeed, were seldom recommended by other groups either.[15]

A White House assistant who had been assigned the task of reviewing the Bureau and Commission lists thought that both were "too tightly drawn to rigid specifications, and . . . someone is going to have to open up the nominations to get representation from the public." An anthropologist himself, he suggested the addition of several social scientists with an interest in solving public problems, such as those affecting the status of women and minority groups.[16] This kind of internal White House advice, supplemented by casual puffs for personal acquaintances, probably contributed to the choice of several persons not frequently mentioned on lists sent to Donald S. Dawson, the presidential assistant who coordinated the selection activity.[17]

* * *

Scientists and engineers may have been intensely interested in the nomination of board members, but the matter could hardly have commanded sustained, high-level attention in the White House during the summer of 1950. On June 25, halfway around the world from Washington, North Korean forces invaded the Republic of Korea, and the resulting crisis raised a question as to whether the activation of NSF might not be put off indefinitely.

To get the Foundation started the President had sent Congress a request for an appropriation of $475,000 for fiscal year 1951. But the House Committee on Appropriations, believing "that new programs which will not provide early aid to our defense effort should not be initiated at this time," struck out the entire amount. The President, said to be "keenly disappointed," instructed Steelman to appeal to the Senate to restore the funds, and Truman approved the Budget Bureau's idea of arranging for Defense Department testimony before the Senate Appropriations Committee "to emphasize the importance of the NSF from the standpoint of national security."[18]

If the President was disappointed, some scientists were dismayed. Lee A. DuBridge, the physicist president of the California Institute of Technology, wrote to Steelman that he hoped "the failure to establish the Foundation is not due to any feeling in Washington that the present emergency has made the creation of a Science Foundation less important or less urgent." DuBridge thought that national defense considerations made the Foundation even more necessary, and he had sent telegrams to the members of the Senate committee asking for restoration of the funds. DuBridge asked Steelman, "Would the possibility of reinstatement [of NSF funds] be increased if the President should promptly announce the creation of the National Science Foundation Board and the activation of this important new agency?"[19]

Instead of restoring the full amount of the request the Senate voted an appropriation of $225,000. Although Albert Thomas, the chairman of the House subcommittee handling appropriations for independent agencies, gave informal assurance that he would not oppose the Senate action in conference, Budget Bureau officials feared that a common conference practice of splitting the difference would result in an "exceedingly restrictive" figure for organizing the new agency. Lawrence R. Hafstad of the Atomic Energy Commission, and chairman of ICSRD, volunteered to speak to Thomas before the conference, but decided that this might backfire if the Texas Democrat felt that he was being harassed. In any event the conference committee agreed to keep the Senate figure, and the Foundation's first budget, of $225,000, was approved by the President on September 27, 1950.[20]

By that time most of the board members had been decided on, following checks for their political acceptability, and on September 30 the President signed letters asking if they would agree to appointment.[21] Some late switches in choice seem to have been caused by such matters as connection with a public or private institution, recommendation by a member of Congress, or party affiliation. On a next-to-final list a few typed names were marked through and others, to whom appointments were offered, inserted in longhand. Instead of Charles S. Johnson, a black sociologist and president of Fisk University in Nashville, an appointment went to John W. Davis, the black president of West Virginia State College, probably on Senator Kilgore's recommendation.[22] Instead of Ernest W. Goodpasture of Vanderbilt University's medical school (like Fisk, a Nashville institution), an appointment went to O. W. Hyman, dean of the University of Tennessee medical school in Memphis. William V. Houston, the physicist president of Rice University in Texas, was replaced by Joseph C. Morris, another physicist and a vice-president of Tulane University in New Orleans. Houston's name had appeared on the Bureau and Commission lists; Morris's had not. It may have mattered that Houston was a Republican, Morris a Democrat.[23]

Two men declined the offer of appointment—Henry Ford II, president of the Ford Motor Company, and Percy L. Julian, a black chemist who was director of research of the Glidden Company.[24] As replacements, the President nominated Charles E. Wilson, president of the General Electric Company, and Robert P. Barnes, a black chemist at Howard University in Washington.

On November 2 the President announced his appointments:[25]

> Sophie D. Aberle, Special Research Director, University of New Mexico
> Chester I. Barnard, President, Rockefeller Foundation
> Robert P. Barnes, Head, Department of Chemistry, Howard University
> Detlev W. Bronk, President, Johns Hopkins University, and President, National Academy of Sciences
> Gerty T. Cori, Professor of Biological Chemistry, School of Medicine, Washington University
> James B. Conant, President, Harvard University
> John W. Davis, President, West Virginia State College
> Charles Dollard, President, Carnegie Corporation of New York
> Lee A. DuBridge, President, California Institute of Technology

Edwin B. Fred, President, University of Wisconsin
Paul M. Gross, Vice President and Dean of the Graduate School of Arts and Sciences, Duke University
George D. Humphrey, President, University of Wyoming
O. W. Hyman, Dean of Medical School and Vice President, University of Tennessee
Robert F. Loeb, Bard Professor of Medicine, College of Physicians and Surgeons, Columbia University
Donald H. McLaughlin, President, Homestake Mining Company
Frederick A. Middlebush, President, University of Missouri
Edward L. Moreland, Executive Vice President, Massachusetts Institute of Technology
Joseph C. Morris, Head of Physics Department and Vice President, Tulane University
Harold Marston Morse, Professor of Mathematics, Institute for Advanced Study, Princeton, New Jersey
Andrey A. Potter, Dean of Engineering, Purdue University
James A. Reyniers, Director, LOBUND Institute, University of Notre Dame
Elvin C. Stakman, Chief, Division of Plant Pathology and Botany, University of Minnesota
Charles Edward Wilson, President, General Electric Company
Patrick H. Yancey, S.J., Professor of Biology, Spring Hill College

The heavy representation of university administrators indicated that the Foundation would develop close ties to higher education. Six members were university presidents, and a seventh had been for more than thirty years the president of a Negro land-grant college. Four of the university presidents had earned their doctorates in the natural sciences, and one, Middlebush, in political science. Only four of the twenty-four did not hold college or university appointments. Private institutions had a few more representatives than did public. Only the Catholic Spring Hill College on the Gulf Coast of Alabama and the black West Virginia State College did not grant graduate degrees.

Fields of science, except for the social, were remarkably well balanced. Mathematical, physical, and engineering sciences accounted for nine members, and so did the biological and medical sciences. A majority of the members gave their primary allegiance to basic research, though for the most part their own work in the laboratory had ended. Applied fields of science might succeed in gaining a voice through the engineers, physicians, and agricultural scientists, but industry would have little direct representation. There were no government officials, but Charles E. Wilson would soon be appointed Director of Defense Mobilization and then resign from the board.

Two blacks, two women: this slightly more than token representation set a pattern often followed in future board appointments. So too did Catholic membership. The University of Notre Dame would be represented on the board continuously for sixteen years. One of the women, Gerty Cori, born and educated in Europe, had together with her husband won a Nobel prize in medicine and physiology three years before her appointment. Sophie Aberle also held an M.D. degree, and she added a social science viewpoint because of her anthropological and personal interest in the Indians of the American Southwest.

Many people had worried that a few well-known East and West Coast private institutions would dominate the board. There were members from Harvard, MIT, Columbia, Johns Hopkins, and Caltech, but the geographic distribution of members was reasonably good. By region of residence when appointed, seven were from northeastern states, six from north central, seven from southern, and four from western.

The board was mature in experience and also in years. Only four—DuBridge, Dollard, Morris, and Reyniers—had been born in the twentieth century. The average age was fifty-six, and one-third of the members had passed their sixtieth birthday.[26]

* * *

Perhaps it was only a clerical slip rather than White House preoccupation with Korea or congressional elections, but eleven days after the board nominations were announced Lee DuBridge still did not know the names of his colleagues. West Coast newspapers had paid little attention to the story. So he wrote to Steelman asking for a complete list of nominees and information on plans for the first board meeting. A few days later Donald Dawson wrote all the members that their first meeting was scheduled for Tuesday, December 12, in the West Wing of the White House, starting at ten o'clock. The President planned to meet with them at noon.[27]

Before they received Dawson's letter some members had heard disturbing rumors that the President might make a political appointment to the directorship of the Foundation. Charles Dollard, after talking with Bronk, Barnard, Fred, and Middlebush, said he had "hope, but not confidence, that we can avert a bad appointment without hurting anyone's feelings."[28]

The rumors were well founded. On November 7 Frank P. Graham had written Truman expressing gratitude that an attempt to assassinate the President a few days before had failed. "The next thing I wish to say," Graham continued, "is that I will take the post which you have in mind for me if it still holds after you consider the advice which the Board is to give you under the law setting up the Foundation." Truman replied: "I am highly pleased with your decision. I think it is a good one and I also think it will be good for the country."[29]

Graham was serving out the tag end of an interim appointment as a United States senator from North Carolina after being defeated for nomination to continue in the seat. A former history professor and president of the University of North Carolina, he had served as an adviser to New Deal and Fair Deal agencies and become identified with internationalist, labor, and civil rights causes. A leading spirit of Chapel Hill liberalism, which came to characterize the university he presided over from 1930 to 1949, he had fought for better opportunities for black and white sharecroppers and textile workers. The President wanted Graham to continue in national service and evidently offered the directorship orally.[30] When the news leaked to reporters they asked Graham as he came out of a meeting with Truman whether he was to be named director. Avoiding a direct reply, he pointed out that the board had to meet first and make recommendations.[31]

Most board members were bound to resist Graham's appointment. They wanted someone trained in science and committed to basic research. William T. Golden, an investment banker who had become familiar with wartime and postwar government science programs and their administrators and who now was investigating the relationships of science and defense for the President, learned in a conversation with Bronk "that he would resent the imposition of such an appointment over the contrary recommendations of the Board."[32] Bronk and other members agreed with the views DuBridge sent them several days before their meeting:

> I have just returned from Washington where I was disturbed by persistent rumors that there are political pressures under way to influence the President to name a political appointee as Director .... These rumors may be wholly without foundation and I hope they are. But in any case they emphasize the fact that the Science Foundation Board must be prepared at its first meeting to consider the matter of the appointment of a Director.... Presumably the President will not or cannot make an appointment until the Board has submitted its recommendations. Consequently, the members of the Board should come to the first meeting prepared to propose candidates for this most important position. I need not stress how the whole success of the Foundation may depend upon the character, prestige and ability of the man selected as its first Director.
>
> In order to get the ball rolling, I am herewith listing the names of a few individuals who have occurred to me or who have been suggested to me as possible candidates.

DuBridge suggested: Alan Waterman, who had led ONR's work of supporting basic research in universities; F. Wheeler Loomis, a University of Illinois physicist who had been associate director under DuBridge at the MIT Radiation Laboratory during the war; and Warren Weaver, a mathematician who had long guided the Rockefeller Foundation's division of natural sciences.[33]

The day before the board meeting Dawson told the President: "There may be substantial objection to Graham on the part of the scientists although we have done as much ground work as is possible in behalf of Graham."[34] Evidently the board did manage to convey its objection to the President. Before its second meeting White House officials had explored several other possible appointments for the lame-duck senator. If Graham did not object, the President's special counsel wrote, "we will quietly pass the word along to members of the Science Board that the President has in mind another position that he wants Senator Graham to take and that therefore he would prefer for the Board not to consider him in connection with the Science Foundation."[35] Thus was averted an embarrassing conflict between the board and the President, and the prospect of conservative, basic scientists prescribing policies to be carried out by an activist eager to solve human problems.

* * *

Only Charles E. Wilson failed to appear when the board met in the White House on December 12—apparently in the Fish Room though the minutes prepared by Barnard and Dollard say "The Cabinet Room." Steelman welcomed the members, and Staats presided until the board elected Conant as chairman. After Fred's selection as vice chairman, the board turned at once to the matter of recommending candidates for director—clearly the most important business facing it, and the most urgent in view of the prospect of an unwanted political appointment. Conant appointed a special committee of seven members, under Barnard's chairmanship, to specify the qualifications the director should meet and to suggest candidates for the position, though they were not to function as a nominating committee.[36] Any member could submit names to Barnard's group. The board agreed to keep the suggested names confidential until after it had made its recommendation to the President.

The President met with the board for a few minutes at noon. One of the group recalled that he greeted each member and then asked what they had been discussing. He smiled when told that the topic was possible directors, and said, "That should be easy, someone who can get along with me." He then talked informally about his hopes for the Foundation and offered to help get an appropriation from Congress.

In the afternoon session Staats, assisted by Carey and Frederick C. Schuldt, Jr., briefed the board on the Foundation's legislative history, its statutory tasks, its relation to other federal agencies, and its budgetary situation and outlook. Other principal matters of business were the election of a nine-member executive committee and discussion of qualifications for the director. The board endorsed the qualifications suggested by Barnard's committee and asked for a more detailed statement before their second meeting on January 3.[37] The statement circulated by Barnard set forth three "desirable" and two "indispensable" qualifications. The director should "be or have been a practicing scientist of recognized ability, or at least should have had experience in administering scientific enterprises or personnel"; should understand how the national government works; and should understand institutions of higher education and American research. He must be able to organize and manage "an institution of moderate size but of high class personnel" and must "be adept in the management of 'public relations.' "[38]

When the board met again Barnard reported that his committee had received about forty names and had decided that eleven of these deserved consideration. The full board cut three names from the list but restored two others that had been eliminated by the committee. After deciding that it was not impolitic to recommend one of their own number, since Bronk's name was one of the remaining ten, the twenty-two members present listed their preferences, with the following result:

1. Detlev W. Bronk, chairman of the board's executive committee
2. A. Baird Hastings, Harvard Medical School
3. Lloyd V. Berkner, Carnegie Institution of Washington
4. Lowell T. Coggeshall, University of Chicago
5. Clyde E. Williams, Battelle Memorial Institute
6. Roger Adams, University of Illinois
7. Alan T. Waterman, Office of Naval Research
8. John R. Dunning, Columbia University
9. Jesse E. Hobson, Stanford Research Institute
10. Everette L. De Golyer, geologist and oil producer

Only two members did not place Bronk at the top of the list, and they ranked him second and fourth.[39]

The board instructed Conant "to name Messrs. Bronk, Hastings and Berkner, in that order, as the candidates deemed by the Board to be most qualified for the position of director; and further, that he should inform the President that Mr. Bronk was, in the unanimous judgment of the Board, the outstanding candidate for the position. It was also agreed that, should the Chairman [Conant] be satisfied upon inquiry that any one of these three was clearly not available, he should proceed in order as far down the list of the ten men named above as necessary to produce a panel of three names to be recommended to the President."[40]

Either Bronk did not suit someone in authority at the White House, or he wanted larger responsibilities for the Foundation than were contemplated by the Administration. In fact, both reasons seem to have blocked his nomination. The democratic President thought Bronk's Academy a snobbish outfit, and he was probably piqued that the board had opposed Graham. Although he was said to have "nodded approvingly" when Conant presented Bronk's name,[41] nods can be misinterpreted.

A few days after Conant's mission to the White House, Donald Dawson, who occupied a key position with respect to the appointment, got a note that did not advance Bronk's chances. The writer, Florence Mahoney, an influential lobbyist for medical research, had heard Bronk give what seemed to her a dismal, long-winded speech, and she characterized his views as "unsympathetic to the administration and what should be done." Baird Hastings, she had heard, "would be better."[42]

John Teeter, clever as always in ferreting out confidential information, also learned whom the board had proposed. Despite his record of opposing the Truman Administration, he did not hesitate to offer it his advice. "Bronk is good, but overworked," Teeter wrote Dawson, "and would be accused of the 'old school tie' affiliation as regards the National Academy of Sciences." Teeter described Berkner, a physicist who had been closely associated with Bush, as "a good administrator who enjoys the confidence of the scientific world." Without mentioning Hastings, Teeter made a general comment that seems to have been designed to eliminate him: "Personally I would avoid any M.D., even though he also had a Ph.D., because the M.D.'s are controversial at this time. If the man now held an M.D. post, he would be labeled as one, even though he also held a Ph.D."[43]

Dawson may have paid little attention to Teeter's advice, but the comment that Bronk was "overworked" came from others too. Golden, in his talent search for the best candidates for science adviser to the President and for NSF director, several times heard statements to the effect that "Bronk just could not say no to things he was asked to do, and then in consequence he would try to do too much and always be behind, overworked and more or less out of breath."[44]

Golden also learned that Bronk laid down the condition that "he would take the job only if the military stuff were included"—apparently meaning that NSF should have a substantial role in supporting defense research in response to requests from the Secretary of Defense.[45] If he did make this stipulation he had sharply changed his views of the Foundation's role, since he, like nearly every other scientist to whom Golden talked, was "crystal clear . . . that the NSF should confine its activities entirely to non-military matters" and not try to get a large budget until it had carefully planned a program.[46] Similarly he and several other board members changed their earlier favorable attitude toward the appointment of a presidential science adviser when they concluded that the Foundation's policy role would thereby be diminished. As Conant explained the switch of members' views, though not his own, in a discussion with Golden and Budget Bureau officials, NSF needed "a National Defense label to get appropriations and manpower (and hold off General [Lewis R.] Hershey [director of Selective Service]) and keep its Board happy."[47] But Golden, on the basis of his intensive investigation, recommended strongly against

NSF involvement in military research. His choice—probably the decisive one—for the Foundation's director was not Bronk.[48] When the board met again, in February, Bronk asked that his name be withdrawn because, as the minutes expressed it, "he was unavailable due to the fact that he had other duties in which he believed he could more effectively serve the national interest."[49]

Meanwhile Golden had been discussing the appointment, first with Budget Bureau officials and then with Dawson in the White House. His first choice was Berkner. If he declined the offer, Golden suggested going beyond the list of three and picking No. 7, Alan Waterman. When Berkner dropped out of the running by accepting the presidency of Associated Universities, Incorporated, the way was opened for Waterman's selection.[50]

Many persons had long thought that Waterman should head the Foundation because of the solid record he had established as chief scientist in the Office of Naval Research. He had been Bush's choice since 1948 at least, and on this one matter, if on few others, Condon and Harlow Shapley agreed with Bush. Writing to Steelman, Condon said that Waterman "stands head and shoulders above any other person I have heard mentioned for this appointment."[51] And at least two board members worrying about a political appointment sounded out Waterman as to his interest in the director's position. He replied that he had only one doubt. Since the national emergency had brought proposals to reestablish OSRD, there was a question as to whether NSF would be excluded from research relating to national defense.

If that is to be the case, then I cannot help wondering whether I ought to leave association with the Department of Defense, after having spent nine years in scientific work with military bearing, at a time when people with this type of experience will be badly needed. If the Board should decide that, in addition to the basic functions of the Science Foundation, it would welcome requests from the Department of Defense for assistance, as authorized in the Foundation's charter, then this doubt in my mind would disappear.[52]

This question remained Waterman's "principal obstacle" when he talked with Staats about the position around the first of March 1951. Since the Bureau also objected to barring the Foundation from defense research, Staats may have given assurance that Waterman wanted. By this time the appointment was rumored to be "imminent." At the end of February Golden penned a note at the bottom of a letter to Waterman: "You will be interested to know that the matter of selecting a Director for N.S.F. is now in the active stage."[53]

Certainly Waterman was a logical choice. Few other persons suggested for the position came close to matching his understanding of university research and administration, federal science programs, and bureaucratic procedures. Also, he was generally acceptable. Hardly anyone would have quarreled with Bush's estimate: "He is a quiet individual, a real scholar, and decidedly effective in his quiet way, for everyone likes him and trusts him."[54]

Yet it is indicative of the temper of the times that someone distrusted even this careful, conservative public servant. Conant thought the nomination of Waterman had definitely been decided on, but learned otherwise after being hastily summoned to the White House, where he was told that the navy's chief scientist could not be appointed because investigators had found that his wife had twice attended teas at the Russian embassy. The "flabbergasted" Conant said this seemed a "ridiculous" reason for blocking a fine appointment. "'So it may to you,' President Truman's spokesman said, 'but with the atmosphere what it is on the Hill, we cannot proceed with this appointment unless you can personally guarantee the man and stand ready to give full public endorsement.' I gave the assurance, and the matter proceeded as scheduled."[55]

Thus a piece of ticker tape carrying an announcement from Key West, where the President was on vacation, came as no startling surprise when Conant read it to his fellow board members the afternoon of Friday, March 9. It told of the President's intention to nominate Alan Waterman as the Foundation's first director. Dollard, acting as secretary, recorded in the minutes: "The Board expressed unanimous approval of the choice." Fred Schuldt, who had brought the dispatch to Conant, saw and heard something more than the approval expressed in the formal minutes: "This news was received by the Board with audible relief and enthusiasm, and Dr. Conant immediately undertook to reach Dr. Waterman to attend the remainder of the Board's meeting."[56]

7
"Welcome Aboard!"

Once it was announced the appointment of the navy's chief scientist as director of the National Science Foundation seemed inevitable from the beginning. "You were my first choice from the start," National Science Board member Edward L. Moreland wrote Alan Waterman. Other MIT officials joined in a chorus of congratulations. The chairman of the Institute's corporation, Karl T. Compton, Waterman's friend since graduate school days and his wartime boss, called the appointment "the best news which I have seen in the paper for a long time. Without any exception every one of the many people whom I have heard expressing themselves as to the best choice for this post has put your name at the head of the list." Julius A. Stratton, director of MIT's electronics research laboratory, wrote: "No one in this country has your experience and depth of understanding of the delicate issues involved in the administration of public funds for the support of fundamental research; nor is there anyone who is held in such universal esteem and who enjoys the complete confidence of his colleagues as you do." Engineering dean Thomas K. Sherwood said he had "argued all along that you were the logical man," and Vice President James R. Killian, Jr. commented similarly, "You seemed to me always to be the ideal candidate for this post."[1]

The praise from Cambridge surely pleased the former Yale physicist, but probably no more than did a letter from a young woman in ONR's London office:

If you have seen Dr. [Charles Eugene] Sunderlin, who should arrive in Washington today, you will have heard with what jubilation we greeted the *New York Times*

announcement of your nomination as Director of the NSF. You were toasted with sherry here in the office by a few of us—strictly against regulations I'm sure—and later, more appropriately, with champagne at Dr. [Maurice E.] Bell's. If by any chance your ears were burning between noon and early evening, Washington time, on 12 March, you'll now know why.
...I think it's wonderful.[2]

Both the author of the letter, Virginia Sides, and Sunderlin, the head scientist of the London office, would soon join NSF, becoming "plank owners," as the first year's recruits proudly called themselves, of the newly commissioned ship. Navy ways and language, brought by the first director and other ONR staff members, characterized the new agency and left traces that long remained discernible. "Aye," Waterman would pencil in answer to secretary Doris McCarn's handwritten queries. And in the middle 1960s new staff members were sometimes puzzled by the invariable greeting, "Welcome aboard!"

Waterman had regarded the Office of Naval Research as an interim surrogate for a national science foundation. It would pioneer new relationships of science and government and then turn over to its successor a part of its basic research projects.[3] His stewardship of ONR won respect from academic, industrial, and government scientists alike. "You have made it clear not only to the services but to scientists all over the world," a Purdue physicist wrote, "that basic science can and should be administered by a government agency without curtailing either the freedom of scientists or the freedom of inquiry." Mervin J. Kelly of Bell Telephone Laboratories and C. Guy Suits of General Electric agreed that Waterman was uniquely qualified for the NSF directorship because of his success at ONR. William T. Golden in his visits with Waterman's federal colleagues heard mamy similar appraisals.[4]

* * *

Alan Tower Waterman had won respect as an organizer and administrator of scientific research more than through personal contributions to knowledge. Born at Cornwall-on-Hudson, New York, he grew up mainly in western Massachusetts, where his father taught physics at Smith College. He completed his graduate studies in 1916 at Princeton, where he had also earned his bachelor's degree. While holding his first teaching position at the University of Cincinnati he met Mary Mallon, an assistant in economics there, and they were married in August 1917. Following two years with the Army Signal Corps' Science and Research Division, Waterman became an instructor in physics at Yale. Promoted to assistant professor in 1923 and associate in 1931, he was still not a full professor when World War II brought him back into national service, first with NDRC and then as deputy chief, and finally chief, of OSRD's Office of

Field Service. Continuing his leave from Yale after the war, he helped the Navy Department's new Office of Research and Inventions plan and activate a program of research support to universities. In August 1946 this office created by the Secretary of the Navy achieved statutory existence as the Office of Naval Research, and Waterman became its deputy chief and chief scientist.

During the long debate over the establishment of a science foundation Waterman remained in the background, attending to his duties in the Navy Department but quietly supporting the Bush group. It seems clear that he came to look on his ONR position as preparation for directing the foundation when it finally materialized. Nonetheless, when legislation at last seemed certain in early 1950 he joined other federal science officials in an attempt to guard their provinces against invasion. He chaired an ICSRD subcommittee which sought to get a presidential statement restricting the foundation's authority to evaluate federal science programs or to take over or limit their research support. Specifically, ICSRD wanted the President to say that NSF's main advisory role would be "to render judgment on the major lines of national scientific strategy"—not pass judgment on agency budgets; its principal administrative function would be to support "undertakings which are inappropriate for sponsorship by existing government agencies"; and it "should administer research grant and fellowship programs in those areas where statutory authority, funds and competence for administration do not exist in other executive agencies."[5]

The restricted NSF role proposed by Waterman's subcommittee—unanimously approved by the whole group—did not accord with the conception held by the Budget Bureau, which persuaded John Steelman to tell ICSRD that it would be premature to settle these issues before the foundation had an opportunity to consider its tasks.[6] Still, the arguments Waterman mustered to deny an evaluation role to the foundation convinced him; and the unanimity of his colleagues posted a caution sign to the administrator of the foundation, whoever he might be. Before accepting appointment as director Waterman made it clear that he did not intend to perform the function that Budget Bureau officers and some members of Congress thought to be NSF's central mission.[7]

The tenacity with which Waterman would cling to the idea that NSF should not attempt to evaluate other federal science programs shows one of his strongest characteristics. It was not an unreasoning stubbornness, but firmness and persistence. Detlev Bronk, who spent fourteen years on the National Science Board, most of them as chairman, described the qualities he had come to know so well that he found in Lloyd Embry's "first-rate likeness," painted after Waterman's retirement: "a man obviously kind and gentle, obviously firm and exacting, obviously a Scotsman persistent in the fulfillment of his duties, and a damned good looking guy as well."[8]

Polite and gentle in manner, a usually clear speaker and a good listener, honest and dependable, Waterman was respected and liked by nearly all of his staff, including those who would have preferred more venturesome and more aggressive leadership. He enjoyed playing softball at NSF picnics and bowling on one of the staff's teams. Once a month Mary Waterman entertained the wives of staff members—"Alan's Wives," she called them—in their home in Westmoreland Hills, a beautiful wooded area just outside the District line in Maryland. Her husband was a talented musician who possessed perfect pitch. He played the piano at NSF holiday parties and, after the Foundation finally found a commodious home on Constitution Avenue, would make a grand entrance in Scottish kilts and skirling his bagpipes before the assembled staff in the auditorium. His musical tastes and repertoire were broad. Invited to Swarthmore College to make a speech, he was also asked to participate in a chamber music group. "I had better play the viola," he replied. As to the choice of music, he would leave that to his host, a former NSF program director, but "Mozart and Beethoven are always fine, and I know and like the Brahms quartets, piano and other. As for the standard quintets, Schumann and Franck are fine if people haven't had too much of them."[9]

Nearly fifty-nine years old when he became director, Waterman enjoyed good health and the ability to relax. He knew the value of vacations. While at Yale before the war he and his friends and their sons would spend a month in the summer canoeing and fishing in the Allagash country of northern Maine. To gain the freedom of traveling without hiring a guide, he obtained a guide's license, which he continued to use even into his seventies. He paddled through the wild country from Moosehead Lake to Fort Kent, a two-hundred mile watercouse, seventeen times, and after retiring as director he sought the help of Justice William O. Douglas to prevent the building of a power dam on the Allagash or the incursion of too many tourists into the area.[10]

For canoeists and licensed guides forethought and caution rank high on the scale of values. So did they for Waterman in his public roles as ONR's chief scientist and NSF's first director. Fortunately for this prudent builder, NSF's guardians in the Budget Bureau restrained the eagerness of National Science Board members who wanted to employ staff to start a fellowship program immediately, even before a director was named.[11] Thus Waterman came to his post without the encumbrance of a staff already in place and with the freedom to construct the agency from the ground up.

* * *

To no one's surprise Waterman looked to ONR for help in organizing and staffing the Foundation. After his confirmation by the Senate in

March and swearing-in by Justice Douglas on April 6, he promptly recruited several key officials. All of them had an ONR connection. To Fred Schuldt, who hoped that the Foundation could help the Budget Bureau impose order on proliferating federal science programs and was watching for missteps, this seemed reasonable "since ONR has been in large measure an NSF under another name, and we have sometimes in the past considered even the possibility of wholesale transfer of ONR staff to NSF."[12]

For his deputy Waterman picked thirty-nine year-old Gene Sunderlin, who had expressed a wish to return to America from London and decided that he preferred the No. 2 position in NSF to being No. 2 in the new science advisory office of the State Department. A Rhodes Scholar who had taught at the U.S. Naval Academy before joining ONR's London office in 1946, Sunderlin had earned his doctorate in organic chemistry. This field would counterbalance his own physics specialty, Waterman told the Budget Bureau, though Schuldt thought a biochemist would have been better for this purpose. In discussing the appointment with Conant, Bronk, DuBridge, and Bush, Waterman acknowledged that the obvious choice would be a biologist, but he rationalized that "in the field of biology and medicine it is likely that any appointee might find himself in one faction and be opposed by another . . . . From the standpoint of working relationships especially and ability, the most logical man would be Sunderlin . . . ." His administrative skill, knowledge of government, and wide acquaintance with American and British scientists gave Sunderlin added strength, Waterman argued.[13]

A Bush protégé, John T. Connor, who had served as general counsel for OSRD and ONR, gave legal advice to Waterman and the board during NSF's formative period. He recommended that the Foundation employ William A. W. Krebs, Jr., a thirty-four year-old Yale law graduate who had also been ONR's counsel.[14] Krebs's appointment as general counsel was announced on May 4, along with Sunderlin's and that of Lloyd M. Trefethen to the post of technical aide to the director and executive secretary of the National Science Board. Trefethen, thirty-two years of age, was an engineer, a doctoral graduate of Cambridge University, a former consultant to the London ONR office, and most recently Waterman's technical aide in ONR.[15]

The heads of three of the four statutory divisions were named later in the year. Soon after learning of his nomination Waterman had sounded out Harry C. Kelly, head of the scientific section of the ONR branch office in Chicago, on his interest in NSF. The State Department science adviser, having lost Sunderlin to the Foundation, now told Waterman that "he was staking a claim on Kelly." But he would lose again, as Kelly accepted the NSF offer to be assistant director for scientific personnel and education

(SPE). A forty-three year-old physicist with an MIT doctoral degree, Kelly had worked in the MIT Radiation Laboratory during the war. From 1945 to 1950, as the chief scientist on General Douglas MacArthur's staff, he aided in the restoration of Japan's scientific and technological programs and won the grateful friendship of many Japanese scientists. When Waterman discussed with the board's SPE committee his wish to recruit Kelly, they cautioned him "about having too many physicists around." Edwin B. Fred said that some other members shared his "feeling ... that biological sciences should receive due attention" in top staff appointments. Waterman assured him that selections of assistant directors for the biological and medical research divisions would meet the need. Kelly's appointment could not wait because the State Department was insisting on an immediate answer to its offer. Besides, Waterman told the board, "the scope of his work for the entire past five years has been over all fields of science and, in fact, in Japan much of it was related to biology and physiology."[16]

Waterman moved quickly to counter the concern about physical scientists' dominance of the Foundation staff. Two days after getting Kelly's acceptance the director talked with John Field II, who would be leaving ONR's biology division in the fall to become head of the physiology department of the medical school of the University of California at Los Angeles. Field, who had received his doctorate at Stanford and taught there for several years, arranged for a temporary leave from UCLA to help organize and staff the Foundation's division of biological sciences.[17]

It took longer to fill the position of assistant director for mathematical, physical, and engineering sciences (MPE). Although Waterman wanted a physicist to lead what he seems to have considered the most important of the Foundation's research divisions, many capable members of his profession were tied up in the booming programs of military research. In view of this he agreed with Robert Oppenheimer that "there would be merit in getting a broad-gauge mathematician or engineer," but he seems to have made no effort to recruit one. In May he urged physicist Robert B. Brode of the University of California at Berkeley to take the job "for a year. There is much to be done and the initial year is especially critical of course in that it will set the tone of the program of the Foundation." Brode declined but did join the staff several years later.[18] In August Waterman offered the post to a former associate in the Office of Field Service, Paul E. Klopsteg, who accepted and began work in November. The only principal early appointee who had not been employed by ONR, the sixty-two year-old Klopsteg was a professor of applied science and director of research in Northwestern University's Institute of Technology. A former chairman of the Argonne National Laboratory's board of governors and a member of AEC's security panel, he also had close ties to industry in Chicago and Detroit. He was the author of several books and articles on the physics of archery, and he was especially well known for his postwar work in the development of artificial limbs. A little more than a year after joining NSF Klopsteg was appointed to a new position of associate director, with broader responsibilities, and the search for an MPE assistant director began again.[19]

An assistant director for the fourth statutory division—medical research—was never appointed. The Budget Bureau's conclusion, even before NSF's establishment, that the division probably should not be activated undoubtedly affected this decision. The Bureau continued to encourage Waterman to consolidate the biological and medical sciences, and its budget examiners indicated their intention to eliminate medical research funds from NSF's fiscal 1952 budget request. Neither the director nor the board wanted to be blocked off from supporting basic research in the medical sciences, and the board protested strongly and successfully against this exclusion.[20] The board established a divisional committee for medical research, and in July 1951 Waterman told board member Robert Loeb that he was "giving active thought to the formation of the division... and particularly the selection of its head." He sounded out Lowell T. Coggeshall of the University of Chicago and R. Keith Cannan of New York University's medical school, but neither was interested. He also explored the possibility of arranging a transfer for a year or two of an NIH official to head the division; Surgeon General Leonard Scheele thought there might be advantages in such an arrangement, but no transfer occurred. Next Waterman tried to persuade Ernest W. Goodpasture of Vanderbilt University's medical school to accept appointment as a consultant to advise the Foundation on its support of medical research. After Goodpasture turned down the offer the board decided to combine, at least for a while, biological and medical research programs in a single division, and finally the separate divisional committees were also merged.[21]

While scrupulous in asking the advice of appropriate board members on possible choices and in confirming the board's approval before making a final offer, Waterman otherwise made the first—and later—decisions on the chief staff appointments on his own. Legally a nonvoting member of the board, he dealt with its members respectfully but not subserviently, and he quickly established a good working relationship with them. Within a few months Charles Dollard was telling Vannevar Bush that "Alan Waterman is doing a bang up job as director and has recruited a number of able and energetic young fellows to help him carry the load."[22] The board, relieved that Waterman had been named director and soon generally confident of his judgment, readily accepted his definition of organization and staff functions.

Waterman outlined his views on these matters immediately after taking the oath of office: The heads of scientific programs—that is, the assistant directors for the research and educational divisions—would report to him and the deputy director. The general counsel would report to the director but would also be "directly available to the Board." An administrative officer, responsible of course to the director and his deputy, would look after fiscal, personnel, and housekeeping services. Civil Service regulations and the 1949 Classification Act would apply to most NSF employees, but not, Waterman proposed, to the deputy director, the division heads, and the general counsel. He advised the board that he intended to fix the salary of the deputy director at $14,000 a year ($1,000 less than his own), the division heads at $13,000, and the general counsel at about $12,500.[23]

* * *

To oversee the many administrative details of creating a new government agency Waterman relied on Wilson F. Harwood. Well-educated and experienced in public administration and management, Harwood had worked as a Budget Bureau analyst and as administrative officer of ONR, where he had been detailed to the office of the Secretary of Defense to direct analyses of the department's research and development activities. Late in 1950 he transferred from ONR to the Bureau of Standards, and he was working there as Edward U. Condon's executive assistant when Waterman arranged for his part-time help in developing the Foundation's administrative organization and staff. Harwood was obviously a leading candidate for the permanent position of assistant director for administration, except for the recency of his transfer to the Bureau of Standards and his resulting sense of obligation to Condon. For several months he divided his time about equally between the two agencies, but in July the Foundation announced his appointment as the full-time administrative officer.[24]

The first need was office space, and neither purchase nor construction was feasible. Here board sensibilities had to be considered as well as working conditions for the staff. For years Bronk cherished a hope of developing a national science center, of which the Foundation would form a part, clustering around the Academy building on Constitution Avenue. A Budget Bureau staff member, George Viault, assigned to midwifery tasks for the Foundation, told the board at its second meeting that space had been "tentatively reserved for it in the YMCA annex at 18th and G Streets, but ... the Board reacted unfavorably to it, expressing a preference for a location nearer to the National Academy of Sciences, in order to use its library." Later, when Viault suggested that NSF might find suitable quarters in a house across from the Naval Hospital in Bethesda, Maryland, Waterman said that offices convenient to visitors near the National Research Council (NRC) and other agencies would be better. Conant similarly expressed a wish for a location near NRC and the Cosmos Club (then a little more than a block from the White House) where several board members stayed when they came to Washington.[25]

The Foundation's first headquarters, occupied early in April, met Conant's preference for location, but it certainly lacked style. A three-story brick residential building on the northeast corner of 16th and I streets, Northwest, the building was, as Waterman described it, "not quite old enough to be antique and not quite young enough to boast any modern appurtenances"—unless an abandoned high colonic irrigation device could be considered one.[26] From the start the space was regarded as temporary, and Harwood at once began a search for more comfortable offices. In May he asked the General Services Administration for 20-25,000 square feet of space to accommodate the growing staff, instead of the 6,000 square feet in the seventeen rooms at 901 16th Street.

> It is difficult to use this space effectively [he wrote]. In two cases access to one room can only be had by walking through two others. Three small rooms, one with tile floor and walls, one with tile floor and a sink, and one with steps to a fire escape, have limited use. The three basement rooms are isolated from the balance of the building because they may only be entered from the street. Under the circumstances, it is estimated that the maximum number of employees that may be housed at this location, even under crowded conditions, is forty.[27]

Bronk might dream of a science center but Waterman reconciled himself to frequent shifts in location. He talked about the problem with Bush, who agreed that "we are bound to look forward to a series of temporary moves as we grow." If NSF tried to stake "a claim for a permanent home" at this fledgling stage, Waterman reasoned, the agency would face a tough fight guarding it against powerful competitors. In addition, the attempt might look like "empire building," and "the changes in personnel around Washington make it difficult to adhere to any long range plan for a matter of this kind." One possibility, which he broached to Conant, was the Devitt School, just off upper Connecticut Avenue and across the street from the National Bureau of Standards. The Bureau controlled the property but might release it to NSF if the Foundation supported Condon's attempt to get other space from the General Services Administration (GSA). One danger of locating next to the Bureau was that NSF might lose its identity, but Conant did not believe this would be a serious problem.[28]

The Devitt School would suit until about one hundred persons were on board. During the first month the Foundation employed fifteen people, and it planned to continue that rate of growth until the staff numbered 145. Larger quarters would be needed before July 1, the director told GSA. Among several other possibilities the Foundation learned of the availability of the Potomac School at 2144 California Street, N.W.[29] Although the California Street building was farther from the heart of the city than desirable, staff members who visited it came back convinced that the Foundation should acquire it, and the director asked GSA's Public Buildings Service to try to arrange for a lease that would permit occupancy by July 1. A lease was soon signed, but modifications of the structure—a patchwork of houses oddly joined to form a school—delayed a move until August. Until then the staff at 16th and Eye had to work in rather cramped offices.[30]

The projected rate of staff growth represented hope more than fact and was exaggerated in NSF's pleas for space. GSA was told in June 1951 that the Foundation expected to have 70 employees by September—"far beyond the capacity of our present space"—yet there were only 56 at the end of the year, occupying nearly twice as much room as in the first headquarters. To make its needs seem more credible NSF's later requests sometimes mentioned not only full-time staff members but a large number of part-time employees and consultants also. Thus in May 1952 the director wrote that NSF was "in imminent need of more space.... We now employ 76 full-time and 61 part-time persons." The California Street offices would be overcrowded by the end of June, Waterman wrote, and the estimated growth in staff and consultants for fiscal year 1953 called for a doubling of the present space.[31]

A few months later Waterman informed the board that the Foundation expected to be assigned four buildings on H Street and Madison Place, close to the White House. One of these (1520 H Street), an early nineteenth-century structure (c. 1818-20), was known as the Dolley Madison House, as the fourth President's widow had resided there during the last years of her life. Two other buildings adjoined this on Madison Place and faced Lafayette Park—a five-story building erected by the Cosmos Club in 1909 and the three-story Ogle Tayloe House, built in 1828. An alley between the Tayloe House and the Belasco Theatre gave access to a parking area, and behind this a fourth building, once the site of Benjamin Ogle Tayloe's stables, provided an auditorium. All of the buildings required a good deal of renovation after the Cosmos Club moved out, but when the Foundation occupied them at the end of May 1953 they made available more than thirty thousand square feet of usable space for the 120 regular employees and a "handsome conference room" for board meetings. The director was pleased to acquire the auditorium, which he anticipated would be used for lectures by distinguished visitors and meetings of local scientific societies.[32]

Late in 1955 NSF began to occupy space in another historic nineteenth-century structure—the Winder Building, located on 17th Street across from the Executive Office Building. Additional offices on Lafayette Square (726 Jackson Place) were occupied by about thirty persons late in 1957, when the total number of regular staff members had passed 250.[33] The growth stimulated by the reaction to Soviet sputniks soon led to new requests to the Public Buildings Service, and in August 1958 the Foundation occupied its fourth headquarters, at 1951 Consitution Avenue, at last moving near the National Academy of Sciences as Bronk had long wished.[34]

The early headquarters buildings left pleasant memories, especially of friendly association, in the minds of many NSF staff members. The California Street building was "not efficient from an office point of view," Virginia Sides recalled, "but rather nice to work in." The staff had "fun" in their early, temporary homes; "working in less than ideal quarters," she continued, "is on the one hand inefficient; on the other hand it adds a something sort of special if you're just not walking down a big government corridor with lots of green walls. . . . our environment in some senses helped to shape us in those early years. . . . It somehow was more intimate than federal bureaucracy normally is."[35] Such memories of course reveal more of the excitement of youthful beginnings, recollected in tranquillity, than they do of physical surroundings.

* * *

On the Foundation's first anniversary, Waterman thanked ONR's fiscal officer for his help in getting NSF started. "I have learned in the last few weeks that there are a multitude of things which must be taken care of in establishing a new agency," the director wrote.[36] April 1951 must have been the busiest month in Waterman's life. Although aided in the organizational chores during the formative period by experienced civil servants in the Bureau of the Budget, the Navy Department, and the Bureau of Standards,[37] the director had to attend personally to many small matters while dealing with large ones—recruiting his chief assistants, planning a program, and preparing a budget.

Writing many routine letters himself and meticulously documenting his telephone conversations and meetings in diary notes, Waterman created a full record of the agency's creation. His ONR experience in government procedures helped get him through this trying period unruffled, as did his ability to delegate tasks to others. Delegation did not mean license. Waterman remained attentive to the work of his staff and did not sign papers placed before him unless he was satisfied with their form and style as well as substance. Documents "signed off on" by several NSF officials often bounced back from the director's office because he had caught a "typo" unnoticed by all other readers. He wrote in a plain, clear style, unmarked by rhetorical flourishes or jargon. While this virtue did not prevail throughout the agency as its paperwork expanded, it did have a wholesome influence in some offices. In time most NSF prose became indistinguishable from the abstract wordiness of other government agencies, but Waterman probably delayed the onset of normal bureaucratic language.

Aware—perhaps overly so—of dangers that might lie ahead, Waterman was careful to avoid unnecessary trouble for the Foundation. But it seems that this did not result in an excess of caution among his lieutenants. They generally remember the early years as a time of zestful creativity, guided by a shared sense of purpose and encouraged by the director. Waterman was scrupulous but not fussy. One long-time associate praises his "tolerance of ambiguity," which permitted some experimentation in the development of programs and a measure of flexibility in their administration.[38]

Fortunately for Waterman and his first division and program directors, choices for program and procedural planning remained fairly open. The Foundation's first budget had not allowed the board to follow its impulse to launch a fellowship program, and the newly appointed director and his principal assistants thus had an opportunity to form their own ideas and recommend them to the board. In this sense too it may have been fortunate that anticipated transfers of Defense Department research contracts did not materialize, since the requirements of administering programs can offer a ready escape from the bothersome job of planning. Poverty is not a happy condition but it can spur creative thought. In planning programs to carry out the Foundation's statutory functions the staff recruited in 1951-52 had time both to draw on their ONR experience and their desire to transcend it.

8
Defining a Program— the 1952 Budget

The Foundation's charter listed eight functions that the agency was "authorized and directed" to perform. The first decisions on the relative emphasis to be placed on these diverse activities were apt to be critical. It would not be easy to double back and take another road. The choices would determine whether the Foundation would give primary allegiance to its public constituency, especially the President, or to its private one, scientists themselves.

For five years the Bureau of the Budget had worked to establish an agency capable of serving the Executive Office of the President. By persuasion and budgetary controls the Bureau continued to try to mold the Foundation into a policy-forming and evaluative instrument. The independent National Science Board, dominated by university scientists and administrators, emphasized instead the support of academic research and education. The director and staff, generally agreeing with the board's aims, devised specific programs and procedures to foster the primary functions of basic research and advanced scientific training, while carefully avoiding conflicts with large and entrenched agencies.

The emergency created by the Korean war, as well as deepening fears of communist aggression and subversion, strongly affected the early thinking about NSF's program. In October 1950 President Truman approved the undertaking of a review by William T. Golden of the rapidly growing military research and development activities and how they related to other federal science programs. Golden spent several months in an intensive investigation which led to his recommendation that the President promptly appoint a science adviser.[1] His studies also resulted in a suggested program for the National Science Foundation.[2]

The Foundation's highest purpose, Golden began, was to advance fundamental scientific knowledge. But the emergency facing the country had brought swift and large increases in Defense Department research budgets and consequent demands on the nation's scientific manpower. The "near-term needs for applied military research" would prevent early expansion of basic research, but it was

> important that current basic research be continued, despite the heavy pressures which will be put on manpower and facilities to shift their emphasis to scientific activities having greater promise of prompt results. And as soon as our expanding military research and development programs are more clearly defined and stabilized it should be possible to divert some effort to increase the attention paid to basic research. This is vital to broaden the foundation of knowledge for our military and industrial strength and the public welfare over the longer term.

Meantime a gradual shift of ONR and AEC basic research projects to NSF would help the Foundation prepare to perform its evaluation function.

One function assigned to NSF by its act was the support of specific research activities—not necessarily basic—requested by the Secretary of Defense. Golden advised—as did nearly all the persons he consulted—against the support by NSF of any applied military research. Other agencies were better equipped to do such work. The Foundation should concentrate on fundamental science. The board should think first not of appropriations but of program, immediate and long-term. As soon as a director and staff were appointed they should undertake, under board guidance, comprehensive surveys of basic research being done by government, universities, and industry, of the support of graduate and undergraduate education in the sciences, and of the nation's scientific and technical manpower. A review of basic research in federal agencies should assist the transfer of "appropriate portions" to NSF. One important program—predoctoral and postdoctoral fellowships—should be started as soon as funds could be obtained, and this activity could be expanded and refined after analysis of the information obtained in the survey of science education. Such studies, Golden said, would lay the groundwork for the Foundation's future program and furnish invaluable information for the investment of public and private funds in research and education.

Although the National Science Board took no action on Golden's memorandum, which had been sent to the members at Conant's suggestion, it did influence their thinking and Waterman's. A majority of the board opposed Golden's earlier recommendation that the President appoint a science adviser, one of whose main tasks would be to "plan for and stand ready promptly to initiate a civilian Scientific Research Agency, roughly comparable to the Office of Scientific Research and Development (OSRD) of World War II."[3] Just as Waterman's chief worry about taking the director's position was the possible exclusion of NSF from defense research, so did the board's majority object at first to exclusion.[4]

These stands surprised Golden. They displayed an "abrupt turnabout" from views given him earlier, by Bronk and DuBridge at least, both of whom had favored the appointment of a science adviser, though Conant had preferred an advisory committee instead. Especially startling was the board's desire to undertake defense research, since nearly everyone Golden had consulted agreed that NSF should eschew military connections. Apparently Conant did not hold a tight rein on the board's deliberations— "things just snowballed" according to DuBridge.[5] But while Conant may have dissented from the majority on the question of military research, as chairman he reported the board's views to the Administration. He told Budget Bureau officials that an OSRD would not be needed even "in the event of an actual outbreak of war," and that limitation of NSF to nondefense research would seriously handicap its "opportunities for recruiting good people and arousing real enthusiasm."[6] The board had concluded that support of military research requested by the Secretary of Defense "might well be one of the most important concerns of the Foundation for some time to come." The board deferred action, however, on a suggestion by Elmer Staats of the Budget Bureau that it establish a Division of Defense Research, as the NSF director, who had not yet been named, should have a chance to say what he thought on this matter. In proposing the establishment of the division Staats was pushing the Bureau's idea of enlisting the Foundation as an ally to monitor expensive military research programs and halt their needless proliferation; in addition, of course, the division would handle defense research conducted at the request of the Secretary of Defense.[7]

The eagerness of some board members to hitch the Foundation to defense research had moderated by the time Waterman's appointment was announced. When he met with Conant and Bronk following the board meeting on March 9, he heard that the members were looking to him for leadership on the question of military research and how it would fit into "the normal functions of the Foundation from a long-range point of view." The lure of quick money had faded when members had second thoughts about the Foundation's real purpose and the danger of subservience to the military and short-term requirements. While the board "would be willing to undertake defense research," Conant told Waterman, it "unanimously agreed that the National Science Foundation should not be put in position of becoming another OSRD."[8]

While Waterman and the board continued to hope for the transfer of research (and funds) from defense agencies, they agreed that it should be basic, uncommitted research. For two different but related reasons, it seems, the board never established a defense-research division: fear that standards of free research and open publication would be endangered by military requirements, and fear that Budget Bureau designs would divert the agency from the support of research and education into the dangerous chore of judging Defense Department and other federal science programs.

Though avoiding entanglement with the military services, Foundation officials won what looked like a chance to influence defense-research policies by another means. Golden's recommendation that the President appoint a science adviser led to the creation of a Science Advisory Committee (SAC), headed by Oliver E Buckley, a recently retired president of Bell Telephone Laboratories, that was placed in the Office of Defense Mobilization (ODM). Among its first members were Bronk, as president of the National Academy of Sciences, Waterman, as NSF director, and Conant, Lee DuBridge, and Robert F. Loeb, members of the National Science Board. In 1952 DuBridge became chairman of SAC, on a part-time basis, and the Caltech president asked Waterman, on the scene in Washington, to be his deputy.[9]

* * *

The Foundation's first budget provided funds adequate only for organization and program planning. But the National Science Board earnestly sought ways of alleviating what nearly everyone agreed was a scientific manpower crisis resulting from the Korean conflict, the draft, and diversion of scientists and engineers into defense work. Disappointed to learn that the meager first-year funds could not be used for fellowships, Conant urged the Budget Bureau to see if there were not some way of underwriting a fellowship program by getting a loan from a private foundation which could be repaid from the fiscal 1952 appropriation. Golden agreed on the importance of awarding fellowships immediately, along with the "war mobilization program or we will be weaker 5 years from now and thereafter." Under this sort of pressure Staats decided that the Bureau should explore the feasibility of transferring $2 million from the Defense Department to NSF for the support of fellowships.[10] Schuldt effectively quashed the idea. Not only were there legal difficulties, but it was already time for receipt of fellowship applications for the coming academic year. "In view of the fact that the Foundation has no Director, much less a staff, to give continuity to the planning," he wrote, "I cannot help but feel that a determination on the part of NSF to launch a program now willy-nilly, may well result in a 'half-baked' program which would haunt the Foundation in the future."[11]

The board surrendered on an immediate program after Staats

explained the difficulties, but it created a temporary committee to come up with a proposal for fellowships beginning in 1952. At the March meeting Charles Dollard recommended a program of pre- and postdoctoral fellowships costing $5 million the first year, $8 million the second, and $10 million the third. The board increased Dollard's estimates to provide for more postdoctoral fellows and to include allowances to universities in addition to tuition stipends. The program was to be administered by the National Research Council, since it would be "foolish for the National Science Foundation to try and duplicate machinery that already exists and is working at a high level of competence."[12]

Although board members unanimously agreed on the desirability of a fellowship program, they obviously needed guidance on its size and its relation to a research program within a budget of no more than $15 million. The Budget Bureau wanted figures quickly for review and submission to Congress, and at the March meeting the board gave Schuldt a rough estimate of a $15 million budget in which research was allocated $7.5 million and fellowships $6.5 million. Waterman had the chore of refining and justifying these estimates before formal submission to the Bureau.[13]

Waterman promptly discussed with M. H. Trytten of the National Research Council details of appropriate stipends, and with AEC officials the possibility of NSF's assuming that agency's fellowship program. The Budget Bureau did not want two agencies awarding general science fellowships concurrently, and it encouraged the assumption of AEC's program by the Foundation, as it would later encourage NSF's assumption of NIH's predoctoral fellowships.[14] The Bureau advised a reduction in the Foundation's fellowships estimate, however, in part because of a belief that studies like those proposed by Golden were needed first to furnish firm data for an extensive program. Waterman did cut the estimate by $1 million and told Conant that the reduction would allow more money for research support; furthermore, the fellowships item would be more defensible and "could pave the way to [an] increase in the budget ceiling by announcing intention of the Foundation to take over the AEC fellowship program" in fiscal 1953.[15] Conant and other board members with whom Waterman discussed this revision did not object and, Schuldt heard, "authorized him to use his best judgment as regards the submission to the Bureau of the Budget."[16]

Since Harry Kelly had not yet reported as head of the SPE division, which would handle the fellowship program, Waterman had to master the details needed to satisfy the board and the Bureau. Schuldt asked why NSF requested funds for only 2,100 fellows when Waterman's data showed that 9,800 graduate science students needed financial assistance. The director replied that not all 9,800 were "fully competent," and the Foundation wanted its fellowships to win prestige by being awarded only to "the most gifted individuals." Bureau examiners who questioned reliance on the National Research Council to administer the program got his assurance that NSF "would be responsible for the Council's administration, and the final appointment of fellows will rest with the Foundation."[17]

The board discussed the director's fellowships plan extensively but inconclusively at its May meeting. Still wanting to start a program quickly, it asked Waterman to study the possibility of awarding some fellowships effective January 1, 1952. The figures of 2,100 fellowships and $1,400 for stipends came in for more serious questioning than the Bureau's. Why not give $500 stipends and support a much larger number of graduate students? But most members seemed to believe that the director had struck a reasonable balance between quality and quantity. Should stipends be uniform? Although the NSF act required that fellowships be awarded "solely on the basis of ability," a means test might be used to adjust stipends on the basis of financial need once fellows had been chosen. The director was asked to study this matter. Should universities receive full costs of education, which might run as high as $3,000 a year, instead of merely a $500 tuition allowance and about $100 additional for such items as laboratory materials? Waterman explained that government policy largely determined these figures. Besides, most fellows would choose to attend well-known graduate schools, already the recipients of the bulk of federal research support, and other institutions would complain that full-cost subsidies were helping the rich universities get richer.[18]

Waterman was as eager as any board member to get the program started. As late as July 5 he was hoping to award two hundred fellowships in September 1951, but lack of a budget and time forced him to drop this notion. At the board meeting in midsummer he proposed to use 10-15 percent of the fellowship budget—still pending in Congress—to make awards effective January 1, 1952. After hearing the director's report on a means test, the board abandoned the idea of adjusting stipends according to individuals' needs. Conant was in Australia, but Waterman used the chairman's arguments "that the fellowships were honors in the democratic sense and made no distinction regarding personal income, [and] that graduate students were over 21 and therefore, in general, would not have private means and should not call on their parents." A discussion of subject-matter fields of science which fellows might study reached no conclusion, and it was understood that later discussion of this question would be based on a staff paper furnished by the director.[19] Fortunately he now had a small staff to do this kind of legwork. Kelly had reported, and he recruited another physicist, Bowen C. Dees, with whom he had worked in postwar Japan, to head the fellowship program.

In addition to graduate fellowships the NSF act authorized the awarding of undergraduate scholarships, an idea pushed by Conant since the issuance of the Bush report. But much had happened since 1945 to raise questions about the estimates and the rationale of the Moe committee's section of *Science—The Endless Frontier*. Billions of federal tax dollars had helped war veterans go to college and graduate school; and a program of scholarships to be administered by the Federal Security Agency, not limited to science and engineering, was being considered. Conant still "strongly approved" an NSF scholarship program but advised Waterman to "proceed very slowly." The Budget Bureau did not demur when Waterman mentioned the possibility of including a request for scholarship funds in the 1953 budget, and a board committee was asked to make recommendations.[20]

The committee, headed by Dollard, recommended a limited program "to dramatize science and to subsidize a small group of men and women of topflight capacity." NSF should include about $1 million in its 1953 budget request for one thousand scholarships to be awarded on the basis of ability in science and not restricting the holders to any special course of study. The Foundation should also endorse the general scholarship program proposed by the Federal Security Agency, and should study the needs and supply of scientific personnel "with particular reference to secondary schools and colleges, in order to develop a satisfactory scholarship plan."[21]

* * *

Important as a fellowship program was to Waterman and the board, they conceived the Foundation's main function to be the support of basic research. And while Waterman as ONR's chief scientist had joined his colleagues in other federal offices in stating a standard bureaucratic view that the new agency's research support should extend only to gaps that they could not legally or appropriately fill,[22] in his new position he insisted, with the board's full backing, on the Foundation's right and responsibility to mount programs in all the natural sciences.

The issue arose first with respect to medical research. The Foundation's fiscal 1952 budget submission in April requested $8.6 million for research support: $1.2 for medical, $2.9 for biological, $4.0 for mathematical, physical, and engineering, and $0.5 for operating costs.[23] The Bureau proposed to eliminate the medical item entirely—though not necessarily in later years—"in view of the large amounts of money now supporting that field." Waterman, knowing the Bureau's design for NSF, replied that "The Foundation could not establish national policy in basic research if it is excluded from operating in any areas." He also resisted Schuldt's suggestion that NSF at least defer support of medical research.[24]

Backing the director, the board reminded the Bureau of the congressional intent that NSF support "basic research and education in medicine" and maintained that there was an "urgent need" for more basic research in the medical sciences. The elimination from NSF's program of "any field of basic science would create a precedent which might, at any time, be made applicable to fields in which there is current support of basic research from other governmental sources." Finally the board used Waterman's clinching argument that elimination "would sharply limit the effectiveness of the Foundation in evaluating and guiding the future of scientific activity in the country because of the intimate relation of medical science to many other fields of science."[25]

At first the Bureau stood by its proposed reductions—$2.7 million in all—from the Foundation's request. Schuldt argued that NSF might become so absorbed in the administration of its research program, which might be enlarged by the transfer of $5-10 million of Defense Department funds, that it would fail to perform its more important evaluation task. Because of the rapid growth of applied research, the scientific community would have trouble absorbing a large amount of new money for basic research. In addition, a Foundation request nearly reaching its $15 million ceiling might anger congressional appropriations committees, who would want to see specific evidence in support of higher research levels.[26]

Waterman made a successful appeal to the Bureau, however, and $2 million for research was restored, including nearly all of the amount for medical research. In the budget submitted to Congress in May the ratio of funds for the three research programs (medical; biological; and mathematical, physical, and engineering) was 1:2:3.[27] The point had been made, to the Bureau at least, that NSF insisted on "a comprehensive program of support for basic research," not simply one of "filling gaps." On the other hand, the Foundation would not attempt to wrest basic research programs from other agencies. Transfers of programs would occur only "in consultation with the agencies concerned." An aim of the Foundation was to enlarge the opportunities for basic research, not to whittle away the support extended by other federal science offices.[28]

* * *

The Bureau backed down on NSF sponsorship of medical research, in part because of the Foundation's argument and perhaps too because it foresaw the need of authoritative scientific support to curb a resurgence of NIH's budgetary growth, temporarily halted during the national emergency. But the Foundation's principal functions in the Bureau's view remained "the development of a national policy for the promotion of basic research and education in the sciences, the evaluation of Federal research programs, and the correlation of NSF's programs with these." Schuldt proposed "to take the line quite strongly" that the Foundation must acknowledge these planning activities as "its first responsibility." He would, however, make one temporary concession. Since "the Foundation has been somewhat awed and overwhelmed by its statutory directive to 'evaluate scientific research programs undertaken by the agencies of the Federal Government,' " it might at first limit its evaluation to federal programs of *basic* research. The new Science Advisory Committee of ODM was supposed to assess military scientific development. Relieved of this much greater chore, NSF should be able to evaluate basic programs "within a reasonable period of time." The Bureau intended to hold the Foundation to these policy duties.[29]

Waterman had said before accepting the directorship that he would not evaluate other federal science programs. The board agreed with his stand. Yet the Foundation could hardly declare one of its statutory functions null and void or ignore Congress's first mandate: "to develop and encourage the pursuit of a national policy for the promotion of basic research and education in the sciences." The hard line that the Bureau proposed to follow in examining the Foundation's first budget request posed a danger of an immediate confrontation.

It turned out that the Foundation's position was strong enough to resist the pressure. Not only did the unity of director and board frustrate the Bureau, but so did the uncertainties about the meaning of national science policy and the obvious difficulties of a small, new staff attempting to evaluate the varied programs of several large agencies. As a result, although the Bureau tried to follow the line suggested by Schuldt, it ended by accepting the Foundation's less direct approach to its policy and evaluation functions, putting off the encounter until another day.

The means of avoiding direct efforts to develop policy and evaluate other programs were suggested in Golden's memorandum on the Foundation's program—though Waterman and the board would have thought of them anyway. Sound policy had to be built on dependable information obtained by comprehensive surveys, and assessment of diverse research programs required operating experience in similar fields.

The emergence of NSF's strategy appears in the evolution of the agency's 1952 budget estimates, which from the start included a line item for surveys of research needs. A press release in April announced the board's plans "for a broad survey of the facilities and personnel available for scientific research in all parts of the country and the needs for developing scientific teaching and research on a broader geographical basis."[30]

At the May board meeting the director reported on the Budget Bureau's criticisms of "the lack of emphasis on policy formulation in the budget proposal," to which he replied "that the Foundation could be an effective policy-forming agency for the sciences only after it had matured in the light of operation of research programs in those sciences." Surveys of the state of research in various fields of science and by various performers, including "weighing the opinions of scientists and examining the needs of Government agencies," would enable the Foundation to add special encouragement "along promising and neglected avenues" to its comprehensive program of research support.[31] By this time the Bureau was succeeding in giving some greater prominence to the functions it considered primary by making "Research Policy Development and Services" the first rather than the last of NSF's several budget categories. The Foundation, in turn, in its budget justification to Congress termed policy development for basic research and education its "most important and fundamental function."[32] The Bureau acquiesced, for the moment, in the Foundation's roundabout approach to policy-making and evaluation.

Within a few months the Foundation publicly announced its ideas on the making of science policy—omitting any mention of evaluation of federal programs—in its first annual report. The statement, which accurately reflects Waterman's views and those of a majority of the board, left ample room for maneuver and deliberation in the performance of the Foundation's first statutory function:

> The development and formulation of a national science policy will take time. At the outset it must be approached with care and thoroughness.
> Among the questions which need to be answered in developing a national policy in basic research and education in the sciences are the following:
> What is the total financial support now being provided for scientific research?
> What is the distribution of this support among the three major sources—Government, industry, and educational institutions?
> What amount of financial support can and should be provided and what is the most desirable distribution from among the available sources of support?
> What is the division of research effort among the various natural sciences?
> What areas need greater emphasis and what less?
> What means can be developed to shorten the period between discovery and practical application?
> What are the present and future needs for trained scientific manpower?
> What is the impact of Government support of research programs on the educational process in universities and colleges?
> What is the effect of Federal research programs on the financial stability of universities?
> A national science policy will stem from many sources and embrace the ideas of diverse groups and individuals. A sound policy, however, must rest on a sound foundation of fact. Developing such a body of fact is one of the chief tasks of the Foundation.[33]

* * *

Two other Foundation functions authorized by Congress gained recognition in the agency's first budget submission—dissemination of scientific information, and maintenance of a register and information clearinghouse on scientific and technical personnel—both under the heading of Research Policy Development and Services. There was never any serious question either in the board or the Budget Bureau about the need to perform these services, though there were some problems associated with the transfer of the National Scientific Register from the U.S. Office of Education to NSF.[34]

The Foundation was directed by its charter "to foster the interchange of scientific information among scientists in the United States and foreign countries." Wholly in accord with the canon that science knows no national boundaries, this function early received the board's endorsement. The budget, the board decided, should include funds for travel to scientific meetings in other countries and for a study of the financial problems of scientific publications, including "consideration of a program of translation of scientific articles published in the Russian language." In fact, the first tentative budget estimates suggested $1 million for publication and translations.[35] Greatly reduced later, the publications item was combined with travel to international conferences in the congressional budget submission. The budget also provided for maintaining the National Register, and the director indicated his intention of assuming responsibility for the Register sometime before June 30, 1952.[36]

One other research service included in the budget, apparently at the request of the Budget Bureau, was the provision of salaries of the secretariat of the Interdepartmental Committee on Scientific Research and Development. The ICSRD, whose establishment had once been provided for in science foundation legislation, had come into existence instead by executive order in 1947. It was assumed that NSF, once organized, would become a member, as it did in June 1951, with the director as the official representative.[37] It was also thought that NSF, because of its general science mission and policy responsibilities, might provide a home for the secretariat.

As the navy's representative on ICSRD Waterman had participated in its cooperative activities and become well aware of his associates' protective feelings for their domains—like his own of course. His experience in that "coordinating" body undoubtedly contributed to his renunciation of an evaluative role for NSF. Thus he was leery of bringing the ICSRD physically under the Foundation's roof, since, as he told Schuldt, such a move "might be viewed with mingled feeling by the other agencies .... If after seeing the Foundation in operation, the other agencies would like to have the Committee operate under the Foundation then the move would be a spontaneous one and not instigated by the NSF." The Bureau agreed that the secretariat might continue to be housed in the agency whose representative served as chairman, and that NSF should transfer the committee's salary-expense funds to that agency. Waterman discussed the matter with Hugh L. Dryden of the National Advisory Committee for

Aeronautics, the current chairman of ICSRD, who also agreed to the arrangement.[38]

The one remaining statutory function not incorporated in the budget was permissive: "to establish such special commissions as the Board may from time to time deem necessary for the purposes of this Act." This provision was a vestige of the foundation bills which provided for various named commissions intended to guide the conquest of awesome diseases. Although the specific commissions were dropped, the power to establish such bodies seemed an appropriate one and was retained. The device would later prove useful, but the board saw no need for any special commission when it formulated its first program in the 1952 budget.

* * *

The NSF budget that went to Congress in May had survived tough questioning by the Bureau.[39] Schuldt still considered its supporting detail inadequate, and he wanted "to bring sharply to the attention of the Board that general plans are not ordinarily sufficient to receive favorable action by the Budget Bureau," if this could be done without causing the board to lose confidence in Waterman. As Schuldt knew, "Waterman had practically no time and no staff to do a real budget job."[40]

Prepared in haste, the justifications for the Foundation's proposed activities varied considerably in specific descriptions. The largest program—research support—had the scantiest programmatic detail, and its credibility rested on a prefatory essay about the importance of basic research to national defense and public welfare. A fundamental premise of the statement—one that Waterman would use again and again to justify support of basic research—was that knowledge is a depletable resource, and hence must be replenished.

> By and large . . . it is only recently that the country has come to recognize that technological advances are made possible only through the application of fundamental scientific knowledge already known. This fundamental knowledge has been a heritage available to us from the accumulated findings of science all over the world. We drew heavily upon this stockpile during the war, very seriously depleting it. Since research has very nearly come to a standstill in most other countries, the replenishment of this stockpile now rests chiefly in our own hands. Certainly, among the Western nations the responsibility is ours, and it is indeed a grave one.[41]

Despite Schuldt's misgivings, Albert Thomas (D., Texas) told Waterman that he "really enjoyed reading" the NSF budget justifications—"a very scholarly job and well done." At the hearing before a House Appropriations subcommittee on June 6 Chairman Thomas began his long, fatherly guidance of the Foundation's program, always with an eye to possible benefits for friends and institutions in East Texas. He listened with seeming patience to what he called "a very learned and scholarly presentation" by the director on the nature of basic research and the way it may ultimately eventuate in practical applications. In his friendly questioning of Waterman and Bronk, Thomas's only disturbing query was: "What do you think about cutting this budget down about 50 percent and taking it very slowly?"[42] On the other hand Thomas struck a responsive chord with them when he said, in what was also a lecture to his colleague Sidney R. Yates (D., Illinois): "... you ought to make it crystal clear that you have no authority under the act, and you have no intention, to tell any governmental agency what to do, how to do it, and how much money to spend. Also, it is not your intention and not your authority ... to tell any university or any private research institution what to do and how they can do it, or how much money they can spend." Waterman's response that "research is no field where master-minding is proper" amounted to a hearty amen.[43]

Yates was confused about the Foundation's purpose, and John Phillips (R., California) was much more so. As Waterman interpreted his questions, Phillips seemed "unaware that the Federal Government was already in the business of supporting research in universities," thought it inappropriate for NSF to undertake this "novel approach," and had trouble distinguishing the fellowship program from that of research support.[44] In his remarks on basic research Waterman had mentioned Jenner, Pasteur, Koch, and Lister. Since they were opposed by their peers or derided as cranks, Phillips said, "you would not have dared give those men a scholarship." Support for research should come from private foundations and industries, in Phillips's view.[45]

Over two months of anxious waiting followed the House hearing. Thomas's question prepared Waterman for "a fairly serious cut," but he thought "our chances are good of getting a fair operating budget. Certainly Congress gives us every indication of treating us cordially and with respect," he told Robert Brode. After all, Thomas had assured the NSF witnesses that "you will certainly make a success of this, and this committee is going to do its best to cooperate with you and help you make a success of it."[46]

Waterman's hopeful estimate of congressional respect for NSF was shattered in mid-August. The House Appropriations Committee report recommended a cut in NSF's budget from $14 million to $300,000—a 98 percent reduction. The committee could not see that the research and fellowship programs offered much chance of "early aid in the present emergency." The recommended appropriation would permit a staff of about thirty persons to continue to plan for future programs.[47] A few days later the House approved the committee's recommendation over the objections voiced by Percy Priest, Brooks Hays (D., Arkansas), and John W. Heselton (R., Massachusetts).[48]

Shocked by the House report, Waterman immediately sought to counter it by convincing the Senate Appropriations Committee of the important connection between the proposed research and fellowship programs and the national emergency—a connection that the House committee had called "not very tangible." Conant was in New Zealand, but the board's vice chairman, Edwin B. Fred, and the chairman of the executive committee, Bronk, approved Waterman's plans to muster support for the Foundation's case.[49]

The first step was the issuance of a public statement. In this press release Waterman said that the House committee had "misunderstood the desperately critical situation ... with respect to scientific manpower and its bearing upon the present emergency." A sharp decline in engineering graduates and a similar shortage of scientists were especially alarming because of the needs produced by a more than threefold increase in military research and development activities. The Foundation's fellowships would directly attack the critical manpower problem. "Research support has equal bearing on the emergency," Waterman said. Here again he emphasized the link to defense. "In field after field—aircraft design, jet engine metallurgy, guided missile development, liquid fuel production, military medicine, atomic power—technical progress is seriously delayed by lack of basic knowledge." Unlike his description before Thomas's subcommittee of the often slow transit of knowledge to application, now Waterman said that "Today, the time-lag between the discovery of a basic scientific principle and its exploitation and application has all but disappeared in great technological areas"—a fair comment perhaps on OSRD's wartime directed research but hardly on the uncommitted research that NSF planned to support. "In 1940," he said, "the Nazis stopped their research" because they believed they could win with weapons already developed. If the United States remembered that lesson, "the full amount of the budget requests for these essential programs will be restored."[50]

It looked like a return of NSF's budget battle the year before. Because of the congressional and public clamor about defense needs Waterman reasoned that it would be a good tactic to gain the backing of the Defense Department and the Office of Defense Mobilization. ODM presented no special problem. Through Oliver Buckley, chairman of the Science Advisory Committee, and Arthur S. Flemming, head of ODM and chairman of the recently established Manpower Policy Committee, he got the help of the White House agency. And support again came, as it had in 1950, in a letter from John Steelman to Senator Kenneth McKellar, who headed the Senate Appropriations Committee.[51]

The Defense Department's assistance seemed to Waterman to be crucial, and here he met difficulties. Robert A. Lovett, Deputy Secretary of Defense, offered sympathetic advice but said his staff all agreed that except for the department's own appropriation, it was improper for the secretary to recommend that one house of Congress correct action by the other; in addition, the congressional emphasis on defense had caused the department to be plagued by agency requests for comments on their budgets. Waterman pointed out that the Senate committee would ask, " 'What does the [Department of Defense] think of the program?' If we answer we have not inquired we are in the doghouse. If we answer [that] the DOD refuses to make a statement or otherwise endorse our program, our program may be thrown out, obviously." In the end Lovett decided that the department could make a supporting statement through its Research and Development Board. To forestall any foot-dragging by this group Waterman gave it positive assurances that NSF would not try to take over any basic research that the board wanted to keep under its wing; but the Foundation could provide valuable assistance by doing research the department would have trouble defending and by increasing the supply of scientists and engineers for military projects. Even so, he was unable to elicit a letter to McKellar's committee and had to settle for one addressed to himself which asserted that an operational NSF capable of performing research at the request of the Secretary of Defense and of awarding fellowships was "imperative." The defense board also agreed to take "appropriate steps," such as sending a representative to the Senate hearing, if Waterman could stimulate a question from the committee about the department's position.[52]

Though the Defense Department's response to Waterman's entreaties fell short of his desires, the letter which he got inserted in the hearing record probably had some influence.[53] The whole episode must have made the NSF director even more wary of taking on an evaluation function, as well as giving him a feeling of relief that his and the National Science Board's careful actions had not raised powerful enemies in the Pentagon.

Other federal agencies were less niggling in offering to help the Foundation in its time of trouble. Waterman sent his statement, with an accompanying letter, to numerous government officials and educational and industrial leaders who might influence legislative action. Many of them responded generously.[54] Among them was Vannevar Bush, one of the first persons Waterman called after he heard of the House committee's action. Though Bush was no longer in the government, his advice still carried much weight in the Senate, especially on the relevance of science to defense. Giving counsel to Waterman by long-distance phone from Cape Cod, Bush arranged for a letter over his name to go that very day to McKellar asking for correction of the House's "grave error," which would "be a crippling blow to the defense program of the nation," and another to his old antagonist Harley Kilgore, now appealed to as a former comrade-in-arms in the battle for a science foundation.[55] Waterman himself talked with at least two members of the committe, Guy Cordon (R., Oregon) and Joseph C. O'Mahoney (D., Wyoming). Cordon, one of the founding fathers of NSF, inserted in the hearing record letters he had received urging Senate reversal of the House action. O'Mahoney told Waterman that he had been particularly impressed by a letter pleading the Foundation's case from his friend George D. Humphrey, a member of the National Science Board and president of the University of Wyoming.[56]

O'Mahoney pointed out to Waterman an important reason for the Foundation's failure to build the public support that might have brought a different outcome in the House: NSF had not told the public what its program would be. The director replied that he wanted to have a full staff before opening the door for business, and it had seemed improper to discuss the program while the House committee still had it under review.[57] But there was no question now of the need for publicity, and Waterman's public statement did create a wider awareness of the Foundation's planned activities and their possibly indefinite deferral. Some major newspapers and news magazines brought the Foundation's plight to the attention of their readers, and science and education journals alerted the people most directly concerned.

The quickest response came in the Sunday "News of the Week in Review" section of the New York *Times*, two days after the committee report. A story by Robert K. Plumb led off with an account of the 98 percent reduction and then described the Foundation's program as outlined in the budget justifications.[58] Apart from news items, however, there was no statement of editorial opinion in the *Times* until September 2, when a tepid endorsement of NSF said that its officials were partly to blame for their troubles, even though "Their inertia is excusable because they wanted to feel their way and to let policies evolve with experience." The *Times* agreed on the desirability of an education program "to overcome a critical shortage of men and women trained in science, engineering, and medicine," but what was most needed, the editors thought, was an agency to study the state of American science and formulate national science policy.

The more friendly Washington *Post* found it "astonishing in this day of 56-billion-dollar defense budgets that the House Appropriations Committee should boggle over a 14-million-dollar fund designed to replenish the armory of scientific ideas from which defense draws its strength."[59] The *Post*'s editorial was called "scholarly and overly-conservative" in an International Latex Corporation advertisement. The House action was "a wind-fall victory for Stalin and his mob" who were "waiting only for the right moment to strike at us," according to this "public service" advertisement.[60] Senator Margaret Chase Smith (R., Maine) showed that she too read *Post* editorials when in her syndicated column she altered only slightly the sentence terming NSF an "armory of scientific ideas."[61] Appearing also in the *Post* was a letter from William Golden, who warned that while meeting immediate defense requirements the nation should not forget its long-term needs for more knowledge and more scientists. The Foundation's functions, he said, "are important in peacetime, vital for wartime."[62] For those who preferred the breezy gossip of Walter Winchell's column, the budget slash was likened to the attack on Pearl Harbor. "On the very day that Congress voted down the scientists it voted to continue its barbershop at the taxpayers' expense. . . . Proving the heaviest thing on a Congressman's mind is a free haircut."[63]

Once again, as during the effort to establish the agency, scientists and educational administrators were encouraged to come to the aid of the beleaguered Foundation. Because NSF had not publicized its plans these pleas were sometimes accompanied by explanations of its functions as outlined in the budget request. Thus Howard Meyerhoff described for the AAAS council the Foundation's projected programs, and he hoped that the members would communicate with their senators, especially those on the Appropriations Committee.[64] The American Council on Education newsletter told educators that they had "both the right and the obligation to speak" on this "matter . . . of grave importance to the national welfare." The newsletter quoted Waterman's public statement in full.[65] Waterman also explained the Foundation's plans in *Science*, and since his paper had been written before the House action, the editors added a footnote telling of the cut and of the danger that it might stand.[66] *Chemical & Engineering News*, which had many readers in industry as well as on campuses, called the House reduction a "completely incomprehensible" piece of "short-sightedness" and hoped that the Senate would restore the requested funds.[67]

In "The Labors of Sisyphus," an editorial in the *Bulletin of the Atomic Scientists*, Eugene Rabinowitch reviewed the frustrations of the effort to create the Foundation, and now to get it started. Analyzing the dilemma that produced Waterman's present strategy of tying NSF to national defense, Rabinowitch said that since World War II military research had played the role of "foster-mother to American science." Science, he continued, "has been treated as if it were deserving of national support only to the extent the military think they need it—and the military was therefore considered the proper agent to support it," Scientists finally convinced Congress that an independent science agency should take over this sustenance, but now, like Sisyphus, "they may have to start from the bottom again."

The root of the problem, Rabinowitch thought, was "not merely an indifference to science, but a sub-conscious hostility to it. This hostility has existed ever since science became an independent agent of progress and change in society; it has not diminished, but rather increased in times when science has produced its most spectacular achievements." Just as an antiscientific mood had helped Hitler's rise and was now evident in Stalin's Russia, "Here, too, science is a magic bird whose golden eggs everybody wants but whose free flight into regions inaccessible to most makes it a suspect creature."[68]

* * *

A week after the House committee made its report, Waterman appealed to the Senate Appropriations Committee for a restoration of $12.3 million of the deleted funds and asked for a hearing. His new budget justifications revealed that the small NSF staff had been hard at work preparing specific plans for programs in the biological and physical sciences, and describing for each program the possible applications of the findings resulting from its research support to health, welfare, agriculture, industry, or (especially) defense. (Thus studies of protein structure and synthesis might lead to plasma substitutes "of vital importance in an atomic bomb blast," and those in upper atmosphere physics would furnish data "vitally needed by the armed forces in developing guided missiles.")[69]

The revised request for a total appropriation of $12.6 million lopped off $1.4 million from the budget submitted to the House in May, since a quarter of the year would have passed by the time Congress took final action. Nearly all of the reduction came out of the estimate for research support. The programs outlined in the biological and MPE divisions would provide funds "through specific grants," evidently to individual investigators. Support of medical research, on the other hand, would be "general" in nature, mainly block grants to preclinical departments in medical schools (half of the departmental-grant money going to "well established departments" and half "on the basis of potential . . . in geographical areas where the need for medical research and education is greatest"); a lesser amount would provide general research support to a few "outstanding investigators."[70]

When board member A. A. Potter, an engineer, saw the new budget justifications, he protested that "Engineering was practically left out," while mathematics, physics, and chemistry were "taking by far the lion's share" of the MPE allocation. Half of the funds for mathematics, Potter said, should go to applied mathematics instead of all for "pure." In view of the AEC support of nuclear studies he proposed shifting all the funds for elementary particle physics and radiation chemistry to engineering fields not mentioned in the budget and deleting the large $300,000 item for solar energy, a "limited area" which MIT was already supporting. Waterman phoned Potter and told him about the necessity of preparing the budget material "literally over night" and assured the Purdue dean that the Foundation would not be bound by the estimates.[71]

The wanderings of board members during the summer and uncertainty about the date of the hearing complicated preparations for it. But the long delay before the hearing was finally scheduled for the afternoon of September 19 not only allowed Conant to return from New Zealand and Bronk to complete a sail along the New England coast with his sons, but also gave time for protests against the House action to gather force. Waterman conferred frequently with board members by telephone, and when they met early in September received their general endorsement of his actions and plans. He had time too to get advice on the strongest witnesses from Staats and Carey in the Budget Bureau and from them and other federal officials on ways of getting the desired kinds of response from McKellar's committee.[72] Yet it was not until the day before the hearing that the witness list was completed: Conant, Bronk, and Potter from the board, Waterman, Harwood, and Krebs from the staff, Buckley as chairman of the Science Advisory Committee, and J. Robert Oppenheimer, director of the Institute for Advanced Study, representing the National Academy of Sciences.[73] In addition, Alexander Smith would appear before the committee to speak in the Foundations's behalf.

The hearing got off to a bad start. The eighty-two year-old McKellar had trouble understanding that the request was for an annual appropriation rather than a deficiency one. Since the House had turned NSF down, he suggested that the appeal be withdrawn. After this confusion was finally cleared up, McKellar commented on the heavy mail he had received urging him to vote for the Foundation's request, and he wondered "if anybody connected with your organization has asked that such letters be written."[74] Schuldt, who was in the audience, thought Conant "demolished . . . pretty effectively" this implication of improper lobbying. More confusion arose because of a typographical error in the budget document's request for authority to employ German and Japanese scientists, and the Foundation agreed to Saltonstall's suggestion that the request be dropped.[75] Fortunately for NSF, O'Mahoney joined Saltonstall in helping Conant and other witnesses over the rough spots, and the other senators generally displayed a friendly attitude. Buckley and Oppenheimer especially stressed, as the Foundation wanted them to, the importance of basic research and fellowships to the nation's defense effort. So what had started as an ordeal ended in satisfaction. "The Foundation representatives," Schuldt learned from Sunderlin, "came out of the hearing with the hope and belief that funds in the order of $7-10 million would be restored by the Senate."[76]

The estimate was a little too optimistic. On October 6 the committee recommended an appropriation of $6.3 million,[77] and the Senate voted this amount a few days later. Apparently McKellar had swung around to a favorable position, since he told an old Tennessee friend that he thought NSF "had an able office" and should have some of its original request restored.[78]

Now the matter was up to a conference committee, and Bronk seems to have discussed with Congressman Priest the possibility of getting friends of the Foundation named to the House group. Priest told him this was not feasible; when Conant heard about Bronk's effort he commented "that we were not well enough aware of congressional procedures etc. to try to enter into the picture unless asked." Probably NSF benefited when the ailing Kenneth S. Wherry (R., Nebraska) was replaced as a Senate conferee by Saltonstall and by the inclusion of O'Mahoney and Cordon among the managers. Of the House group only Thomas was an identifiable friend. Waterman wrote to conferees from both chambers pointing out that the House hearing had occurred only two months after his appointment; by the time of the Senate hearing over three months later, he said, "it was possible to present a complete and detailed statement of the Foundation's program." The implication was that if the House committee had possessed this fuller information it would have acted differently.[79]

A few days after the Senate hearing Priest had told Bronk that he "felt that the House would hold the position taken by the Senate."[80] But Foundation officials knew enough about conference committees to expect a compromise somewhere close to the middle of the extremes, which was what resulted. The conference report recommending $3.5 million nearly split the difference, and this was the NSF appropriation for fiscal year 1952 passed by both houses on October 20.[81]

Earlier in the month Waterman had presented to the board breakdowns for budgets of $6.3 million and $3 million. One member wanted to drop the fellowship program if the appropriation was only $3 million, but this was the only dissent from the view that both fellowships and basic research should be supported, even on a much reduced scale from that planned. The board granted discretion to the director in deciding allocations for an appropriation between the two figures.[82]

Talking to Conant a few days after final approval of the appropriation, Waterman reported that "there were no strings attached" to it. The act had restored language deleted by the House so that the appropriated funds would be available for use after the end of the fiscal year—that is, they were "no year" funds. And a worrisome technicality that had threatened a serious limitation on salaries would not apply. Conant agreed with Waterman's allocations. What was important, they concurred, "was that this would permit us to get into operation with a complete staff and . . . would get us off the ground."[83]

FIRST NATIONAL SCIENCE BOARD

Seated, left to right: John W. Davis, Sophie D. Aberle, Detlev W. Bronk, James B. Conant, Alan T. Waterman, Gerty T. Cori, Patrick H. Yancey, S.J. *Standing*, left to right: Harold Marston Morse, Elvin C. Stakman, Chester I. Barnard, Paul M. Gross, Frederick A. Middlebush, Joseph C. Morris, James A. Reyniers, O. W. Hyman, Lee A. DuBridge, Robert F. Loeb, Robert P. Barnes, George D. Humphrey, A. A. Potter, Charles Dollard (Photo by Harris & Ewing)

JAMES B. CONANT
Chairman, 1950-51

CHESTER I. BARNARD
Chairman, 1951-55

ALAN T. WATERMAN
Director, 1951-63
(Photo by Harris & Ewing)

DETLEV W. BRONK
Chairman, 1955-64

FIRST DIRECTOR AND BOARD CHAIRMEN

LLOYD M. TREFETHEN
NSB Secretary, 1951-53

VERNICE ANDERSON
NSB Secretary, 1953-82

WILLIAM A. W. KREBS
General Counsel, 1951-53

WILLIAM J. HOFF
General Counsel, 1953-73

BOARD SECRETARIES AND NSF GENERAL COUNSELS

PAUL E. KLOPSTEG
Assistant Director, MPE, 1951-52;
Associate Director, 1952-58

C. E. SUNDERLIN
Deputy Director, 1951-57

WILSON F. HARWOOD
Assistant Director, Administration, 1951-57

HARRY C. KELLY
Assistant Director, SPE, 1951-59

WATERMAN'S FIRST LIEUTENANTS

16TH AND
I STREETS, N.W.,
1951

H STREET
AND MADISON
PLACE, N.W.
(OLD COSMOS
CLUB), 1953-58

1951 CONSTITUTION AVENUE, 1958-65

2144 CALIFORNIA STREET, N.W., 1951-53
(Courtesy Potomac School)

NSF HEADQUARTERS BUILDINGS

ELMER B. STAATS
(Courtesy Office of Management and Budget)

WILLIAM T. GOLDEN
(Photo by Lewis L. Strauss)

FREDERICK C. SCHULDT, JR.
(Courtesy Office of Management and Budget)

WILLIAM D. CAREY
(Courtesy Brooks Photographers
and the *Washington Post*)

A WHITE HOUSE ADVISER AND BUDGET BUREAU OVERSEERS

"I'll Be Glad To Lend You My Sickle"

from *The Herblock Book* (Beacon Press, 1952)

"Let You In On A Secret. There's A Connection Here"

from *The Herblock Book* (Beacon Press, 1952)

9
Ways and Means of Administration

Nearly a third of fiscal year 1952 had passed before the Foundation received its first operating budget. But the small staff—now numbering about sixty and settled in at the former Potomac School—had been busy deciding on means of transforming the generalities of budget justifications into operational programs. Soon approved by the board, these administrative policies and procedures reveal, as much as dollar allocations to particular programs, the values the Foundation attached to scientific research and education. The nature of the federal system and the variety of American higher education would prevent NSF from following the practices of the British University Grants Committee, which some hoped it might use as a patronage model, but both board and staff intended for their organization to stand for simplicity and quality as much as any private foundation. If it was possible for a government agency to avoid bureaucratic fussiness, the Foundation meant to.

While the director was discussing the intricacies of fellowships with officials of the National Research Council, the Atomic Energy Commission, and the Public Health Service, his staff was investigating techniques of fostering research. They looked into the practices of public patrons and into those of the Rockefeller Foundation, Carnegie Corporation of New York, and the Research Corporation. Their investigations resulted in an argument for grants rather than contracts to support the research of individual investigators. This choice of the project-grant system as the typical form of NSF research support received the board's approval and was ready for use when the fiscal 1952 appropriation became available.

The choice of the project-grant system also entailed a variety of subsidiary decisions. For help on these matters an elaborate machinery of advice had to be developed, both to ensure the quality of the research receiving support and to protect the Foundation's integrity. But these prudential aims sometimes ran counter to the desire for simplicity. Patterns of behavior characteristic of government bureaucracy were bound to set in eventually.

* * *

In July 1951 the NSF comptroller, Charles G. Gant, drafted a paper presenting his, Krebs's, and Harwood's views on the varied means of supporting research that were available to the Foundation under the wide discretionary authority extended by Congress—"contracts or other arrangements (including grants, loans, and other forms of assistance)." Intended to provoke board discussion, the paper set out the three-man committee's preliminary conclusions. Among these were: "As between the contract and the grant, the grant should be used by the Foundation wherever possible because of its simplicity, ease of administration, and greater acceptability among research personnel"; and ". . . the typical grant will be made to an institution for use by an individual for specified work and covering a definite time period."[1] The board expressed general approval of the staff paper at a meeting a few days later, though it suggested changing "specified work" to a broader term and making the grant available either to an individual or a group of individuals, but took no formal action since Waterman was simply seeking advice.[2]

In fact, the director wanted the board to refrain from setting a policy that might limit the staff's flexibility in supporting research. When the board returned to the subject in October he again emphasized that the procedures outlined in an expanded version of the staff paper should be considered tentative. The staff recommendations applied "to the usual or typical case of research support," and Waterman asked the board to approve them as "a general and interim basis of operation."[3] In giving its unanimous approval,[4] the board endorsed the project grant as the usual form of research support and agreed to the staff's list of characteristics of the "typical grant"—e.g., it "should be as simple as possible," allow for the payment of indirect costs at a uniform rate and travel and publication expenses, and permit the grantee institution to retain equipment obtained with grant funds.[5]

Of all these matters none was more troublesome, and more threatening to the wish for simplicity, than indirect costs—that is, overhead expenses such as library services, utilities (light, water, heat, etc.), and administrative services not attributable to a particular project but essential to an institution's total program. Gant's draft suggests the intensity of staff debate on the question better than the higher level of abstraction of the later paper.

The committee's inquiry about whether indirect costs should be paid, and if so how much, turned up "equally weighty arguments on both sides of the question." Private foundations' grants usually did not include indirect costs; government contracts normally paid them in full. NIH and AEC allowed their inclusion at a uniform rate of 8 percent of total direct costs. Administrators of universities and other research institutions argued strongly for reimbursement of indirect costs; individual researchers usually opposed.

Some contended that while indirect costs were indeed part of the expense of doing research, a distinction should be made between research being done for the government and research initiated by an institution. In the latter case the Foundation might claim that it had no moral obligation to pay overhead and "that a contribution on the part of the recipient is at least an indication of its own interest and faith in the proposal and a kind of surety for its successful performance." But if the institution had to furnish the funds, they would have to come from money intended for other purposes, and this diversion would mean special favoritism for the natural sciences to the harm of the humanities and social sciences. Some said that this effect would put NSF into "a position which it should seek to avoid at all costs"; others responded that the unfortunate result was "beyond the Foundation's cognizance." Inclusion of indirect costs in NSF grants would reduce the amount of research the agency could support. In addition, the equipment acquired by institutions with grant funds constituted a subsidy they did not get through most forms of government support. "While true," the other side answered, "the argument does not meet the central question of who pays the additional cost."

Those who appealed to the private foundation example held that NSF intended to allow its grant recipients equal freedom in the use of its money; hence, like the private patrons it should omit overhead payments. But NSF grants would ultimately overshadow the limited research support of the private sector, and as Foundation support grew the indirect costs to be borne by the universities would become more and more burdensome.

On balance, the staff concluded, NSF should pay at least part of the indirect costs. But the practical question still remained of whether to pay the full amount, which would require detailed inquiries into the varying accounting practices of institutions, or to pay at some uniform rate which might or might not approximate the full overhead costs. For "simplicity and ease of administration," the staff chose a uniform rate, later fixed at 15 percent of the total direct costs.[6]

In choosing to use grants instead of contracts NSF followed the pattern of private foundations and, alone of federal science agencies, the Public

Health Service. (The departure from ONR's cost-type contracts might have seemed surprising except that ONR had not been empowered to make research grants.) Although simplicity and verbal connotations largely determined the choice of the grant, the staff mustered several other arguments against following the normal contractual procedure. A contract implied that something definite and describable was to be "delivered" to the purchasing agency, which would have control over the work being done for its use. The object of basic research support on the contrary was to benefit the nation, not to get delivery of a product or service to the government, and its outcome could not be defined or described in advance. Control over research might be just as restrictive under a grant as under a contract, but "the difference lies in the manner of exercising control rather than in its intensity, in one case the manner being formal and overt, in the other informal and subtle." But generally scientists believed that the grant offered them more freedom and was simpler, cheaper to administer, and less cluttered by requirements for auditing and formal evaluation of results.[7]

A secondary choice was the project grant instead of the broader institutional or block grant. Although the latter should be used when appropriate, the staff paper concluded, the project grant seemed better suited to two of NSF's main objectives in sponsoring research—ensuring a comprehensive national research program, and encouraging outstandingly important basic research. These objectives required a rather precise assessment of work that needed doing. Through use of the project grant NSF could review the comprehensiveness of the country's research effort and select "the most competent and promising investigators" for work of special importance. A third objective of the Foundation's research program—"strengthening research organizations as a basis for future achievement"—might occasionally require "judicious use of the institutional or block grant," since for this purpose institutions needed flexibility in deciding how to develop their research potential. Institutional grants had hazards, however, for a government agency which must assure the Bureau of the Budget and Congress that its funds were being spent only for science, not for general educational purposes, and that its programs did not overlap those of other federal research agencies. Finally there was the very practical point that NSF's research budget for some time would be so small as to force it "to determine rather narrowly the particular areas in which the Foundation will sponsor research." Grants for general research support and institutional development would have to wait.[8]

The Foundation expected unsolicited proposals from talented scientists to determine the flow of its research support. But though unsolicited and shaped by the interests of the individual researchers, all proposals would at some stage have to yield certain items of information on which a grant could be based. And as a government agency aware of the sensitivities of congressmen and of "have-not" colleges and universities, NSF had to let all who might be interested know that it was ready to do business and on what terms. Early in December 1951, using mailing lists of the AAAS and the American Council on Education, the Foundation distributed a brief mimeographed guide for the submission of research proposals.[9]

The statement, announcing that NSF was now prepared to evaluate proposals and make grants for basic research in the mathematical, physical, medical, biological, and engineering sciences, encouraged prospective applicants to discuss their projects informally with appropriate NSF program directors before submitting regular proposals. When a proposal was received its reviewers would especially seek to determine "the scientific merit of the suggested research, including the competence of the investigator." The principal investigator's institution might prefer to pay his salary, but the grant would "normally provide sufficient funds . . . for such items as the salaries of personnel, materials, equipment, necessary travel, publication, and other direct costs" and "indirect costs up to 15% of the total direct costs."

The guide suggested that the proposal describe the intended research, the general procedure to be followed, and the facilities and equipment available. Biographical and bibliographical information on the principal investigator and other professional persons participating in the project should be included. The budget should estimate the total cost and duration of the project and itemize amounts for salaries, permanent equipment, expendable equipment and supplies, travel, other direct costs, and indirect costs. To assure the Foundation that the proposal had the approval of the institution originating it, one copy "should be signed by the principal investigator, by the department head, and by an official authorized to sign for the institution." An attached sample grant letter explained the conditions that would govern revocation of the grant, the return of unused funds, and applications for patents.

In listing the policies applicable to the administration of a grant, the guide added one to those previously discussed with the board as characteristic features of a typical grant—a safeguard for national security. Reflecting the anxieties of the time, this provision stated: "In cases where there is a reasonable chance that information may be developed that should be classified in the interest of the national security, clearance may be required for investigators on the project. When, in the judgment of the principal investigator, information is developed that should be classified, he should notify the Foundation immediately."

How the Foundation would evaluate proposals was not explained, but no doubt everyone understood that there would be some sort of peer review. The board had already learned that after the program staff had first evaluated a proposal it would then be considered by advisory groups or consultants and by the appropriate divisional committee, after which would come a broad NSF staff review and a decision by the director about a recommendation to the board. The NSF act required board approval of all awards, and a large number of grant recommendations would obviously impose a detailed chore on that policy-making body. To ease the task as much as possible, the staff intended to present for each proposed grant a brief summary of the project and its evaluation.[10]

* * *

The first research grants—twenty-eight in biological and medical sciences—received board approval on February 1, 1952, less than two months after the mailing of the guide for submission of proposals. Even though a good many proposals had been received before the mailing, this timing shows remarkable expedition by John Field's group of staff scientists in processing proposals through the network for advice, review, and approval. As the board minutes summarized the process:

The sequence of events was: an independent evaluation of each of fifty-eight proposals by at least three expert reviewers; a two-day meeting of a screening panel of eleven consultants expert in the fields represented; a meeting of the newly-formed Divisional Committee regarding general policy and program within the field of the Division; and consideration by the full staff of the Director.

In short, the recommendations had "necessitated considerable effort and accurate timing on the part of all concerned."[11] Actually, the biologists had got off to a flying start by simply shifting their ONR programs to NSF.

All but two of the grants were awarded to colleges and universities. (The exceptions were the Institute for Cancer Research and the National Academy of Sciences.) Private and public institutions shared nearly equally in the number of grants and the amount of funds. Yale University and the California Institute of Technology each received four grants. California institutions had the largest number of grants (7), followed by Indiana (6). Nearly half of the awards went to midwestern colleges and universities, but only two to southern (Johns Hopkins University and the University of Mississippi) and, except for a $780 grant to the University of Minnesota, only one (the University of Kansas) in the vast area between the Mississippi River and California. Three grants were made to undergraduate institutions, two of them to Wabash College in Indiana. The largest award ($50,000) was also the one of longest duration, five years, to support research in genetics by I. Michael Lerner and Everett R. Dempster of the University of California at Berkeley.[12]

The board readily approved twenty-seven of the grants but had qualms about the recommendation of an award of $24,000 to the National Academy of Sciences for operating expenses of the Pacific Science Board.

Some members were uneasy about the terms of the proposal and its differences from the other straightforward research projects. The Pacific Science Board, a group of eleven scientists with an executive office in Washington and a field office in Honolulu, provided various kinds of assistance to scientists doing research in the Pacific Ocean area. It had requested funds, to be administered by the Academy, for such operating expenses as staff salaries and travel, supplies, and publications. The NSF advisory panel took note of the "block grant" nature of the proposal but recommended it as worthy of support. National Science Board members raised several policy questions: "Should funds be granted to a body which then makes independent decisions as to how it will grant these funds to other individuals or institutions? Should financial assistance to the Pacific Science Board be charged to the Division of Biological Sciences? Is general support for scientific studies for a geographic area such as Micronesia a proper function of the Foundation?"[13] Some board members may also have been disturbed about the Academy connection. Bronk, president of the Academy and chairman of the board's executive committee, and Marston Morse had left the room while the proposal was under discussion, and they abstained from voting on it later. Earlier in the day the board had discussed Krebs's memorandum on conflicts of interest and a suggested guide for board members' actions on grants and contracts, compensation, political activity, and public statements. The three negative votes on the Academy proposal and the nine abstentions in addition to those of Bronk and Morse may have indicated concern, heightened by the general counsel's paper, about procedure as well as substance.[14]

* * *

The lateness and size of the 1952 appropriation forced the Foundation to make drastic changes in its fellowship plans. It abandoned the idea of a pilot program starting January 1 and scaled down the estimated number of fellowships from more than two thousand to a few hundred. Adjustments in program plans were further complicated by the resurgence of sharp differences of opinion among board members on such matters as appropriate stipends and allowances, whether fellows should be permitted to supplement their incomes by working, and whether some means should be adopted to prevent concentration of fellows in a small number of graduate schools. Despite the board's arguments, however, the Foundation managed to announce the program in November and, with the assistance of the experienced panels of the National Research Council, to make its first awards of predoctoral and postdoctoral fellowships in April 1952.

The fellowship program was predicated on a need to attract bright young persons to scientific careers in order to overcome a severe shortage in skills of critical importance to the nation's security and welfare. But a fellowship program large enough to increase significantly the amount and quality of the nation's scientific manpower could seriously disrupt university arrangements for the support of graduate students and rob talent from other fields of learning or the professions. Careful adjustments had to be made to win for NSF fellowships a mark of special distinction while at the same time they kept in line generally with institutional policies and those of other federal agencies.

Charles Dollard's seminal paper first brought these complicated issues before the board in March 1951.[15] The paper sought to answer the questions of how many fellowships NSF should offer, how to allocate them among three years of graduate study, what stipends and allowances were appropriate, and how the Foundation should administer the program. On all of these matters later discussions by Waterman and staff with officials of NRC, AEC, and PHS resulted in substantial modifications of the program outlined by Dollard's committee, but some conflicts of values continued, especially on stipends and allowances. Dollard's committee thought that NSF should offer enough money "to attract the best student" and enable him to give full time to his studies but should not try to compete with industrial salaries or so exceed normal fellowship stipends as to play hob with other programs. It might be too bad if high salaries lured top-notch students into industry, but this loss could not be avoided. "The life of the scholar will never be as remunerative as other professions," the paper said, "and perhaps graduate school is the first place to learn this lesson."[16]

The board accepted the committee's view that NSF should award substantially more first-year fellowships than those for the second and third years of graduate study. The aim was to attract college seniors into graduate school; too often they chose careers other than scholarship because universities reserved most of their fellowships for advanced students. The board agreed too that stipends should be higher in the second and third years but decided, over the objection of some members, to raise rather than lower the committee's recommended figure for beginning graduate students.[17]

The board accepted the staff's proposal that family allowances be provided for married graduate students who were beyond the first year but continued to debate whether to impose an upper limit on the amount of an individual's fellowship. Some members wanted a uniform amount for all recipients in a particular year of study, out of which they would pay tuition and travel expenses. This arrangement would encourage fellows to enroll in low-tuition institutions close to their homes—that is, state universities especially. The majority, however, favored payment of full tuition and travel in addition to a uniform living allowance, though this policy would surely lead to criticism from advocates of geographic distribution who wanted to encourage the growth of new centers of graduate work. While most members seemed to believe that fellows, particularly those with families, would have a hard time living on their stipends and allowances, the board accepted the policy proposed by the staff that full-time study would be the general rule, "with the proviso that work which demonstrably contributes to their scientific education may be undertaken subsequent to approval in each case by the Foundation." And though NSF could not dictate to the Internal Revenue Service, the board wanted publicity about fellowships to make it clear that they were only for educational purposes, not payment for services, and thus presumably not taxable as income.[18]

The announcement of predoctoral fellowships said that applicants would have to take a fellowship examination (the Graduate Record Examination administered by the Educational Testing Service) and that NRC panelists would use the test scores along with college records and letters of recommendation in evaluating their qualifications. An appointment would be for one year but might be renewed. Both pre- and postdoctoral applicants, who must be U.S. citizens, would have to submit the affidavit and loyalty oath required by the NSF act. The fellowships would support advanced work in the mathematical, physical, medical, biological, and engineering sciences, and interdisciplinary fields of the natural sciences.[19]

* * *

Nearly 2,700 persons applied for the first predoctoral fellowships and took the required examination. NRC panelists recommended 932 of these as having superior qualifications, and the Foundation staff, after making analyses of fields of science, years of study, and geographical distribution, proposed 569 awards to the board. Well above an earlier estimate of 400 fellowships, the increase was made possible by a shift of some funds allocated to research support and by an estimate that about 15 percent of those offered fellowships would decline them. The use of the declination estimate enabled NSF to avoid establishing a list of alternates and the complications that would entail.[20]

For a while Waterman had hopes of further increasing the number of fellowships by a transfer of $100,000 from the air force, which broached the idea of using the NSF machinery to award fellowships to persons interested in research careers in aviation. Waterman rejected the idea of selection of individuals by the air force, both because of administrative difficulties and a wish to avoid close ties to the military, but said that the Foundation might tell the service the names of fellows doing research on subjects related to aviation and allow its representatives to talk with them if neither the fellows nor their institutions objected. The air force responded that it wanted "more explicit recognition and contact with fellows" than this arrangement would permit. Waterman then suggested that the Foundation might, in its selection, take special account of the fields of science of particular interest to the service. Despite the efforts to work out the problem, however, the air force Office of Scientific Research was told that the plan did not accord with air force policy.[21]

All along, the Foundation had intended to award far more first-year fellowships than those for the other two years combined. Dollard's committee had suggested 2,500 first-year awards, 175 second-year, and 60 third-year, though renewals in later years would reduce these differences. Later, when planning for 400 predoctoral fellowships, the staff proposed a distribution of 320, 50, and 30 for the three years of graduate study. But an unexpectedly small number of applications for first-year awards as compared to those for continuing graduate study greatly changed the final pattern of awards—170 first-year, 169 second, and 230 advanced. Nonetheless, NSF emphasized that the 30 percent of the awards to beginning graduate students represented "a sharp departure from previous Federal fellowship programs" and reflected the Foundation's aim to attract a greater number of competent persons into science and engineering.[22]

The departure was much less sharp than NSF had intended. In fact, the whole selection process looks as if it were designed to achieve an unexceptionable balance, particularly among fields of science and geographic distribution of fellows. (If there had been an active feminist movement, exception would have been taken to the fact that fewer than 50 of the pre- and postdoctoral fellowships were offered to women, though the proportion may have reflected the relative numbers of applications.) Only two states (Rhode Island and Nevada) had no fellowship winners, and NSF pointed out to possible critics that "the applications and awards were roughly proportional to the total population and the population attending colleges of the various regions." By field of science, 158 fellowships went to biological sciences graduates, 140 chemistry, 137 physics, 75 engineering, 62 mathematics, 36 earth sciences, 7 agriculture, 6 astronomy, and 3 anthropology.[23]

The nature of applications for postdoctoral fellowships also altered the Foundation's plans for that program. When NRC panelists began to examine the nearly three hundred applications, they found that much the larger number came from recent recipients of the doctorate, and it was almost impossible to compare these with the scientists who had earned the degree some years before. NRC therefore recommended two kinds of fellowships and furnished the Foundation with separate lists of five highly qualified senior scientists and 113 recent doctoral graduates. The board accepted the staff's recommendation to offer fellowships to all five of the senior group and to fifty of the younger scientists.[24]

Just as the program of research support aimed at comprehensiveness of coverage of the fields of science and responsiveness to unsolicited proposals, so too in its first fellowship program the Foundation showed no inclination to tamper with the general directions of graduate study. Dollard's paper had stressed the opportunities afforded by a program of fellowships to avoid duplicating existing patterns and to "encourage the development of new fields that show great promise." Through exercising "judgments of the very highest order" in deciding how many fellowships to award in each field, NSF could make "its largest contribution in the direction of the whole fellowship program."[25] But in the event, the Foundation chose the laissez-faire course of relying on the wisdom of the marketplace.

* * *

The existence of the National Research Council relieved the Foundation of a complicated administrative chore in awarding fellowships but not of creating other advisory machinery for that and other programs. For each division of the Foundation, the agency's charter provided, there should be a committee to "make recommendations to, and advise and consult with, the Board and the Director with respect to matters relating to the program of its division." The board was to appoint the divisional committees and might decide whether its own members should serve on them. To carry out this mandate the board decided that each divisional committee should contain at least two of its own members and that every board member should serve on at least one divisional committee. A poll of the members' interests determined their assignment to temporary committees, corresponding to the four statutory divisions, consisting only of board members. These temporary committees were later reconstituted as committees of the board.[26]

The board's decision that its members should serve on divisional committees came before Waterman's appointment as director. He obviously did not like the idea, and his temporary general counsel, John Connor, also opposed it. Congress had intended the divisional committees to advise the Foundation on its actual operations, Connor told the board, and for board members to participate in actions at that level and then to review and approve programs recommended by the director on the advice of divisional committees would confound their policy-making responsibility. While some members argued that sitting on the committees was desirable because it would help the board make informed decisions, the majority concluded that they might become advocates of particular programs and lose the broad view necessary for wise policy. Rescinding its earlier action, the board left the matter open for later determination.[27]

Some board members continued to believe that they should serve on divisional committees, along with other eminent scientists in their fields, and they did not give up that view readily. But the director, sure that they were wrong, pleaded for a clear distinction between committee advice to his assistant directors and that to the board. A committee's effectiveness, he said, depended on "equality of authority and responsibility among the members"; a mixture of board and nonboard members would negate that principle. An assistant director's independence of judgment would suffer if his committee contained persons whose authority in the organization was superior to his, and his value to the director would be lessened. The board's judgment would also suffer since policy review should not occur until after executive decisions and recommendations by the director. "If members become immersed in operational activities," Waterman argued, "their preoccupation with these is almost certain to diminish their effectiveness as policy makers in the broad sense." After laying out six objections he applied an emollient. Naturally scientists on the board wanted close association with NSF programs in their special fields, but there were various ways to promote a sense of participation and he mentioned several.[28] Some of the board's biologists remained unconvinced, but a majority of the members finally accepted their divorce from operations, agreeing to their exclusion from divisional committees advisory to the Foundation's assistant directors. Committees advisory to the board, on the other hand, would be composed of board members.[29]

The hazy fringe between policy and operations would continue to cause the board to stray occasionally onto boggy ground, but on the issue of divisional committees the members at least forswore their intention to do so. They soon appointed committees to advise NSF divisions on their programs and to appraise their procedures, but appointment of a committee on medical research was delayed. The staff biologists thought a separate medical committee would be pointless, and the divisional committee for the biological sciences agreed that it would be "a poor administrative arrangement" to have two committees advising the same staff. The board nevertheless carried through its plan to establish a medical committee, which met in May 1953 and discussed inconclusively whether the merger of biological and medical sciences should continue and, if so, whether there should be two advisory groups. Later in the year the medical and biological committees met jointly and decided to tell the board that while they were "not unwilling to serve on the committees as designated," they thought a combined committee would be better. The board then merged the two groups, as it did its own corresponding committees.[30]

Like the board, divisional committees sometimes showed a human tendency to wander beyond what others considered their proper bounds. Giving advice on proposed programs often impinged on the board's policy-making responsibility, just as evaluation of the peer review of proposals might veer into criticism of a program panel's scientific judgment of a particular project rather than of the soundness of the staff's procedures. Staff notes on divisional committee meetings, which normally occurred from two to four times a year, give the impression that assistant directors and program officers usually managed to enlist committee members as allies in advocating new activities and bigger budgets. It soon became customary for one or more board members to attend divisional committee meetings, which for the board was a way of keeping watch on the staff and committee as well as a means of vicarious participation in operational activities, and for the staff and committee a way of influencing the board. Similarly the board occasionally invited divisional committee chairmen to its sessions.

Divisional committee members tended to be somewhat younger than board members—averaging fifty years of age in 1952—and most of those on the research committees were still active scientists. On the committee for scientific personnel and education, however, all but one of the academic members were high-ranking administrators; this group also contained the only woman divisional committee member, Katharine McBride, the president of Bryn Mawr College. Except that none of the thirty-four persons came from a state college—not surprisingly since the faculties of these teacher-training schools contained few well-known scientists—and only a few from liberal arts colleges, institutional representation on the divisional committees seems reasonably well balanced, as does geographical. There was less spread among the institutions where members had done their graduate study; four had earned their doctorates at Harvard, and three each at Yale, Columbia, and the University of Pennsylvania.[31]

To review the merit of research proposals the Foundation from the start relied on individual consultants and program panelists. Nearly all of the 101 panel members listed in NSF's second annual report were active researchers, though some were primarily administrators. It was a completely male cast, averaging 48 years of age, and mainly from universities (7 each from Harvard and the University of Illinois, 6 from Yale, and 5 each from Princeton, the University of Chicago, and the University of California at Berkeley). Seventeen had completed their graduate study in foreign universities, 15 at Harvard, 10 at Princeton, 8 at Berkeley, and 5 each at Stanford, MIT, and the University of Illinois.

Through the referee system of consultants (mail reviewers) and panelists the Foundation intended to secure high quality in its sponsored research and a safeguard against bureaucratic rigidity. As Waterman explained the purpose of the reviewing system as it had developed during NSF's first year of operations, "The general aim is to ensure that not only the selection of research for grant award, but also the conduct of the research and its relation to the educational program of the institution, conform to the best traditions of freedom of inquiry and integrity in research." Because of the staff's concern about preserving flexibility, no uniform rules had been laid down, and programs in the two research divisions used somewhat different ways of judging proposals, though both sought to answer the same kinds of questions about scientific merit, the ability and resources of the principal investigator and his associates, the institution's interest in the project, and the reasonableness of the budget. The reviewing process sought to assess not only the intrinsic merit of a proposal but also its standing with respect to other proposals in the same field.[32]

Geographical distribution was an important factor in the making of choices on proposals of substantially equal quality, Waterman told the board, both because NSF's charter forbade "undue concentration" and because the agency wanted to develop new research centers. Of the proposals received, he estimated that about 40 percent deserved support, though nearly all of them asked for more money than seemed reasonable, especially in view of the Foundation's small budget. During fiscal 1952 NSF granted only one dollar of research support for every fourteen requested; but no proposals were turned down for budgetary reasons alone. In every instance so far, Waterman said, negotiations between the agency's staff and the scientist investigator had succeeded in adjusting the budget to their mutual satisfaction. (Here of course lay a possibility for trouble if agreements between NSF program managers and faculty scientists to scale down budgets should put the onus of rejecting grants on campus administrators.) The staff did reject a few proposals without submitting them to review by consultants or panels if they proposed applied research or research in clinical medicine or if they came from persons obviously incompetent to do the work proposed.[33]

Through this advisory apparatus and board approval of the director's recommendations, by the end of fiscal year 1952 the Foundation had awarded $1.1 million in research grants, nearly three-fourths of this amount in the fields first staffed in NSF, the biological and medical sciences. The grants averaged about $11,000 in amount and a little less than two years in duration. Slightly over half of the grant funds was budgeted for stipends and salaries of graduate students and other research assistants, and about one-fourth for such other direct costs as equipment and supplies, travel, and publication costs; faculty salaries constituted only a small part of the average grant dollar.[34]

Distribution of the awards among the country's four geographic regions (Northeast, North Central, South, and West) corresponded fairly closely to the distribution of graduate students, though on this score the northeastern states were shortchanged. Institutions in the North Central region—extending from Ohio through the second tier of states beyond the Mississippi—got a third of the funds, while the shares of the other three regions were nearly equal—21 percent for the Northeast, 23 for the South, and 22 for the West. California institutions, led by Caltech, which got six grants, received the largest share among the states ($163,500); of the other states, only Indiana and Illinois institutions tallied above $100,000. Fifty-five of the 60 grant recipients were colleges and universities, and at least 10 of these did not grant doctoral degrees. Two of these were black colleges. All of the largest amounts, however, went to Ph.D.-granting institutions: Caltech ($73,700), Indiana ($55,400), Yale ($47,700), Purdue ($44,600), Johns Hopkins ($41,400), Pennsylvania ($41,400), and Illinois ($40,400). Surprisingly, Harvard does not appear in the list—for the simple reason that the university, whose president chaired the National Science Board, had decided not to endorse proposals to NSF.[35]

* * *

In September 1951 Waterman introduced to the board Robert C. Tumbleson, the chief of the Foundation's new Scientific Information Office. More than NSF's public relations arm, Tumbleson's office would be responsible for much of the task required by the charter of fostering "the interchange of scientific information among scientists in the United States and foreign countries." This function, as the Foundation conceived it, encompassed such activities as the encouragement of publication of research results, improvement of abstracting and clearinghouse services, translations of foreign-language reports and the easing of restrictions on international exchange of scientific and technical information, and provision of travel funds for scientists to attend international conferences.

Editors and business managers of scientific journals in the early 1950s were struggling to stay afloat in a flood of reports meriting publication while trying to cope too with rising printing costs. Authors whose articles had been accepted had to endure interminable delays before publication, and the printing of abstracts and indexes fell further and further behind. As the bulk and subscription prices of periodicals grew, so did individual and library cancellations. Several journals appealed to NSF for help. *Physical Review*, S. A. Goudsmit and George B. Pegram told Waterman, was running in the red about $35,000 a year, and they hoped to get enough money "to cover the deficit for two years" while they searched for longer-term answers to the problem. The Foundation responded with a grant of $50,000. Similarly NSF joined with six other agencies in extending emergency aid for *Biological Abstracts*.[36]

Both the director and the board worried about such direct subsidies and agreed that they should be given only temporarily and to journals that seemed likely to survive. Payment of page costs on the other hand could appropriately be tendered in research grants since "research is not complete until it is published."[37] In order to learn what problems scientific periodicals and their sponsors faced, one of the first undertakings of the Scientific Information Office was the mailing of a questionnaire to about two hundred journals. Various other surveys and reviews soon followed, by which the office sought to acquire a factual basis for its program and to assist the Foundation in developing information policies both for itself and other federal agencies.[38]

Waterman viewed these studies as one way of meeting the Foundation's responsibility for national science policy. Collaboration with other federal agencies, whose rules on such matters as page costs differed, was essential, particularly because federal research support and Cold War regulations had aggravated many of the difficulties. Fortunately Waterman's ONR experience acquainted him with the problems, and he now served on a special committee which supervised the Defense Department's technical information agency. One thing needed, Waterman believed, was a central clearinghouse to handle information generated by federal research support. Technical reports were piling up in the offices of sponsoring agencies but stayed there, unknown to possible users. The Library of Congress, which had assisted ONR, should be the clearinghouse, Waterman suggested, and he and Sunderlin conferred with Luther Evans, the Librarian of Congress, and his chief assistant, Verner Clapp, to move toward the creation of a central information service. The library promptly began to help, but the necessary surveys and interagency discussions clogged progress toward the goal. A full year later Waterman told Don Price: "Our view here is that there would be advantage in pooling information as to present handling of scientific information, the adoption of somewhat standard procedures to the extent possible and the use of the Library of Congress as the central library for material beyond the working needs of each agency. At least this would do as a starter."[39]

Apprehensions about communism, foreign or domestic, also hindered the publication and exchange of information. While to many American scientists the early Soviet success in developing a nuclear weapon proved the futility of secrecy requirements, the achievement created public alarm, which was whipped up further by accusations of disloyalty, and contributed to excessive classification of research related to defense and the raising of barriers to distribution of its results. Waterman joined his colleagues on ICSRD in deploring restrictions on the mailing of technical data to Iron Curtain countries; the members argued that the USSR could obtain any information it wanted except that classified at the source, but the flow of material from eastern Europe was limited because of the U.S. requirements. The executive secretary of the group "was instructed to present a strong case to appropriate authorities" to change the undesirable rules.[40] And when asked by an interdepartmental committee on internal security to recommend means of strengthening government security programs, Waterman urged the widest possible dissemination of information. NSF would cooperate in safeguarding the relatively small amount of scientific information which should remain secret; but, he added:

I believe we may safely say . . . that where there is genuine uncertainty as to the strategic intelligence value, we should be least apt to err . . . in deciding to release the information. Any slight possible advantages which might accrue to a potential enemy in the release of such information would undoubtedly be offset by the disadvantages to ourselves arising out of official limitations upon the normal flow of scientific information, and probable retaliation, resulting in curtailing of highly desirable incoming information.[41]

NSF early showed a lively interest in Soviet science. The Foundation assembled information on current Russian scientific literature, made a grant to the AAAS for the publication of several papers on Soviet science, and with funds transferred confidentially from the Central Intelligence Agency encouraged the preparation of a new Russian-English scientific and technical dictionary.[42] Expansion of these and similar activities during the next few years would help prepare the American scientific community—though certainly not the public at large—for the shocks of Russian H-bombs and sputniks.

Finally, as parts of its diverse science-information tasks, NSF in its first year of operations made twenty-three international travel grants, enabling American biochemists and mathematicians to attend conferences in Paris and Rome, and awarded $8,400 to the librarian of the John Crerar Library in Chicago to study the functions and organization of information services in scientific libraries.[43]

* * *

In requiring that NSF "maintain a register of scientific and technical personnel and in other ways provide a central clearinghouse for information covering all scientific and technical personnel in the United States, including its Territories and possessions," Congress apparently intended to ensure quick mobilization of scientists and engineers in a national emergency. But the legislation left the Foundation a good deal of latitude to decide how and for what purposes to carry out the mandate. An obvious first step was to take over the operation of the Office of Education's National Scientific Register, and Waterman began negotiations for this transfer soon after his appointment as director. These discussions led to an agreement that the Office of Education would continue to maintain the Register, with NSF footing the bill, until January 1, 1953, when the shift would occur.[44]

For expert advice on appropriate uses of the Register the Foundation turned to Dael Wolfle, director of a recently established Commission on Human Resources and Advanced Training. His report on the registration and clearinghouse function laid out clearly the kinds of activities the Foundation might engage in, depending on which of several purposes it chose to emphasize: employment and placement services, the publication of biographical directories such as *American Men of Science*, a tool for the administration of manpower controls, or a resource for statistical studies on scientific and technical manpower. Wolfle concluded that professional scientific and engineering societies were better suited than NSF for the placement-service function but that the NSF staff could assist the societies in developing uniform records and, by coordinating their work, provide a basis for a quick transition to a more comprehensive register to meet mobilization requirements. So long as private means remained adequate for the publication of biographical directories, NSF need not take on this role; otherwise it would be a suitable activity. Although some other agency than the Foundation would have responsibility for manpower controls in the event of national mobilization, the science agency in planning its Register functions should consider how they could be useful in the administration of such controls. Finally Wolfle suggested a function that fitted in with Waterman's ideas on the Foundation's policy-development role:

> The most generally useful clearinghouse of information service which the Foundation can offer lies in the field of statistical studies of America's scientific and specialized populations. There is great demand for such information. A number of agencies are partially satisfying that demand, but coordination of available data is necessary and leadership in planning for continuing studies is highly desirable. The Foundation has an opportunity to play an important role— one consistent with its responsibility for developing national scientific policy—by taking the lead in conducting an integrated and continuous series of supply and demand studies of America's scientific and specialized personnel.[45]

Wolfle estimated that the Register activities he recommended would cost NSF only $100-150,000 a year. Not only would these functions furnish valuable services to manpower planners and colleges and universities, but they would also provide insurance for the meeting of mobilization demands. Waterman accepted the recommendations, and the board added its note of approval.[46]

As Wolfle had said, there was "great demand" for the kinds of services the Register might provide. The Office of Defense Mobilization hoped that NSF could extend the Register's coverage to include economists and rare-language and area specialists. A member of the SPE divisional committee, which discussed the Register repeatedly and at great length, pointed out that cartographers would be especially needed in wartime and urged their inclusion. Requests came for support of a new edition of *American Men of Science*. And the possible availability of data stimulated program planners to conceive of multiform ways of aggregating information that might be useful for their special purposes. Memories of World War II and fears of a third growing out of the "present emergency" pervaded manpower planning; if there should be universal military training, a call-up of scientists in reserve units, and an emptying of science classrooms, the Register must help meet the nation's need. It was fortunate that NSF had adopted clear policies for the Register since clients suggested so many different roads it might take. As a consultant employed to assist in starting the function said, the Foundation had "a bear by the tail."[47]

Nevertheless NSF managed to stick fairly closely to the policies recommended in the Wolfle report. Scientific societies, aided by NSF grants and technical advice, cooperated in the registration activity and moved toward uniformity in their personnel records. Registration of engineers posed some special problems, in part because many of them did not belong to professional societies and did not engage in research; a "finders list" instead of complete registration was suggested for them and for certain other groups outside the natural sciences. The Foundation itself, as its new Program Analysis Office began to plan surveys of American science—ambitious enough in the conception of some of the planners to bear comparison to the Conqueror's Domesday Book—eagerly looked to the Register to furnish much of the requisite manpower data.

Waterman, as ever, held more moderate ideas, but he too saw in the Register an important element in what he had called, at the Budget Bureau's insistence, NSF's "most important and fundamental function"—the development of national policy for basic research and science education. But that is a much bigger topic than the maintenance of a register and clearinghouse. The Bureau's and the Foundation's differing views on policy development and the ways and means NSF devised to perform the function are the burden of the following chapter.

10
Evaluation and Policy

Immediately after the board meeting where his nomination as director was announced, Alan Waterman had a long discussion with James Conant and Detlev Bronk, the chairmen respectively of the board and its executive committee. One subject "of primary interest" to them was the mandate to NSF to evaluate federal scientific research programs. Waterman summarized their views: "This is a matter which must be handled with extreme care in order to avoid (a) actual evaluation of research programs because of the difficulty and danger of doing so, and (b) failure to provide the President, the Bureau of the Budget and Congress with information which is evidently called for by this clause. If the Board's effort in this direction should at any time be regarded as inadequate the Foundation would be in trouble."[1] This minute gave an accurate forecast of rough weather ahead and a hint of the maneuvers the Foundation would use in skirting it. Somehow, information must be passed off as evaluation, and given an added gloss to cover the other troublesome charge of developing national science policy.

The Budget Bureau pointedly raised the policy and evaluation issues two months later when its examiners quizzed NSF officials on their proposed 1952 budget. "What relative priorities does NSF give," they asked, "to (1) the development of a national policy for the promotion of basic research and education in the sciences, and (2) the actual initiation of research and education programs? . . . What are the plans for exercising the 'evaluation' function?"[2] Although the Bureau reluctantly acquiesced in the Foundation's first temporizing response to these questions, it soon renewed the effort to use the agency to rationalize federal science activities. Given the Foundation's diffidence and other agencies' resistance, a clear solution of the problem of bringing coordination and control over diverse and competing programs was impossible to achieve. But an accommodation of sorts came in March 1954 with the issuance of Executive Order 10521. This vague definition of policy permitted the Foundation to aspire to become the principal federal patron of basic research and a protector of academic virtue, while relieving the agency of dreaded policing duties.

The first moves toward that policy statement had begun nearly three years earlier, when Willis Shapley set down the Bureau's expectation that NSF "would make some sort of evaluation and coordination" of federal basic research programs and "take over the sponsorship of some basic research now supported by other agencies." Shapley suggested that agencies supporting basic research by grant or contract—that is, external or extramural research—be told promptly that the Administration expected these developments to occur. Not that all such basic research would come under the wing of NSF, which in any event would have to acquire staff and competence to handle the transfers. And there must first be an accurate inventory of current and planned programs, accompanied by agency indications of those that might be shifted. Since simple requests to designate appropriate transfers would "draw a complete blank" from the Defense Department, it should be given "a target figure" and asked to earmark projects for transfer totaling this amount.[3]

While Bureau staff members deliberated the best way of carrying out Shapley's suggestions, some agency officials showed a willingness to transfer certain basic research projects and even a desire for program evaluation and policy leadership by the Foundation. Three days after his nomination Waterman had visitors from the Army Ordnance Department who said that they would welcome an evaluation of their new research program and "would be glad to transfer funds" for any projects on their list that NSF wanted to support. "In short," Waterman recorded, "they expressed themselves as very willing to cooperate with the Foundation in every way."[4] The National Research Council, to which these research officials also turned for advice, was in a better position than an unstaffed NSF to assist in arranging for review of proposals in their new program, and there seems to have been no sequel to their visit nor any transfer of projects to the Foundation.[5]

There was nothing remarkable about Army Ordnance research officials (one of whom had worked in ONR) turning to Waterman for assistance in starting their program, but for those from the Public Health Service to do so may have seemed a little startling. Nevertheless senior PHS officials in a meeting with Waterman and Sunderlin sought to suggest how NSF could provide guidance to them by collecting "the kind of basic information and [formulating] the kind of policy judgments which an operating agency in the research grant field needs if its activities are to be most productive in the national interest." They agreed that NSF should support medical research, but primarily to gain the experience needed for informed answers to policy questions. Charles V. Kidd, the head of research planning at NIH, found Waterman's attitude disappointing. "I believe as a citizen as well as an employee of the Public Health Service," Kidd told Fred Schuldt of the Budget Bureau, "that if the Science Foundation pays only cursory attention to the basic factors underlying the place of science and research in our culture and our economy and to the basic factors affecting the productivity of research, a great opportunity will have been missed and the potentialities of the Science Foundation will have been lost." "Amen!" added Bill Carey.[6]

People in the Bureau recognized that if NSF was to perform such feats, it needed help as well as a push. To provide both, Schuldt and Shapley elaborated on the latter's earlier suggestion and drafted a presidential policy statement to inform the heads of executive departments and agencies of NSF's responsibilities and of their duty to cooperate. Shapley had followed with increasing alarm the expansion of "general purpose basic research" in the military departments, occasioned in part by a Research and Development Board policy statement intended to keep basic research in balance with applied research and development. Although some Defense Department officials acknowledged that general-purpose basic research belonged in NSF, Shapley wrote, "in the absence of any formal guidance as to the role of the NSF they are not in a position to block the expansion of basic research support by the military agencies."[7]

The congressional debates leading to the Foundation's establishment caused a dilemma for the Bureau's draftsmen. Although the Bureau had succeeded in knocking out of the legislation a provision that NSF's activities were not to take over or limit those of other agencies, a good deal of legislative history to the same effect had been made on the floor of the House. It seemed essential, then, to try to block the initiation of any new general-purpose basic research programs, to resist the increase of those already in being, and to encourage "the gradual and *partial* transfer of existing support programs" to NSF.[8]

The draft presidential statement called on science agencies to furnish information that NSF would need in its evaluation of basic research programs, a function that would be of value both to the agencies and to the Executive Office of the President "in planning and improving the organization and management of the Federal scientific research program as a whole." In its first research support the Foundation would emphasize "significant problems now receiving inadequate attention." (Here, as in its examination of NSF's 1952 budget estimates, the Bureau evidently conceived the agency's main research role as one of filling gaps.) This selective support would demand "close coordination" of the Foundation's program with those of other agencies and determination of their "proper scope" and "areas of responsibility." Ultimately the Foundation should "become the principal agency of the Federal Government for the support by grant or contract of basic research," probably in part through its assumption of support currently extended by other agencies. There might be instances in which other agencies should continue to sponsor general-purpose basic research, just as NSF might support projects in which they had "a very direct interest." But all parties should be assured that careful consideration would precede any changes in the pattern of basic research support, and there would be no disruption of existing programs.[9]

Schuldt and Shapley argued that the Bureau had to take the lead in defining NSF's and other agencies' duties on basic research policies. The assistant director of the Bureau, Elmer Staats, preferred instead to allow NSF "to assume the initiative in getting such policies worked out and adopted," though Carey warned him of the need for a quick resolution since Defense Department science officials were planning "to more than double their support of basic research in 1953."[10]

Staats's desire to persuade rather than compel the Foundation led to a meeting between Bureau and NSF officials and a follow-up letter from the Bureau indicating the desirability of "an authoritative statement, possibly a Presidential letter," along the lines of Shapley's earlier suggestion. The statement should be issued quickly while time remained to alter Defense's 1953 research plans. (Indeed, early issuance might permit transfers of some programs to NSF in fiscal 1952, and at this time the Foundation still did not have an appropriation.) Staats said that the Bureau looked forward to getting advice from the Foundation on other agencies' 1953 research budget requests. "The benefits to the Bureau resulting from this cooperative relationship would probably take the form of securing, both now and in the future, some general judgments from the Foundation as to the ability of the Nation's research facilities and scientific personnel to absorb further expansions of the Federal program in major basic fields and disciplines, rather than specific judgments or recommendations concerning the programs of particular agencies." In other words NSF need not be afraid of gagging on the bitter pill of evaluation.[11]

The Bureau's plan offered a possibility of funds for a still penniless agency, and the National Science Board decided that "evaluation" might not be so hazardous after all. Discussion of Staats's letter "showed strong feeling throughout the Board" that NSF should assume a role of leadership for science. Without a dissenting vote the members indicated their willingness "to consider transfers of funds from other agencies for support of research" and to cooperate with the Bureau in reviewing 1953 research budget requests. Forswearing any intention to monopolize basic research support, the board nevertheless held that "uncommitted, as opposed to programmatic, research is more appropriately handled by the National Science Foundation." The board's resolution made no reference to a presidential policy statement and left it up to the director and the executive committee to carry on discussions with the Bureau and with other science agencies.[12]

If the board action suggested that the Foundation was indeed ready to grasp a leadership role, appearances were deceiving. Waterman's chief concern was to increase the Foundation's appropriation to the statutory ceiling of $15 million as soon as possible, and then to persuade Congress to remove the limitation. While the hope of direct transfers of funds faded, the Bureau's design to make "comparative transfers"—accretions to NSF's budget through cuts in other agencies' requests—offered another route toward the goal of making the Foundation the "principal agency" for federal support of basic research, if the ceiling could be lifted. Waterman asked for its removal, but he thought it might be best to delay the legislative move "to permit full development of the Presidential policy concerning the role of the Foundation."[13] Yet he did not push this development. Following the board's seemingly favorable consideration of Staats's letter in October, Waterman gave only desultory attention to the issuance of a presidential policy statement until the Bureau renewed its prodding in the spring of 1952.

* * *

In the early months of 1952 Budget Bureau staff members showed signs of irritation with NSF and growing skepticism about its ability to evaluate federal science programs. When the Foundation's first annual report arrived at the Executive Office Building in January, Carey said that the document reminded him "of the Spiritual Exercises of Saint Ignatius. It takes its place with the advocates of sound money, peace, ethics, and American motherhood." Since NSF had neglected to furnish a transmittal statement for the President's signature, Carey suggested that Schuldt try his hand at writing one that would "bring us back down to earth" from the lofty prose about Thales of Miletus, Hans Christian Oersted, and Louis Pasteur.[14] Schuldt, who had talked earlier about taking a strong line with NSF about evaluation and policy development, now had only faint hopes that the agency would ever "be very effective in these respects," though it should still have "sufficient opportunity to demonstrate its presumed inadequacies."[15]

A full year after Shapley's suggestion of an Executive Office policy statement on basic research, Carey resumed the effort to force the Foundation into action. Taking with him a draft letter from the Budget Bureau's director, Carey visited Waterman in his California Street office, where he found a leisurely, genteel environment. "It is an excellent residence for the dean of studies. And this is how the Foundation is being run," he decided.[16] The draft letter reminded Waterman of the government's "need for a thorough and objective evaluation of basic research activities, and the eventual establishment of goals toward which future efforts can be guided." NSF should be ready by October 15 to give the Bureau policy guidance in its consideration of basic research budget requests; further, the Bureau would like to have "specific advice" which might lead to economies in research expenditures. These services would require NSF "at a very early date" to make an inventory of federal basic research activities, as a first step toward appraising their adequacy and the establishment of goals, and in addition, the draft continued, "it will be desirable for the Foundation to keep itself informed" on government-supported applied research and development. Finally NSF could do government planners a great service by identifying research areas "where a start should now be made toward filling gaps in basic science and training manpower for future needs."[17]

Carey waited three weeks for Waterman's considered reaction and then "went after" him on the telephone. "In brief," Carey told Staats,

it seems that he checked around with "key" members of the Board, and found a "general feeling of apprehension." They all want to do everything we proposed to ask, but they are afraid the existence of the Bureau's letter would become known and would drive basic research underground in the agencies. The major concern is that the Foundation may come to be regarded as a precinct station of the Budget Bureau. They do not wish to let the impression get about that NSF is policing the research agencies at the behest of the Bureau.

Only Chester Barnard, Conant's successor as chairman of the board, thought that the Bureau letter was a good idea. Carey agreed to let Waterman "take a crack at softening the letter so as to make it less specific just as long as he didn't make it so vague that any letter would be pointless."[18]

Waterman's redraft eliminated the October 15 date, but Carey took the director's word that NSF would be ready by then to advise the Bureau on research budgets. And the Foundation would formulate definitions to get started on an inventory of federal basic research activities. The two men discussed bringing the Defense Department's "wholly unrealistic" basic research estimates under control, a problem compounded by the department's policy requiring that 6 percent of its research and development expenditures, averaged over five years, be for basic studies. Waterman had succeeded in getting a recommendation to the Secretary of Defense to remove this floor and substitute for it a special committee, of which he would be a member, to decide on an amount for basic research. Carey agreed that this was "a major achievement." On another matter, Waterman liked Carey's suggestion that NSF bring up to date the Steelman report of 1947 as a way of restating "long-term goals for basic research." Carey in turn endorsed the director's idea of an NSF study of the effect on colleges and universities of the "easy money" flowing from federal research offices, but warned Waterman "to avoid an open break with the Office of Education."[19]

While Carey was willing to accept the softer version of the proposed letter, Waterman's board was not. In a long discussion of NSF's evaluation function the board agreed with the director that research could not be validly appraised "except in the light of history," and that scientists themselves had to decide what needed doing in their particular fields. NSF had recently arranged for a comprehensive study of the status of the physiological sciences by the American Physiological Society. Out of such surveys of fields of science or from studies of special topics within the disciplines, conducted by those most acquainted with the subjects, there would gradually accumulate a body of soundly based knowledge which the Foundation could use to plan its program and to assist other agencies "in a cooperative manner" as they assessed their basic research support. Thus while NSF should be wary of sitting down with Budget Bureau examiners to review the requests of other agencies, it should take over the Bureau's chore of gathering figures on federal expenditures for research and development in nonprofit institutions and refine the information and make it more precise. In contrast to the urgency felt in the Budget Bureau, the board's minutes reveal an insistence on gradualism, deliberation, and the lodging of policy planning in science rather than government.

> Members of the Board expressed the general feeling that this evaluation function should be approached carefully and agreed that it could only be successfully done in collaboration with the scientific fraternity, with constant awareness of the dangers involved. Under no circumstances should the Foundation attempt to direct the course of research for the programs of other institutions or agencies. Any solution of this problem must inevitably recognize the freedom, independence, and integrity of those engaged in basic research. The members of the Board, the Director and staff are in full agreement on this point.[20]

Waterman explained the board's views, which were also his own, to Staats a few days later. Staats agreed to drop the letter from the Bureau but asked that NSF send one explaining its evaluation plans, which as Waterman saw them encompassed, in addition to collecting information on federal research activities:

    a. A continuous long-range survey of research across all the fields of science, and
    b. Study of basic research underlying specific important areas, which should be of special interest in the emergency.

The Foundation would aim for an analysis of American scientific research updating the Steelman report. The idea of NSF eventually becoming the "principal agency" for the support of basic research, which had been announced in the President's 1953 budget message,[21] might be included in the letter to the Bureau along with an assurance that the Foundation did not intend to monopolize federal sponsorship of basic research. Significant of the different values attached to evaluation was the omission from Waterman's diary note on the conference of a topic recorded by Staats: "Waterman indicated that they would be quite willing to advise with the Bureau informally with respect to programs submitted by the agencies for fiscal year 1954."[22]

NSF did not delay in carrying out the activities agreed on by the board and explained to the Bureau. A new Program Analysis Office was soon established to plan and schedule studies on research and development and to serve as the "focal point" for their coordination. Waterman and Bronk agreed tentatively on a few intensive studies that might be started quickly "on topics of importance in defense, general welfare or in scientific progress." And the director promptly talked with top officials of AEC, PHS, and Defense's Research and Development Board to explain the Foundation's approach to evaluation and to calm their apprehensions.[23] But not until October did he send the promised letter to the Bureau, and then only after the Budget Director asked him for it. There seems to be no ready explanation for this delay except the persistent edginess about encounters with sister agencies, as reflected in the minutes of a summer board session:

> Dr. Bronk ... stated that the Executive Committee had considered the problem of the effect upon inter-agency relationships that might result from the evaluation of the research programs of Government agencies. The evaluation responsibility cannot be evaded, but the evaluation should be conducted in such a way as to strengthen the relations between each agency and the Foundation. The Committee recommended that this be achieved through frank discussions with other agencies, encouraging them to remedy weaknesses by their own initiative, rather than by compulsion. An essentially constructive evaluation procedure will assist other agencies, be appreciated by them, and will, therefore, be best in the long run for science and for the nation.[24]

An affirmation of Waterman's earlier commitments to Staats, the letter offered the Foundation's services "in a consulting capacity" to the Bureau or other agencies on questions of research policy. While ready "to take the lead" in supporting basic research, NSF believed that other agencies should also sponsor fundamental studies when they were "directly related to their statutory functions." The Bureau evidently concluded that these assurances were all it could hope for from NSF for the time being. A few days later Waterman wrote Barnard: "I had a very good talk with Elmer Staats today. I believe we have a good understanding with the top administration there."[25]

* * *

While Waterman was expressing his satisfaction with the understanding he had reached with the Bureau's top administrators, those working in the vineyard of Carey's Labor and Welfare Division were seeking better answers than those NSF had come up with to the problems of organizing and managing federal science programs. Under Carey's direction they wrote a 53-page paper which they hoped would provoke discussion and decisions once the budget season in the closing months of 1952 was out of the way. Carey confessed his and his colleagues' unhappiness with the paper, since there had been little opportunity for staff in other divisions to contribute and especially because Willis Shapley, the resident expert on Defense Department research and development, had not even had time to comment on it.[26] The paper suggests a somewhat desperate feeling that government science and technology were getting out of control, that the center could not hold unless NSF could be transformed not simply into the *principal* agency for the support of basic research but the *sole* federal sponsor of "nonprogrammatic" scientific research.

The paper cast the problem in historical terms. Three comprehensive reports on federal research activities—by the National Resources Committee (1938-41), Bush (1945), and Steelman (1947)—had emphasized the need for "high-level coordination" and "direction" of research conducted in government laboratories and the inadequate organization of the Budget Bureau for dealing with research programs and budgets on a government-wide basis. Since the issuance of these reports the problems of coordination and direction had grown enormously, especially as new military offices made contracts for extramural research, often with universities and technical institutes. Efforts to bring a measure of unified coordination and direction had availed little. ICSRD had "restricted itself pretty much to problems of research administration and ... steered away from attempting to deal with policy and coordination of policy problems." NSF was "barely beginning" its evaluation and policy development, and the harvest was apt to be "a long time off." The Science Advisory Committee of ODM had produced "little noticeable effect" on federal science activities. And competing military programs had flourished despite the effort to achieve central control through the Research and Development Board, which could not force "a new concept of policy upon unreceptive service departments" without the backing of the Secretary of Defense.[27]

Of the big unsolved problems facing the government, such as confused and overlapping agency assignments and inadequate exchange of information on research throughout the country, the most serious from the

Bureau's viewpoint was "the lack of a clearly defined Federal research policy which can guide the development and evaluation of research programs." This lack hindered progress toward several Bureau aims, among them the achievement of an overview of the total national research effort "as a framework for a sound Federal research program," a rational division of government research activities, adequate coverage of all important areas and elimination of unproductive research, a good balance between basic and applied research, and thrifty administration.[28]

Swelling federal funds for science confronted colleges and universities with equally serious difficulties: coping with "big business" problems of organization and management; subtle forms of control and distortion of academic programs owing to concentration of federal support in the natural sciences; the loss of talented faculty members from liberal arts colleges—traditionally prolific in graduating future scientists—to federal-contract universities; and divisiveness in these "favored" institutions because of salary differentials, the establishment of autonomous research institutes, and the proliferation of administrators insulated from faculties. Besides these dilemmas, government money flowing to universities too often *purchased* applied and developmental research rather than *supported* fundamental studies, caused shifts of emphasis by private foundations, and created confusion and irritation because of widely varying requirements on such matters as accounting and reporting and allowances for overhead.[29]

Searching for ways to answer these problems Carey's logicians found a formula in a distinction between programmatic and nonprogrammatic research. This distinction differed from the conventional one between basic and applied, since occasionally programmatic research was basic—e.g., "research in nuclear cross sections which is essential to the development of improved nuclear reactors"—while some applied research was not essentially related to the programs of sponsoring agencies—e.g., much medical research. "In general," the paper said, "programmatic research is the kind of research which an agency can justify as being an integral part of a program to solve an immediate agency problem. It is characteristic of such research that it can be planned in some detail and that the desired results of such a project can be related closely to a previously agreed upon goal." It followed that the Defense Department in contracting with universities for basic studies that promised "ultimate military application" was operating in the nonprogrammatic area, as was PHS when it undertook to stimulate research in small colleges.[30]

The Bureau group proposed to use this distinction and Ockham's razor to achieve better administration of government research. The assignment of all nonprogrammatic research to NSF would cancel the need for interagency coordination of currently overlapping jurisdictional zones. Each agency would remain responsible for planning and evaluating the research necessary to carry out its assigned tasks. When more than one agency had an important programmatic interest in a research topic—e.g., nutrition, with which Agriculture, Defense, and PHS were all concerned—the Bureau should designate one as having responsibility for leadership. The federal research program as a whole should be evaluated by NSF "in terms sufficiently detailed to allow analysis of its general direction and its impact on the Nation and on the scientific community." If this comprehensive assessment revealed a need for adjustments, the need should be brought to the attention of the President or the Bureau.[31]

But apart from supporting programmatic research necessary to carry out agencies' statutory missions, why should the government engage in research at all? In dealing with this question the Bureau group went beyond the customary justifications that new knowledge was needed as a base for the structure of applied research and development and for the solution of social problems. The writers emphasized instead the importance of strong colleges and universities as the home of science. ". . . it seems clear that the Federal Government's interest, in the case of non-programmatic research, is in subsidizing colleges and universities in the performance of one of their two traditional functions"—the advancement of knowledge.[32]

Instead of individual project grants the paper suggested "general purpose research grants" to institutions. The arguments that support of individual projects ensured balance, prevented gaps and duplication, and ruled out inferior research, all of which had been strongly advanced by NSF, seemed unconvincing to the authors. Rather than having government agencies review proposals from individual investigators, "we should have one Federal agency handle all non-programmatic research by making general purpose research grants to a large number of colleges, universities, and other non-profit research institutions." This policy would require the use of some kind of formula and financial participation by the institutions to guarantee "adequate project review at that level and . . . to prevent indirect subsidization of university functions unrelated to research." The cost-sharing formula could be used to resolve questions of indirect costs, and institutions could decide such matters as whether to pay page costs to scientific journals or use the grant funds to support additional research.[33]

The shifting of research decision-making from the capital to the campus would not relieve NSF of making studies of balance and gaps in research, but these studies "would be only for the information and guidance of colleges and universities and would not be directives to them." Even though based on the opinions of eminent scientists, NSF's studies would still be "only guesses," and a guess on the campus, where a person's colleagues were in position to judge his quality, might be as productive as peer review conducted from afar. The social sciences should be eligible for support under the broad institutional grants, and NSF's evaluation studies should include the social sciences as well as the natural.[34]

Government fellowship and training programs should be governed by similar principles, with one agency—perhaps NSF, the Office of Education, or the Department of Labor—being responsible for manpower studies. These studies might occasionally reveal deficiencies in certain fields that NSF should take into account in selecting fellows, but normally awards should be made "irrespective of the applicant's field of special interest."[35]

One can understand Carey's unhappiness with the paper. Some of its questionable judgments probably came from hasty composition to meet a deadline, while others may have originated in annoyance, either at bureaucratic empire-building or at Olympian dicta emanating from the scientific community. A final, brief section on the Bureau's internal problem of organizing to deal with government research suggests the authors' uneasiness about finding satisfactory solutions. While some people might argue that the federal research dilemmas fell in NSF's province because of its responsibility for science policy, "NSF will not be able to operate effectively in implementing policies on a government-wide basis without backup from the Bureau."[36] But whatever the inadequacies of the analysis and the suggested solutions, the paper showed the Bureau's conviction that the problems were important and urgent. Thus Waterman's "good understanding" with Staats did not signify an indefinite remission of the Bureau's pressure on the Foundation to become an evaluating and policy-making agency.

* * *

"I am currently recruiting a well-trained individual to serve as a special assistant to me to head up a Program Analysis Office," Waterman told John T. Wilson in June 1952. Meanwhile Wilson, a psychologist who had recently transferred from ONR to NSF's biological sciences division, was to direct the new office, assisted by Charles Gant, who would relinquish his position as comptroller.[37] Wilson was probably amused by the reference to "a well-trained individual." Only a short time before, when the position of assistant director of his division became vacant, Waterman had said to him, "John, would you do this until we get someone who is qualified?" Wilson replied, "Well, if you put it that way, I can't resist."[38]

Waterman had trouble recruiting a head of program analysis. His first choice, Dael Wolfle, was unavailable, and his second, S. Douglas Cornell, a physicist with the Research and Development Board, took a position with the National Academy of Sciences instead. After prolonged negotiations Raymond H. Ewell, a chemist and economist with the Stanford

Research Institute, came to head the office well over a year after its creation.[39] A great deal had happened in the interim as Wilson and Gant elaborated plans for studies that would pass muster with the Bureau of the Budget and at the same time dispel the suspicions of science administrators in other agencies.

Agreeing with Waterman that NSF would be "clobbered" if it tried to sit in judgment on federal science programs and budget justifications, Wilson proposed a carefully staged progress toward the goals of policy and evaluation. The Foundation had chosen "deliberately to move extremely slowly" in performing these functions because their importance and ramifications demanded prior experience in operating research and fellowship programs. Among the concerns of national science policy, as he saw them, were such matters as

the total effort to be expended by the nation in the support of science; the areas of science to be supported; the division of responsibility among various agencies, particularly agencies of the Federal Government, in the execution of this support; the recommended methods and means in the execution of the support; the best manner and means of modifying, with changing conditions, the policies which guide such support, and so on.

Answers to these questions could come only from comprehensive factual knowledge of the needs and opportunities of science and of the nation's scientific resources, including research facilities and manpower. As for evaluation, that could be done only in accordance with standards and criteria developed through broad surveys of fields of science and intensive probing of specific areas. These studies would arouse the interest and enlist the services of scientists, who best knew the problems of their fields. While the studies were under way NSF could help improve the organization and management of government science by collecting factual information on federal programs and, by raising relevant questions on agencies' missions and objectives, stimulate them into greater "self-criticism and self-evaluation." Wilson suggested as a "minimum goal" in fiscal 1953 that every NSF program director get at least one study started bearing on his area of responsibility.[40]

The office took over from the Budget Bureau the compilation of statistical information on federal science activities, and within a year the Foundation published the first two parts of its continuing series on *Federal Funds for Science*, covering funds for scientific research and development in nonprofit institutions and R&D budgets of federal agencies. In addition to the study of physiology already in progress, the Foundation soon supported surveys of psychology and of research and training needs in applied mathematics. Conferences and symposia, usually jointly sponsored with other agencies and institutions, on such topics as photosynthesis and solar energy, low-temperature physics and chemistry, and high-energy particles constituted the third element of NSF's fact-finding and policy-development activity. A related service grew out of the recommendation of a presidential commission that NSF appoint a special committee to propose a program of basic research and technical development for the exploration and discovery of minerals.[41]

These undertakings might lead eventually to recommended policies and criteria for evaluation, but by no means did they provide the coordination of government science programs that some Budget officials and members of Congress wanted. In NSF's House appropriation hearing in January 1952 Albert Thomas wondered whether the several programs could not "be consolidated under one head," or at least better coordinated. "Instead of having everybody working all over the lot and throwing balls in every direction, let us have somebody calling the signals," he chided. Republican committee members John Phillips and Norris Cotton pressed harder. One of the main reasons for creating the Foundation, Cotton claimed, was to get an agency to "coordinate, clarify, organize, and prevent waste and duplication" in government research.[42]

A year later Phillips was sitting in the chairman's seat when the Foundation presented its case for an appropriation. The November elections had brought to power an economy-minded Republican Congress and Administration. Truman's request for a $15 million budget for NSF, still the legal maximum, was cut back to $12,250,000, and the new Budget Director, Joseph M. Dodge, told Waterman that he expected the Foundation to "initiate, at the earliest possible date, a comprehensive study of the Nation's present effort and needs in research and development, with particular emphasis upon the extent of the Federal Government's responsibilities during and after the current emergency."[43]

Dodge's peremptory summons to action, followed by an oral indication that the Bureau expected the "comprehensive study" to be substantially completed in a little more than a year, forced NSF to shift into a higher gear. "To date, we have been developing the policy study and the program analysis effort . . . on a very slow and deliberate basis," Wilson wrote the director, but now there must be "more vigorous action" if the Foundation was to meet the deadline with a report comparable to Steelman's. The agency might use the authority given in its charter to establish a special commission to prepare the comprehensive study, though Wilson did not favor that tack. He thought that the organization and plans he and Gant had formulated would serve the purpose if "an all-out attempt to recruit a full-time Head" and additional staff for the office were made and if the staff in other divisions changed their insouciant attitude toward the policy role. The new head should have the rank and responsibility of an assistant director, Wilson thought, and further, "it will be necessary to create a feeling throughout the Foundation that the policy function . . . is from this time on, just as important in the Foundation's efforts as the grant-making and fellowship-granting functions. I do not believe that such a feeling now exists."[44]

It turned out that time was not as short as Wilson feared. Bureau officials gave NSF another year for the completion of the first, major part of the study, and other portions might appear in continuing reports. Nonetheless Dodge's letter put an end to leisurely cud-chewing about science policy, and for the next few months the Foundation staff, even in the research and educational divisions, gave unwonted attention to a program of studies relating to the neglected function. In May the board received a general outline of the activities planned by the Program Analysis Office—studies covering research and development by government, industry, and educational and other nonprofit institutions; studies on the status and progress of science; and studies of special scientific problems (e.g., manpower, information programs, and international activities) and areas (social, medical, and agricultural sciences). In July the board received a refined version of this program of studies, estimated to cost $800,000 in fiscal 1954.[45]

In presenting the plan to the board Waterman reinterpreted the Foundation's policy and evaluation functions by quoting language, which he liked better than that in the founding act, from the Hoover Commission Report of 1948.[46] He then derived the following statement of NSF objectives which the program of studies would help achieve:

(a) to develop and maintain the maximum potential of the nation in scientific research; (b) to assure that the research undertaken and supported by the Federal Government is soundly conceived and administered; (c) to assure, in the national interest, the effective utilization of the results of research; and (d) to determine the relative responsibilities of the Government and other public and private agencies in bringing about these results.[47]

Congressman Thomas might have found it difficult to discern his single signal-caller in this abstract statement of objectives; but for Waterman it conveniently dropped the charter's unpleasant words "evaluate," "appraise," and "correlate," though their replacements might be just as troublesome if taken literally.

Dodge had called for a study of research *and development*. The board took the stand that "*The NSF should confine its major attention to science and matters related directly to science*. This means that the Foundation should not assume leadership with respect to developmental matters, since they involve considerations other than science." Responsibility for evaluating development and related applications belonged solely to the sponsoring agency. NSF's proper role was to assist other agencies by advising them on the basic research needed for development, the kind and supply of scientists required, and perhaps on the necessary organizational arrangements.

Finally, a qualified affirmation: "The NSF should be ready to accept a position of leadership with respect to the basic research programs of the Federal Government, in the sense of leading a cooperative enterprise within the policies already stated by the NSF and by the Administration."[48]

By this time the Budget Bureau had again picked up the idea of a presidential definition of the Foundation's policy responsibilities and the reciprocal obligations of other federal agencies. The board statement laid down the terms which NSF would be willing to accept gracefully. While during the months ahead the Bureau tried to persuade the other suspicious parties to agree to an executive order, the Foundation proceeded with its program of studies, generally as they had been presented to the director and by him to the board, though under new direction in the Program Analysis Office the plans became more elaborate and the procedures more formal than those outlined by Wilson. There were angry charges of reneging on solemn agreements, of gathering information that could serve no useful purpose, and of upsetting informal cooperative arrangements between NSF program directors and their counterparts in other government bureaus. Bickering continued throughout the autumn, but by the end of the year the chores of gathering and interpreting data were reasonably well understood and, however unsatisfactorily in the view of some, were going forward.[49]

* * *

The new Administration's alarm about budget deficits sparked revived interest in a presidential statement on research policy. After three months in office President Eisenhower, Budget Director Dodge, and Secretary of the Treasury George Humphrey admitted to Republican congressional leaders that they had not been able even to halve Truman's projected 1954 deficit of nearly ten billion dollars, let alone wipe it out as they had hoped. Senator Robert Taft angrily warned Eisenhower: "With a program like this, we'll never elect a Republican Congress in 1954. You're taking us down the same road Truman traveled. It's a repudiation of everything we promised in the campaign!"[50] Soon after that outburst Dodge wrote to Waterman about the congressional and executive branch concern that too much money was being spent on research and development and the consequent need to evaluate science programs and eliminate unnecessary duplication. NSF had not made much progress in its policy-development duty, and Dodge wanted to discuss this matter with Waterman as soon as possible.[51]

When they met, Dodge asked whether NSF or ICSRD could carry out the review of research budgets necessary for economy and efficiency. Neither could, Waterman replied; ICSRD representatives were all parties at interest, and he had concluded before accepting the directorship that it would be improper for NSF to attempt the task. The Foundation's responsibility was only for basic research, and the way "to increase efficiency and economy" in this tiny portion of the total R&D budget "was to center more of this support in the NSF . . . while leaving to the other agencies basic research in fields directly related to their statutory missions." In time NSF might be able to comment helpfully on other agencies' applied research, but not on proposed developmental activities except in general on the adequacy of research and manpower to support them. The critical requirement was that each agency have "a strong set-up for planning its research and development operations." The heaviest expenditures of course were for defense, and since the question of science advice on security matters had become active again with the change of Administration, Waterman suggested the desirability of having a young scientist available to the National Security Council "to answer or get answers to spot questions and make available the most competent scientific advisers on call as needed." Perhaps because the discussion veered in this direction, Dodge said he would like to pursue the topic in a later meeting with White House officials.[52]

In June Waterman and Barnard, representing NSF, and Hugh L. Dryden, ICSRD, attended a meeting which ranged over the same subjects but served the purpose of educating the President's Special Assistant for National Security Affairs, Robert Cutler, other presidential assistants Gabriel Hauge and Emmet J. Hughes, and ODM director Arthur S. Flemming on the problems of controlling federal research expenditures and providing science advice to the White House. Dodge raised the question foremost in his mind, Who would assist the Bureau in evaluating research and development? All agreed with Dryden that ICSRD was not up to the job, and Waterman argued that no part-time committee could do it effectively. He claimed that the existing system of informal coordination of basic research was working smoothly; all the important research agencies received good scientific advice, and the main concern was the prevention of undesirable duplication or competition. When Dodge asked if NSF would take responsibility for basic research, Waterman replied that it would but with his usual qualification "that NSF exercises no control but only leadership." NSF would not make "detailed budget examinations of other agencies' programs," but it would answer specific questions raised by the Bureau if it had the competence to answer them. Dodge then said he would draft an Administration paper on NSF's responsibility, and he dismissed Barnard's view that the board did not like the idea and rejected Cutler's proposal that NSF prepare the statement. Both Waterman and Dryden warned against the issuance of "any order which required the other agencies to report to NSF in evaluation of programs."[53]

While the Bureau was drafting executive orders—originally two instead of the final one—alarm began to spread among scientists, in and out of government, about shrinking support for basic research and disasters that would result if NSF should be designated as its sole federal patron. Wisecracks by Secretary of Defense Charles E. Wilson to the effect that basic research was the kind that provided no returns to those who paid for it, and that he was not interested in learning why potatoes turned brown when frying, bothered E. R. Piore, Waterman's successor in ONR, as much as they did scientists in academia. Piore saw little enthusiasm for fundamental research in AEC, and he feared that makers of military research policy, faced with cuts in R&D budgets, would drop the R in favor of the D. The result, he warned Lee DuBridge, would be that "our first team will suffer the bruises of this retrenchment"—that is, "Harvard, MIT, Caltech, Chicago, etc."[54] DuBridge, after talking with Deputy Secretary of Defense Roger M. Kyes and AEC Commissioner Lewis Strauss, concluded that research cuts in those agencies would "be much less than Piore fears," but the Caltech president had equally weighty worries of his own. He had read Senator Alexander Smith's argument for removing NSF's $15 million appropriation ceiling—a charter amendment that became law in August 1953—and was disturbed by Smith's repeated emphasis that the amendment would result in bringing all basic research sponsorship under NSF. DuBridge told Waterman that he "would be bitterly opposed" to such a consolidation. By contrast with the "shortsighted policies" of NSF—that is, failure to pay full overhead costs—those of Defense and other agencies were "more considerate of the welfare of universities." Since Budget Director Dodge seemed to want NSF to monopolize federal support of basic research, it might be wise to tell him and the President that the National Science Board did not agree.[55]

DuBridge was mistaken about Administration policy, Waterman replied. There had been no change from the stand announced by Truman that the Foundation should become the principal, but not sole, federal sponsor of basic research. Obviously the economizing mood would prevent any immediate increase in government support, but the aim should be to maintain the level for basic research through additions to NSF's budget while cuts were applied to development. Waterman did not agree with DuBridge on the benefits of military links to university campuses. "I believe one cannot escape the conclusion that in the long run a civilian agency should carry forward the bulk of general basic research support in the universities," he wrote. And grants were preferable to complicated contracts for the support of academic science. Some government agencies allowed no participation by their scientific staffs in negotiating and administering research contracts. "As for the indirect costs difficulty, which I know looms large in your thinking, I have hopes that if we plug away at this matter, we can reach a satisfactory settlement; I certainly hope so."

Waterman ended with a barb. He had thought DuBridge was clear on NSF policy. Could he have been absent when the board discussed these matters?[56]

Senator Smith's remarks and rumors about Budget Bureau intentions also brought disquiet to government agencies. Waterman knew that the proposed executive orders would add to the uneasiness of his fellow research administrators, and he set out to prove the Foundation's friendship. Meeting with top officials of research offices in AEC, Agriculture, and all the military services, he explained NSF's stand and encouraged them to continue their support of basic research. But the missionary work did not lay the fears to rest, and the Budget Bureau's drafts of two orders—"Pertaining to Coordination of Research and Development" and "Pertaining to the Functions and Responsibilities of the National Science Foundation"—tended to confirm suspicions. Even Waterman's good friends in ONR thought the orders "would be interpreted as a move to have all basic research go to the Foundation" and would cause agencies with no real interest in fundamental science abruptly to drop support of university research. The acting assistant secretary of defense for research and development, a newly established office, also saw a probability of "top-level decision being too precipitate."[57]

The concern about sudden disruption of university research arose from related sections of the two orders. The draft NSF order provided:

In cooperation with educational institutions the National Science Foundation shall appraise the impact of Federal research programs and their administration on such institutions and shall . . . recommend to the President policies to guide agencies in relieving such institutions of responsibility for research and development deemed more appropriate to industrial or Government-operated facilities or which, in the judgment of the institutions concerned, tend to disturb the proper relationship between education and research.

Other agencies in turn, according to a section of the companion order, were to use the NSF-formulated policies in appraising their grants and contracts with universities and discontinue those that were inappropriate to an academic setting.[58]

Comments he heard on his good-will missions led Waterman to recommend to Carey that the troublesome section be dropped from the order pertaining to other agencies. Carey, knowing that "universities have nightmares at the thought of losing Federal money which has been generously available up to now," alerted Dodge to the opposition the Bureau would face from such academic officials as DuBridge and MIT's James R. Killian, Jr. Both were members of the Science Advisory Committee, and Flemming had turned over copies of the first, limited-circulation drafts to DuBridge who, to Carey's dismay, quickly placed them on the committee's agenda.[59] In fact, even before the committee met, DuBridge, writing as its chairman, fired off a seven-page denunciation of the orders to Flemming.

To put the matter very bluntly, I would be strongly opposed to issuing these orders in their present form. I believe that science would suffer and that the agencies engaged in scientific work would be burdened and confused to an extent which would reduce their scientific effectiveness. I also believe that these orders would place upon the National Science Foundation responsibilities for which it is not prepared and for which its basic composition makes it unfitted.

NSF, DuBridge continued, "is not charged with making general research policies for the Government and is not suitable for this task." ("Read the Act," Carey jotted in the margin.) Caltech "would go broke very promptly if all of its basic research support were suddenly transferred to the National Science Foundation." (Carey: "Heart of the matter.")[60]

The moderate NSF director, trying to reason with DuBridge, pointed out justifications for the orders: (1) the need for "increased efficiency and economy" in federal R&D programs (appropriations had more than doubled between 1949 and 1952, and tripled in Defense—from $500 million to $1.6 billion); (2) the need to correct the imbalance between applied research and development and basic research in universities (the ratio was four to one, even excluding nonacademic university research centers); and (3) the need "to clarify or assign responsibilities for dealing with these matters."[61] Waterman had come to believe that a presidential statement was desirable, though characteristically he wanted to guard every important interest. Thus he told Hauge that he welcomed the consideration of the orders by the Science Advisory Committee, and he suggested that after the Bureau had analyzed agencies' comments, a group of university officials be called together to advise Dodge. Hauge recommended this step to the Bureau and said that he too wanted to proceed "very deliberately on this project."[62]

As expected, the Science Advisory Committee did strongly oppose the orders but drafted a substitute single order, because, as Waterman noted, "the general attitude was that since matters had gone thus far some form of order had best be put out."[63] NSF's official view, drafted by Waterman and the Foundation's new general counsel, William J. Hoff, suggested that the Bureau consider, as an alternative to their issuance, "a statement covering the same ground but permitting less formal and fuller discussion of the policies involved." Otherwise NSF suggested several textual changes based on the criticisms Waterman had heard in his conversations with officials of other agencies and in the recent meeting of the Science Advisory Committee.[64]

The strongest opposition to the orders—and to the later single form—came from AEC and Defense. Lewis Strauss thought they would tend to centralize direction and control over federal research activities and "make far reaching changes . . . which we believe would not be in the public interest."[65] Defense asked for a conference to discuss the fundamental questions raised by the orders, and after this meeting Donald A. Quarles, the new head of the department's research office, thought that because of his "fairly strong position . . . the executive order idea may have been slowed up and may be modified."[66]

To Carey the changes later proposed by Defense "would make the order useless." He was about ready for a showdown. The department's views, Carey thought, "reflect a deep antagonism toward the NSF in all particulars. I believe that the Bureau cannot alter the proposed order according to the wishes of the Defense Department without surrendering completely to the prevailing attitudes of that agency, which are not compatible with the motivations of the order." He proposed to discuss the Defense letter informally with Waterman and David Z. Beckler, a science aide to Cutler and Flemming. If they agreed with Carey, he suggested that the Bureau "tell Quarles we can't go along, and that we will make one final circularization of the current unofficial draft before delivering an order to the White House."[67] Waterman, in the role of mediator, dealt directly with Quarles and worked out some mutually acceptable changes, though Quarles continued to object to a designation of NSF as the principal agency for basic research support, and in the long run Waterman had to give up on his effort to insert "primary agency" in the order.[68]

Agency comments on the latest version of the order arrived in the Bureau in its busiest season, and Carey turned them over for review by Beckler, who was "subjected to all kinds of pressures by the private scientists who make up the ODM Science Advisory Committee, and by the Defense people." Besides Defense—essentially the separate services more than Quarles's office—AEC gave the most trouble, but Waterman worked out satisfactory arrangements with that agency. By mid-January Carey thought the order was about ready to send to the White House, and on February 10, 1954 Dodge sent the order to the Attorney General and the President.[69]

After opening his press conference on March 17 with an allusion to St. Patrick's Day and an announcement that an investigation of coffee prices was nearing completion, President Eisenhower mentioned "one other little item"—an executive order to be published that afternoon on research and development. A statement accompanying the order pointed out that less than one-tenth of the federal expenditures for science went for basic research, too small a fraction in the President's opinion.[70]

The first five sections of the order set out NSF's duties: (1) to recommend to the President federal policies to "strengthen the national scientific effort" and help define the government's proper role in research: (2) to continue studies of research and resources in science, giving particular attention to federal activities; (3) to review federal research programs to assist in strengthening their administration, to determine gaps or undesirable duplication in basic research, and to make recommendations on basic research to agency heads; (4) to become "increasingly responsible" for providing the federal government's support of general-purpose basic research, although other agencies should continue to conduct or sponsor basic studies "closely related to their missions"; and (5) to study the effects of federal support of research and development on educational institutions and recommend ways of guarding their strength and freedom. The other sections were intended to ensure that other agencies managed their science programs efficiently and economically, shared research equipment and facilities, consulted with NSF on their basic research policies, and cooperated in improving the classification and reporting of scientific activities. (The text of the executive order appears in Appendix 1.)

"I believe that the introductory statement by the President is quite helpful," Waterman wrote DuBridge, "especially in its emphasis upon the need for more support of basic research.

"Now that all of the tumult is over, I trust that this will be properly interpreted and on the whole be beneficial. I believe it should certainly be so with respect to Congress. At any rate, we in the Foundation will try to uphold the proper interpretation."[71]

End of the Beginning

The issuance of Executive Order 10521 had little effect on federal science, but it provides a convenient halting place to look back over the Foundation's beginning as an operating agency. The order, by defining NSF's role in policy development and evaluation as a cooperative rather than a regulatory one, eased the danger of conflict with other agencies while it left the Bureau of the Budget still saddled with the difficult job of coordination. With a strong sense of relief, the board and the director concluded—somewhat too readily—that they could now concentrate on what they and most of the staff thought to be NSF's main function—the support of basic scientific research and closely related educational activities in universities and colleges.

Waterman regretted that the order did not name NSF as the principal federal sponsor of basic research, but at the time that could only have been a millennial hope anyway. Though Congress had removed the $15 million appropriation ceiling, NSF's budget for fiscal 1954 was only $8 million, half of which would be obligated for research grants. The Foundation's allocation for research was less than 3.5 percent of the government's total for basic science and only 0.2 percent of the budget for federal research and development.

By the end of fiscal 1954 the Foundation had awarded $6.7 million in 643 research grants.[1] Although the policy was to divide the research budget equally between the two research divisions (BMS and MPE), the life sciences group had got a substantial headstart in the first year, and their grants for the three-year period aggregated somewhat more than those for the MPE programs. Regulatory biology led all other programs with approximately $950,000 in grants, followed in order by physics, chemistry, molecular biology, and engineering. Lagging far behind all other programs in fourteenth position was environmental biology with thirteen grants for $76,760.

With so little wealth to spread and so many worthy supplicants, the Foundation was in a good position to answer critics of the geographical and institutional distribution of its research awards. Besides pleading poverty, NSF soon developed another response that would become customary: research grants corresponded closely to the institutional and geographical concentrations of graduate students. (Of course the Foundation by its research awards and especially by permitting fellows to choose their graduate schools helped to reinforce the patterns of concentration.) Not that NSF's policy makers and administrators were unconcerned—Waterman and some of the staff worried particularly about the decline of science in undergraduate colleges—but their overriding interest was the advancement of science through support of its ablest practitioners.

Only two states (Arkansas and Nevada) had no recipients of research grants during the first three years. The largest winner among the states was Illinois ($600,500), followed by California ($527,900), Massachusetts ($518,400), and New York ($492,700). No other state received as much as $300,000.

By geographic region, the 9 states of the Northeast received 32 percent of the funds; the 12 North Central states 32 percent; the 16 of the South and the District of Columbia 19 percent; and the 11 of the West 16 percent. Grants to the territories of Alaska and Hawaii and the Commonwealth of Puerto Rico and to a few American researchers in other countries accounted for the remainder of the funds.

Southern institutions and those of the Great Plains and Rocky Mountains lagged considerably behind those of the Northeast, East North Central, and Pacific Coast in the receipt of research grants. Eighteen universities had grants amounting to more than $100,000:

University of California, Berkeley	$292,400
Yale University	245,750
Harvard University	231,000
University of Wisconsin	218,920
University of Illinois	211,600
University of Chicago	189,000
University of Pennsylvania	173,100
Princeton University	131,300
University of Minnesota	129,680
Washington University	127,200
Purdue University	125,000
Indiana University	122,900
Columbia University	119,900
Pennsylvania State University	116,400
Johns Hopkins University	112,400

California Institute of Technology 106,500
University of Washington 106,500
Northwestern University 103,500

Their $2.9 million in research grants made up 43 percent of the total.

Although the bulk of the funds was concentrated in graduate-level universities, the concern shown in Waterman's correspondence, and in several NSF-sponsored conferences, for the maintenance of high-quality science in free-standing liberal arts colleges was evidently shared by program directors and their consultants and panels. Such highly regarded colleges as Antioch, Bryn Mawr, Haverford, Mount Holyoke, Oberlin, Reed, Smith, and Wabash all received at least two research awards, and many similar colleges received one. Predominantly Negro colleges fared less well—only five managing to get a total of six awards—and state colleges whose main function was the training of public school teachers were not even that successful.

NSF's fellowships showed similar patterns. The Northeast led all other regions in the number of successful applicants. Of the 1,866 pre- and postdoctoral fellows by June 30, 1954, 36 percent resided in states of the Northeast, 31 percent North Central, 18 percent West, and 15 percent South. Except for the North Central region, which had a high success rate, these percentages corresponded closely with applications: 37 percent Northeast, 26 percent North Central, 20 percent West, and 17 percent South.

Although more NSF funds for research went to the life sciences than to the MPE disciplines, this was not so of fellowships. Students in the life sciences received only 29 percent of the fellowships, a little below their percentage (32) of applications; those in chemistry received 23 percent, physics and astronomy 22 percent, engineering 12 percent, mathematics 10 percent, and earth sciences 5 percent.

Harvard and MIT easily led all other universities and colleges in the number of baccalaureate graduates winning NSF fellowships. Their 200 fellows were more than 10 percent of the total group. As the following list shows, four liberal arts colleges (CCNY, Swarthmore, Oberlin, Brooklyn) ranked in the top twenty institutions where NSF fellows earned their first degrees; several others (Amherst, Pomona, Reed, Wesleyan, and College of Wooster) graduated from 11 to 17 fellows each. Institutions graduating more than 20 fellows were:

Harvard University 103
Massachusetts Institute of Technology 97
University of Chicago 68
Cornell University 53
California Institute of Technology 48
City College of New York 40

University of Illinois 40
Swarthmore College 39
University of California, Berkeley 39*
Columbia University 36
Carnegie Institute of Technology 33
Stanford University 33
University of Wisconsin 30
University of Michigan 29
University of Minnesota 29
Oberlin College 29
Ohio State University 24
Brooklyn College 23
Northwestern University 22
New York University 21
University of Pennsylvania 21
University of Washington 21

(*Estimated; the fiscal 1952 figures combine all campuses of the University of California.)

Fellows naturally tended to choose graduate schools with outstanding reputations in their fields of science. Again Harvard and MIT ranked at the top. The twenty institutions attracting the largest numbers of NSF fellows were:

Harvard University 171
Massachusetts Institute of Technology 163
University of Chicago 146
California Institute of Technology 110
Princeton University 103
University of Illinois 102
University of Wisconsin 102
University of California, Berkeley .... 96 (est.)
Columbia University 78
Yale University 74
Stanford University 67
Cornell University 58
University of Michigan 48
Johns Hopkins University 45
University of Minnesota 40
University of California, Los Angeles .... 35 (est.)
Ohio State University 32
Purdue University 30
Iowa State College 27
University of Pennsylvania 27

These twenty institutions enrolled 83 percent of the fellows, and the top ten accounted for 61 percent.

Southern institutions, except the marginally regional one of Johns Hopkins, and those of the Plains and Mountains attracted few fellows. Thus of the first group of fellows only 8 percent chose to attend southern universities, and of the 16 percent in western institutions nearly all studied in graduate schools in California.

The Foundation's plan to award undergraduate scholarships, withdrawn when it seemed that Congress might establish a general program under the Office of Education, was under consideration again by 1954. But while a scholarship program would remain in limbo, other designs to expand NSF's educational activities—notably institutes for science teachers in schools and colleges and the preparation of new, up-to-date science courses—were in the take-off stage. Also bubbling up from eager staff members were ideas for new ventures in research. By 1953 the Foundation's annual report listed in its life science programs one entitled Anthropological and Related Sciences, and a year later a wary board began to debate the director's recommendation that the limited research support for the social sciences be publicly acknowledged as a full-fledged program. From the conferences and symposia organized by research program directors came other ideas, such as the construction of large-scale facilities for radio astronomy, marine biology, and high-energy physics, that would move NSF into national programs of "big science" in the coming years. Already in preparation was a worldwide research program, in which NSF would coordinate the funding of United States activities, the International Geophysical Year of 1957-58.

The executive order may have freed NSF from some policy responsibilities it did not want, but it also recognized the Foundation's special interest in the health of academic science. It encouraged studies of the effects of federal programs on universities and colleges and recommendations on government science policy toward higher education. NSF's board and director welcomed this opportunity and were getting ready to exploit it. Still another need for the development of federal policy—one which the Foundation grasped unhesitatingly—came from the ominous growth of loyalty and security requirements for government-supported research.

The President's order scarcely marked a historical watershed, but it came at a time when the Foundation was showing a growing interest in new endeavors and in developing means to undertake them. In this sense the order and the closing of the third year of operations may be taken to signify the end of the Foundation's beginning.

Part III:
Cold War Growth, 1954-57

"Growth is the only evidence of life."
Cardinal Newman

11
Men and Means

Measured by size of staff and budget the National Science Foundation was an insignificant agency when the Soviets launched Sputnik I on October 4, 1957. The staff, numbering a little over 250, had grown by only about one hundred during the three and a half years since the issuance of Executive Order 10521. The director, general counsel, administrative staff, and members of the Office of Special Studies occupied the Dolley Madison House and other former Cosmos Club buildings on the northeast side of Lafayette Park, along with the research program staffs—except for the tiny social science program (two professionals and a secretary) which shared lodging with the Office of Scientific Information across the park on Jackson Place. Somewhat isolated, but still only two blocks farther away, in the Winder Building on 17th Street, were some sixty persons who administered NSF's education and manpower programs and served the President's Committee on Scientists and Engineers.

The budget had grown somewhat more impressively. Only $8 million in fiscal year 1954, it doubled that figure two years later (finally exceeding the onetime statutory ceiling), and then quintupled it the next year, when Congress appropriated $40 million for fiscal 1957. An economy mood held the fiscal 1958 budget at the same level, until alarm over successful Russian satellites and American fizzles resulted in a supplementary appropriation of close to $10 million. Besides these basic appropriations NSF received other funds to administer the United States share of the International Geophysical Year (IGY), and these totaled $43 million between 1954 and 1958. But this kind of relative affluence needs to be viewed in terms of the huge expenditures for defense research, which finally evoked President Eisenhower's warning against a "military-industrial complex"—to which adjectives some critics would have added "academic."

If against this background NSF was still a dwarf among giants, its own expansion, even before Sputnik I, was owing largely to fears and needs of "the national security state."[1] Cold War concerns during the years 1954-57 fostered growth in the Foundation's first research and educational activities and the rise of new ones. NSF both capitalized on the desire for security and helped halt the stifling effects of security requirements. Drawing on the ideas and services of scientists in the nation's leading research institutions, the Foundation's staff pushed, often successfully, for greater scope for their programs and for new departures. These achievements, which will be detailed in the following chapters, gave NSF a more consequential role in national—and international—science than its small staff and meager appropriations might imply.

* * *

Following a policy of rotation in office for assistant directors, Waterman in March 1954 asked Marston Bates of the University of Michigan if he would succeed H. Burr Steinbach, about to return to the University of Minnesota, as head of NSF's biological and medical sciences division. Steinbach had filled the position for a year, following a similar short tenure by Fernandus Payne of Indiana University. Bates, a member of the BMS divisional committee, knew the offer was coming and had already made up his mind. He wrote: "The Foundation has had a most reassuring beginning under your leadership; but obviously you cannot keep this up without complete and understanding cooperation from your colleagues in science. The sort of cooperation that isn't hedged by personal convenience or personal ambition. Believe me, it is with the utmost reluctance that I beg to be excused." Bates had joined the zoology department at Ann Arbor only two years before and, despite his belief in NSF's importance, said that he was "scared even to try another move when . . . only beginning to feel adjusted here." He wished Steinbach could stay on for another year but sympathized with his desire to return to research.[2]

"The sort of cooperation that isn't hedged by personal convenience or personal ambition"—here Bates touched on matters that strongly affect academic scientists, causing dilemmas for them and adding to Waterman's recruitment difficulties. Professional obligations—in this instance to a struggling federal agency devoted to basic science—often conflicted with personal loyalties to students, colleagues, and institution and with the fascinations of research. The next person Waterman sought for the position—this time successfully—well revealed in his replies the conflict of duty and desire.

Lawrence R. Blinks, director of Stanford University's Hopkins Marine Station, was about to mail an application for a Fulbright research appointment in Australia when Waterman's offer came. He had to weigh "the chance for a year of undisturbed research, against a year of very busy administration." Like Bates, he thought his decision involved more than "personal preference: I honestly believe there is a real duty on the scientists of the country to join in the work of the Foundation, to keep it in close touch with many aspects of their science." He considered Waterman's rotation policy "an admirable one. The more working biologists who understand the problems and the opportunities of the Foundation, the better it will be in forging it as a strong instrument of American science. Of this I have no doubt"—but then the lament of the dedicated scientist— "and of the inexorable march of time cutting ever shorter the time for active research. Ars longa—."[3]

A week later, writing from Boston just before taking off for a month in England, Blinks stated his willingness to come to Washington for a year. A visit with some of NSF's "permanent staff" the day before had convinced him that they had matters "well in hand." Steinbach had told him "that he *does* have time to think, a little above the melee," and Blinks hoped that he too, like his predecessor, would be able to meet his "obligations to students and research assistants.... It would be unfortunate if connection with the Science Foundation meant divorcement from Science itself." He had not caught Potomac fever, and he worried about scientists seduced by bureaucratic gamesmanship.

> I think I shall never understand the ramifications of the Washington labyrinth, the interdepartmental, inter-agency relations. I am more than a little appalled at the mixture of science with these but I suppose it must be. Science seems so much simpler than its Machinery! I wonder, from the outside, whether the engineers of that machinery do not become fascinated with the turning wheels for their own sake. For this reason I think it highly important that there do enter in sceptical, simple minded people from the outside each year, who query the "Operations". I hope this will always remain the policy of the Foundation. It is with the feeling that someone must do this that I am willing to try, though the endeavor is really far from my experience or ambitions.[4]

The practice of importing outstanding scientists as assistant directors for terms of a year or less no doubt had merits, but also inherent handicaps. A new division head administered a program shaped by someone else, and in turn placed his stamp on that of his successor.[5] If inexperienced in federal budget-making and administrative procedures, he often suffered bafflement and frustration, especially if he hoped to achieve quick changes during his brief stay. Persons skilled in university politics and administration perhaps adjusted more easily to the ways of government than those who had spent most of their time in the lecture room and laboratory.

Waterman abandoned the rotation system for BMS assistant directors after Blinks's return to Stanford. John Wilson, who headed the psychobiology research program and had acted as the division director once before, was named assistant director in 1955 and continued in the position until 1961, when he left NSF to join the University of Chicago as special assistant to the president.

But the search continued to find someone to head the MPE division. Raymond J. Seeger, who had been employed to be the program director for physics research, long held the assistant director's position in an acting capacity while Waterman tried to recruit eminent physical scientists to accept a year's appointment. Early in 1954 Waterman thought that Harvard physicist J. Curry Street might be interested, but Street's active research program at the Brookhaven National Laboratory made him reluctant to take on an administrative chore. Besides, Street had become alarmed by rumors about an impending shift to NSF of ONR and AEC support of university basic research—a mistaken policy, he thought. Waterman, who was in the middle of the negotiations for the executive order dealing with this problem, was acutely conscious of such fears, and he tried to assure Street that "an internal staff paper from the Bureau of the Budget which seems to have had wide circulation ... has no official status"; NSF hoped to expand federal support of basic research, not consolidate it. Unable to get Street, Waterman made renewed efforts to recruit physicists Frederick Seitz of the University of Illinois and Robert Brode of the University of California at Berkeley.[6] Failing again, he continued Seeger in the acting position until 1957, when a one-year appointment was accepted by E. A. Eckhardt, a retired geophysicist who had long directed research for the Gulf Research and Development Company and had recently headed an NSF committee investigating the desirability of establishing a geophysical institute in Hawaii. Finally, in the summer of 1958, Randal M. Robertson, a physicist and scientific director in ONR, accepted an appointment on a permanent rather than a rotating basis.[7]

In contrast to the transitory or "acting" leadership of the research divisions, the Foundation's education programs remained under the continuous direction of Harry Kelly. Two others of Waterman's principal early appointments, however, left NSF in the middle 1950s—Sunderlin, the deputy director, for a position in Belgium, and Harwood, the assistant director for administration, for one in Iran. The director decided not to appoint another deputy, in part perhaps because he had by this time established a second associate directorship.[8]

Research and educational program directors were also recruited occasionally as "rotators" for terms of one or two years, but generally the persons holding these operating-level positions qualified for Blinks's designation of "permanent staff." Thus in the life sciences division the programs of environmental, molecular, regulatory, systematic, and psychological biology had the same directors throughout the period 1954-57, as did those of chemistry, mathematics, and physics in the physical sciences division. Although some research program staffs consisted only of a scientist head and a secretary, normally there was also a professional assistant and occasionally a clerk-typist. With the help of a few administrative persons in the assistant director's office, the specialized programs maintained considerable autonomy and offered unusual opportunity—unusual in government service at least—for their heads to acquire feelings of importance and leadership.

"Everyone wants to be a program director" was repeated so often in staff meetings that it became an adage. While usually aimed at top officials who were "interfering" in operations, the saying reflected the satisfactions of independence and status enjoyed by the key program administrators. " . . . it is really the program director's decision that counts," one of them commented on his experience in NSF. "Of course, officially he only recommends, but if his recommended decision is not illegal, immoral, or fattening it's going to stick. And we used to fight to establish this right in the old days."[9] Through reviewing proposals the program director kept abreast of new developments and ideas across the whole range of his discipline and throughout the nation. In panel meetings and conferences he formed friendships with the leaders of his profession. As a patron of research he could bask in reflected glory when one of the scientists in his "stable" won election to the National Academy or the ultimate distinction, the Nobel prize. There were dangers of ego inflation of course—he might be dubbed "Mr. Chemistry" or "Mr. Molecular Biology" by introducers at science conventions—but he did occupy a central position in his discipline and had a chance to influence its directions, not only through his recommendations on proposals but more importantly through budgeting for his program. Since budget-making was a long-term process, permanent program directors had a decided advantage over rotators; often it took two or three years to formulate a rationale and justification for a "new thrust" and to persuade one's superiors of its desirability.[10]

Nearly all of the program directors were men, but in the life sciences division and in the offices which gathered, studied, and disseminated science information women filled many positions as professional assistants and research analysts. In his public speeches Waterman several times emphasized the need to attract women into scientific careers—a need heightened by the concern during the 1950s over severe "manpower" shortages in science and engineering.[11] These statements might have been less frequent had his speech writer been a man rather than the talented Lee Anna Embrey, but there is no reason to question their sincerity. Virginia Sides, looking backward from the days of the women's liberation movement, thought "it quite remarkable that [Waterman] was as unsex-biased as almost anybody you could think of at the time. . . . I think he probably always had a feeling that women in science were perfectly acceptable people."[12] Certainly, however, the membership of NSF's divisional committees and advisory panels showed the dominance of science by men. The Foundation's annual report for fiscal 1954 showed that Katharine McBride was still the only woman member of a divisional committee, and all of the 112 members of advisory panels were men. Four years later Mary I. Bunting, dean of Douglass College of Rutgers University, had joined McBride on the SPE divisional committee (as some years later she would join her on the National Science Board), and four women sat with 151 men on advisory panels.[13]

* * *

Jack Teeter, who had an unshakable conceit that it was his political magic that had caused the creation of the National Science Foundation, stopped by Vannevar Bush's office in the spring of 1954 to complain about Alan Waterman. Teeter reported that people on Capitol Hill "seem to think that the NSF needs a good 'goose.' " Under Waterman's "too passive" direction NSF had "fallen into the 'old school tie' control"—Teeter's shorthand for the National Academy of Sciences—"and has no one who understands political maneuver or the approach to Congress. The time is ripe now for the N.S.F. to take the lead but there must be stronger men at the helm. If they do not accept the leadership now Congress will assume them incapable and the other agencies will keep the N.S.F. in wraps." Bush answered that he was "just as troubled about it as you are"; it seemed clear to him "that the Science Foundation now has to do a job or else disappear from the scene as far as any strong influence is concerned."[14]

Aside from engaging in a favorite pastime of stirring up trouble, Teeter may have been reflecting accurately congressional unhappiness about the Foundation. In the recent House budget hearings Republican committee members had let Waterman know that they considered coordination of federal research NSF's most important job, and they deplored the agency's failure to perform it.[15] Still, in its action on NSF's budget request for fiscal 1955 the House treated the agency better than usual. Heretofore the House had voted—as it would again the following year—to keep the appropriation at about the current level, which was always substantially below the request in the President's budget. Partial rectification came in the Senate and in the compromise figure agreed to in conference. The table summarizes NSF's appropriation history, 1951-58, excluding the supplemental appropriation for fiscal 1958 and IGY appropriations.

NSF Appropriations, 1951-58
(**dollars in thousands**)

FY	President's budget	Approved by House	Approved by Senate	Final appropriation
1951	$ 475	$ 0	$ 225	$ 225
1952	14,000	300	6,300	3,500
1953	15,000	3,500	6,000	4,750
1954	12,250	5,724	10,000	8,000
1955	14,000	11,000	14,000	12,250
1956	20,000	12,250	20,000	16,000
1957	41,300	35,915	41,300	40,000
1958	65,000	40,000	40,000	40,000

The table does not show the reductions, often substantial, in NSF's requests to the Bureau of the Budget. In the fiscal 1956 submission, for example, the Foundation asked for $23.6 million, despite the President's call for bare-bones estimates. Challenged in the Bureau's hearing, Waterman argued that greater support of basic research was an essential "antidote" to the overwhelming federal emphasis on applied research and, in addition, a good way of increasing the supply of highly trained scientists and engineers. When the Bureau nevertheless set a figure of $15.9 million, the NSF director and his senior staff mustered eight "cogent reasons" why the Foundation's research request should be restored, and cited in defense of its science education budget the draft report of a special interdepartmental committee which pointed out the threat to "our way of life" in the growing numbers and quality of Russian scientists and engineers.

In justification of the fiscal 1956—and later—estimates Waterman referred to Executive Order 10521 and statements of Presidents Truman and Eisenhower that NSF should become "increasingly responsible" for government sponsorship of general-purpose basic research. Yet the agency's fraction of the total was "ridiculously small." So too was basic research itself in comparison to applied—only about $130 million out of a total federal R&D budget of $2 billion in 1954—and this gross imbalance deflected universities from their traditional and proper function of advancing fundamental knowledge. Proposals from academic scientists showed that many highly qualified scientists wanted to undertake important investigations but were stymied because the Foundation's budget could fund only a fraction of their projects. Research support increased the number and enriched the education of graduate students who found employment as research assistants—a better kind of training, some thought, than that furnished by fellowships, and like fellowships "vital in improving or indeed maintaining our position in scientific manpower relative to the U.S.S.R."[16]

These arguments, varied and amplified in later years and tied together with a national security ribbon, were insufficiently persuasive in the White House and Congress to yield massive budget increases before the first Sputnik launchings, but they did result in growth that seemed fairly impressive at the time.

NSF's appeal to the Bureau in 1954 (on the fiscal 1956 budget) managed to get much of the original request restored, though the Budget Director thought "it was a risk in going to Congress with as high an amount" as $20 million.[17] Two years later a deep cut in the agency's preliminary estimate for fiscal 1958—from $104 million to $55 million—caused Waterman to consider a direct appeal to the President. The Foundation had predicated its estimate on a national emergency in science, one which required provision of the "raw material" of new knowledge for military and industrial development; protection of colleges and universities against loss of their science faculty members to industry; "identification, motivation and training of boys and girls with aptitude for science, beginning in secondary schools"; and support of such costly research facilities as radio and optical astronomical observatories, nuclear reactors and accelerators, university computers, and specialized biological laboratories.[18]

These ambitious plans failed to sway Budget Director Percival F. Brundage, whose hold-the-line policy was reinforced by a letter from Albert Thomas. Congress had allowed a big increase (from $16 million to $40 million) in NSF's budget the year before, and Thomas let the Administration know that he would not approve a further rise "until some tangible results can be appraised." Brundage first told Waterman that the Bureau would allow a request of $60 million, but when the NSF director protested, Brundage slashed another $5 million.[19] Angered by this bullying technique, Waterman discussed with Gabriel Hauge in the White House a personal appeal to Eisenhower, but held it in abeyance when Brundage said he did not really object to a $60 million figure. Earlier Waterman and Bronk, who was now chairman of the National Science Board, had agreed that NSF should present the matter to the President if the Bureau cut the estimate below $75 million, but Brundage finally persuaded them not to "press the matter further." As it turned out, another $5 million was added when the President submitted his budget to Congress.[20] This time the Senate failed to follow its usual practice. It agreed with the House in holding NSF's budget at the current level. But soon national alarm over Russian technological feats and a crumbling of faith in American public schools and primacy in science prepared the way for crash programs in education and research and big budgets in the years ahead.

* * *

When budget hearings moved from the Executive Office Building to Capitol Hill, Waterman and his colleagues entered a very different world. Here bureaucratic and scientific abstractions had to be explained to laymen who spoke the language of Main Street. Congressmen, addressing the witnesses as "Doctor"—often, one suspects, with mock deference—and betraying a profound ignorance of differences between science and technology and between basic and applied research, almost invited patronizing lectures from their scientist supplicants. Question and answer sometimes sailed by like ships in the night just barely in hailing distance.

In the pre-Sputnik years hearings on NSF's regular appropriation never lasted more than two days—one before the House appropriations subcommittee and one before the Senate. The Senate hearings were usually perfunctory but not those before the House subcommittee. There NSF witnesses were often subjected to detailed section-by-section quizzing and homilies on what the agency could and should do.

Except for two years (1953-54) when Republicans controlled Congress, Albert Thomas presided over the annual House hearings like a benevolent despot. When in the minority he answered Republican carping about the Foundation's failure to coordinate federal science by arguing that Congress had given the agency "a lot of pleasant words" but no real authority. After his return to the chair, however, he discovered in NSF's basic act an "artfully drawn" array of implied powers. "I think you can do anything on earth under it," he told Waterman. "Do not ever change it, because if you do, you might cut off some of your authority."[21]

Some of NSF's activities Thomas considered a waste of time and money. He derided the gathering of data on research expenditures as "chasing rabbits." These "science policy" studies would cause NSF to "bog down in statistics and paperwork" and divert it from its main work of educating enough scientists to meet the Soviet challenge. Thomas's worries about Russia—and about Texas—largely determined his views on the programs the Foundation should emphasize. He knew that most academics disliked loyalty oaths but warned that Congress would not "tolerate your spending money to send some of these Communist boys to school." For a while he shared some of his colleagues' skepticism about Russian scientific capabilities; but then he read Nicholas DeWitt's *Soviet Professional Manpower* (1955), a heavily documented book sponsored and published by NSF, which completely reversed his ideas and fed his fear that nuclear physicist Edward Teller's dark portrayal of Russia's scientific progress and America's inadequacies might be accurate after all.[22]

To Waterman and the National Science Board the support of basic research in university laboratories was NSF's paramount mission. Thomas had a higher priority. To him the fundamental problem was the shortage of scientists "that is created by a lack of high-school teachers." He thought

DeWitt's book ought to be placed in the hands of every high school superintendent in the country, and he startled Waterman at a hearing in 1956 by asking if NSF could not use $9-10 million instead of the $3 million it requested to modernize science and mathematics instruction in secondary schools through a program of institutes for their teachers. Thomas and others on the committee evidently saw the new program as a way not only of strengthening American science but also of providing federal aid for education without accompanying federal control.[23]

Besides helping to reach these goals the institutes program could benefit many colleges and universities that failed to win NSF's research funds—teachers colleges in East Texas, for instance. Stephen F. Austin State College in Thomas's home town applied for support of a summer institute, and the congressman wrote the Foundation in its behalf. Waterman, fearful that the college might accept only white teachers and thus not qualify for a grant, talked with White House officials—first Hauge and then Maxwell Rabb, secretary to the Cabinet—for suggestions of ways to avoid offending the powerful chairman. Rabb advised Waterman to let Thomas know of NSF's integration policy "to avoid having a burning issue arise." It turned out that there was no obstacle, and soon Waterman happily informed Thomas that the Nacogdoches institution had been selected, and that Baylor University, Southern Methodist University, and the University of Texas would also serve as hosts to summer institutes.[24]

Thomas's frequent importuning bothered the NSF director, who earnestly tried to keep his agency above politics. But Thomas obviously considered his entreaties normal and appropriate for a congressman in a position to exert influence. In a sense, NSF belonged to him. He enjoyed his colloquies with the distinguished board members who testified at NSF's hearings, and he urged Waterman to bring the entire board with him, or if not all 24 at once, at least 10 or 12.[25] He encouraged NSF support for the research of an Iowa doctor friend and for several medical researchers in Houston, for joint funding by NSF and AEC of a nuclear reactor in Texas, for the establishment of a center in Houston to evaluate American and foreign scientific work, and even asked for the drafting of a baccalaureate address he was to give at East Texas State Teachers College.[26] The commencement address breached none of Waterman's canons, but NSF may have bent its rules on the selection of research projects. Internal NSF communications show Waterman's and Klopsteg's sensitiveness to Thomas's pressure but also the firmness of some NSF program staff in adhering to regular procedures and standards of quality.[27]

Thomas's interventions on behalf of his friends and congressional district may have produced little except headaches for the Foundation, but his dominance of the Independent Offices subcommittee certainly helped shape the agency's program. Though sure that his Republican colleagues' attempt to require NSF to "coordinate" federal science—that is, reduce government spending—would result in nothing more than windmill-jousting, he did, when he returned to the chair, continue their opposition to an increase in the Foundation's staff and budget. The subcommittee thought as he did that many of the science policy studies were "of doubtful value and should be curtailed."[28] But if he and his fellows were niggardly in approving appropriations, he tried to break the Foundation's prudent behavior patterns. In shifting from a narrow to a broad interpretation of NSF's charter he stopped scoffing at the Foundation's impotence and led Waterman and the board members who accompanied him to a vista of ample opportunities in science education, including subsidy of educational institutions.[29]

Thomas was unpredictable and therefore unsettling to NSF officials. In the 1955 hearing he took them by surprise by accusing the agency of controlling academic science: NSF's consultants and panels were hired to do its bidding. This charge especially disturbed Waterman, who believed that individual researchers not only should but did determine the course of science.[30] While Thomas in later years occasionally expressed concern about federal sapping of institutional autonomy, he seems to have worried less as his vision of national need and of NSF's possibilities broadened along with his power to guide the Foundation.

The Senate proved much more generous than the House in furnishing the means by which NSF financed its gradually expanding programs in the 1950s. No senator, however, ever played a part approaching Thomas's in importance to the Foundation or loomed so large and constantly in the thoughts of Waterman and his associates.

* * *

Thomas's allegation that NSF's consultants simply ratified agency decisions may have contained some truth—but not much. Of course staff members did not merely transmit suggestions gleaned from their scientific communities; their own interests, ambitions, and sense of what needed doing naturally affected their recommendations on program budgets and grant awards. Yet their unceasing contacts with proposers of research or educational projects, participants in specialized conferences, and members of ad hoc committees, advisory and review panels, and divisional committees exposed them to a wide range of ideas from the "Republic of Science."[31] They filtered these ideas and came to judgments on priorities; but these judgments were still subject to review, modification, and reversal. Waterman had good reason for believing that NSF did not "mastermind" the direction of science but reflected instead its autonomous decisions.

The diverse influences of the outside scientific world on particular programs and budgetary decisions are evident in the advice given the Foundation in the meetings of its divisional committees.[32] In these sessions heads of NSF divisions and programs won strong backing for well-conceived experiments, but often got temporizing requests for further study of risky projects and half-baked notions. As partisans of the programs they counseled, members of a research divisional committee usually managed to gain not the preponderant budgets they might want, but a rough equivalence with the other research division, since Waterman and a few chief advisers, on the staff and on the board, discreetly maintained enough of a balance to avert internecine warfare.

In fact, for most of the pre-Sputnik period the Foundation held to its policy of equal budgets for BMS and MPE research projects, though a reduction in the Defense Department's basic research budget in fiscal 1955 resulted in a temporary larger allocation (but by no means equaling the $3 million Defense cut) to MPE programs.[33] But when the Foundation began to support such costly research facilities as astronomical observatories, nuclear reactors, and university computers the scale tipped heavily on the MPE side. The education and manpower programs administered by the SPE division failed to grow proportionately with those of research, until the House subcommittee gave NSF its big, unwanted boost for institutes for high school teachers. The following table shows obligations for research and education programs through fiscal year 1958.

NSF Obligations, FY 1952-58
(dollars in millions)

	1952	1953	1954	1955	1956	1957	1958
Basic research grants							
BMS	$0.8	$0.8	$2.0	$3.6	$4.8	$7.4	$8.5
MPE	0.3	1.0	2.0	4.4	4.7	7.6	9.4
Social science	—	—	—	—	—	0.3	0.6
Antarctic	—	—	—	—	—	—	0.9
Research facilities							
BMS	—	—	—	—	0.1	0.9	1.0
MPE	—	—	—	—	0.4	4.5	5.0
Education							
Fellowships	1.5	1.4	1.9	1.8	2.1	3.4	5.6
Other education programs	*	*	0.2	0.3	1.4	10.9	13.7

*Less than $100,000.
Source: NSF annual reports, 1952-58.

While marshaling arguments for more favorable treatment of their division as a whole, members of a research divisional committee also wrestled with the problem of allocations of funds to its specialized programs. Here the heterogeneity of MPE programs (astronomy, chemistry, earth sciences, engineering, mathematics, and physics) and their organization along traditional departmental lines caused difficulties that the close kinship and functional organization of the biological programs did not present. Proposal pressure—that is, the number and dollar amount of meritorious proposals—was generally considered the principal element in determining a rational distribution of funds. MPE divisional committee members, who threshed over the allocation dilemma at nearly every meeting, hoped that better information on the numbers of researchers in each discipline and on available research funds might make it possible to construct a sophisticated formula for long-term budget planning. But for the short term, they agreed, data on meritorious proposals received by each program would have to serve—at least for 90 percent of the research grant funds available to the division; the other 10 percent should be reserved for flexible use by the division director.[34]

The "meritorious proposal" formula method of allocation soon had its critics. Divisional committee members representing engineering became "perturbed at the apparent relative low ratings of engineering sciences proposals and the possible restriction on program funds," and Seeger soon told the committee that it was "highly desirable to eliminate a noncooperative spirit of competition that is incipient within the Division, and at the same time to put the matter of fund distribution on a more stable basis."[35] By March 1956 the committee recognized that a rigid formula based on meritorious proposals had not worked well and threatened to "lead to an inflation of ratings" which could undermine the peer review system. Instead, budget allocations (which must not be made without the NSF director's approval) should take several factors into account: the previous year's budget; the number and dollar amount of program proposals over a period of several years; support from sources other than the Foundation; measures of research potential such as numbers of doctorates and graduate students; and such special considerations as the need to develop new research fields and encourage young Ph.D.'s.[36] Even so, proposal pressure continued to be the main justification both for requests to Congress for an overall increase in NSF's research budget and for allocations of this increase among the disciplines.

The MPE divisional committee spent much more time reviewing the detailed operations of the several disciplinary programs and recommendations of their advisory panels than did the members of the BMS committee. The two research committees not only functioned differently, but quite separately. Information on activities in the other—and rival—research division came mainly through comments by the director.

Well-wrought minutes which generalize rather than proceed methodically through a committee's agenda usually give an impression of coherent, germane debate ending in clear decisions. So it is with the summaries of the BMS advisory group's sessions in the 1950s. Obviously the biologists' counselors must have indulged in a good deal of rambling, off-the-point talk, but the record shows purpose and coherence. Rather in contrast to their MPE counterparts, they seem to have had nearly complete confidence in the good sense of the BMS staff and gladly joined their efforts to explore innovative ways of advancing biological research and research training. While the MPE committee listened to detailed, quantitative analyses of program operations, argued over self-serving recommendations from disciplinary panels (whose chairmen sometimes met with the committee), and warily tried to ensure that proposals to support large-scale physical facilities would not cut into the budget for individual research projects, the BMS advisers quickly dispatched the review of past activities, acted on suggestions of staff-named ad hoc committees rather than program panels, and pushed the director and board to experiment with broader, more flexible forms of research support than the project grant.

Yet the committees had common concerns, ranging from the relatively minor but remarkably irritating matter of insufficient travel money—for themselves, staff, panel members, and American delegates to international conferences—to budgetary provision for expensive research equipment and facilities. (These two concerns, in fact, were constants.) Consensus on plans and proposals for large facilities was of course an essential element in building NSF's case for larger appropriations, and long before a facilities "line item" appeared in the budget it had been argued at length in committee.

In the MPE group, disciplinary rivalries hampered the reaching of agreement on large facilities, but by January 1957 the committee had settled on several general principles. Although NSF should continue to put most emphasis on research projects, the committee recognized that "in many areas the large facilities are essential if science is to progress on a broad front." The job of setting priorities was one for the staff and board. In view of the enormous need for facilities—$350 million over a five-year period in the physical sciences alone, according to NSF staff studies—and the inadequacy of money to build them, evenhanded treatment of all fields of science was out of the question. The committee hoped that the director and board would "have the courage to support many which are not popular choices in that they help only one area of science, though they do this at a critical stage. The best guide is the enthusiastic endorsement of the working scientists—not the promoters—of the discipline in question."[37]

The BMS committee, conscious of its handicaps in competing for equal funding against costly but salable physical science facilities and against popular medical research laboratories which were becoming available through NIH's spreading programs, endeavored to stake claims in NSF's budget to meet a variety of needs in biological research. Relying on suggestions of inventive staff members and ad hoc groups of specialists, the committee encouraged support for biological field stations, laboratories for germ-free animal research, controlled environment chambers for plant experiments (phytotrons, or "goldplated greenhouses"[38]), equipment for general use or too expensive to include in an ordinary research grant, and graduate laboratories in universities. Constituting themselves as a review panel, the divisional committee assayed the findings of "site-visit teams" in order to recommend the support or declination of proposals of these kinds. Through these actions the committee helped establish a program of basic research facilities in the biological sciences, set policy and precedents on a case-by-case method, extended the coverage of project awards to expensive equipment, and prepared the way for an autonomous graduate-laboratories program by the end of the decade.

Considerably more than either of the research divisional committees, that for SPE actively participated in the planning of the programs under its jurisdiction. Meeting four times a year—more frequently than the research advisers—the SPE group developed rapport both with the NSF staff and with the board SPE committee, with which it regularly held a joint annual meeting. Besides giving advice on programs—at first only fellowships and the National Register—and their budgets, the divisional committee dealt with broader questions of NSF's relation to the U.S. Office of Education and to a presidential committee created in response to a growing worry about shortages of scientists and engineers. But most important, the divisional committee stimulated the SPE staff to think of ways to extend NSF's educational activities beyond the apparently narrow range authorized by the agency's charter.

Finding no authority for educational support except through scholarships and fellowships and the exchange of scientific information, NSF's director and general counsel long thought that amendments to the act would be required before the Foundation could yield to pressure from staff and committee for new programs, except "experimental" ones of limited duration under the mandate to develop national science policy for education in the sciences. Checkreined by this limitation, the staff nonetheless displayed ingenuity in suggesting ideas for experiments in education in the sciences, and the divisional committee subjected them to rigorous but sympathetic criticism. In time, as Albert Thomas told Waterman that the Foundation could "do anything on earth" it wanted to, and as Congress earmarked about a quarter of NSF's budget for heretofore "experimental" institutes for high school teachers, the agency's strict interpretation of its charter began to appear much too conservative.

New departures began slowly, but even before the orbiting of Soviet sputniks opened the floodgates, NSF had undertaken a variety of educational activities that capitalized on the rising concern about national security. The following chapter describes the Foundation's broadening educational mission.

12
Quality and Quantity in Science Education

In the tug of war between elitists and levelers the National Science Foundation has nearly always pulled for the quality side. Most of its research grants have gone to the best scientists who, quite naturally, happened to be at the best universities. Its fellows, whose right to choose their graduate schools was one of NSF's firmest principles, have flocked to an embarrassingly small number of these same institutions. At the start the Foundation committed itself to excellence. James B. Conant, echoing his earlier words in *Science—The Endless Frontier*, wrote in NSF's first annual report: "In the advance of science and its application to many practical problems, there is no substitute for first-class men. Ten second-rate scientists cannot do the work of one who is in the first rank." He charitably omitted his earlier slight that "second-class men often do more harm than good."[1]

Yet egalitarian pressures and regional demands have brought change. Though mainly coming from the outside, as when Congress required a huge increase in the teachers' institutes program, the impulses for broadening and diversifying the Foundation's activities have often originated in the staff or its advisory groups.

In the 1950s external and internal forces combined to break down some of the walls around NSF's education programs. Well before Sputnik raised general alarm about the quality of American education, thoughtful observers of the nation's schools had begun to focus on the inadequacies of their teachers and curricula as a central problem. Better pay, the critics believed, would attract and retain a larger number of competent teachers. Better textbooks and visual aids would stimulate students' interest in fundamental subjects, inspire more of those who were talented to enter college, and give them a firmer foundation for college-level study. Instructional deficiencies were not only in science and mathematics of course—the high school coach was more apt to teach social studies than physics—but Cold War fears made science and mathematics seem crucial, and more and more critics of "progressive" education concluded that "Life-adjustment educators would do anything in the name of science except encourage children to study it."[2]

Alarm over Soviet scientific progress spurred not only Congress but also the Cabinet and led to the establishment of first an interdepartmental and later a presidentially appointed national committee to awaken the country to a dangerous shortage of scientists and engineers. The Foundation resisted this intrusion into what it considered its business and worried that the Cabinet-inspired move might cause panicky crash programs. Unable to prevent the appointment of the national committee, NSF nonetheless urged that it give primacy to quality, not numbers.

The Foundation's advice boiled down essentially to this: Improve science and mathematics instruction in schools and colleges. Motivate more bright students to go to college. Sift choice grain from the baccalaureate chaff for graduate training in science and engineering. Furnish greater opportunity and more money for basic research. Through such an interrelated program NSF would brush up the old Jeffersonian design for providing the nation with an aristocracy of talent.

But the proposed school reforms required either amendment or looser interpretation of the Foundation's charter. When Harry Kelly's SPE staff members advocated new programs that did not clearly fall under one of the statute's few authorizations for science education, the director on advice of counsel suggested the necessity of charter amendments. Repeatedly considered, charter revisions kept being deferred, largely because they might threaten local control of schools or open troublesome conflicts with the U.S. Office of Education. In the long run Congress helped resolve the dilemma by ignoring the statutory limitations that bothered Waterman and his general counsel. And after Sputnik even the Bureau of the Budget acknowledged that NSF had ample authority for its program of education in the sciences.

* * *

No question of legality affected the awarding of fellowships, but the NSF act did contain restrictions on the selection of recipients. A provision that a fellow should be selected only because of his ability suited the

Foundation's policy makers, as did the fellow's right to choose where he wanted to study. Still, these statutory terms caused difficulties for the staff in picking fellows and in answering charges of elitism. The further stipulation that wide geographic distribution should influence choice among applicants of substantially equal ability added another complication.

A sketch of the procedures followed in selecting a single class of graduate fellows may help to clarify some of the complications and give a basis for understanding the criticisms of NSF's principal fellowship program in the pre-Sputnik years.

In March 1954 the National Science Board approved Waterman's recommendation to award 657 predoctoral fellowships and honorable mention to 1,355 other finalists in the competition. The awards resulted from 2,865 applications sent to the National Research Council, which under its contract with NSF established screening panels consisting of 122 scientists (selected for field of science and geographic distribution). The screening, costing the Foundation $135,000, resulted in lists of the applicants in six quality groups, those in each group being considered as of approximately equal ability. The SPE staff decided that the program had enough money to recommend all the applicants in the top quality group and 52 percent of those in the second. All other finalists in the second, third, and fourth quality groups were proposed for honorable mention—a category intended to help graduate schools recruit teaching assistants. A slightly higher percentage (28.5) of life science finalists were recommended for fellowships than those in the mathematical, physical, and engineering sciences (26.3), but there were nearly three times as many finalists in the latter group. Distribution by subject-matter field was similar to doctoral degrees awarded in the years 1949-53, but percentages of fellowship awards were somewhat lower in the life sciences and quite a bit higher in physics and astronomy. Only four states were unrepresented among the successful applicants; but once again institutions chosen for graduate study showed a heavy concentration, though twenty schools had not been on the list the year before.[3]

The Foundation's arrangements with NRC provided that the top quality group would contain substantially fewer candidates than the number of projected awards. While this disposition meant that the SPE staff would have to fill many slots (255 in 1954) from about equally able persons in the second quality group, it allowed leeway for balancing years of graduate study, fields of science, and states and regions of residence. The choices were not easy but they were impersonal; they did not involve rescreening of applicants' papers or ad hominem arguments. Much as if they were manipulating a complicated formula, the staff of the fellowship program shuffled cards so that the selections would first meet the statutory requirement of wide geographical distribution and then fit NSF's policy emphasizing the first year of graduate study and ensure a defensible spread among science fields.[4]

The Foundation's fellowship policies did not suit everyone. Sharply differing views of spokesmen for particular disciplines or graduate schools generated several suggestions for changes. A chemist on the MPE divisional committee argued that NSF's awards for beginning graduate study did not really increase graduate enrollment; the first-year fellows would have entered graduate school anyway. (But while most of the exceptionally capable and ambitious NSF fellows would have found other sponsors, graduate enrollments could expand if universities maintained their own fellowships and teaching assistantships.)[5] Some persons wanted to discontinue awards to second-year fellows, both to reduce the shortage of qualified teaching assistants and to ensure that good students gained valuable teaching experience. Others favored nearly automatic renewals or making the original awards two-year fellowships. (Though acknowledging the benefits of teaching experience, NSF raised a barrier against it by normally prohibiting additional compensation during a fellow's tenure.)[6] The achievement of balance among fields of science, with applications and awards nearly in proportion, failed to attack personnel shortages in critical areas (e.g., nuclear engineering and aeronautical engineering); some persons wanted special fellowships established for this purpose. (But the fragility of information on critical areas made it difficult to set priorities and devise a special program. Perhaps for this purpose institutes would be preferable to fellowships.)[7]

The concentration of fellows in a few institutions caused the strongest complaints. Waterman and most members of the board, like the SPE divisional committee, thought that the critics were unfair, and he argued against changing the law giving fellows freedom of choice. It was wise policy, he wrote a board member,

that in the best interest of progress in science . . . the top candidates for awards for graduate study . . . be permitted to select the institutions at which they wish to study. This is a small group, after all, less than two per cent of the whole graduate school population. Such a highly selected group presumably will make their selection with the best advice and in general exercise good judgment. This policy was explained clearly to the Congress and was not questioned. After all, it is a good American custom. Any alternative whereby they are allocated to certain schools would certainly, in my opinion, bring out much stronger reactions in opposition. Among these would be government control of science, directly or indirectly. I do not mean to imply that we do not understand the criticisms which have been voiced. We are well aware of these. However, it seems to me that the situation will tend to correct itself automatically.[8]

Explaining the policy to the president of the American Council on Education, Waterman said that NSF considered a fellowship to be support for an individual, not an institution, "and should be administered with the welfare of the individual pre-eminent." He did not see anything critical in the concentration.[9]

Yet the concentration of fellows did not automatically correct itself, and the only obvious cure—limiting freedom of choice—remained unacceptable to the Foundation, which took some comfort in the fact that each year some fellows chose schools that had not been selected before. Just one NSF fellow at an undistinguished university, Kelly argued, "exerts a disproportionately large salutary effect on the department and school. His presence . . . evokes a local sense of pride, renewed effort, and higher standards on the part of both staff and other students." In addition, the SPE divisional committee believed, competition for the best students provided a valuable challenge to lesser known schools to gain on the leaders.[10]

The Micawberish attitude that things would get better ignored steady evidence to the contrary. Of the 1957-58 pre- and postdoctoral fellows, 129 chose to study at Harvard, the same number as the year before. The University of California at Berkeley and MIT were each selected by 66, Caltech and the University of Chicago by 51 each. Below these top five institutions were Princeton (43), Wisconsin (41), Stanford (38), Illinois (31), Columbia (30), Michigan (30), Cornell (29), and Yale (28). Only five other institutions were selected by as many as 10 fellows. While the 1957-58 fellows chose to attend 80 different U.S. institutions, four-fifths of the class gathered at only 18 graduate schools. Generally the leaders had held or increased their drawing power during the six years since the start of the program.[11]

Despite continued sniping from critics, NSF held its ground on fellows' free choice. The promise of a larger budget in the aftermath of Sputnik, however, opened a way for new forms of support for graduate training. At the end of 1957 Waterman responded to an Indiana professor's complaint about the piling up of NSF fellows with his standard defense that they had every right to attend the schools where they could get the best possible education. But he added: "While this is true of our regular predoctoral program, we feel that we now have a fellowship plan which will take care of the point that you mention."[12] Before long the Foundation would add to its roster of educational programs one for "cooperative graduate fellowships," which fostered much wider institutional participation in NSF-supported graduate study.

Meanwhile NSF had added two other fellowship programs and rejected ideas for several others. From the outset of the postdoctoral program the incongruous mixing of applications from mature scientists with those from new Ph.D.'s had caused difficulties, and in fiscal 1956 the Foundation began to award senior postdoctoral fellowships, intended to give opportunities to advanced scientists to study and do research in their special fields, gain interdisciplinary research skills, or revitalize their teaching by spending a year at centers where they could associate with productive scientists. Teachers who were eligible for sabbaticals but unable to take them on the usual half-salary basis tended to sink into a rut, repeating the same lectures and demonstrations year after year.[13]

The other new program aimed to improve science teaching in undergraduate colleges. Predictions of huge enrollments within a few years and doubts about the competence of college teachers, many of whom had dropped out of graduate school before earning the doctorate or had long been on the job without much chance to keep pace with advances in their subject, furnished justifications for college faculty fellowships. Obvious advantages of the program to NSF, which awarded 100 of the new fellowships in the first year (1957), were that it manifested an interest in undergraduate instruction and helped counter charges of elitism.[14]

Few substantial objections were raised to the inauguration of the senior postdoctoral and college faculty programs, but several other suggested kinds of fellowships failed to win approval. The divisional committee turned down a proposal of fellowships for government scientists and showed little enthusiasm for summer fellowships for high school teachers or for fellowships in critical areas of science and engineering. (NSF nevertheless requested funds for special or critical-areas fellowships for fiscal 1958. The committee after all was simply advisory.) Nor did the committee like the idea of awarding ten "distinguished service fellowships" a year to outstanding American scientists. Katharine McBride "questioned whether prizes are a meaningful way to build up prestige and suggested that the funds might be spent better for bona fide fellowships."[15]

The Foundation moved slowly toward awarding fellowships in the social sciences. Psychology (except clinical), physical anthropology, and physical geography were first to join the natural sciences, mathematics, and engineering. Later the defining adjective "physical" before anthropology and geography was dropped. In 1954, under the tutelage of Harry Alpert, a sociologist on the staff, NSF began to support basic research "in the areas of convergence of the natural sciences and social sciences," and the fellowship program, following suit, cited mathematical economics, demography, information and communication theory, and the history and philosophy of science as eligible "convergent" fields, along with interdisciplinary fields of the natural sciences and mathematics (e.g., biochemistry, biophysics, geochemistry, statistics and statistical design, and oceanography).[16] Three years later a cautious National Science Board sanctioned research support in particular social science areas that did not necessarily meet the convergence rule, and Alpert recommended that the fellowship program be similarly extended.[17] But Harry Kelly, the division head, opposed the inclusion of any named social sciences. He lost the argument and the fellowship announcement issued in the fall of 1958 finally let into the fold both the convergent fields and econometrics and sociology—apparently a dread word for some even though it was modified by "experimental and quantitative." Like "convergent areas" before, the newly eligible social sciences had to meet standards of "objectivity, verifiability and generality" that governed in the natural sciences.[18]

The NRC continued to handle the administrative chores of the pre- and postdoctoral fellowships, but Bowen Dees, who headed the programs, thought that the Foundation should take over most of these details though continuing to use the Educational Testing Service to administer examinations and NRC to select the screening panels and administer the review process. NSF control over fellowship administration, he argued, would eliminate confusion over responsibility for the programs, result in better management, ensure proper interpretation of Foundation policies, promote staff interest, and save money. Waterman called Dees's presentation of these arguments "an important paper to keep in mind," but he took no steps to carry out its recommendations. Bronk's presidency of the National Academy of Sciences may have kept the director from pursuing the idea. Later, when Kelly recommended that in the college faculty program NSF should ask the Association of American Colleges to evaluate applicants, he cleared the matter with Bronk, who "indicated that he would go along" but hoped the association would check with NAS-NRC for advice from scientists.[19]

NSF staff members also wanted to bring under Foundation control all federal general-purpose science fellowships, a plan fostered by the Bureau of the Budget. For a while there was movement toward this goal. AEC gave up its predoctoral awards and NIH soon followed, as the Foundation's fellowship budget was raised by an amount approximating that which NIH had been spending on its predoctoral program. But postdoctoral fellowships were another matter. For these NIH had a much larger budget than NSF, and while the two agencies discussed the feasibility of shifting "general purpose" or "non-disease-oriented" postdoctorals, the health agency decided to define practically all of its fellowships in "disease-oriented" or "special purpose" categories. It encouraged NSF to expand its own postdoctoral programs, but not at NIH's expense.[20]

More than that, in 1954 NIH decided to revive its predoctoral program at its former level. The agency's special relationship with Congress aided this move. When Waterman heard that NIH had asked its appropriations subcommittee for funds to restore the program, he assumed that the Budget Bureau must have approved the request. But NSF's fiscal officer, Franklin C. Sheppard, learned that the Bureau had received no advance information of NIH's plan.[21] There was nothing NSF could do to block the restoration. The NIH director told Waterman that his agency was "in full agreement with the NSF on the conditions under which this [is] undertaken, namely special training to round out the training of individuals who are expected to go into public health or related fields."[22]

By 1956 AEC concluded that NSF's fellowship programs were too puny to meet the needs for nuclear scientists and engineers. The Foundation had agreed that NIH had a right to award fellowships related to its mission, and it could hardly take a different stand with AEC. But Waterman pointed out to Willard F. Libby and Lewis Strauss of AEC that the stipends they proposed to offer were out of line with NSF's and those generally available in universities. He hoped the Commission's training grants would not be called fellowships, which properly meant awards based on merit and gave the recipients maximum freedom to decide where and how to study.[23]

Libby told Waterman that undergraduate scholarships were needed as well as graduate fellowships in "an all-out effort to train scientists and engineers in general and for nuclear engineering in particular." When Waterman said that other agencies should limit their training programs to their particular fields of interest, Libby

disclaimed any intent on the part of AEC to cover training in education in the sciences in general. He did remark, however, that AEC's position in all these matters was that they hoped the NSF would be able to take general responsibility for education and training in the sciences, but that if NSF was not successful in securing adequate funds they felt that they could broaden their activities to fill the gap. This is exactly typical of the AEC philosophy.[24]

NSF objected to proposed amendments to the AEC act that would give the Commission "additional general authority in connection with education and training of scientists, duplicating that already possessed by the National Science Foundation," though specific authority for "specialized training activities in fields directly related to the programs of the Commission" would be appropriate.[25] Responding to AEC suggestions of programs to speed the training of scientists and engineers, Waterman said that NSF did not favor undergraduate scholarships limited to science and doubted that loans would do much to stimulate college attendance. The improvement of high school and college science teaching was a general problem, not one suitable for specialized agencies. NSF should do more about the problem, but the entry of AEC or other mission agencies into the activity "could not help but lead to serious problems of coordination and duplication." Similarly Waterman tried to dampen AEC interest in other ideas for improving school and college education in science, though naturally he thought it "extremely important for the AEC to engage in programs within their specialized competence and responsibility directed toward training of persons in fields peculiary related to atomic energy."[26]

The proliferation of fellowship programs alarmed Bowen Dees. Not only did AEC intend to make awards to first-year graduate students in nuclear engineering, but there was "a strong possibility" that the agency would try to start a scholarship program for college seniors too. Plans were being made elsewhere for specialized fellowships in vocational rehabilitation and water-pollution control. The Defense Department was thinking about sponsoring fellowships in particular areas of the physical sciences. Congress was giving NIH even more money than it had asked for, and its fellowships might be expanded three or four times.[27] Any hope of the Foundation's controlling federal science fellowships faded, and even though various agency programs promised greater total support, the resulting competition compounded the problems of coordination of standards and stipends.[28]

Competition came from inside NSF too. Early in 1957 Waterman asked the board to approve two proposals recommended by the research divisions, one for thesis support of graduate biology students at Caltech, the other to aid graduate students in mathematics at Yale. To Dees and Kelly these grants would simply establish locally administered fellowship programs. Besides raising policy questions, the proposals carried "jurisdictional overtones" disturbing to domestic tranquillity within NSF. But on the ground that the grants were experimental means of supporting research, the board approved them.[29] The awards exemplified the wish of some staff members for broader forms of research support than simply the individual research project and for flexibility both for the Foundation and for the institutions winning its funds.[30]

* * *

Although Waterman told AEC that the Foundation opposed undergraduate scholarships limited to science students, this was hardly a firm conviction. For years NSF talked about, and sometimes halfheartedly proposed, starting a scholarship program. Ultimately the national anxiety about American education following Sputnik brought the simmering discussion to the boiling point and forced a resolution.

A decision to push for scholarships would have been easier if the difficulties of administering the program had not loomed so large. The same statutory requirements governing fellowships applied to scholarships. Ways of selecting scholars solely on the basis of ability, but widely distributed geographically, who could choose their colleges freely, challenged the ingenuity of scholarship proponents. While SPE staff members thought up ways around these obstacles, and even of taking students' financial means into consideration, they still faced the dilemma of whether it was right to single out science students for favored treatment. At the undergraduate level, nearly everyone agreed, a scholarship program should be across the board for all fields of study. Yet some held the pragmatic attitude "that there is often virtue in 'taking what one can get,' " and science scholarships might be justified as a pilot operation that would chart a course for a later general program.[31]

The Budget Bureau had rejected NSF's first request for $1 million for scholarships because of the possibility of a general program under the Federal Security Agency.[32] In 1953 Kelly again suggested asking for $1 million for scholarships (for fiscal 1955) even though the Bureau was still skeptical about such a program.[33] In August the Foundation called a two-day conference of representatives of several national associations of higher education to get their advice. While the educators held widely different views and offered many qualifications, an observer discerned a consensus that "the Foundation should support a nation-wide scholarship program of some type, and that such a program would not have adverse effects upon other fields of intellectual activity." Nevertheless NSF decided to put off requesting funds because of "the need for further study of the more basic problem of how to identify competence among our young people and to stimulate them to continue their training."[34]

Again the next year an SPE staff study recommended that the Foundation request $1 million for scholarships and outlined a plan for the testing and screening of high school seniors and the awarding of 1,200 to 1,500 scholarships, with stipends ranging from a nominal amount of $50 up to $1,000. (While ability would be the basis for selection, a scholar's financial need would determine the amount of the stipend.) Unsuccessful finalists would get certificates of merit—comparable to honorable mention in the predoctoral fellowship program—and a list of these meritorious students would be sent to all the nation's colleges for use in their recruiting efforts.[35] NSF senior staff members differed sharply on initiating the program, but a joint meeting of the board and divisional SPE committees gave it a qualified endorsement. After all, one board member observed, at the level of only $1 million the program would scarcely deflect large numbers of students away from other fields into science.[36]

To study the feasibility of a scholarship program and to develop plans for it, the Foundation turned to the College Entrance Examination Board. While awaiting the outcome of this study NSF again put off a request for funds.[37] Meanwhile a number of bills in Congress showed a rising public interest in federal loans or scholarships to encourage talented young people to enter college. The Foundation, when giving its views on these bills, showed its preference for scholarships over loans, and unfailingly dropped reminders that it had statutory authority to award them. But, as Waterman commented on one of these bills, "In general we feel that more staff work is needed before a Federal loan or scholarship program is inaugurated."[38]

Although the College Entrance Examination Board developed a standby program for NSF, the plan remained on the shelf. By the spring of 1955 the SPE divisional committee had concluded that scholarships were not the best means available to the Foundation to increase the number of qualified scientists. Any federal program should be general rather than limited to the sciences, but the committee "was not at all sure that it would enthusiastically endorse any scholarship program." In recommending that NSF not ask for scholarship funds for fiscal 1957, Kelly pointed to the increasing percentage of young people going to college and adopted the committee's view that improving the competence of high school teachers would better serve to interest students in science careers.[39] A year later NSF's preliminary budget estimates for fiscal 1958 included $12 million for an experimental program of four-year scholarships to test the validity of the argument that many able high school graduates who did not go to college would if they had the means, but there was not much steam behind the request. The divisional committee endorsed the experiment but urged that the request not exceed $4 million.[40] Even this amount got knocked out of the President's budget.

Until Sputnik NSF continued to show a disinclination to push for science scholarships. An editorial by Dael Wolfle in *Science* pointed out some of the reasons why, after long study, the agency had resisted the temptation "to be stampeded into adopting measures designed to strengthen science at the expense of other areas of human endeavor," and concluded: "In the long run it seems likely that science will profit at least as much from increasing the over-all number of students of high ability as it would from a more narrowly conceived effort, and that society as a whole will profit more."[41] A scholarship program was lumped with "Priority II Questions" by the SPE division near the end of 1956. Similarly Waterman told an insurance company vice-president who had written President Eisenhower about the need for federal science scholarships that the Foundation believed the first priority should be the improvement of instruction through the strengthening of high school and college teachers of science.[42]

Not even Sputnik—"a scientific Pearl Harbor" as Waterman called the Soviet satellite launch in speaking to the SPE divisional committee—resulted in NSF scholarships, though it did bring reconsideration of a program. Knowing that there would be enormous congressional pressure for the Foundation to "do something," Kelly's staff worked long hours and weekends from Thanksgiving to Christmas arguing over and revising budgets. One of these called for the astronomical sum of $248.3 million for SPE programs, including undergraduate scholarships despite "still serious reservations" about them. Although the divisional committee continued to take "a dim view of scholarships," the members did show alarm when they heard that the U.S. Office of Education (OE) might start a program limited to science and mathematics. They believed "it would be infinitely better to have the Foundation operate it by virtue of its statute, experience and trained personnel."[43]

Kelly never expected the quarter-billion dollar budget to be taken seriously, and at the same time he presented a much more modest proposal asking for $90 million. In still another revision he proposed NSF scholarships and a loan program, without requiring a means test, though "political and emotional reactions might force" one.[44]

Scholarships were only one of ten possible new education programs that Waterman discussed with James R. Killian, Jr., the newly appointed (and first) Special Assistant to the President for Science and Technology. And at the insistence of the Budget Bureau, which was showing concern about overlap in the science education plans of NSF and the Office of Education, discussions also occurred with OE officials. "Dr. Killian has played a key role in arriving at the final decision," Waterman told the National Science Board—a decision which followed conferences in the White House involving the Director of the Budget. The resulting delineation of the roles of NSF and OE reserved activities limited to science to NSF but provided that OE would propose a program of general scholarships for high school graduates.[45] The eventual outcome would be a program of student loans, not scholarships, and the effective end of NSF's sporadic, hesitant efforts to award them.

* * *

The Foundation also showed much hesitance in its early years about undertaking support of high school science. Doubtful authority was one reason, but more fundamental was the disparity between resources and problem: The chance that NSF's limited funds could make a significant change in the nation's schools seemed slim; better to spend the money on research and fellowships where it could make a difference. Apart from the lack of statutory obligation, some questioned whether the Foundation had even a right to engage in matters traditionally under state and local control. Whatever role the federal government had in schooling belonged to the Office of Education, and while NSF scientists sometimes looked down on OE's "educationists," they avoided provoking conflict with them. Still another reason for the hesitance was a feeling that the Foundation would demean itself by involvement with schools.[46] Small colleges, perhaps, since they had been remarkably productive of scientists and were widely regarded with sentimental affection. (Daniel Webster's plea for Dartmouth—"It is, sir, as I have said, a small college, and yet there are those who love it"—still struck a nostalgic chord.)

College teachers were, in fact, the beneficiaries of NSF's first two institute grants. In the summer of 1953 eighty-one college teachers, most of them without NSF stipends but attracted by the mountain setting and climate of Boulder, Colorado, assembled for eight weeks of lectures by distinguished mathematicians. The institute, or "conference," though sponsored by the University of Colorado at the Foundation's suggestion, had been planned and organized largely by the Committee on Regional Development of Mathematics of the Mathematical Association of America. Harry Kelly's practice, in this instance and later, of turning to a professional society to plan a program avoided the appearance of federal masterminding and fitted Waterman's philosophy of science policy-making by scientists themselves. The other 1953 institute was held at the University of Minnesota, where twenty-one physics teachers from small colleges in the Midwest and upper South attended a five-week summer session, along with a group of high school physics teachers in a companion institute supported by the Fund for the Advancement of Education.[47]

J. W. Buchta of the Minnesota physics department, who had promoted the latter institutes, had been pressing ideas for the improvement of science teaching on the Foundation almost from the beginning of the agency. His main interest was in gaining support for "summer institutes for selected high school teachers in various sciences and in different parts of the country," including one he proposed to NSF for his own campus. Unsuccessful at first in persuading the National Science Board to back the high school venture, he advanced the cause by getting help from a private foundation. Reports on the successful mixing of college and secondary school teachers in the 1953 Minnesota institutes eased NSF's tentative step down to the high school level the following year.[48]

Encouraged by his divisional committee, Kelly submitted a fairly ambitious plan for the 1954 summer program of Research Education in the Sciences. (This title, which almost invited incursions on SPE's domain by the two research divisions, was soon changed to Education in the Sciences.) Kelly proposed eleven college teachers institutes, eight of them in biology, chemistry, mathematics, and physics and three interdisciplinary; a program to bring outstanding scientists to small-college campuses for short periods to lecture, advise on research and curricula, and confer with students on career opportunities; and summer grants to college teachers to allow them to visit research centers. In addition, he suggested the awarding of one or two grants, comparable to one already made to Science Clubs of America, "to inform and encourage the qualified and interested youth of the nation who wish to consider science as a career."[49]

Associate Director Paul Klopsteg considered Kelly's plan too expansive,[50] and it was cut sharply. Three college teachers institutes were supported from the SPE budget, none of them interdisciplinary, and a fourth, emphasizing research, for college biology teachers by the BMS division at the University of Minnesota's summer station on Lake Itasca (again in conjunction with an institute for high school teachers supported by the Fund for the Advancement of Education). And NSF also decided to support a proposal from the University of Washington for a four-week conference for high school mathematics teachers. "The Office of Education was not entirely enthusiastic about the Foundation's supporting the Washington Conference," Kelly reported to his divisional committee, "but raised no objections."[51]

The "experimental" grant to the University of Washington, intended to help NSF decide whether it should have a program for high school science teachers, followed various successful institutes sponsored by industry, universities, and private foundations. These demonstrations encouraged NSF to make its first sortie into what it regarded as a dangerous area, but also one that was arousing more and more concern. Cold War worries about shortages of scientists and engineers were intensified by trenchant criticisms, like those of Arthur E. Bestor in *Educational Wastelands* (1953), of the failure of American schools to teach basic subjects. The scholarship conference held by NSF in the summer of 1953 often drifted into discussions of the importance of high school teachers as identifiers and motivators of talent and of the consequent need to increase their competence and interest.[52] Often untrained in the disciplines they were charged with teaching, they needed subject-matter instruction that might not be available to them in universities' regular summer sessions; if teachers were able to stretch their poor salaries to pay for summer school, they usually studied teaching methods or school administration instead of mathematics or chemistry.

NSF wanted the institutes to emphasize subject matter and keep courses in educational methods to a minimum. There were differences of opinion on the offering of academic credit, but since graduate training, and especially a master's degree, nearly always brought a better salary, most high school teachers preferred to receive credit. In time, among various forms, some "sequential" institutes permitted teachers to attend for several summers and earn a master's. "Unitary" institutes by contrast were one-shot affairs. Some institutes offered no credit, some only undergraduate, and some an option. Besides shaping institutes to meet diverse needs, NSF hoped to induce universities to change their normal academic-year and summer-session patterns so that they would regularly provide discipline-centered programs for schoolteachers—a hope that largely failed.[53]

Especially influential in promoting the institutes program was a University of Chicago mathematics professor who advised the SPE division in 1954-55. Eugene P. Northrop chose the title of "consultant" rather than program director—"a vacuous title in the absence of a program"—in part because it allowed him to serve concurrently as an adviser to the Fund for the Advancement of Education and to speak out freely on NSF's shortcomings. Northrop soon saw that instead of initiating educational activities NSF mainly reacted to occasional, unsolicited proposals. He set out to develop a coherent program to attract more bright young persons into scientific careers and to improve their education. While many factors that would affect the program were unknown, he argued that prudence should not stand in the way of action. Continuing study of means of identifying, stimulating, and educating scientifically talented youth could help sharpen the program later.[54]

Northrop chided NSF for spending so little money on education, apart from fellowships. The proposed 1956 budget called for $500,000 for education in the sciences, or only 2 percent of the total request, despite the division's recommendation of twice that amount and the approval by the SPE divisional and board committees of $750,000. Fortunately for his case, a draft report of an interdepartmental committee forced the Foundation to look again at its budget estimates and resulted in an increased allocation for fiscal 1955 and a revised request for as much as $1.5 million more, or a total of $2 million, for fiscal 1956.[55]

The increased request came to Albert Thomas while he still worried about federal bureaucratic controls over education and before he had read Nicholas DeWitt's *Soviet Professional Manpower*. Even so, thanks especially to the Senate, NSF's education in the sciences program ended up with an allocation of $1.3 million for fiscal 1956. The number of institutes grew from eleven in the summer of 1955 to twenty-seven the next year (two of them for a full academic year). The Foundation still regarded the teachers' program as experimental, but reports on the institutes and efforts to evaluate them showed that they were popular and helping to mitigate a big problem.[56]

Some members of NSF's board and staff, however, saw a trend that bothered them. William J. Hoff, the general counsel, believed that the continuation of institutes and some other educational activities "on an expanded and more or less permanent basis" would require changes in the NSF act. Valid as pilot projects under the Foundation's authority to develop national policy for education in the sciences, these activities ceased to be legitimate when they became "support of the actual teaching of science."[57] But the kind of amendments Hoff thought necessary disturbed the board's chairman, Chester I. Barnard. He did not want a broad extension of authority, he told Waterman.

I see no objection, and much merit in the pilot type of training study, but I would raise a good deal of a question as to whether we should get into the training or educational functions as a substantial or permanent operating matter. I believe we shall soon reach the stage where to protect our main functions we shall have to resist pressure from within or outside the organization for expansion of activities.[58]

The Bureau of the Budget also questioned the expansion of the institutes program when the Foundation proposed a large budget increase for fiscal 1957. Rather than provide direct financial support, NSF might better encourage the growing interest of private industry in sponsoring refresher sessions for teachers. Hugh F. Loweth of the Bureau, expressing a widely held view, thought "that more pay for teachers is the real answer to the problem," and obviously that solution required a public awakening beyond the Foundation's influence. Special emphasis on science education seemed questionable to Bureau staff members. And while OE had failed to seize opportunities, NSF "should have a formal agreement with the Office of Education as to what each will do."[59]

But as shown by a White House Conference on Education at the end of November 1955, the national mood was swinging strongly behind increased federal aid for public schools. A month later, in a speech to the AAAS on "The Crisis in Science Education," Waterman traced the long growth of federal participation in education. Playing on the ominous contrast between schooling in science and mathematics in Russia and the United States, he built a case for expanding NSF's programs of institutes for teachers, visiting lecturers, traveling high school libraries, and curricular reform.[60]

The Administration's budget decisions reflected the rising demand to help the schools: The fiscal 1957 estimate for NSF's program of education in the sciences was increased by more than $4 million over the year before, to $5.4 million, of which $3,850,000 would be for the strengthening of science teachers ($3 million for academic-year institutes for high school teachers, $850,000 for summer institutes for high school and college teachers), $910,000 for the improvement of science curricula, and $615,000 for studies and activities on motivation of able students to consider careers in science and science teaching.[61]

By the time this budget reached Congress Albert Thomas had experienced his conversion. Instead of $3 million for "refresher" courses for high school teachers, he told Waterman, the Foundation should be asking for $9-10 million. Getting ambiguous answers from Waterman, Kelly, and Paul M. Gross, the board's vice chairman, as to whether the Foundation could use that much money in fiscal 1957, Thomas said: "Dr. Waterman, when you and your group get back to the office, send us a little note in the mail tomorrow on this, please."[62]

Since some of the committee's comments had indicated that any increase in the institutes budget would come at the expense of other programs, Waterman and some board members became alarmed. Kelly recommended an enthusiastic expression of NSF's ability to use the funds effectively, coupled with a plea for flexibility in deciding on the number of summer institutes and in arranging for three-year grants for some of them.⁶³ But Kelly's letter, drafted in time to meet Thomas's short deadline, was not the one sent three days later.

Although the Budget Director warned Waterman against a response that would endanger the "narrow margin" of balance in the total federal budget, NSF's comptroller pointed out that the President's policy called for honest answers to congressional questions, even if they might lead to breaking the budget.⁶⁴ But Waterman was more concerned about safeguarding the research program than in multiplying institutes. He even grasped at the chance that AEC's interest in science education might offer a way of protecting the research budget. He hoped to convince Lewis Strauss that any AEC plans for large expenditures for training might be dropped in view of NSF's increase. Thus there need not be offsetting cuts in the Foundation's research appropriations, and AEC poachers on NSF's educational preserves would be warded off too.⁶⁵

Detlev Bronk, Barnard's successor as chairman of the National Science Board, at first advised Waterman to take a hard line and tell Thomas that it "would be unwise and difficult" to expand the education program more rapidly than planned. But after hearing Gross's advice that NSF "might compromise a bit by suggesting some compensating reductions elsewhere," Bronk conceded the possibility of a slight readjustment, though he feared that "such a move might encourage the Committee to make similar suggestions in future years"—a well-justified fear.⁶⁶

So instead of Kelly's proposed enthusiastic response, Waterman's reply to Thomas emphasized the "balanced approach" of the Foundation's budget request, designed to promote "progress in the numerous problem areas confronting us in science today."

> Therefore, after consideration of the matter, I do not believe that the Foundation should increase its Education in the Sciences program at the expense of other Foundation activities. The gravity of the long-range problem confronting the Nation in the area of scientific manpower cannot be exaggerated. However, the Foundation's activities providing support for several other areas of science contribute equally as much to our national strength.⁶⁷

Thomas's subcommittee held to its priority, however, and the House stipulated that at least $9.5 million be spent for supplementary training for high school teachers, leaving only $500,000 for all other activities in the program of education in the sciences. Still more disturbing to NSF was the halving of the requested increases for basic research and research facilities.⁶⁸

Waterman appealed to the Senate to correct the House mistakes. The cut in the basic research request, he said, would wipe out approximately five hundred projects giving advanced training to about twelve hundred graduate students. The Senate need not return to the exact figure for each item in the President's budget, but if it would restore the full amount of the request and eliminate the stipulation on training for high school teachers, NSF could then "conform to the spirit of the House action" and "provide the balance and flexibility necessary for the development and conduct of well-balanced programs in all areas important to the national scientific effort."[69]

The Senate did what Waterman asked, but that was not the end of the affair. Knowing that Thomas would probably stick to the House position in conference, Waterman tried an indirect approach to the chairman of the House Appropriations Committee, Clarence Cannon, a Missouri Democrat, through Frederick A. Middlebush, president emeritus of the University of Missouri and a member of the National Science Board.[70] The House members of the conference did not back down, however, on the requirement on training high school teachers, though they did agree to ease some of the other stringencies in a final appropriation of $40 million.

The fiscal 1957 appropriation transformed the institutes program into a truly national one. Its funds grew in a single year from 7 percent of the NSF budget to 25 percent. The number of summer institutes jumped from 25 in 1956 to 96 in 1957, academic-year institutes from 2 to 16, and in-service institutes (evening and Saturday training courses) from 2 in the spring of 1957 to 21 in 1957-58. From 309 teachers receiving instruction in the summer of 1955, the number rose by about one thousand in all institutes in fiscal 1956, and then grew fivefold (to 6,565) the next year.[71]

The rapid growth caused changes in standards and in NSF administrative procedures. At first the practice of institute directors was to enlist eminent scientists as lecturers. An institute was normally limited to a single field of natural science or mathematics, and its purpose was to present recent developments in the discipline to teachers who had been selected for their ability and promise. Yet the Foundation had always been concerned about schools in rural areas or small towns where bright students had almost no chance to study science. Bowen Dees reported to the SPE divisional committee that when the 1953 school year began, 268 high schools in North Carolina had no science teachers, and many of the schools had to employ persons who had received no college science instruction.[72] Graduates of such schools were often so deficient in mathematics that they avoided college science or engineering courses. Unfortunately, teachers in small high schools, perhaps because they feared rejection, seemed less inclined to apply for institute training than their city counterparts, and thus the gap in quality may have widened.[73]

The desire to improve the least qualified teachers ran counter to the original purpose of informing the best qualified about recent developments in their subjects. Soon NSF added to the roster of single-discipline institutes presenting advanced knowledge others in general science or multiple fields, sometimes for teachers who needed to learn the elementary matter of the courses they would have to teach. While these low-level institutes, taught not by eminent scientists imported from leading universities but increasingly by faculty of the host institutions, served a high purpose, they caused qualms for some NSF board and staff members who cherished the idea of a federal agency devoted only to the best science.

But if not serving the best science, the rapidly growing institutes at least helped NSF answer charges of elitism and maldistribution of grant funds. In 1957 there were summer institutes in all but five states and in three territories. Many state colleges whose main function was teacher training and small liberal arts colleges received NSF grants for the first time. So too did several predominantly black colleges, nearly all in southern states where segregation still prevailed in most institutions of higher education and where public officials often proclaimed their undying resistance to integration.[74]

Racial segregation posed a difficult problem for NSF.[75] The Foundation earnestly wanted to improve education in the South, where it lagged behind the rest of the nation. Though Waterman and most board members (with the decided exception of the Reverend Theodore M. Hesburgh, president of Notre Dame) were hardly crusaders for social justice, they were men of conscience who opposed subsidizing segregation in either all-white or all-black institutions. Anxious both to avoid publicity and to support institutes in the South, NSF in the early years of the program tried to achieve as much integration as possible. The provision of shared accommodations for living and eating was then unacceptable to nearly all southern institutions, and even though NSF preferred such arrangements, a black member of the board, Robert P. Barnes, told Kelly that he would settle for less in the interest of better science schooling in the South. And while the first summer institute in the region—for college teachers of mathematics at the University of North Carolina at Chapel Hill in 1954—offered fully integrated facilities, NSF refrained from announcing a policy against segregation until 1955. Then, in a form letter to institute directors, Kelly stated the Foundation's "understanding" that no one would be barred from participating or unfavorably discriminated against because of race, color, or religion. The policy kept some institutions from applying for institute grants and caused others to be turned down.

The statement of policy seems to have helped some institutions eager to qualify for grants to move toward complete integration. The policy may also have been effective in getting the support of liberals in Congress for the large fiscal 1957 appropriation for institutes. If so, there was an ironic result.

NSF had to spend the flood of new money quickly, and it would be most unwise to anger powerful southern congressmen by awarding institute grants only to other regions. The Foundation had to reach a quick decision whether to hold to or to ease its nondiscrimination policy. Black colleges, probably willing to accept and accommodate white applicants though unlikely to attract them, had submitted proposals for 1957 summer institutes. Should NSF make grants to these colleges but not to all-white institutions that, following the defiant mood of "massive resistance" in most of the region, would probably find ways to exclude blacks and certainly would not furnish integrated living and eating arrangements for them?

Waterman called Gabriel Hauge in the White House for advice. The director's note on the conversation shows the Eisenhower Administration's passive attitude toward enforcement of the integration policy laid down in the *Brown* decision of 1954:

> Dr. Hauge emphasized the fact that the Supreme Court decision was not the sole factor in this situation, but the President had made this a part of his policy. He, therefore, endorsed the position of the National Science Foundation that in our dealings with colleges and universities we conform with this policy. . . .
>
> Dr. Hauge's analysis indicated that a satisfactory policy would be to insure that any institution or agency granted funds by the Foundation for this purpose should spend these funds in accordance with the President's policy position. Arrangements made by individuals or otherwise, outside the agency dispensing the funds, would then not be a concern of the Foundation. For example, if the agency arranging for an institute makes no arrangements for living quarters for participants but leaves this to the individuals, then the program would be satisfactory provided the actual planning of the institute conformed to the President's policy.[76]

This counsel tolerated ambiguity. Official policy called for nondiscrimination in the selection of institute participants but did not require the host institution to furnish integrated living quarters and dining rooms. The White House advice may have helped NSF accommodate Albert Thomas's interest in getting an institute for Stephen F. Austin State College without "having a burning issue arise."[77] The Foundation soon dropped the earlier statement of "understanding" and gave the following guidance to directors of 1957 summer institutes: "Each institute will establish its own criteria for admission within the general Foundation policy that candidates should be considered primarily on the basis of professional competence and promise as teachers of science and/or mathematics." But lest the test of merit block the selection of poorly trained teachers—perhaps especially blacks—one's "capacity to develop as a teacher" was to be a principal criterion along with "professional competence." While NSF guarded against any clear violation of federal law, the agency supported institutes whose participants were either all black or all white; in other cases both blacks and whites were accepted but lived and ate apart. Although the Foundation looked with favor on proposals that promised integration, and thus encouraged the breakdown of racial barriers—an achievement in which southerners on the SPE staff took just pride—many of its grants went to segregated institutions until the practice was sharply attacked by a report of the U.S. Civil Rights Commission in 1961 and at the same time a more vigorous White House policy of enforcement replaced Eisenhower's.[78]

The rapid growth of institutes also entailed procedural changes. Instead of relying on professional societies to evaluate proposals by mail review, NSF shifted to the use of advisory panels which assembled in Washington. As a consequence of bigness, informal and varying practices that had prevailed before were supplanted by system and uniformity in stipends for participants, guidebooks for directors, and checklists for visiting observers. Naturally the greater work load required some growth in NSF staff as well, so that by 1957 there were directors for separate programs of education in the sciences, academic-year institutes, and summer institutes.[79]

After the big jump in 1957, however, the prospect for further expansion the next year seemed unlikely. NSF did not ask for an increase in the budget for institutes, and the fiscal 1958 appropriation was the same as the year before, with $9.5 million again earmarked for the training of high school teachers. By the spring of 1957, when planning was under way for fiscal 1959, Waterman expected little if any increase in NSF's appropriation. He showed some interest in increasing the number of institutes for college teachers, but he and the board began to consider phasing out the "experimental" programs for high school teachers. The academic-year program came under special question because it aggravated the shortage of teachers by removing some of the best ones from the classroom for a full year.[80]

There was some disillusion too as results fell short of expectations. Universities and colleges showed little inclination to incorporate institute "reforms" into their regular teacher-training programs. Private industries and foundations that had pioneered the institute idea now withdrew their support when the government moved in. And what was especially discouraging, many high school teachers who most needed the refreshment of new knowledge and skills showed no interest in applying for admission to institutes.[81] A large mass of unreachable teachers preferred, often for quite sensible reasons, to spend their summers more profitably or more pleasurably elsewhere than in college classrooms.[82]

By the early fall of 1957 the Foundation was moving toward a no-growth policy for summer and academic-year institutes, though the SPE staff was eager to start other experiments to improve science education. Then the launching of Sputnik changed the outlook dramatically. It brought another big boost in the institutes budget and a chance to try out a variety of other educational projects, some of them reaching down into the elementary school. Some schemes were hastily concocted because of prospective bounty from a Congress suddenly aroused by public alarm. Others had been in preparation for several years. Among the latter were designs to bring into the schools up-to-date, relatively rigorous, and entirely new science textbooks, accompanied by coordinated teachers' manuals, demonstration experiments and apparatus, and film strips.

Sputnik created an intellectual climate that encouraged the early adoption of these new courses of study. NSF institutes furnished a tested means of preparing teachers to teach the new courses in physics, chemistry, biology, and mathematics and of speeding their transit into the schools.[83]

* * *

In the spring of 1954 American anxiety often bordered on hysteria. It was the time of the Supreme Court decision outlawing segregation in the nation's schools, of the televised Army-McCarthy hearings, of proclamations of "massive resistance" to racial mixing at home and "massive retaliation" against communist aggression abroad. Many Americans of normally placid temperament became convinced that Moscow was directing a conspiracy, reaching around the globe, to bury western democracy, and their fears were intensified by the speed of the Russian development of nuclear weapons. Belief in a substantial margin of American superiority began to crumble.

A sense of impending, perhaps imminent, danger moved Eisenhower's Cabinet to act. The Cabinet's concern about the relative scientific and technological strength of the United States and the Soviet Union led to the establishment in May 1954 of a special interdepartmental committee to review the trends in American education of scientists and engineers and to explore "the possible steps which might be taken to increase the supply of fully-trained persons in these and related fields." Arthur S. Flemming, director of the Office of Defense Mobilization, asked Waterman to serve on the committee, along with the secretaries of Defense, Labor, Commerce, and Health, Education, and Welfare, and the chairman of the Atomic Energy Commission.[84]

Much of the atmosphere of crisis was generated by ODM, which had submitted the reports that had alarmed the Cabinet and was of course concerned about the nation's readiness to mobilize essential scientific manpower quickly if an emergency occurred. In outlining the work to be undertaken by the committee, ODM said that "we are experiencing for the first time a serious shortage of scientific and engineering talent." Since the Russians were speeding up their training programs, "the security of the nation is at stake." But the ODM paper moved beyond the question of possibly immediate mobilization requirements and raised issues about the long-term development of scientific manpower, a matter that NSF understood to be one of its special responsibilities. America's specialized manpower was not growing nearly fast enough to meet rising military and civilian needs, the paper said. Not only were enrollments of graduate science students declining, but far too many able youth did not even enter college. According to ODM's figures, "Of the top 2 percent of high school graduates, in terms of both intelligence and high grades, only two-thirds graduate from college. Of the top quarter of high school graduates... only 42 percent graduate from college." Although the ODM paper said that the committee should "consider quality as well as quantity," the main emphasis was on increasing the "supply" of trained scientists and engineers.[85]

At least NSF saw the top priority being given to numbers and reacted defensively. At the committee's first meeting Waterman "heartily endorsed" a statement by another participant mentioning "the importance of high quality scientists rather than just numbers."[86] Throughout the life of the committee and its successors, NSF representatives sought to counter what they thought was undue emphasis on quantity. And in response to Flemming's pressure to complete and publish a report quickly, NSF members of the task force created by the interdepartmental committee stressed the complexity of supply-demand relationships and argued for careful accumulation and scholarly assessment of data. They wanted to ensure against a slapdash, impassioned public appeal. In their view, the report should take account and encourage government support of the solid work already being done under private auspices to understand and improve the manpower situation. Further, the report

should almost totally avoid making recommendations as to specific approaches to the solutions of these problems. It should explicitly state that the problem of training more and better scientists and engineers is one which involves all levels of our educational system. Through some means, it should demonstrate that the problems existing in other professional fields have not been ignored. The report should make clear the reasons for Federal interest in these problems while demonstrating an understanding of the fact that these problems are neither susceptible to solution by the Federal Government nor such that the Federal Government should, because of its interest, attempt to gain any measure of control over education in the United States. It should not attempt to create or inspire the creation of a Federal organ to coordinate the various activities in this field, and finally, it should recognize the current programs of Federal agencies, in particular, the Office of Education, the Foundation, and possibly the Atomic Energy Commission, the Office of Naval Research, etc.[87]

By contrast to NSF's characteristically studious approach to the problem, James H. Taylor of ODM asked each committee member to produce a "single best" suggested solution. The Foundation instead listed its several educational and related programs.[88]

The SPE divisional committee shared the staff's irritation at ODM's haste and its interference in the Foundation's business. The task force, headed by Taylor, intended to recommend the appointment by the President of a national committee on the training of scientists and engineers, and Kelly asked his advisers' opinion on an appropriate stand by the Foundation. While deploring the failure to recognize NSF's "constant and quiet study" of the problems of scientific manpower and fearing that the citizens' group to be appointed by the President "would produce only pious platitudes and publicity," the SPE divisional committee nonetheless counseled cooperation so that the Foundation's judgments would not be ignored. Kelly was also disturbed because the task force expected NSF to serve as the staff for the proposed citizens' committee. But rather than let OE provide such staff services, burdensome as they might be, an SPE adviser argued that if there was "to be distortion and emphasis on particular fields" (that is, science and engineering), the Foundation was the better choice. Thus the logic of self-protection pulled NSF into serving a distasteful cause.[89]

But worse was yet to come. A few days after the divisional committee reluctantly advised cooperation, Kelly received an ODM working paper that proposed recommending to the President not only that he appoint a national citizens' committee but also "issue an executive order creating an interdepartmental committee on the training of scientists and engineers, to be chaired by the Office of Defense Mobilization." Kelly and the Foundation's general counsel, William Hoff, believed that the duties of the two committees would largely duplicate the statutory responsibilities of NSF and those defined in the recent Executive Order 10521. Hoff told the director that the kind of representation suggested for the national committee paralleled that of the National Science Board, and the committee's proposed objectives seriously overlapped those of the board. As for the interdepartmental committee, its duties would be the same as NSF's except that it could start any new programs it thought desirable, and "without any reference to needed funds." Was the interdepartmental committee intended to study mobilization needs? If so, NSF would be glad to cooperate. But if it were intended to solve long-range problems of scientific manpower, the committee would be assuming responsibilities belonging to the Foundation. Hoff advised the director to discuss the matter "candidly with Taylor and if necessary, Flemming, with a view to ascertaining what objectives they seek to accomplish."[90]

ODM dropped the explicit recommendation for an interdepartmental committee and made several other revisions requested by NSF. But the Foundation failed to carry its most important point. The National Science Board and the staff opposed the formation of a national committee, but held that if one were to be appointed, it should be named by NSF and report to the President through the science agency.[91]

The argument carried little weight, however, in the absence of strong support from other federal agencies. At a meeting of the special committee Waterman contended that manpower shortages were uncertain, confined to a few fields, and likely to improve. Too much dramatic stimulation might lead to a glut that would be difficult to absorb. The government's main concern should be the long-term problem of developing highly qualified scientists. A Defense Department representative also questioned whether a presidential committee was needed, but Flemming assumed that there was a consensus favoring a recommendation for its appointment. He said that the plan was to assign administrative responsibility for the committee to NSF "except for matters of the use of manpower for national security."[92]

The SPE divisional committee then tried its powers of persuasion on Taylor and his deputy, John Hilliard. The ODM officials did not back down. They refused to worry that their efforts might result in an oversupply of scientists and engineers or shortages and second-fiddle feelings in other important fields of knowledge. Hilliard told the committee that ODM had watched NSF's development "occasionally with impatience, hope and pessimism." Those "bitter-sweet words," a committee member observed after the ODM officials had left, may have represented an effort "to get steam behind the Foundation."[93] That surmise was undoubtedly accurate. The ODM officials' draft report had in fact already prompted NSF to put in a request for more money for education in the sciences.

At length Waterman agreed to accept a somewhat modified draft report.[94] After a great deal of fretting, NSF had concluded that the appointment of a presidential committee would not seriously disrupt the Foundation's activities or undermine its authority. Kelly's note on a telephone conversation with Carey of the Budget Bureau probably reflects accurately a weary, what-does-it-matter attitude:

> Mr. Carey asked if we had any objections to the report. I told him no—that at first we had some misgivings as to possible duplication with the Foundation's activities, but that these possible difficulties had been removed. I stated that the National Committee was a kind of citizens' committee with whom it would be possible to have a kind of self-help in mutual exchange of activities and views. The Foundation's role would be to act as liaison with the Federal Government . . . .
> The conversation was very brief indeed, and I gather that Mr. Carey was interested solely in collecting gripes.[95]

Later developments indicate that nearly everyone had been overwrought. ODM had tried to whip out a quick report designed to arouse the public about a dangerous manpower shortage and to promote far-reaching changes in education. To ODM the objections raised by the Foundation must have seemed self-serving and, in view of the assumed peril to national security, fussily academic. But by the time the draft report was completed and approved by the Cabinet early in 1955, the mood of crisis which had inspired it had noticeably relaxed. A revulsion against McCarthyism had dissolved many of the popular fears of domestic subversion, and foreign-policy spokesmen were now talking less about "massive retaliation" and more about "coexistence."

The sense of urgency was gone. The draft report, scheduled for Cabinet consideration in January 1955, was at length approved on April 29. In September, on a trip to California, Waterman sounded out Robert G. Sproul, president of the University of California, on his interest in heading the national committee. In December, following Sproul's declination, Waterman received other suggestions for chairman from one of his board members, and finally, in February 1956, the director heard from Flemming that Howard L. Bevis, president of Ohio State University, had agreed to take the position.[96]

Not until April 3, 1956 did President Eisenhower announce the establishment of the National Committee for the Development of Scientists and Engineers and Bevis's appointment. Although calling attention to the challenge to America's technological primacy "by those who use science for aggression and conquest," the generally temperate presidential statement said that the new committee's work for science and technology "will not distract us from continuing our efforts on behalf of all the other important fields of education." While "the Government has a responsibility for increasing the supply and improving the quality of our technological personnel, the basic responsibility for solution of the problem lies in the concerted action of citizens and citizens' groups organized to act effectively." Hence he was appointing a national committee, composed of well-known scientists, engineers, educators, scholars, and spokesmen for state and local government, business, and labor, for which NSF would provide staff services and enlist the cooperation of other federal agencies. Neither the establishment of the committee nor the naming of its chairman seemed newsworthy enough to draw a question from the press corps at the President's news conference the following day.[97]

Waterman's statement on the Foundation's support of the committee dwelt on the development of "highly-trained and creative scientists and engineers." "For the race ahead, we must emphasize excellence," it said.[98] The national committee's executive secretary, NSF announced, would be Robert L. Clark, an authority on manpower resources who had been a consultant to ODM.[99] Clark served on the Foundation staff until the committee wound up its business at the end of 1958. By that time, thanks to the Russians, the public had been more than enough alerted to the threat to American technological supremacy.

Meanwhile a flood of contradictory testimony had inundated the national forum. The emotions of a presidential election year contributed to the making of pronouncements, and strong denials, about dire shortages of skilled technicians. The respected science writer Waldemar Kaempffert warned that unless there was a strenuous national effort the USSR would equal America's scientific strength in five years and surpass it in ten—a prediction picked up by many others, including the President's national committee in a post-Sputnik report.[100]

But the best-known spokesmen for science and engineering tried, as did the Foundation, both to take advantage of the growing interest in science and to quiet popular alarm. All five speakers at a symposium held at the National Academy of Sciences soon after the appointment of the President's committee agreed that the United States should not get into a manpower-production race with Russia but "should concentrate on raising the quality of scientific education." Emphasis only on numbers, they said, would weaken American science by endangering professional standards. Similarly, Lee DuBridge, speaking at a conference held in connection with a meeting of the national committee, urged an end to the hysteria about Russia's forging ahead of America. True, more science and technology degrees had been awarded in the USSR than in the United States the year before, but DuBridge said "So what?" Perhaps the massive Soviet effort was due to a century of Russian neglect of technology. Rather than trying to match the number of Russian engineering degrees, America's concern should be the informed building of strength in particular scientific disciplines according to their needs.[101] But while people differed on whether quantity or quality should have top priority, nearly all seemed to agree that the central problem was the failure of the public high school to teach science and mathematics.[102]

* * *

The public babel made all the more important the acquisition of reliable information on scientific personnel. The Foundation's commitment to that task, which it viewed as the continuous, progressive refinement of exacting techniques of data collection and interpretation, caused resentment of ODM's pressure for the creation of a citizens' committee—a public-relations crusade as NSF tended to see it. To some, the Foundation showed an excess of caution on a vital matter, and an occasional study under its auspices, done for the best of purposes, might even prove harmful to the effort to change national attitudes. Just as NSF's attempts to prevent the establishment of a national committee seemed to soft-pedal manpower shortages, so did one of the studies it supported—on methods to explain movements in the supply and demand for scientific manpower—cause consternation when it cast doubt on the reality of a shortage.[103]

Amid the general clamor the Foundation's manpower program continued on course. Under the guidance of Thomas J. Mills, program director for scientific manpower, the National Register of Scientific and Technical Personnel extended its coverage to include 140,000 scientists and 12,000 engineers by the summer of 1957. Removal of the Register's records center from Washington to the "non-target area" of Raleigh, North Carolina showed the roster's primary purpose of ensuring readiness for mobilization in a national emergency, and several tests of its adaptability for mobilization requirements were performed. But NSF also regarded the Register as an essential source for its manpower studies, and the agency resisted some ODM efforts to extend coverage beyond natural scientists, mathematicians, engineers, and demographers to other specialists who might be needed in an emergency. The SPE divisional committee spent much of its time, for example, debating an ODM request for the addition of persons with unusual skills—"rare birds" they were usually called—and the best means of identifying them quickly.[104]

By the late 1950s more and more graphs, charts, and tables in books and articles carried the notation "Source: National Science Foundation," a designation that was becoming a stamp of authenticity. However shaky NSF's figures on scientific personnel and on research and development might be, and they were largely estimates, they were far more accurate than those available before and were becoming steadily better. Thus when the Foundation published its first "fact book" (*Scientific Personnel Resources*) late in 1955, Dael Wolfle, a leading authority on the subject, called it "the best half-dollar bargain on the current book market." NSF's "fact book," Wolfle said, "is now the place to look if one wants to know the percentage of physicists with Ph.D. degrees, the age distribution of mathematicians, the expected number of engineering graduates in 1960, the number of high I.Q. high-school graduates who do not go to college, or if one wants information on any of quite a large number of similar questions concerning scientists and engineers in general or those in a particular field."[105] For a society becoming increasingly dependent on information, the Foundation's work in gathering and disseminating reliable data was indispensable.

13
Little Science

A telephone call in March 1954 from Alan Waterman inviting AEC's director of reactor development to a panel meeting on ultra-high-energy accelerators illustrated the NSF director's intention not to be blocked out of any important area of the natural sciences.[1] For an agency whose research budget was then only $4 million to try to stake a claim on the research frontier of high-energy physics may have seemed preposterous to custodians of "big science," but this step was only one of several that NSF took early in 1954 to develop what in its jargon were termed "large-scale facilities." Although the Foundation failed, within the next four years, to gain a foothold in accelerator construction, a growing budget and careful selection of targets enabled NSF to share in sponsoring the development of nuclear reactors, university computing centers, radio and optical astronomical observatories, biological field stations, and controlled-environment laboratories. Though still chiefly a patron of individual research projects at universities and colleges—little science—NSF had also gained a role in larger and sometimes collaborative programs—if not quite big science yet, at least much bigger.

The guardians of traditional little science, the subject of this chapter, worried that the larger efforts would cut into the budgets for individual projects and jeopardize academic research. But since university administrators dominated the National Science Board, and university scientists most of NSF's other advisory bodies, the advancement of academic science through the research-project system remained, along with education and the study of science resources, a central Foundation mission. The staff's values too were more professorial than bureaucratic.

The Foundation's custodians also worried about extending its patronage beyond the natural sciences and engineering. While NSF insisted on its right to support research in nuclear physics, it had to be coaxed into an "uneasy partnership" with the social sciences.[2] Starting as a small research program for anthropology and related sciences in the life sciences division, the social sciences next managed to plant a base in the other research division as "socio-physical sciences," and at length emerged as an autonomous program (but not yet an office or division) in 1957. Still a minor activity and not touching all principal subject-matter fields—political science was still excluded—the Foundation's grants for social science research nevertheless constituted an important part of the total federal support of basic work in the social disciplines.

Although the extension to the social sciences may have indicated a growing latitudinarian spirit among the Foundation's policy makers, it did not seem so to some program officers. By the summer of 1957 no-trespassing signs were going up where they had been roaming freely. Several factors contributed to a mood of frustration: the end of budgetary growth; the stopping of experimental programs; a feeling that NSF should actively stimulate research in certain science areas; and a desire to break out of the confines of narrow project grants. The director, backed by the board, hindered change by insisting that the Foundation should not "mastermind" the course of science. But then came Sputnik and the walls came tumbling down.

* * *

Research-grant procedures continued generally in the pattern set during NFS's beginning years. The wish to keep matters simple—for the scientist, the college or university, and the Foundation—remained strong. Still, comparison of an April 1955 edition of NSF's most important occasional publication, *Grants for Scientific Research*, with the brief mimeographed guide issued in 1951 shows a bureaucratic creep toward greater specificity and tighter regulation—as well as overuse of the passive voice and minatory shalls and wills. The slender, fifteen-page handbook, which clearly described procedures for submitting research proposals and administering research grants, aimed at achieving "some uniformity" among proposals to assist their consideration, but rather than setting up a formidable array of precise stipulations to be met, the brochure read like an invitation to seek support. And if successful in their applications, researchers need not feel bound to a "strict adherence to the original budget estimates" so long as they informed NSF of "contemplated major deviations . . . and the reasons therefor."[3] (In fact, research-grant budget estimates tallied closely with actual expenditures. An analysis of completed grants in 1955 revealed "a very tight relationship" between estimated and actual costs of salaries, permanent equipment, expendable equipment and supplies, and other items of expense in the "average research grant."[4])

Although budget allocations in Walter R. Kirner's chemistry program may have differed considerably from those, say, in Leon W. Cohen's mathematics program, the "average research grant" provides a convenient way of looking at the totality of NSF's research programs. Overall, research-project budgets allocated the bulk of grant funds to salaries, though the fraction gradually became smaller—from three-fourths (74.6 percent) of the total direct costs in fiscal 1955 to two-thirds (67.1 percent) in fiscal 1958. Less than one-fifth of the salary payments went to principal investigators, and that mostly for research during the summer months rather than the academic year. Postdoctoral research associates accounted for about one-fourth of the salary budgets and graduate student research assistants for about one-third. Other salary and direct labor charges usually ran between a fifth and a fourth of the total. While the salaries portion of the average research grant declined, the share for equipment rose somewhat. By fiscal 1958 permanent and expendable equipment and supplies together amounted to nearly one-fourth of the budget. Travel and other costs remained fairly constant at 4-5 percent each. Budgets for indirect costs, which throughout the period were limited to 15 percent of direct costs, gradually rose from 12.5 percent in fiscal 1955 to 13.6 percent in fiscal 1958.[5]

By 1958 the dollar amount of research grants in the mathematical, physical, and engineering sciences was beginning to run ahead of that for grants in the biological and medical sciences, but the two divisions' totals for the seven years since the first awards in 1952 were quite close—$28.1 million for BMS, $29.6 million for MPE. Grants in the social sciences accounted for another $1.3 million, or a total in all research programs of $59 million.[6]

NSF's research programs were indeed "little science." The average amount of the 4,053 research grants awarded during the seven years was $14,558. In fiscal 1952, grants of both divisions averaged about $11,000, and the figures remained around $9-11,000 until fiscal 1955, when an upward trend began. By the end of fiscal year 1958 the average grant in the BMS division had reached $14,680, in MPE $20,403, and in the new social sciences program $14,815. In the life sciences programs the averages for the entire seven years ranged from $8,515 for systematic biology to $17,909 for molecular. In the MPE group, engineering had the lowest seven-year average ($13,218) and physics the highest ($20,580). For fiscal 1958 alone, the average sizes of grants in physics ($31,003) and astronomy ($30,843) considerably exceeded those of the other four programs, all of which fell in the $17-18,000 range.[7]

NSF research grants, FY 1952-58

		% of total
Biological and Medical Sciences	$28,126,312	47.7
Developmental biology	1,573,232	2.7
Environmental biology	2,477,660	4.2
Genetic biology	2,365,100	4.0
Metabolic biology	1,482,350	2.5
Molecular biology	6,142,780	10.4
Psychobiology	3,411,450	5.8
Regulatory biology	5,866,825	9.9
Systematic biology	3,142,105	5.3
General	1,664,810	2.8
Mathematical, Physical, and Engineering Sciences	$29,553,300	50.1
Astronomy	2,733,530	4.7
Chemistry	8,083,800	13.7
Earth sciences	3,334,820	5.7
Engineering sciences	4,917,050	8.3
Mathematics	3,834,200	6.5
Physics	6,523,900	11.1
General	126,000	0.2
Social Sciences	$1,323,450	2.2
Anthropology and related sciences	722,400	1.2
Economics	93,300	0.2
History and philosophy of science	66,450	0.1
Sociology	182,100	0.3
Socio-physical sciences	259,200	0.4
Total	$59,003,062	100.0

The early patterns of geographic and institutional distribution of NSF research funds underwent little change in fiscal years 1952-58.[8] The Northeast and the West gained a little; the North Central region and the South lost a little. Percentages of NSF research dollars going to these regions for the entire seven-year period 1952-58 were:

```
Northeast ............................................ 35
North Central ........................................ 30
West ................................................. 18
South ................................................ 16
    Territories and possessions ...................... 1
```

Regional percentages of research grant dollars corresponded fairly closely to dollar amounts in proposals submitted to NSF and to numbers of graduate students, but less so to total population; here the South lagged well behind the other regions, and the West and Northeast ran well ahead.[9]

But regional aggregates hide significant particulars and variations. The South would have trailed even more except for substantial NSF grants to such governmental and semipublic institutions in the District of Columbia as the National Bureau of Standards, the Smithsonian Institution, and the National Academy of Sciences-National Research Council. Mississippi institutions received only $62,700 during the seven years. The University of California (whose particular campuses were not usually identified) received $1.4 million in fiscal 1957 alone, nearly three-fourths of the funds awarded that year to all eleven western states—more, indeed, than the total dollars to the twenty-seven lowest ranking states of the whole country.

Over the seven-year period the University of California received more than $4 million in NSF research grants. Though attribution of some grants to particular components of that prototypical multiversity is questionable, the Berkeley campus seems to have led all other U.S. institutions in winning NSF research funds. The following universities had received more than $1 million each in NSF research grants by the end of fiscal 1958:

1. University of California, Berkeley $2,595,295*
2. University of Chicago 2,239,500
3. Harvard University 2,158,240
4. Massachusetts Institute of Technology 2,005,150
5. University of Michigan 1,872,800
6. University of Wisconsin 1,805,920
7. Columbia University 1,749,000
8. Yale University 1,638,600
9. University of Illinois 1,531,000
10. California Institute of Technology 1,235,650
11. University of Pennsylvania 1,154,600
12. Johns Hopkins University 1,113,350
13. University of Minnesota 1,111,630
14. Purdue University 1,073,400
15. Cornell University 1,062,550
16. Indiana University 1,016,700

*Some grants attributed to the Berkeley campus may have gone instead to other components of the University of California. The total of research grants to the University of California, 1952-58, was $4,009,645.

The $25.4 million awarded to these sixteen universities amounted to 43 percent of the Foundation's grants for basic research. The other 57 percent was divided among several hundred institutions—approximately 250 in 1958.[10] Besides universities and colleges, which made up much the largest number, the recipients included a variety of other organizations (museums, botanical gardens, academies of science, hospitals, nonprofit research laboratories) and several individual scientists without institutional affiliations. Some funds went to each of the forty-eight states, the territories of Alaska and Hawaii, the commonwealth of Puerto Rico, and a few foreign countries.

Only one readily identifiable junior college appears in the long annual lists of recipients of research grants, but, in contrast to the first three years, the names of state colleges once specializing in teacher education recur fairly often. Evidently they were in transition toward a general education program and were aided in this course by NSF research support. While doctoral universities were the big money-winners, a large number of independent liberal arts colleges received research awards. Not all of the following institutions offered only undergraduate degrees, but their awards during the years 1952-58 show the continuing ability of these generally elite colleges to compete effectively for research funds:

1.	Swarthmore College	$145,800
2.	Reed College	120,600
3.	Carleton College	97,200
4.	Smith College	97,000
5.	Haverford College	89,600
6.	Bryn Mawr College	89,100
7.	Amherst College	81,100
8.	Grinnell College	76,200
9.	Barnard College	71,900
10.	Earlham College	71,500
11.	Bowdoin College	60,000
12.	Wesleyan University	56,200
13.	Pomona College	52,700
14.	Mount Holyoke College	50,300
15.	Oberlin College	49,250
16.	Antioch College	46,150

Dozens of other undergraduate institutions received grants of smaller totals.

Only eleven of the nation's approximately 120 historically black colleges received NSF research awards. Howard University ($86,200) easily led the others—in rank order, Tuskegee Institute, Morgan State College, Texas Southern University, Fisk University, Central State College (Ohio), Meharry Medical College, Philander Smith College, Xavier University of

Louisiana, Tennessee Agricultural and Industrial State University, and Atlanta University.

Any grants to Radcliffe College were attributed to Harvard University, but all the other six of the "seven sisters" (Barnard, Bryn Mawr, Mount Holyoke, Smith, Vassar, and Wellesley) received funds, ranging from Smith's high of $97,000 to Wellesley's $8,200. A number of other women's colleges, and not confined to the Northeast, also won awards—e.g., Goucher, Hunter, Sarah Lawrence, Randolph-Macon Woman's College, and Mundelein.

The diversity of the Foundation's research clientele perhaps indicates some sensitivity of program directors and their advisers and reviewers to accusations of elitism. Nonetheless, the heavy flow of funds to 15-20 doctoral universities and to a similar number of well-known private colleges shows NSF's dedication to the best science. The breadth and nature of a few of the grants to liberal arts colleges indicate not only a concern for maintaining the fertility of these seedbeds of excellence but also an effort by some NSF staff members to move beyond the individual-project grant to more flexible forms of institutional support.

* * *

The preceding section generalized about the "average research grant." This one particularizes about a single research program, regulatory biology, in the mid-1950s. That is not to say that this program was typical (none was), nor was its program director, but his annual reports deal with problems common to all research programs, especially how to stretch program funds to support as many worthy proposals as possible. His reports also illustrate the range of activities related to an NSF program director's main function of evaluating proposals.[11]

First, this program director's professed canons: His "guiding philosophy" was "to provide as much assistance as possible to basic research and to activities ancillary to research." He did not solicit proposals, nor did he favor any special areas of biology, since all needed investigation and he saw none that clearly lagged behind the others. "There seems little doubt," he wrote, "that 'masterminding' research by allocating money to specific areas, whether they be called programmatic work, the filling of gap areas, or by other names, results in work of lower quality than if the problem is chosen by the investigator only because he has an interest in it and has ideas about how to attack it. . . . the over-riding criterion is that of scientific merit."

The program director and his assistants must have felt at times that they were on an accelerating treadmill; they ran faster and still lost ground. The flow of good proposals kept increasing, and so did the backlog of those approved for funding which had to be carried over to the following year. With a budget of about $430,000 for fiscal 1954, only $74,000 remained at the end of the third quarter (when the report was written). Funds had been obligated for 29 projects (12 of them carried forward from the year before), but other proposals approved at the fall panel meeting remained unfunded and 47 others would be up for evaluation at the spring meeting. The program head expected that there would be an unmet requirement of $525,000 by June 30 and a carryover of about 30 approved projects. He estimated that the program should have at least $1,250,000 in fiscal 1955 to meet the need for the most worthy projects if proposals continued to come in only at the current rate; if the rate grew the requirement would be $2 million in 1955 and $3 million in 1956. The rate did grow. On May 15, 1955 the program had 44 approved proposals needing $790,000 to activate, but only $150,000 left in its budget; now the unmet requirement was $640,000. A year later it would be $737,000, and by the end of fiscal 1957 nearly $1 million.

The work load also grew. The addition of a professional assistant helped ease routine program chores, but the nine-member advisory panel had to read more proposals every year and rate them in their fall and spring meetings as highly meritorious, meritorious, acceptable, doubtful, or unacceptable. The formidable task led to three panel meetings a year beginning in fiscal 1957, since the number of proposals requiring evaluation had grown from 114 three years before to 210. Besides the panel, whose membership changed somewhat each year, a large number of mail consultants assisted in the evaluation, and the number of these referees reading one or more proposals rose from 110 in 1954 to 228 two years later. (From the start, BMS programs tended to follow the NIH pattern of relying mainly on the collective judgment of panels in deciding the merit of proposals; most MPE program directors based their decisions mainly on their reading of mail reviews. For one MPE program director's experience with peer review which relied both on mail reviews and panel advice, see Appendix 2.)

Although the dollar requests in proposals were usually pared down in negotiations following panel approval, the program sought to fund all proposals rated highly meritorious or meritorious. Any hope of supporting those rated acceptable soon evaporated. But a large proportion fell in the two meritorious categories—133 out of 151 in fiscal 1955, 89 out of 184 in 1956, 122 out of 218 in 1957. In a "new" program of metabolic biology in fiscal 1958, created to reduce the load on the regulatory and molecular programs, 64 percent of the proposals were rated highly meritorious or meritorious and 21 percent acceptable.

One reason for the many high ratings, according to the program director, was "self-selection" among scientists owing to a spreading awareness that NSF supported only work of high quality. Another was that as grants expired the investigators applied for continuation of support and were nearly always successful. The program director expected that eventually about 30 percent of the grants would be renewals. Nearly half of the approved proposals in metabolic biology in fiscal 1958 were renewal requests—hence the high percentage falling in the two meritorious groups.

The high percentage of good proposals and the tight program budget had the unhappy effect of limiting the duration of grants. Longer-term grants would not only have given investigators a sense of security and relief from frequent renewal applications but would also have reduced administrative costs and lightened the burden on the program and its reviewers. The growing pile of approved unfunded proposals, however, frustrated the program director's wish. He regretted that only one grant made in fiscal 1956 would run for five years and that forty-two would last two years or less. The average duration of the year's awards was 2.4 years, slightly better than the year before and better than the Foundation-wide average of 2.1 years.

The program supported research in several ways in addition to subsidizing individual projects. One of these was the sponsoring of conferences or symposia, usually in cooperation with private foundations, other federal agencies, professional societies, or universities. Dealing with special topics that often crossed disciplinary boundaries, the research conferences provided a good means of exchanging the latest information on matters of rapidly developing interest and, since the proceedings were usually soon published, of disseminating new knowledge to other interested scientists. The regulatory biology program normally sponsored three or four conferences a year on such specific substantive areas of science as The Mammalian Fetus—Physiological Aspects of Development, Comparative Endocrinology of Vertebrates, and Neurophysiology of the Synapse.

Similarly the program supported the travel of scientists to international congresses and meetings. Here again NSF often collaborated with other organizations and enlisted the advice of specialized groups. For example, the program joined with the American Society of Biological Chemists and the American Chemical Society in paying for scientists' travel to the Third International Congress for Biochemistry in Brussels in 1955. The three sponsors decided on joint announcements, application forms, and rules, and the NSF program managed the operation. A committee representing the two professional societies and a national committee for biochemistry, with the NSF program director serving ex officio, chose 27 grantees from the 188 applicants. Nineteen of the grants came from NSF funds. Although such grants consumed only a small part of the NSF budget, this form of research support was highly valued by the Foundation, and of course by the scientists whose proficiency and prestige were enhanced by attendance at international congresses. It was a cause for dismay when the House of Representatives, fearful of letting the Russians learn any more American scientific "secrets," excised a request for travel funds to international conferences from NSF's fiscal 1956 budget.

Some "research" conferences actually dealt with undergraduate education, a matter of much interest to the program director. He and a colleague who headed the molecular biology program had earlier arranged for a survey of the status of physiological science by the American Physiological Society, and that study led to a number of related cooperative undertakings by NSF and the society, among them a series of summer workshops on the teaching of physiology in undergraduate colleges.

Not only the college teacher but students too benefited from the program's interest in introducing them to the challenges of research and possible careers as biologists. Grants to Harvard University and Reed College in 1955 to support research by juniors and seniors were followed the next year by similar awards to Carleton College and Johns Hopkins University. The grant to Hopkins even extended to high school students, giving them an opportunity to discuss their research or science fair projects with members of the university's biology department.[12] Since it seemed infeasible to make such awards directly to a large number of colleges, the program head attempted to develop a plan to deal with state or regional groups of institutions. At his encouragement a group of Indiana colleges and universities submitted a proposal through the Indiana Academy of Sciences. Referees endorsed the proposal, but its approval hinged on a policy decision favorable to this kind of extended activity by a research program. The National Science Board, however, in discussing NSF's responsibilities in education turned thumbs down on support of students in secondary schools or colleges, choosing instead to emphasize the improvement of teachers' competence.[13]

Although balked in his effort to extend the program's support of undergraduate research through cooperative state or regional arrangements, or even to make any more grants for that purpose to individual institutions, the program director did manage to continue another type of student research support. A former medical school professor himself, he thought that there was a serious shortage of medical investigators trained in research methods. The activity began with a single three-year grant of $6,900 to Washington University in fiscal 1954 to give selected medical students a firsthand research experience during the summer months. Encouraged by the BMS divisional committee, the program director prepared a program plan which won endorsement by the committee and the board. The Universities of Minnesota and Wisconsin received grants in fiscal 1955, and then six more medical colleges the following year. But since the "program" had never been officially announced, it had a sub rosa quality that bothered the regulatory biology director. He proposed sending an announcement of the program to all medical school deans and establishing an advisory panel to evaluate applications—if, that is, he could get a budget big enough to meet a reasonable number of the requests.

The announcement resulted in applications from sixty medical schools requesting $1.8 million. Originally allocated $150,000—three-fourths of the amount asked for—the program received a supplemental allocation which permitted it to offer 18 awards, though two schools declined them since no funds were allowed for indirect costs. The response to the announcement furnished adequate justification for a continuation of the program and for a request (unsuccessful) for a bigger budget.

An important part of the program director's work may be defined as "coordination" with his counterparts in other federal agencies. In fiscal 1954 when draft executive orders stirred apprehension about Budget Bureau plans to centralize basic research in NSF, the Foundation's director, it will be recalled, visited other science agency heads and let them know that he had no imperial ambitions. Similarly the regulatory biology director organized a meeting, attended by seventy-five representatives of seven agencies supporting extramural research in the life sciences, which he believed helped dissipate "vague antagonisms previously held toward the Foundation." Although he intended to hold more such meetings, the exchange of information and plans normally occurred more casually, often in telephone conversations.

Not all interagency sessions were harmonious. Serving as an NSF representative on the governing board of the Bio Sciences Information Exchange, the program director soon learned that the impingement of BSIE's information-gathering functions on those of his NSF division created a "rather delicate" problem that had to "be handled with skill and tact." BSIE's growing cost and its efforts to solicit information and to satisfy subject-matter requests from individual investigators seemed to him to "go far beyond" the organization's main purpose of "providing an exchange among the participating agencies of information concerning projects supported or being considered." But since a majority of agency representatives thought otherwise, he suggested that NSF rethink its continued participation in BSIE.

Both time-consuming routine chores and matters of policy for biological science fell to the program director because of NSF's special responsibility for basic research. He served as a member of a staff committee attempting to write a comprehensive general report on national science policy; in cooperation with NIH and congressional staff members he helped prepare a summary report on House hearings emphasizing the need to support basic research in order to advance medical practice; with fellow BMS program directors he sought to develop "a functioning flexible system" of categorizing information derived from life science research so that it could be readily stored and retrieved; he acted as secretary for an ad hoc committee, appointed at the request of NSF by the Federation of American Societies for Experimental Biology and Medicine, on facilities for research on germ-free animals; to keep abreast of his field and in touch with working scientists, he traveled 60-80 days a year visiting colleges and universities and attending professional meetings; and in addition to his program duties he served as deputy division director.

Like his fellows in other programs, the regulatory biology head occasionally found reasons to complain to his superiors. He wanted a bigger budget of course; but though he made a strong case for more money, he evidently recognized that his program was not unique. He sought more help in the office and more funds for travel. These were conventional complaints, common to nearly all programs. The one really bitter note sounded in his annual reports concerned the policy decisions cutting off the BMS division's grants for undergraduate research and campus-controlled graduate student research unconnected with NSF research projects. These "unorthodox" grants, he said, had responded to needs expressed by scientists. The ending of some of these pioneering activities and the assignment of others to a division (SPE) that had shown little interest in them meant that BMS would "become essentially restricted to the routine business of considering 'research proposals.' " He pleaded for a reversal of the decisions stifling the kinds of "imaginative and constructive action" on which scientific progress and the Foundation's "role of leadership in the advancement of science" depended. The vehemence of the indictment shows a degree of frustration that less strong-willed program directors must also have felt sometimes under the Foundation's cautious leadership; but it displays too how important a research program director considered his work to be.

* * *

The social sciences gained admission to the NSF canon through constant citation of authority, step-by-step diplomacy, and pressure from a few members of Congress. With little support (and a good deal of opposition) from the communities of natural scientists and engineers, the National Science Board, and much of the NSF staff, those seeking a share of the Foundation's small budget for the social sciences had an uphill struggle. But by astute exegesis of the gospel of Vannevar Bush and by thoughtful studies and recommendations, a study director who joined the staff early in 1953 succeeded in winning eligibility of most areas of the social sciences for support through NSF's research and fellowship programs.[14]

A sociologist who had analyzed public opinion and statistics for the Office of War Information, the Office of Price Administration, and the

Budget Bureau, Harry Alpert came to NSF as a member of John Wilson's Program Analysis Office. With Wilson's backing he promptly began a systematic survey not only of the possible role of NSF in social science research but also of the scientific status of the social disciplines.[15] In this wide-ranging activity Alpert and his professional assistant, Bertha W. Rubinstein, conducted the kind of study that Bush had avoided but said social scientists should make to establish the validity of federal support for their subjects. Despite his doubts about some of the social sciences, based in part on his loathing of New Deal social planning, Bush had concluded that the congressional decision to permit but not require their support was sensible.[16] In testifying on the legislation he had said: "The proposed foundation should allow an opportunity for effective integration and partnership between the natural and social sciences and I believe that this pattern should be the result of careful study by the foundation after its establishment."[17] Alpert quoted those words time and again as a basis for his studies and for the formulation of a program based on the convergence of the natural sciences and the social.[18]

To win friends on the board was critical. Alpert, accompanied by Wilson, started with the chairman, Chester Barnard, who urged them to limit NSF's role strictly to the "hard science core" of the social sciences.[19] Alpert added Barnard's "hard science core" to Bush's "effective integration and partnership" as a shibboleth to rally support for his cause. There would be no hint of softness or of association with controversial subjects that could give openings to attack by "pure" scientists or conservative members of Congress.[20]

After a year of intensive study Alpert presented recommendations for a social science research program, whose aim of "effective integration and partnership between the natural and social sciences" should be pursued cautiously and experimentally for three years.[21] Research supported through the program should be methodologically rigorous, important for national welfare and defense, convergent with the natural sciences, and characterized by "objectivity, verifiability, and generality."[22]

Many natural scientists insisted that the social sciences were applied studies rather than basic, aiming to find solutions to social, economic, and political problems, and thus did not qualify for NSF support. Much of Alpert's effort was necessarily devoted to showing the need for *basic* research in the social sciences. His rationale was not unlike the one natural scientists used in justifying their own basic research programs. Instead of talking about the cultural value of new knowledge, they often spoke of its practical social utility—usually unanticipated, sometimes long deferred, but nonetheless certain. With somewhat greater expectation of a quicker use for knowledge, Alpert could cite evidence that dealing with such problems as unemployment and inflation required more "understanding of the determinants of the economic behavior of the basic decision-making units of the economy. Intelligent policy-making ... has more to gain in the long run from this kind of basic research than from direct attempts to enlist present knowledge in the solution of policy problems."[23]

Alpert and Rubinstein's study of the status of the social disciplines and of their public and private support showed a need for both greater emphasis on basic research and a larger supply of highly qualified social scientists. Federal social science research programs had recently been sharply cut. Private foundations had heavily supported the social sciences—the recently established Ford Foundation most notably—but mainly in "problem-oriented rather than research-oriented" activities. The Ford Foundation's behavioral sciences division was attempting to overcome the relative neglect of fundamental studies, but the bulk of its social science support went into action programs related to peace, education, democracy, and economic welfare.[24]

In contrast to Waterman's stand that NSF should support research in all important areas of the natural sciences, Alpert proposed a limited social science research program, sharply defined in relation to work sponsored by public and private organizations. "Risk capital" for chancy and unorthodox ventures would have to continue to come from private foundations, and so would support for evaluative studies and those—on sex and politics, for example—which might cause public controversy.[25]

Because the program in its experimental phase would be based on the idea of convergence with the natural sciences, it should have a home in both research divisions. And since the quality of NSF's own work of gathering and interpreting data on scientific manpower and research depended on precise application of social science techniques, the Foundation's "policy" arm also needed the guidance of a social scientist. Thus Alpert proposed a three-hat position for NSF's chief social scientist, who would divide his time between being program director for anthropological and related sciences (BMS), program director for statistical and related sciences (MPE), and study director for social science research (Program Analysis Office).[26]

Although social science research supported through the research divisions was sharply defined, Alpert conceived the program analysis task as much broader than simply collecting and publishing reliable statistics about scientific resources and manpower. The study director should be concerned "with science as a human social activity," encompassing studies of such matters as scientists' motivation and creativity and the functions of scientific organizations in the advancement of science. Similarly studies in the sociology of science would be valuable in showing the effects of science and technology on society and the economy, public attitudes toward science, the role of science in international relations, and other impacts of science on the social order. A related contribution to the understanding of science and a stimulus to its theoretical development would come through studies in the history and philosophy of science.[27]

Other recommendations for the social sciences dealt with fellowships, extension of the National Register to cover special skills, a budget of $258,000 for fiscal 1956, and consideration, after two years of program experience, of combining the research activities into a division of anthropological, sociological, and economic sciences.[28] After slight modification of some of Alpert's recommendations in a senior staff meeting,[29] Waterman submitted the paper and proposals to the board in May 1954.[30]

Several newly nominated board members were present for their first session. Perhaps their unfamiliarity with the touchy issue caused it to be put off until a later meeting.[31] Before that came, Alpert discussed the staff paper with board member Charles Dollard, president of Carnegie Corporation of New York, who invited two fellow Carnegie executives, James A. Perkins and John W. Gardner, both social scientists, and the president of the Social Science Research Council, Pendleton Herring, to join them. "Mr. Dollard," Alpert informed Waterman, "stated that he thought the approach of the Staff Paper was very reasonable and basically sound." To furnish the director with an additional argument should it be needed, Alpert quoted a recent statement by Vannevar Bush pointing out that differences between the natural and social sciences were often exaggerated and commending the progress of the social sciences toward precision.[32] When the board members next met, in Berkeley, California in the conference room of the state university's board of regents, they unanimously approved "the implementation of a limited program in the social sciences."[33] In effect, the board sanctioned a program that was already in being on a small scale.

The board approval was soon followed by the establishment of a program of socio-physical sciences in the MPE division (a counterpart to anthropological and related sciences in BMS), but in addition to such "convergent areas" as mathematical social science, human geography, economic engineering, and statistical design, the program supported research in the history, philosophy, and sociology of science. Raymond Seeger, the acting MPE division director, had a special interest in the history and philosophy of science, and though proposals in these subjects might fall within the scope of any research program or cut across divisional lines, his interest evidently made it politic to lump them with socio-physical sciences. In February 1955 NSF and the American Philosophical Society jointly sponsored a conference on the history, philosophy, and sociology of science, and at length an advisory panel was formed to give guidance to the program and help evaluate proposals in those disciplines.[34]

In carrying the good news of NSF's social science program to associations of psychologists, sociologists, geographers, and members of related professions, Alpert always mentioned its cautious, exploratory character.[35] Waterman too continued to emphasize how gingerly the Foundation was stepping into dangerous waters. "As you know, the Congress expects us to move cautiously and carefully in the direction of the social sciences," he replied to one inquiry. "It is anticipated that as a result of our experience and study over the next few years, we shall be in a sound position to consider appropriate next steps in the development of our social science research program."[36]

Waterman struck the same prudent note even when answering congressional entreaties to give *more* emphasis to the social sciences. Alpert may have taken heart from signs of a congressional shift from hostility to encouragement of the social sciences,[37] but the director worried about being pushed into applied research. ("Applied research drives out basic" ran his proverb.) So too did the National Science Board. Senator Estes Kefauver (D., Tennessee), wrote to all board members urging NSF to undertake fundamental research on the underlying causes of juvenile delinquency. A strong contender for the Democratic party's nomination for the presidency, Kefauver could not be treated lightly. Waterman said he shared the senator's concern, but he was sure Kefauver would "agree that it has been necessary for the Foundation to proceed cautiously in the area of the social sciences and only after serious study." The board worried also about NSF being dragooned into studies bearing on juvenile delinquency, even if the senator's call was for basic research.[38]

Alpert at least seized the opportunity presented by Kefauver's letter to suggest, most discreetly, that NSF might do more to "fill this gap" in basic social science research and move beyond the experimental phase of his program.[39] He had already recommended that the fiscal 1958 budget provide some funds for research support "in social science disciplines proper," and Waterman agreed to add to his half million dollar request for the program $100,000 more "for basic scientific research not covered by the criterion of convergence."[40] The board approved the extension, apparently without question, and it did not even come to the attention of congressional appropriations committees.[41]

The expanded research program included economics, experimental sociology, social statistics, and experimental social psychology. While requesting more money for these "non-convergent" fields in fiscal 1959—and extension of the fellowship program to make its coverage congruent with that of research—Alpert assured the director that "We have followed, and will continue to follow, the Congressional mandate to proceed cautiously in the social sciences." There would be no support of research on applied or mission-related subjects which fell in the scope of other agencies. But NSF was the only federal patron of basic research in anthropology economics, demography, and the history and philosophy of science. Their support by NSF was all the more important, Alpert suggested, because the Ford Foundation in 1956 had decided to shift all of its behavioral science efforts into action programs.[42]

While promising to heed the warning from Congress nearly a decade earlier to go slowly, Alpert exploited opposite advice now coming from the Hill. A report from the Senate subcommittee on juvenile delinquency reemphasized Kefauver's plea to NSF to support the social sciences "on a reasonable scale," and both Alpert and the Foundation's public information officer, Clyde C. Hall, brought the report's strong recommendations to Waterman's attention.[43] In the spring and summer of 1957 Senators Wayne L. Morse (D., Oregon) and Hubert H. Humphrey (D., Minnesota) spoke for the social sciences during consideration of NSF's fiscal 1958 budget, and Morse said that Warren Magnuson, the chairman of the subcommittee handling the appropriation bill, agreed with him that the Foundation should spend $1 million of the $40 million appropriation for social science research and fellowships.[44] Soon after Sputnik Vice President Richard M. Nixon began to become interested in the Foundation's social science activities as well as those of other federal agencies.[45]

The social sciences did not get as much money as Morse urged, but the separate research programs were unified in August 1957 and removed from their obscurity as "anthropological and related sciences" and "sociophysical sciences." Now designated as a *program* for social science research—not an office or division—Alpert's combined functions came under the general direction of the associate director for research.[46] A consolidated advisory panel was established which was broadly representative of the four main program areas (anthropological, economic, and sociological sciences, and the history and philosophy of science).[47] The unified program, clearly labeled as social science and no longer requiring that proposals meet the convergence criterion, quickly attracted a large number of research proposals—more than one hundred in fiscal 1958, requesting about $4 million, of which 49 were approved and $725,950 granted.[48]

As described in the preceding chapter, Harry Kelly resisted Alpert's move to name specific additional social science disciplines as eligible for NSF fellowships. This battle had also been won by the spring of 1958, though quarreling continued over whether any certain amount of the fellowship budget was to be committed to awards for the social sciences.[49]

By this time Alpert was preparing to leave NSF to become graduate dean of the University of Oregon. At their last meeting before his departure the members of his advisory panel signed a letter to Waterman expressing their appreciation of Alpert's accomplishments. They hoped that the steady advances he and Rubinstein had made could be ensured by the establishment of a division dedicated to "basic, hard-core social science."[50] Still, the war was not over. In the Senate Morse joined in the call for divisional status, a bigger budget, and better representation for the social sciences on the National Science Board. In the House Morse's fellow townsman—and soon Alpert's too—Charles O. Porter (D., Oregon) added his plea for a larger budget. Later Porter, like Morse, criticized President Eisenhower for failing to nominate a single eminent social scientist to the board; since Dollard's and Sophie Aberle's terms expired in 1958, the only one of the twenty-four members educated as a social scientist was Frederick Middlebush, the University of Missouri president emeritus, and his field (political science) was not among those eligible for NSF support. "I cannot escape the conclusion," Porter said, "that the President's action will be a blow to the small but promising social science research program of the National Science Foundation."[51]

Meanwhile the National Science Board was trying to decide whether to continue Alpert's expanding by inchmeal or return to the rule of "convergence." Early in 1958 the growing clamor from Capitol Hill and the Vice President's interest in behavioral research contributed to the appointment of a board committee to consider NSF's future role in the social sciences.[52] It was a distasteful subject for some board members, among them the recently appointed Kevin McCann, president of Defiance College and a speech writer and friend of President Eisenhower's. ". . . one of these days soon, I feel," McCann wrote Middlebush, "we have to face up to the fact that the social sciences—except for a few extremely limited areas—are a source of trouble beyond anything released by Pandora." So much needed doing for the natural sciences, quickly and with too little money, that "the Foundation should not be fragmentized by a vain effort to comprehend the entire universe of human search."[53]

At the suggestion of the Reverend Theodore M. Hesburgh, chairman of the four-member board committee, Alpert prepared a staff paper on the main "problems, issues and suggested resolutions" that needed to be considered. Alpert's comments on these matters naturally defended the policies and course he had followed.[54]

After stormy arguments the four board members, evenly split, settled on a report saying that the program so far had been "safe" and "conservative." The two "more liberal members" questioned its "restricted parameters." The committee's division prevented any forthright recommendations except making the "program" into an "office," which should follow "the same general philosophy as in the past, with the possible listing of special areas in the social sciences to be supported." If the activities of the office reached a level like that of the existing divisions, then the board should consider elevating it to divisional status. Finally, advisory committees should be expanded somewhat to ensure representation of the several social science disciplines. Father Hesburgh's conclusion sounds rather discouraged:

It perhaps should be noted that what is reported here would be a minimal statement of the various and conflicting points of view that were expressed on the part of members of the committee. It would be possible to report opinions far to each side of this minimal statement. Some members of the Committee take a dim view of the social science activity generally, unless very tightly restricted to its "scientific" aspects, and other members of the Committee feel that the area should be considerably broadened beyond the present safe policy statement. However, the above report may be taken as a reasonably accurate lowest common denominator of the various opinions expressed and, as such, should certainly be exposed to a much broader discussion on the part of the whole Board.[55]

Even this "minimal statement" was nearly thrown out by the board. But since Hesburgh was on a trip to Africa, Bronk asked the board to wait until the committee chairman was present to defend the report. Bronk told Hesburgh privately that he would probably have to modify the report to get it through. Hesburgh thought it ridiculous to draw what little blood still remained from the anemic statement and, at a board meeting near the end of 1958, presented the report essentially as originally written. Perhaps, as he recalls, the members this time were in a good mood or perhaps they hesitated to challenge his obvious conviction. In any event, they approved the report.[56]

* * *

The summer of 1957 was a season of discontent in some NSF offices. John Wilson, writing his division's annual report to the director, saw disturbing signs that the Foundation might be entering "a static phase," which in the normal course of organizational change would be "rapidly displaced by movement in a backward direction, accompanied by a marked deterioration of staff morale and heightened interest in individual and unit welfare," sharply contrasting with "the cohesiveness and singleness of purpose" of the agency's early years. Then program directors had "enjoyed a great deal of latitude in initiating ways and means of assisting the country's scientific enterprise" and had shown "imagination and administrative skills" in solving difficult problems. But now government "retrenchment," in which NSF shared—for the first time its budget was showing no gain—along with narrow interpretations of the Foundation's statutory authority, seemed to foreshadow the end of exciting change. With program directors limited essentially to "routine processing of research-support applications," NSF would have trouble recruiting and holding first-rate people. To prevent drift toward mediocrity and dreary routine, the Foundation should perhaps review its programs and mode of operation. If budgetary growth had come to an end, it might be best for NSF to modify its traditional system of research support to an experimental one whose successes could be adopted by other government agencies.[57]

Wilson avoided a direct challenge to the conservatism of the board and director by casting this "prospectus" in a speculative tone as if his fears might be completely illusory. Yet there is no mistaking the restlessness he and his colleagues in BMS felt about restraints that increasingly hindered their attempts to foster research in ways other than through individual projects. A year later, as mentioned above, the program director for regulatory biology expressed his frustration much more bluntly.

These BMS officials spoke of the "routine processing" of research proposals as if this highly professional work were dull and undemanding. Obviously it did not alone offer a sufficiently stimulating challenge to them. The complaint discloses a desire to influence the course of science that is not quite in keeping with the customary disavowal of "masterminding." In fact, NSF scientists and their advisers often expressed ambiguous attitudes about the agency's appropriate role in the support of research.

The ambiguity shows in recurring debates in advisory committee meetings over the desirability of giving special emphasis to "gaps" and slow-moving areas of science or of relying instead on "random" proposals to reflect the wisdom of the scientific marketplace. Although there was broad agreement on supporting the best science, differences multiplied over the ways to pursue excellence.

Wilson kept pushing for grants broader and more flexible than those for individual projects, though he knew Waterman's mind better than to advocate departmental or institutional grants. Thus, shortly after Sputnik resulted in the prospect of supplementary appropriations, Wilson wrote for his division:

> ... we would not recommend a departure in the direction of institutional grants, but rather hold to a concept of a grant covering an area of science, but with considerably decreased specificity over that which is now commonly regarded within the Foundation as a satisfactory project proposal. We would go so far as to recommend that the extension include the searching out of highly qualified individuals for the purpose of granting funds to support their activities, in contrast to the more passive practice of stimulation through program director visits, and then awaiting proposals.[58]

Ten days before, Waterman had told the BMS divisional committee that he and the board agreed that research grants might be broadened, but not by providing departmental support. It was possible to assess the merit of individual scientists, but efforts to judge the quality of an organizational unit made up of persons of varying competence would put NSF in an untenable position.[59]

While the like-minded program directors in BMS and their advisers tended to speak with one voice on the desirability of greater breadth and freedom in NSF's research-support policy, this was less true of the MPE group, mainly perhaps because of differences among the several disciplines and their felt needs, though the "considerable amount of internal dissension and discord" within the division observed by one MPE panel chairman may have prevented unity too.[60] Spokesmen for mathematics urged government agencies to "move in the direction of group grants," but the MPE divisional committee thought that while "block grants" might appropriately cover the research programs of three or four professors, they should not encompass whole departments.[61] Engineering groups, unhappy that their success rate in winning NSF grants was so low—and no doubt because they resented the snobbery of many academic scientists—sometimes urged special programs of research and education aimed at improving the quality of persons entering their profession and at achieving parity with the natural sciences. A retired board member who had considered himself a representative of industry regretted that NSF had not made "a special case" of engineering research, "or at least relax[ed] the policy that first and overriding consideration be given to the scientific merit of a proposal."[62] There were occasional pleas from advisory committees for favoritism for young scientists, and surely some program directors and their panelists did give them an advantage; yet, others may have agreed with a division director who advocated "supporting preferentially and predominantly the mature scientists who are probing at the frontiers of knowledge."[63]

Most board members accepted Waterman's research-support ideas without serious question. In June 1957 the board spent most of a two-day session at MIT's Endicott House discussing the Foundation's policies, especially those on the criteria for selecting areas of research to receive the greatest support and the methods that should be employed to appraise proposals. Waterman enumerated three considerations that he thought most important: first, the progress of science; second, the health of science departments in colleges and universities; and third, the development of the individual scientist. Of this triad, only departmental well-being did not receive direct emphasis in NSF's research policy, he said, though the Foundation did take care not to harm the growth of institutions of higher education. Warren Weaver, speaking out of long experience in the Rockefeller Foundation, urged a more active role by NSF's professional staff in seeking out lesser-known scientists who were working on "the frontiers of science" in specified areas; and the board agreed that the agency was now mature enough to "exert leadership in certain avenues of research provided this is done judiciously." The Foundation's "highest ideal," to which other aims were incidental, should be "to stimulate the furtherance of research as a vital part of the intellectual, moral, and cultural strength of America." This lofty aim required a highly competent NSF staff, and the board conceived its duty to be to help the director recruit such a staff, to provide it with ample travel funds to become familiar with pioneering research, and to educate Congress on the Foundation's objectives.[64]

Reflecting on the board meeting in a letter to a member who had missed the session, Waterman expressed some reservations about Weaver's suggestion. Admittedly, the director wrote, "we cannot avoid 'managing' national research" so long as NSF's budget remained small, but the Foundation should try to avoid "putting pressure on scientists to conduct research on special topics and certain areas." Although Weaver had described his method of encouraging research as "suction" rather than "pressure," Waterman evidently thought they amounted to the same thing. "I pointed out," he wrote, "that a Federal agency should do this with great caution and not by trying to persuade scientists to do research against their inclination but rather to stimulate special fields by conferences and informal contacts to make certain that individuals competent in such areas have the funds and equipment they need. I have had quite a bit of experience with this method and it works quite well."[65]

Most differences were over means, not ends. Nearly everyone, on the staff and on the board, agreed that NSF should support the best science, which meant the best scientists. If one asked a research program director to state his guiding philosophy, his ready response in this prefeminist time was apt to be: "Support the man, not the project." Those he considered his clientele would have answered the same way. When William V. Consolazio, program director for molecular biology, asked several leading biologists about the kinds of help they needed from NSF, Lawrence Blinks ended his thoughtful reply with a brief summary: "It works out to this: people rather than projects; fair support for many without undue concentration in 'research factories'; *time for thought*. Good luck in providing it!"[66]

But an NSF program director did not have Warren Weaver's free range in discovering and encouraging talented persons. When Consolazio tried to promote a long-term grant for the nuclear physicist Leo Szilard to continue his new studies in theoretical biology on a roving assignment at five universities, the BMS divisional committee, after a tiring debate, "regretfully recommended" declination, in part because they thought "a firm and responsible connection with a single institution" better than "multiple weak institutional connections." The proposal did, however, lead the committee to suggest the possibility of a competitive "career investigatorship program."[67] When a board member reported to Waterman that a group of Berkeley physical scientists thought NSF should award an investigator support on the basis of a more or less specific proposal, [but] telling him off the record to use his own judgment in how he spends the grant while keeping reasonably within the bounds of his original proposal," Raymond Seeger commented that the Foundation could hardly "allow people to ask funds on one basis and then allow them indiscriminately to use these on another basis." Waterman of course agreed. NSF favored freedom, but not that much.[68]

Although not as free as they wanted to be to influence the directions and conditions of research, NSF program directors sought to use the hands-off, essentially reactive system of reviewing unsolicited individual proposals to support science of high quality. In his annual report for fiscal year 1958 the assistant director of the MPE division wrote that "the Foundation's aim should be to make the peaks higher and to leave the filling of the valleys largely to others."[69] But by that time Sputnik had ended the "retrenchment" that so discouraged John Wilson a year before. Instead of "a static phase" and then retrogression, an era of flush times was about to begin that would even permit NSF to raise the level of scientific valleys.

RAYMOND J. SEEGER
Acting Assistant Director, MPE, 1952-57

JOHN T. WILSON
Program Director, Psychology, 1952-55;
Assistant Director, BMS, 1955-61

ALBERT THOMAS
Chairman of NSF's Appropriations
Subcommittee, 1950-52, 1955-66
(Courtesy Albert Thomas Papers,
Woodson Research Center,
Rice University Library)

BOWEN C. DEES
Program Director, Fellowships, 1951-56;
Deputy Assistant Director, SPE, 1956-59

ADMINISTRATORS OF RESEARCH AND EDUCATION PROGRAMS
AND A CONGRESSIONAL PRIME MOVER

DORIS McCARN, THE DIRECTOR'S
SECRETARY, AND WATERMAN

VIRGINIA V. SIDES, SPE

MILDRED C. ALLEN
Program Analysis Office and
Office of Special Studies with
JOSEPHINE K. DOHERTY (RIGHT), BMS

BERTHA W. RUBINSTEIN
Program Analysis Office and
BMS, with Waterman

KEY STAFF IN THE EARLY YEARS

LAURENCE M. GOULD (LEFT)
AND THE REV. THEODORE M. HESBURGH IN ANTARCTICA

HARRY ALPERT
Program Director, Social Science Research, 1953-58
(Courtesy University of Oregon Archives)

LLOYD V. BERKNER
President, Associated Universities, Inc.
(Courtesy Brookhaven National Laboratory)

PROMOTERS OF BIG SCIENCE AND SOCIAL SCIENCE

BIG SCIENCE: SIGNING THE RADIO ASTRONOMY CONTRACT

Seated: Lloyd Berkner and Waterman. *Standing,* left to right: Lee Anna Embrey, Wilson F. Harwood, James M. Mitchell, Franklin J. Callender (Grants Administrator), C. E. Sunderlin, Charles B. Ruttenberg (Attorney), William J. Hoff

DON K. PRICE

JULIUS A. STRATTON

J. W. BUCHTA
(Courtesy University of Minnesota News Service)

WILLIAM G. COLMAN

COMMITTEEMEN AND REPORT WRITERS

SCIENCE ADVISORY COMMITTEE OF THE OFFICE OF DEFENSE MOBILIZATION

(meeting with President Eisenhower and ODM Director Arthur S. Flemming). *Seated*, left to right: Flemming, Eisenhower, Lee A. DuBridge, I. I. Rabi. *Standing*, left to right: Emanuel R. Piore, Oliver E. Buckley, Alan T. Waterman, James B. Fisk, Detlev W. Bronk, Bruce S. Old, James R. Killian, Jr., David Z. Beckler, Robert F. Bacher, Jerrold R. Zacharias, Charles C. Lauritsen.

14
Bigger Science

On a trip to the West Coast in February 1954 Alan Waterman talked with physicists at Stanford and Caltech about how NSF might help meet their research needs. While in Pasadena he also talked with two of the nation's leading astronomers, both observatory directors, about requirements in astronomy.[1] These conversations dealt with matters of "big science"—high-energy physics research on the one hand, and photoelectric, solar, and radio telescopes on the other—that would command an increasing portion of the Foundation's attention and money during the next four years.

The larger ventures brought larger problems for NSF's advisory groups, research program officers, and management. Program directors, unaccustomed to the new scale of scientific entrepreneurship, regional and institutional competition, and accusations of monopoly and power bids, sometimes concluded that they were now engaged in politics or big business, not science. Those administering predominantly "little science" programs feared that they would lose some of their "share" of the Foundation's budget, and even those getting increases for large projects worried about taking on long-term commitments for maintenance and operation of the new research centers that might steadily grow and drain the resources for individual investigators.

Other developments warped administrative tidiness and simplicity. Emerging scientific fields such as oceanography, geophysics, and atmospheric sciences cut across traditional disciplinary lines, requiring adjustments in NSF's patterns of evaluation and support. Some of these new interests demanded expensive equipment and facilities and the cooperation of many widely dispersed investigators and data collectors; thus they increased the pull toward big science. Occasionally they carried an element of applied research, as when cloud physics verged into weather modification, that might divert NSF from its exclusively basic-science role.

The Foundation's financial administration of U.S. activities in the International Geophysical Year (IGY) especially expanded the agency's scientific horizons. In this cooperative endeavor, rhetoric about the international character of science became concrete reality. But so too did national rivalry. If NSF's interest in putting satellites into space sprang from desire for new knowledge of nature, the Russian success in getting there first had an enormous public impact that lifted the Cold War and the Foundation to a new stage of development.

* * *

The trouble with the many small astronomical observatories that dotted the American landscape, Otto Struve wrote in 1940, was that they had to search for something they were "able to do instead of what is scientifically important and interesting." He suggested an extension of the kind of cooperation represented by the two observatories he headed— Yerkes in Wisconsin and McDonald in Texas. Five or six universities should join in asking a private foundation to help them organize a new and more powerful observatory in the good-seeing area of the West Texas mountains.[2]

Not a private, but a public foundation seemed a more promising source of aid with the establishment of NSF a decade later. The American Astronomical Society lost little time in publishing its hoped-for support from the new agency. And almost as soon as NSF was open for business, three state universities—Arizona, Indiana, and Ohio State—submitted a joint proposal for locating in the Southwest a new observatory for photoelectric research in astronomy. The proposal—unsuccessful in itself— had consequences. It was one factor leading to the meeting of an ad hoc group of astronomical consultants, soon to become a formal NSF advisory panel, who favored the creation of a photoelectric observatory which would represent a larger number of cooperating institutions and be open to astronomers throughout the country.[3]

Following the advice of another ad hoc group, the Foundation arranged a conference in the summer of 1953 at the Lowell Observatory in Flagstaff, Arizona to discuss photoelectric astronomical problems, techniques, and instrumentation. Near the end of the two-day session Leo Goldberg of the University of Michigan, a member of the Foundation's MPE divisional committee, proposed that the participants think more broadly than about a photoelectric telescope and seek instead an observing center for all branches of optical astronomy. His suggestion of a cooperative interuniversity observatory changed small thinking to big and resulted in a conference recommendation that NSF appoint a committee to study the technical requirements and a desirable location for a new observatory.[4]

A few months later Waterman appointed an advisory panel for a "national astronomical observatory." Its chairman was an experienced and forceful administrator, Robert R. McMath, an industrialist, codonor and director of the McMath-Hulbert Observatory, and a colleague of Goldberg's in Michigan's astronomy department. During the next four years McMath guided the complex investigations by astronomers and worked harmoniously with NSF officials. Though he and the Foundation's astronomy program directors had trouble in prying a letter of intent through the NSF director's office, the agency gradually made a firm commitment to establish a national observatory for optical astronomy.[5]

Meanwhile scientists interested in a new way of probing the universe—one where the United States lagged behind several other countries—had similar success in getting NSF to support the development of a national observatory for radio astronomy. In contrast to the optical astronomers' smooth and businesslike progress toward their goal, however, the course of the radio group was rough and stormy.

Both observatories had similar origins and for a while followed parallel paths. Like the optical astronomers who collaborated in the Arizona-Indiana-Ohio State proposal, a group of scientists at Harvard and MIT wanting to build a large "dish" for radio astronomy soon concluded that their need exceeded their resources. They turned not directly to the Foundation but to Associated Universities, Incorporated (AUI), an organization sponsored by nine private northeastern universities which operated the Brookhaven National Laboratory on Long Island under contract with the Atomic Energy Commission. AUI, headed by Lloyd V. Berkner, whose expansive imagination inspired several "big science" enterprises, was deeply involved in most of the later negotiations with the Foundation. Just as the photoelectric conference at Flagstaff led to the appointment of McMath's panel, an advisory panel for radio astronomy, headed by Merle A. Tuve of the Carnegie Institution of Washington, resulted from a conference in January 1954 sponsored by NSF, Caltech, and the Carnegie Institution. Another conference, in May, called by AUI and chaired by Berkner, recommended that AUI ask NSF to support planning and feasibility studies for a large radio astronomy facility.[6]

In reviewing AUI's request NSF's radio astronomy panel recommended that the search for a site be limited to the area within three hundred miles of Washington, in part because most scientists and engineers interested in the technique lived in the East and a radio facility there would offset the West's advantages for optical observing. The panel's recommendation of a grant was approved but without being referred to the National Science Board, since at the time the NSF staff assumed that planning and feasibility studies did not require board approval. This omission, coupled with the exclusive control of AUI by elite private institutions of the Northeast, may have contributed to the dissatisfaction with that organization's plans soon to be shown by some southern members of the board.[7]

The simultaneous development of plans for optical and radio astronomy observatories—and for NSF support of university nuclear accelerators, reactors, and computers—forced decisions on what conditions should govern the agency's investment in these expensive undertakings and how they could be fitted into the Foundation's budget. In May 1955 the National Science Board adopted the following recommendations of its MPE committee:

1. The NSF should recommend as a national policy the desirability of government support of large-scale basic scientific facilities when the need is clear and it is in the national interest, when the merit is endorsed by panels of experts, and when funds are not readily available from other sources.

2. A national astronomical observatory, a major radio astronomy facility, and university research installations of computers, accelerators and reactors are examples of such desirable activities for NSF.

3. Funds for such large-scale projects should be handled under special budgets.

The "special budgets" provision was meant to prevent any encroachment "upon the regular established programs of the Foundation." Moreover, the board wanted "an appraisal of future commitments or requirements . . . prior to being required to approve specific projects."[8] Informing Gabriel Hauge in the White House of the board's action and of NSF's intention to ask for funds for large projects in its fiscal 1957 budget, Waterman said that the recommended national policy would extend to fundamental science the kind of government support given to applied-science facilities for defense.[9]

While the board was recommending policy, AUI was proceeding with its feasibility study. The choice of Green Bank, West Virginia as the best available location got the approval of Tuve's advisory panel, but his and some board members' opposition to AUI as a possible manager of the observatory began to build during the early months of 1956. Tuve distrusted Berkner, but most of the avowed objections rose from the regional character of AUI; the panel held that the managing organization should be more broadly national in its makeup, and so did three southern scientists—Paul Gross, Joseph Morris, and William Houston—on the National Science Board. Raymond Seeger may have been imagining a bit when he suggested that the location of the observatory in West Virginia made the southern board members feel that Yankees were "once more invading their sacred territory without an invitation," but undoubtedly sectional pride influenced their stand.[10] Besides the criticism of AUI's narrowly regional constituency, opposition was based on the organization's primary responsibility to the Atomic Energy Commission. An observatory in the West Virginia hills with a paraboloid dish 140 feet wide, budgeted to cost $3.5 million in fiscal 1957, might loom large in NSF's thinking but seem only an inconsequential sideline to the managers of the Brookhaven National Laboratory.[11]

Berkner's reluctance to allow other institutions than the AUI nine to share in the direction of the proposed observatory continued to be the main obstacle. In response to Waterman's urging of wider representation, Berkner suggested alternatives—a "visiting committee," for example—that did not satisfy the objectors on the board or Tuve, who chaired a deeply divided panel, three of whose seven members favored management by AUI. Tuve and Bart J. Bok, a Harvard astronomer on his panel, at an informal meeting in Berkner's office "kept pointing out . . . that he should not take an inflexible attitude toward having the AUI Trustees controlling the facility." Helen S. Hogg, NSF's program director for astronomy in 1955-56, recorded that "Dr. Berkner's attitude softened noticeably with time, and the next day he said that AUI, albeit with regret, would accept a different trustee setup."[12] Still, the National Science Board's MPE committee, hearing of AUI's continuing "reservations" about extending its membership, concluded that a decision on management of the observatory should be put off until after NSF had called a conference to discuss the feasibility study "and the whole question of a pattern for a truly national organization to further radio astronomy research."[13]

If Tuve's objections to the AUI plan had been only technical, they might have been resolved amicably. But other matters greatly disturbed him, among them the driving ambition and strong-mindedness of Berkner, his onetime colleague in the Carnegie Institution. Tuve called the feasibility study's provision for a separate NSF advisory board for the radio observatory "poisonous," the proposed visiting committee a "whitewash," and the ultimate goal of a vastly expensive 600-foot dish an AUI "power bid." Tuve said he disliked leading an effort to replace AUI by a more representative organization because he had become *persona non grata* to Berkner, and AUI might discriminate against him or his younger colleagues when they sought to do research at the new observatory. Nonetheless he did win assurance that the forthcoming conference would give a hearing to alternative management schemes and he took steps to see that one would be presented.[14]

Nearly fifty people attended the conference on radio astronomy in Washington on July 11, 1956, proposed and presided over by Detlev

Bronk. Representatives of AUI, of the Tuve and McMath panels, of the National Science Board's MPE committee, of a score of research institutions, and members of the NSF staff and invited observers from the Naval Research Laboratory and the Office of Naval Research sat through a day-long session that one experienced government hand said was unlike anything he had ever seen before. Joe Morris, describing the diversity of opposing views to fellow board member Julius A. Stratton, provost of MIT, paraphrased Winston Churchill: "Never have so many thought so differently on so few matters!" "Oh, it was a dramatic day!" a then-brand-new program director remembered many years later.[15]

The amenities were quickly forgotten. Tuve, next on the agenda after Waterman's statement of the purpose of the conference, attacked what he called the scheme of "a very small group of men" as grandiose, opportunistic, and self-serving. The AUI plan, he said, would develop a specialized technology of electronics and split the discipline of astronomy. There was nothing wrong with Green Bank as a site for radio observations, but NSF should at least ponder keeping astronomy intact by constructing a single optical-radio observatory in Arizona. Reminding his audience that this was the Foundation's first venture in developing a large facility for a basic science—a matter that weighed on Waterman's and board members' minds too—Tuve urged deliberate efforts to integrate a promising new technique with traditional astronomy, to guard against a commitment to huge expenditures later, and to choose a form of control and operation that would keep science tied to its university base rather than entrust it to peripheral "self-approving groups of 'experts'." NSF should get its policies clear first, not have to repent later.

Berkner tried to cool the air. To those who feared that the Green Bank observatory under AUI's direction would be an independent laboratory, he said that instead it would, like Brookhaven, be "national in every sense, . . . open to qualified members of every college, university, and institution." Supported by Donald H. Menzel of Harvard and Jerome B. Wiesner of MIT, he urged NSF to decide quickly on the management organization, which should then select a director and staff.

Goldberg made the issue more explicit when he insisted that in a national observatory "there should be something more than a liaison between the facility and the universities. Its operation should, in fact, be controlled chiefly by the universities." While only a few institutions were then engaged in radio astronomy, the number would grow, and the organization operating the observatory "should be sufficiently flexible to permit both the addition of new members and the subtraction of older ones in order to insure that at all times the policies of the facility are controlled by those universities that have a vital stake in it."

An alternative to AUI, inspired by Tuve, was proposed by William G.

Pollard, executive director of the Oak Ridge Institute of Nuclear Studies (ORINS). He described that organization and offered it as a model for a corporation of national scope, made up of "a sizable group of universities" including all that had "a valid interest in this facility" and permitting the election of new members. The members would elect a board of directors which would manage the corporation's affairs. Pollard had already discussed the proposed corporation with President Irvin Stewart of West Virginia University, who was willing to start the necessary action promptly. Naturally some delays would occur, but "in the long haul," Pollard argued, "one would end up with a corporate body of universities who felt that in a real sense this facility belonged to them." Brief comments from National Science Board members Houston and Morris showed their approval of Pollard's idea.

The argument grew more heated in midafternoon. Wiesner accused Tuve of unfairly putting an "onus on AUI" as "people that loved to manage things." Perhaps the Cambridge group who had sought Berkner's help had made a mistake in dropping their original idea of an eastern regional facility for a "national" one, but Berkner could make it work. "I don't think you could find a man of equal stature," Wiesner said.

Tuve warned again that the AUI plan would split optical from radio astronomy. "We have got a limited divorce," he said; "if you are going to confirm it, today is when it happens." Bart Bok disagreed, arguing that "the tensions in the family are lessening." Other speakers thought division would be a disaster and, while willing to allow separate panels to guide the development of optical and radio observatories, they insisted that ultimately there should be a single astronomy panel.[16]

The sharp conflict of views left little ground for consensus. At length Edward Reynolds, administrative vice-president of Harvard and an AUI trustee, rose to say how disturbed he was by the "atmosphere" of the conference. Extending his arm full length and pointing toward Tuve, Reynolds looked to an observer like Jove hurling thunderbolts from Olympus. "I have no fear of contradiction from my colleagues as Trustees of AUI," Reynolds said; "we don't want this contract under this atmosphere. You are going to have to want us enthusiastically if we are to take it. Then we can do a good job for you."

Since so much of the day's argument had revolved around the "regional" versus "national" question, Bronk, in bringing the conference to a close, reminded the antagonists that "great universities are neither regional nor national, they are international." Though a consummate chairman, Bronk could perform no miracle of synthesizing points of agreement—except one that he and Waterman had come to during the debate: McMath's and Tuve's panels would have to meet together to consider their relationship.

Too many advisers were planning menus for the NSF astronomy

kitchen. Obviously "depaneling" would make life simpler for the Foundation. If that desire was not immediately achievable, then at least the different groups should keep in close touch. NSF arranged that not only the two observatory panels should meet jointly but that the regular astronomy program panel should attend the conference too. Held at Ann Arbor with McMath presiding, the joint session on July 23 reached agreement that NSF "should proceed toward 'unity' in all aspects of both the optical and radio facility plans and operation." While the separate panels would presumably continue in existence until the observatories had begun operations, the Foundation's regular panel would then become the responsible advisory body. "In the meantime, to assure the promotion and preservation of unity in astronomy, close liaison or alternatively partial or complete merger of the panels would be indicated."[17]

Waterman and his legal office moved promptly to arrange for the acquisition of the Green Bank site and for zoning regulations that would ensure its fitness for radio observations. Although a West Virginia congressman up for re-election accused NSF of tipping off his opponent of the site selection before its announcement, the agency seems to have managed rather well to keep rumors under control and the state's officials satisfied and cooperative.[18]

But the problem of construction and management of the observatory remained. Following the July 11 conference in Washington, Pollard quickly revised his proposed agreement for an interuniversity association and asked a dozen astronomers and university presidents if they would serve as original incorporators. Tuve, the prime mover in this effort to block AUI, wanted an immediate response to the invitation so that the first meeting of the trustees of the new corporation would take place within a month, thanks to the cooperation of administrators in West Virginia University.[19]

Menzel, director of the Harvard College Observatory, was one of those invited to be an original incorporator. Still seething over Tuve's accusations at the Washington conference and angry at the request for an immediate answer, Menzel asked Waterman to try to postpone a decision on Pollard's proposal. "Harvard definitely will not be stampeded," he said; it favored AUI instead of a new corporation. In telephone conversations with Seeger and Frank K. Edmondson, NSF's program director for astronomy, Menzel blasted this gun-to-the-head demand, suggested that Tuve be rotated off the radio astronomy panel, and blamed a southern "pork barrel interest" and "selfish motives on the part of the Carnegie-Cal Tech axis" for the attempt to discredit AUI.[20] Menzel also wrote directly to Tuve and castigated him for stirring up sectional emotions in letters to southern educators and for the "false" statement that AUI was too busy directing the big operation at Brookhaven to ensure "full and unbiased attention" to Green Bank. Menzel understood that Tuve had made this statement in the name of his panel without consulting its members. At the "stormy" Washington conference, Menzel wrote, the only questioning of AUI's competence had come from Tuve and his Carnegie-Caltech allies. While the Pollard proposal was "offered in the best of faith," it would delay the radio observatory by at least two years. AUI could move ahead immediately. "I have good reason to believe," Menzel said, "that AUI will broaden the representation on its board of trustees to include astronomers on a basis that will strengthen the national character of the program." To Waterman this point was crucial.[21]

Waterman did ask Tuve not to proceed hastily, yet a letter from Berkner offering to make a proposal for the construction and operation of the observatory made no mention of enlarging the AUI board. Waterman invited AUI to submit a preliminary proposal, which NSF would consider along with any others it might receive;[22] but because of the vehement opposition to AUI he talked with several board members about a possible way out of the dilemma. As Berkner was sure to hear of these conversations, they would serve to put pressure on him to expand his board.

One of those whom Waterman telephoned was Stratton, who had first suggested to his Cambridge colleagues wanting a radio telescope that they get the help of AUI. Morris had already appealed to Stratton to persuade AUI to broaden its geographical base, and he replied that the "intemperate" opposition to Berkner's group, even if ill-founded, was a convincing reason not to select AUI to manage the facility. But to organize a new interuniversity group would consume valuable time and hardly seemed justifiable. He preferred a contract with "a specific university with demonstrable experience and interest," or perhaps with an industrial corporation. Waterman's suggestion was for NSF to make a contract with West Virginia University. Stratton and the other board members with whom he discussed the idea had a high regard for Irvin Stewart, who had effectively assisted Bush and Conant throughout World War II, but some of them questioned the engineering and managerial strengths of his institution. And what if he should leave the presidency? Waterman agreed that the competence of the university needed investigation, but he continued to cling to the idea even after Stewart expressed his hesitance to take on the responsibility alone. Stewart was interested, however, in jointly administering the observatory with other institutions through representation in a new corporation or an expanded AUI.[23]

Closer to Green Bank than the campus of West Virginia University was Charlottesville, and Waterman next explored the chance of management by the University of Virginia. President Colgate Darden said his institution would be willing to serve, perhaps in association with Stewart's, but his polite reply, relayed through a member of the university's physics department, showed no eagerness for the job.[24]

Several other institutions were mentioned as candidates for sole manager, and Waterman continued to cast in hope of a strike almost until his board met on August 24. Owing to some members' insistence, which he evidently shared, that AUI should be ruled out unless it added trustees, he mentioned receiving word that the organization would agree at its annual meeting in October to admit "three satisfactory outside representatives to its Board from the rest of the country at large." Since Waterman had failed to find an institution eager to be the sole contractor and since the formation of a new corporation on the ORINS model would probably entail long delays and might set a bad precedent for other large-scale facility projects, the prospects for selection of AUI improved greatly when it gave in to demands for broader representation. Bronk's advice to the director may have tipped the balance decisively. The National Science Board chairman still believed, as he obviously had at the July conference, that "it would be more satisfactory to have management in the hands of an existing organization." Waterman thought so too. He shared some of Tuve's mistrust of the AUI president and, though he never really liked the Tuve-Pollard scheme, wanted to throw Berkner off balance by encouraging the offering of alternative forms of management. All along Waterman's strategy had been to put pressure on Berkner to "keep AUI in bounds" and force him "to develop a national plan."[25]

At the August board meeting Waterman presented the AUI plan, Pollard's proposal, and a letter from the University of Virginia expressing its willingness to manage the observatory. He reported that options to purchase the land had been obtained and zoning restrictions passed by a special session of the West Virginia legislature. Now the board had to decide on management. Bronk, emphasizing the importance of this first NSF experience on a big project of this sort, hoped that the board would manifest "the unanimity which has characterized its actions in the past." Morris submitted a resolution from his MPE committee authorizing the director to negotiate a five-year contract with AUI to establish and operate a radio astronomy observatory, with the understanding that at the end of that period NSF would consider establishing a common management for both the radio and the optical observatories; in selecting the director and an advisory committee for the observatory, AUI should consult with the Foundation's director. To pay for land at the site, additional studies, and beginning operations, the resolution authorized expenditures up to $800,000. Although the resolution got unanimous approval, a residue of mistrust of AUI prompted a board request that AUI should always emphasize "that they were acting under arrangement with the National Science Foundation to provide a Radio Astronomy Observatory for the use of the Nation's astronomers." Finally, at the board's October meeting Waterman should present the proposed arrangements with AUI. If AUI did not agree with the board's terms, then Waterman should offer other plans for developing the facility.[26]

AUI did accept the terms, and Berkner's assistant, Richard M. Emberson, worked agreeably with NSF officials in deciding on contractual arrangements. Three trustees-at-large were added to the AUI board, and a contract for $4 million for the establishment, construction, and operation of the observatory was signed in November 1956.[27]

From the outset the Foundation had considered the prompt appointment of the observatory director critical for the development of the facility. So too, apparently, had Berkner and his associates. Even before completing the agreement with NSF he had picked a nominating committee, headed by Menzel, and got the Foundation's concurrence on the intended appointment procedures. The committee members were not likely to be candidates themselves, but most of them, in Edmondson's view, probably did not know who the best radio astronomers were. In mid-November the position, sweetened by the tender of a professorship in any of the nine associated universities, was offered to Goldberg, but he chose not to abandon his research in optical solar physics in the stimulating academic environment of Ann Arbor for "the relative isolation of Greenbank."[28]

Perhaps others responded similarly. In any event the directorship long stayed vacant, to the unhappiness of NSF officials. Many months after the signing of the contract, when the Foundation's MPE division director complained about the delay Berkner is reported to have dismissed the grievance bluntly, saying "I'm the director." Fortunately Emberson was well qualified to oversee the development and got along well with members of the NSF staff. Still, the failure to name a director quickly seems symptomatic of some of Green Bank's growing pains and may have been partly responsible for them. Not until July 1959, nearly two years after ground-breaking ceremonies had occurred at Green Bank, did Otto Struve become the observatory's first director. Ironically, Struve, as a member of Menzel's nominating committee, had originally been ruled out of consideration.[29]

Serious technical and managerial problems delayed the building of the 140-foot equatorially mounted dish that was planned to be the principal instrument of the radio observatory.[30] Several years later a member of the National Science Board, reflecting on the difficulties that had plagued the first of NSF's large-scale undertakings, wondered whether there had "been adequate engineering analysis at the feasibility stage or was the project simply swept along enthusiastically on its scientific merits? . . . He felt it was important for the natural enthusiasm of the sponsoring scientific group to be rationalized with the engineering possibilities." Another member wondered to what extent the review panels on such project "were composed of the people who were primarily interested in the proposals."[31]

Such hindsight observations might seem to call into question the wisdom of Waterman's principle that there should be no "masterminding" from Washington, that NSF should simply respond to the needs of science as expressed by the scientific community. But in this instance there was no unified community. Few optical astronomers understood the electronics of radio astronomy, though the original division between the two groups was being narrowed, largely through the agency of the American Astronomical Society. This lack of understanding may have hindered the rationalization of scientific enthusiasm and engineering possibilities, but certainly the problems of Green Bank's early development were also due to personal, regional, and institutional antagonisms.

* * *

The more prolonged but less troubled development of a national observatory for optical astronomy was in the main a successful example of NSF behaving as its director said it should. Leading astronomers largely controlled events, with NSF's blessing. This is not to say that there were no misgivings. Waterman and some of his staff had doubts about the term "national observatory," since the Foundation was forbidden to operate laboratories, and thought about giving the facility a less conspicuous name. The deputy director, Gene Sunderlin, reminded the senior staff that a substantial grant to support the McMath panel's studies might constitute a moral obligation to pay for something quite expensive later. Similarly the MPE divisional committee and the board worried about continuing maintenance and operating costs and about diverting money from the regular program of research grants. McMath himself, it is said, would have quickly abandoned the grand design if it seemed likely to reduce the Foundation's budget for individuals' astronomical research.[32]

Despite such apprehensions NSF steadily supported the panel's deliberations, culminating in an intensive survey and testing of possible observatory sites in the Southwest and then delicate negotiations with the Papago Indians for permission to place the astronomers' "long eyes" on their sacred mountain Kitt Peak, about fifty miles from Tucson, Arizona. Initially the observatory was to have two major reflecting telescopes—one 80-inch, the other 36-inch—and auxiliary photoelectric and spectroscopic equipment.[33]

To build and operate this national center under contract with NSF, seven universities formed a corporation with the felicitous acronym AURA (Association of Universities for Research in Astronomy—the name chosen earlier for Pollard's aborted organization). Negotiations between NSF and the organizers of AURA proceeded more calmly than those with AUI, though hurt feelings and institutional pride sometimes threatened to crack the smooth surface. No one dissented from the principle that the observatory should be available to all qualified scientists. There were, however, differences over admission to membership in AURA.

Paul Gross, vice chairman of the National Science Board, wanted AURA to be open-ended, allowing easy admission for interested institutions. McMath insisted on the principle set forth by Goldberg in the conference on radio astronomy: control should be held by universities having "a vital stake" in astronomical research. While NSF staff members supported McMath and Goldberg's stand against an open-door policy, the astronomy program director did urge the Michigan astronomers to admit to membership in the proposed association all three of the universities that had started the ball rolling in the first place. There was no question about including Indiana, but Goldberg at first omitted Ohio State from his organizational-meeting invitation list, saying that the Midwest would be too heavily represented, and he excluded Arizona because it did not offer the doctorate in astronomy. A protest from Geoffrey Keller of Ohio State, soon to become NSF's program director for astronomy, supported by the Indiana incumbent in the position, managed to change Goldberg's mind about Ohio State. Eight institutions, all having Ph.D. programs in astronomy and at least three departmental faculty members, received invitations to the organizational meeting in Ann Arbor in March 1957, and all but Caltech chose to become original incorporators of AURA.[34]

While holding to standards of demonstrated competence and Goldberg's "vital stake" idea, the AURA organizing group showed none of AUI's reluctance to expand its board by the election of directors-at-large. Edmondson's personal diplomacy, in which he suggested to Goldberg the desirability of broader geographic and small-institution representation, helped gain at-large seats on the AURA board for Edwin F. Carpenter of Arizona and Peter van de Kamp of Swarthmore, the latter NSF's first program director for astronomy. The seven original university members of AURA (California, Chicago, Harvard, Indiana, Michigan, Ohio State, and Wisconsin) and two others that soon joined (Princeton and Yale) were represented by two directors each, an astronomer and an administrative officer; in addition, directors-at-large represented nonmember institutions (Arizona, Swarthmore, and Vanderbilt), and two other at-large positions were filled by a treasurer and an assistant secretary.[35]

Although AURA was not incorporated until October 1957, the National Science Board in May of that year authorized Waterman to begin negotiations with the proposed association and instructed him to explore the possibility of arranging for "user participation" fees to help pay the observatory's operating costs—a matter of concern to the House Appropriations Committee as well as to the board. During the summer NSF's assistant director for MPE sciences and the general counsel's office worked out contract terms with Goldberg, using the AUI contract as a model, and in

December the board authorized making a contract with AURA for $3.1 million to build and operate the observatory.[36]

As the new year opened the first NSF-AURA contract was signed; Aden B. Meinel, who had conducted the meticulous and sometimes dangerous search for an ideal site, had been named director of the observatory; the McMath panel had gone out of existence, and McMath himself had resigned from the Foundation's MPE divisional committee and been chosen president of AURA; and Edmondson, the program director responsible for explaining the astronomical community and NSF to one another, was now AURA's vice-president and, in the words of Geoffrey Keller, his replacement at NSF and recently a member of Goldberg's organizing committee, the "contact man between AURA and the Foundation."[37] If such shifts looked like a game of musical chairs, they illustrated perfectly how a small, well-organized scientific community, some of whose members held strategic positions on NSF's staff and advisory bodies, could win its goals in Washington.

* * *

In the fall of 1953 a phone call from Wisconsin began a long and frustrating chapter in NSF's effort to share in sponsoring the construction of high-energy nuclear accelerators. Ragnar Rollefson, calling on behalf of his associates in fifteen universities banded in the Midwestern Universities Research Association (MURA), asked Seeger if the Foundation would consider supporting preliminary design studies on a new type of accelerator that the group hoped to build. AEC and the Ford Foundation had turned down their proposal. In any event MURA would rather not be supported solely by AEC, whose aims, Rollefson said, were unlike those of universities; nor did the midwestern physicists want to be restricted to the machines available to them at the AEC's Argonne National Laboratory, operated under contract by the University of Chicago, which concentrated on reactor research. Seeger thought that the Foundation could "perform a useful function, at least in helping in the national planning of such facilities, even though NSF itself might not be responsible in the long run for their actual funding." Since MIT and Harvard physicists, nearly through with their accelerator-design studies, also expressed an interest in getting NSF support, he arranged a conference attended by representatives of the MURA and Cambridge groups and the chairman of the Foundation's advisory panel for physics.[38]

The conference favored NSF support of the MURA design studies, provided AEC and the managers of Argonne were "sympathetic" to the idea. In addition, NSF should use its authority to develop national science policy to establish an advisory committee on ultrahigh-energy accelerators—at that time those with an energy level greater than one billion electron volts (then called bev, later GeV)—which should discuss how many such accelerators were needed, how much money would be required over the next decade to build and maintain them, and what policies should govern those outside federal laboratories. AEC's Brookhaven and Argonne laboratories came in for some strictures from conference participants, who claimed that the government facilities could not replace university-based research and fell short of meeting the needs of university staff members and graduate students. "Students are found to stagnate, there were not sufficient classes and the environment was in no way equivalent to that of a university," wrote J. Howard McMillen, NSF's physics program director, in summarizing the criticisms.[39] Academic values linking basic research and education would furnish a principal argument during the next several years for NSF to enter into accelerator development and, along with the Defense Department, to break AEC's virtual monopoly of a frontier field of science.

Although managing to win AEC's assistance in securing an appropriation for nuclear research reactors at universities,[40] NSF had serious handicaps in trying to edge into accelerator development. In the first place, the Foundation's charter forbade the agency to sponsor nuclear energy research without AEC's concurrence. Another big obstacle of course was the expense of accelerator construction and operation. As Waterman told Donald Quarles of the Defense Department, who asked if NSF ever expected to finance some accelerators instead of AEC, it seemed "not likely as long as the costs represent such a large portion of our budget for research."[41] Congress would not consider providing NSF with funds to undertake an accelerator project unless both the Budget Bureau and AEC gave their blessing. And both the Bureau and AEC could rightly question whether a large, earmarked addition to NSF's tiny budget would not distort the agency's general program and whether the Foundation would be able to keep paying the unknown but certainly heavy operating costs of an accelerator after its completion.

But at least the Foundation could try to help MURA. Believing in the skill and the ideas of the midwestern scientists, and in the desirability of locating a major accelerator in their region under the control of an academic community, NSF officials became more and more committed to MURA, while AEC's antagonism grew correspondingly.

The MURA physicists, backed by their university presidents, felt acutely that AEC was favoring their professional rivals on the east and west coasts; even if the agency decided to build a powerful accelerator in their region, they feared that it would probably be located near Argonne rather than their preferred site near Madison, Wisconsin, and not built according to the promising design they were trying to perfect. (As it turned out they were right on both counts.) Adding to their dilemma were new competitors for federal funds, not only the physicists in Cambridge but others at Princeton and Stanford. On a trip to California in February 1954 Waterman was asked about the possibility of NSF support for stepping up the power of the Stanford accelerator.[42]

While on the west coast Waterman made arrangements for an NSF-sponsored panel to consider questions about accelerators like those raised in the meeting convened earlier by Seeger, and he persuaded Robert F. Bacher of Caltech to serve as the panel's chairman. This ad hoc committee later became a formal advisory panel on high-energy accelerators, under the chairmanship of Leland J. Haworth, director of the Brookhaven laboratory and vice-president of AUI. By 1956 this group was recommending that NSF and the Defense Department, as well as AEC, "engage directly in the support of high-energy physics" and "extend their support in this field to maintain important positions." The Foundation's physics program's regular advisory panel followed up by recommending that NSF plan to budget $15-20 million a year by 1962 for accelerator research, and the MPE divisional committee endorsed this advice. By mid-1957 estimates of the rate of expenditure for the support of high-energy accelerators were running at $70-100 million a year by 1962 instead of the current $40 million.[43]

The National Science Board not only concurred in the recommendation of the high-energy panel but referred specifically to MURA as an appropriate regional organization to manage one of the machines. After all, the board had approved several large grants for the MURA group's design studies, though always recording that NSF was not committing itself to finance an accelerator. Indeed, NSF's strong financial and moral support, along with backing from the Office of Naval Research, helped keep the MURA team from disintegrating in the face of discouragement and even hostility from AEC.[44]

Waterman kept pegging away at AEC, especially with Commissioner Willard F. Libby and Thomas H. Johnson, director of research, on behalf of MURA and for aid in getting Budget Bureau and congressional approval for NSF to help build research reactors and accelerators. He always insisted that the Foundation had no interest in competing with the Commission and would not fund MURA proposals without AEC's sanction. But, he argued, NSF must support basic research across the board, and a comprehensive program "could not afford to have gaps as important as research with large nuclear accelerators." While AEC had an interest in basic research, its primary concern was the practical one of developing nuclear energy; the overall accelerator program would be "healthier" with NSF participation, and so would university research and education.[45]

In negotiations with MURA and AEC, Waterman relied increasingly on his associate director for research, Paul Klopsteg, who had close ties with both groups; he had been an AEC adviser, chairman of Argonne's board of governors, and an administrator in Northwestern University, one of the MURA institutions. By March 1957 Klopsteg concluded that AEC was so "fed up" with the MURA physicists that it would probably cut off their funding when their current contract expired. Then, AEC officials thought, "the less emotional" of the MURA scientists would be willing to join in designing and constructing an accelerator at the Argonne site. Klopsteg saw little that NSF could do "to rescue MURA" except to make a grant to help the group finish its design studies.[46]

The following month Klopsteg met in Madison with MURA administrators and scientists and the Wisconsin governor, Vernon W. Thomson, who had recently written about AEC's treatment of MURA to Sherman Adams, President Eisenhower's chief assistant. Klopsteg pondered over some possible solution to what seemed an irreconcilable conflict: AEC wanted MURA liquidated; MURA refused to become an Argonne satellite. "Somehow," Klopsteg told Waterman, "the way must be found of preserving and increasing the potential of such a devoted group as exists in MURA." Perhaps Governor Thomson's letter to Adams offered a way out of the dilemma. Klopsteg advised Thomson to hold off a while before talking to his fellow midwestern governors. A conference called by the White House might open a way for MURA to be supported without AEC funds and without AEC opposition.[47]

Lacking AEC's approval there was nothing NSF could do to help the MURA physicists, whose chances of getting an accelerator of their own became even slimmer when Stanford came in with a completed proposal—to AEC, Defense, and NSF—for a multibev machine estimated to cost $78 million. Expensive as this was, the price was lower than the $100 million accelerator MURA wanted to build, and the depleted midwestern group still had to do more studies to test the feasibility of their design. And money was not the only factor. Since the accelerators would do different kinds of science, the kind of scientific findings they might yield weighed heavily on the decision-makers. The Foundation, wanting to keep at least part of the MURA group together, got encouragement from Admiral Rawson Bennett in the Office of Naval Research, who thought that MURA's plight offered a good opportunity to expose AEC's "monopolistic" attitude. Although a rumor circulated that AEC would object to the Foundation's granting any more money to MURA, arrangements were made by the end of 1957 for a seventh NSF award to the group; altogether NSF support to MURA since fiscal 1954 amounted to nearly half a million dollars. While continuing to fund MURA's accelerator-design work despite threats of a cutoff, AEC did not retreat from its decision not to build an accelerator at a midwestern location other than Argonne.[48]

Stanford was a different matter. Russian satellite launchings caused increased anxiety about losing the "race" in high-energy research as well as in space and missiles; and since the scientific promise of the Stanford plan met with general favor in Washington, the likelihood of its early development seemed strong by the close of 1957. The only question was, what federal agency or agencies should pay for the accelerator? The Budget Bureau wanted support to come from only one agency, and if AEC was unwilling to undertake the task, Defense seemed to have the inside track. As William Carey told Foundation officers, the Stanford project might be too big for NSF to digest. Waterman solicited the help of the President's new science adviser, James R. Killian, Jr., for a share in the funding, arguing that "since accelerator research is frankly so basic, it seems to me a bad precedent to have the project depend entirely on military funds." Killian and the Science Advisory Committee agreed, and Defense too favored tripartite funding, but AEC continued to stall. In mid-January 1958 a discouraged ONR physicist, Randal M. Robertson, told Seeger that the project was "still on dead center," and more than four months later Klopsteg assessed the situation the same way: "I believe we are on dead center and see little hope of getting off."[49]

Early in 1958 E. A. Eckhardt, assistant director of the Foundation's MPE division, accurately expressed the agency's consistent view and thwarted hope: "... co-equal funding would insure equal voices and avoid domination by any one agency.... Scientists feel strongly that there should be more than one government agency to which they can go to solicit support for their projects. Monopolies are just as bad in science as they are in other areas where they are forbidden by law." And as for MURA, that group "represents an extremely valuable scientific resource which should not be permitted to go sour through frustration."[50]

MURA's fight was not finished; nor was the Foundation's effort to help the group and to share in accelerator development. Yet, NSF's commendable desire to help a talented scientific team in a neglected region and quickly to forge for itself a prominent role in high-energy physics may have been overeager. In January 1956 the Foundation's advisory panel for physics debated the wisdom of the agency's move to take over the financing of the Princeton and Cambridge accelerators after their construction with AEC money. To the Stanford physicist Wolfgang K. H. Panofsky, a member of the panel, that procedure was "completely unrealistic," given the Foundation's meager budget and the great and unpredictable fluctuations in costs of accelerator modification in the early stages of operation. And, Panofsky charged, the way government agencies had planned the kinds of machines and the level of their support would "inevitably lead to 'master-minding' of the high-energy research program from Washington"—that is, to commit what Waterman considered a grievous sin. It would "be very much healthier," the Stanford physicist said, if NSF followed its normal practice of responding to proposals from university scientists and supporting meritorious projects if funds were available. Instead of trailing in AEC's wake, the Foundation should start from scratch "by supporting both the construction of and research with a machine at a given installation." If a multibev machine was out of NSF's budgetary bounds, then the agency should start in a lower-energy range.[51]

Similar counsel of moderation came to the Foundation's physics program nearly two years later from Frederick Seitz of the University of Illinois, a member of the Haworth panel. He considered NSF's and ONR's concern for powerful machines in the 100-bev range, like those proposed by Stanford and MURA, "entirely proper"; but others in the "more modest" 5-10-bev range, operated by universities, either singly or in pairs, would "probably give us very rich information during the next ten or fifteen years." Here, Seitz thought, was a good opportunity for NSF and Defense to take a responsible role in supporting high-energy research.[52]

Accustomed to moderation as NSF was, such cautionary advice needed to be heard. The ambitions of high-energy physicists and the costs of big accelerators would soar to even greater heights in the post-Sputnik years.

* * *

In the fall of 1953 the National Research Council asked NSF to take responsibility for obtaining and administering government funds for U.S. participation in the Third International Geophysical Year, a worldwide scientific research program that would extend from July 1, 1957 through December 31, 1958. The lapse of a half-century between the First International Polar Year (1882-83) and the Second (1932-33) suggested a renewal in 1982-83; but the need for more knowledge of the earth, its oceans, and its atmosphere and the development of technology capable of yielding that knowledge made geophysicists restive about waiting so long. Besides, if the interval were halved, the third "year" would occur during a peak period of solar activity, a phenomenon of intense scientific interest. Thus when a group of scientists gathered in James A. Van Allen's living room in April 1950 to talk with a British visitor, the distinguished geophysicist Sydney Chapman, they responded eagerly to Lloyd Berkner's suggestion that the time was at hand for a new effort.[53]

The idea won the approval of the International Council of Scientific Unions, which established a Special Committee for the IGY with Chapman as president and Berkner as vice-president. This committee guided, coordinated, and interrelated the research activities planned by the many national IGY committees. Eventually 67 nations participated in what Berkner later described as "perhaps the most ambitious and at the same time the most successful cooperative enterprise ever undertaken by man."[54]

In recommending acceptance of the National Research Council's request, Waterman told the National Science Board that "the broad program of research envisaged involving both public and private institutions and requiring flexibility in administration" made NSF the logical federal banker. The board agreed, and it saw the program as a potentially bountiful supplement to the Foundation's small budget for basic research. But a congressional appropriation for the IGY must be clearly separate and distinct from the Foundation's regular budget.[55]

In any event it was already too late to submit an IGY budget along with NSF's request for fiscal 1955. Although Waterman expected to seek a single, nonrecurring IGY appropriation, the Budget Bureau thought it unwise to ask immediately for the full amount—estimated at $13 million, exclusive of logistic support to be provided by the Defense Department. Instead, the Bureau recommended $2.5 million for fiscal 1955—probably enough to cover obligations that must be made immediately—with the balance of $10.5 million to be requested the following year. Waterman worried that the later big request might adversely affect NSF's regular 1956 budget, and though William Carey conceded that possible danger, he said that the Bureau would do everything it could to keep the two budgets separate. To get the backing of the Bureau, and of Congress later, the Foundation solicited letters endorsing the IGY plans from the Office of Defense Mobilization, the departments of Defense, State, and Commerce, and the AEC. A letter from President Eisenhower to the board chairman, Chester Barnard, hailing the IGY as a contribution both to science and technology and to international cooperation, further supported the request to Congress.[56]

The witnesses Waterman headed before NSF's House appropriations subcommittee on July 1, 1954 became well-known visitors on Capitol Hill during the next few years. They included Bronk, Berkner, Joseph Kaplan, chairman of the U.S. national committee for the IGY, Hugh Odishaw, its administrative secretary, and Laurence M. Gould, a member of the national committee, chairman of its Antarctic committee, and a member of the National Science Board. The hearings—especially before the House subcommittee after Albert Thomas resumed the chair in 1955—increasingly resembled love feasts, as attentive members of Congress learned about the researches of thousands of investigators around the world on such matters as aurora, cosmic rays, geomagnetism, glaciology, ionospheric physics, meteorology, oceanography, seismology, and solar activity. And after a White House announcement in July 1955 that the United States would launch an unmanned earth-orbiting satellite, representatives and senators alike often displayed a childlike curiosity in questioning the IGY wizards.[57]

Of course the adversary relationship customary in NSF's regular appropriations hearings did appear occasionally—as when Thomas told Waterman "Now I am going to jump on you in a nice way," because the Administration had announced an expensive satellite program without consulting Congress.[58] In the first House hearing the subcommittee chairman, John Phillips (R., California), and Charles R. Jonas (R., North Carolina) thought that the Foundation might be exceeding its authority by entering the international arena, but Waterman was prepared for that challenge and responded by reading the clear statutory sanction. Phillips and his colleagues showed some concern, as senators did too, as to whether other nations would contribute their fair share to research whose findings would flow into world data centers and be available to all scientists and engineers. For a while it was not known whether the USSR would join in the effort, but when it did, the NSF witnesses could cite the Russians' full participation as an argument against scrimping; the success of the carefully articulated plan depended on the United States meeting all the expenses of its part of the total program. Thus IGY proponents enjoyed an unusually advantageous position in their approach to Congress.[59]

Still, the House, which habitually cut NSF's regular request deeply, could hardly let the IGY estimates get through scot-free. It trimmed $1 million from the first request of $2.5 million. Senate restoration of the full estimate resulted in an appropriation of $2 million, and NSF managed with this amount to pay all the fiscal 1955 bills without dipping into its regular funds—an anguishing possibility for a few months.[60]

Congress cut another million from the next year's request ($11 million), but then NSF asked for a supplemental appropriation of $28 million to pay for the satellite program and other newly planned activities which had been approved by the international committee. Another modest cut of $1 million resulted in total IGY appropriations for fiscal 1956 of $37 million.[61]

The Defense Department, headed by a secretary unsympathetic to basic research, was less cooperative, especially after the U.S. IGY plans were extended to include earth-orbiting satellites, to be launched by the navy. Nongovernmental scientists, whose anxieties NSF shared, worried about military aims and secretiveness; and when the Defense Department tried to acquire nearly all of the 1956 IGY supplemental appropriation to cover deficit financing of the satellite program, Waterman had to appeal to the Budget Director and presidential aides to safeguard the budget for the scientific program.[62]

Early in 1954 when Waterman talked with Donald Quarles and Earl G. Droessler in Defense about logistic assistance to the IGY program, in particular to an Antarctic expedition, he was told that any Defense expenditures should have a relationship to the department's functions. Since the planned research contained obviously defense-related matters, the department would be "in the boat," but owing to the international nature of the program, Defense would not want to put in a claim for any of the IGY budget. Waterman explained that the plan necessitated financial administration by a single agency (NSF), which would transfer funds or make grants to the various other agencies and institutions engaged in the program. "If each agency insists upon using its own funds," Waterman told Droessler, "then the plan could hardly be properly unified and effectively run. To all of this Droessler agreed."[63]

Despite Defense's interest in the planned Antarctic research, the department estimated that its costs in handling an expedition to the continent would amount to at least $8 million for an "austere effort" and might run above $25 million; since "there was no current military requirement for such an expedition," the department argued that it should not be asked to foot the bill. Waterman told Carey he had expected such a response and that the estimate was much too high. To meet this objection both Carey and Gabriel Hauge encouraged NSF to get the State Department and the President to endorse the expedition as a matter of national interest.[64] The State Department offered proper encouragement, and in March 1955 the White House announced that an Antarctic expedition would get under way in November.[65]

The satellite program, announced by the White House on July 29, 1955,[66] caused serious problems for NSF. The Defense Department tried to shift to the Foundation responsibility for meeting some of the enormous and constantly rising costs of developing, launching, and tracking a series of orbiting satellites. NSF conceived its role to be paymaster only for the instrumentation of the satellites to carry out the scientific program devised by the national IGY committee, with its headquarters in the National Academy of Sciences. The scientists at the Academy became uneasy and angry when Defense tried to get NSF to transfer to it $20 million of the supplemental IGY appropriation; after difficult negotiations the Foundation did transfer $5.8 million to the Naval Research Laboratory for launching vehicles, but the Budget Director turned down a Defense request for an additional transfer of $7.4 million.[67]

By the spring of 1957 the problem of satellite funding became critical, and Defense, under orders not to let the scientists' plans interfere with the development of guided missiles, threatened to halt the program altogether. Whether or not there was a real danger of ending an activity that had aroused great public excitement, at home and abroad, Waterman and Bronk seemed gloomy about the prospect. They mustered all the support they could at the White House and in the National Security Council, which reached a decision that, Waterman told Carey, "seemed quite agreeable" to all participants. The responsibility for requesting additional funds was left to the Defense Department.[68]

More important than money to the IGY national committee was private control of the scientific program. Suspicious that national military interests would result in the subversion of an internationally recommended plan, the committee nagged at Waterman to keep the program pure and Defense in a cooperating role. Joseph Kaplan told the NSF director that he foresaw "grave danger if the Committee, or any scientist involved in the program, permits any discipline to become cloaked in governmental authority or even the appearance of governmental authority." To help guard against any tendency toward "the nationalization of science," Kaplan asked for a "full disclosure" and documentation of governmental policies and decisions relating to the satellite program since its inception. Waterman replied that he shared the committee's concern about some aspects of the program, but he curtly dismissed the request for written documentation. They had already discussed the matter orally, and Kaplan knew what had occurred.[69]

The IGY national committee's uneasiness continued. When the Soviets announced their intention to put a satellite in orbit, the worries about the floundering U.S. program grew, as did the pressure to win the "race," for there was an effort to be first despite the post-Sputnik disavowals. In July 1957, shortly after the official beginning of the year, Waterman compared rumors with Odishaw at the Academy that "the military is going into a 'crash' program and . . . that corners will be cut." Odishaw saw unfortunate "international implications" in a hurried effort to put up a "ball," not for the purpose of scientific experimentation but to "get one up first." Waterman tried to reassure Odishaw that the scientists' original purpose would be upheld. While it was too bad that they lacked full information, Waterman said, "we should not jump to conclusions until we have the facts."[70]

Waterman and Bronk also tried to dispel the apprehension of National Science Board members about military control of the satellite program and its diversion into military applications. Both told the board that "every precaution was being taken to make the true scientific purpose clear." But as one board member, Warren Weaver, commented two weeks after the launching of Sputnik, "we obviously had very little to say about what was happening, and it was still more obvious that we were involved in an enterprise, various features of which were tied up with security and the military." What especially irritated Weaver was a newspaper story quoting Charles E. Wilson, Secretary of Defense in Eisenhower's first term, blaming scientists rather than his own department for the failures of the American satellite effort. Another board member, Father Hesburgh, writing from Vienna four days after Sputnik, offered Waterman one bit of wry consolation. Admittedly the " 'Red Star' in the sky" was "really a home run" for the Soviets, but one person had remarked sympathetically, "Well, the Americans shouldn't feel too badly, because the Russians have had a lot more experience with satellites."[71]

At least one board member expressed concern about the nature of NSF's connection with other aspects of the IGY program. Just as Weaver complained that money for instrumentation of satellites "was flowing through, or at least flowing past, the NSF" without any real board control, Earl P. Stevenson worried about similar departures from normal board procedures on other matters. Although Waterman and Laurence Gould were able to give him some reassurance, Stevenson still wondered about delegating to an Academy committee responsibility regularly exercised by the board. He had no quarrel with a policy statement from board chairman Barnard as it applied to the regular grants program:

> All we ask is that the recipient of the funds honestly carry out what he undertakes to do. If it produces no result of interest from any point of view whatever, that is absolutely all right. Never should the recipient be regarded as performing a function for the National Science Foundation.

But Stevenson thought this policy inapplicable to IGY grants. Here he evidently conceived that the delegation of authority—which he doubted the board could legally make—required the performance of some specific activity.[72]

Partly in response to Stevenson's questions, Waterman arranged a full discussion before the board of the Academy-Foundation responsibilities and procedures on IGY projects. Although NSF could not delegate to the national committee responsibility for the expenditure of public funds, he said, the Foundation did regard the committee and its technical panels as the architect of IGY programs, responsible for their "planning and execution . . . and for certifying to their scientific merit." The Foundation and the Academy, he and others explained, had to cooperate closely and use "the simplest of procedures consistent with fiscal integrity as well as flexibility" to meet tight schedules.[73]

Continuing to mull over the differences in administering IGY grants to universities and regular research grants, Waterman noted that while NSF's normal policy was to support an individual or a group of investigators, the policy with respect to IGY grants was to assist in the accomplishment of a program whose individual parts had been designed to fit into an overall plan. Thus, in the latter instance "the aims of the individual or the group are subordinate to that of the contribution to the IGY program." Since IGY projects had definite goals and deadlines, proposed departures from the research plan or schedule had to receive immediate attention to prevent jeopardizing the program as a whole.[74]

* * *

Great as was the popular excitement aroused by the announcement of the American intention to put a satellite into orbit around the earth, NSF's first and most enduring interest in the IGY was scientific discovery of the unknown continent of Antarctica. To scientists of earth, oceans, and weather, Antarctica was, as Roger Revelle, director of the Scripps Institution of Oceanography, told Albert Thomas in one of his subcommittee's reviews of the IGY program, "a kind of library of what has happened in the past locked up and frozen," or "a big icebox" preserving millennia of geophysical events.[75]

In the early stages of IGY planning Berkner told Waterman that Laurence Gould would be the "outstanding choice" to head the U.S. Antarctic committee. Waterman and Bronk agreed that "it was particularly important to have someone in this spot to avoid trouble with other people moving into the area" and that Gould would do well.[76]

A member of the National Science Board and president of Carleton College, Gould had served as second in command and chief scientist on Admiral Richard E. Byrd's Antarctic expedition of 1928-30. (Berkner had been a radio engineer on the expedition.) Gould was a friend of both Minnesota senators—Edward J. Thye (R.) and Hubert H. Humphrey (D.)—and had access to Eisenhower's White House, and he obviously enjoyed using his considerable influence in behalf of Antarctic research and of NSF. "I have the deep feeling that if the IGY is exploited properly," he wrote Waterman, "it may be one of our most effective tools in securing adequate appropriations from Congress."[77] With some apparent reluctance he accepted a chore of shepherding members of the House Committee on Interstate and Foreign Commerce on a trip to the Antarctic; he feared that members of NSF's House appropriations subcommittee would take offense at not being invited, and besides he would much rather associate with scientists and the naval support force than congressmen on a "junket." But once he reached McMurdo Sound he changed his mind. He wrote in longhand to Waterman:

> This has been a very good idea. The congressmen are being genuinely impressed. The Chairman Oren Harris [D., Arkansas] is an intelligent and perceptive man and he is seeing things right!!! The committee is very proud of the fact that they sponsored the NSF and that it is playing such an important role in this program. As for post IGY Harris said "I believe this committee is the only one that can sponsor the right kind of legislation."[78]

Although Gould later became bitter at the closing of the Little America station and disappointed at what he considered NSF's laggard effort to promote the post-IGY Antarctic program, he had an influential part in popularizing a wide-ranging research effort on the frozen continent and in ensuring its continuance.[79]

With support provided by the navy, the United States established six scientific stations on the continent before the official opening of the International Geophysical Year. By its close, arrangements had been made for a continuing program of Antarctic research under the Foundation's direction, and in 1959 the United States and the eleven other nations engaged in Antarctic operations during the IGY signed a treaty reserving the continent for peaceful and scientific purposes. International cooperation in science, especially as shown in Antarctica, was an important political legacy of the IGY.[80]

* * *

The Antarctic Treaty helped confirm scientists' belief in the internationalism of science. During the IGY, and perhaps especially amid the perils to life in Antarctica, the many instances of cooperation and growing friendship among scientists of different countries increased their impatience with Cold War regulations that stifled their efforts to advance science through personal association and easy exchange of information. One of the objects of their irritation was the U.S. State Department. State had followed through on a Berkner recommendation of 1950 to create a science advisory office but, after a hopeful start, had let it dwindle into virtual extinction.[81]

In 1955 Nelson A. Rockefeller, then a presidential assistant heading a committee on government organization, asked NSF to prepare a report on the federal government's role in international science. This report, written under Sunderlin's direction and labeled "preliminary," was delivered to the White House in December. Two years later Waterman was still trying to find out from Rockefeller what comments he had and if anyone could give NSF a "green light" to go further.[82] The dragging pace shows the difficulty of winning official encouragement of international scientific cooperation during the Cold War and the general indifference of the Administration's chief foreign-policy makers toward science as an instrument to achieve their goals. Nonetheless the report is a valuable summary of the Foundation's views on international science.

Obviously intending to ward off criticism that the report was self-serving—that is, how can foreign policy help science?—its authors sought to prove the usefulness of science for foreign-policy objectives: the building of "free world" strength and the easing of international tensions. But the report asserted that an aim of foreign policy should also be to further the progress of science at home and in friendly and neutral countries, including less-developed nations where the United States could demonstrate its peaceful purposes by helping them bolster their self-esteem and prestige and improve their standard of living.

Surveying the current U.S. activities in international science (exchange of scientists and scientific and technical information, scientific representation and liaison abroad, and participation in scientific programs of international organizations), the report characterized them as "diffuse and ill-defined," nearly all "specifically oriented toward identifiable military, economic, intelligence, or political objectives and . . . not directed toward the support of science as an activity important in its own right as a contributing factor to national and international welfare." Moreover, there were many gaps in existing programs, especially in basic research, and few programs dealing with science in its "increasingly global" nature. (Here the writers were surely thinking of the plans being developed for the IGY.) Some activities, such as the enforcement of visa requirements and controls over the flow of information, even undermined U.S. leadership in science and aroused hostility among foreign scientists.

The report recommended a variety of ways to overcome these deficiencies, some of the proposed steps clearly showing the special interests and emphases of NSF. First of all, the government should increase its support of international science activities and provide for their consideration "at a level which will ensure complete and effective coordination." The support need not be related to specific economic, political, or military goals—indeed, support of basic research abroad should come from nonmilitary sources—but should encourage "foreign, or cooperative U.S.-foreign, endeavors of outstanding scientific merit as an immediate scientific objective of U.S. foreign policy." Naturally we would not build up Soviet scientific strength, but through fostering communication among scientists of the East and West we could help "break down artificial barriers erected by totalitarian countries."

The bulk of the report's specific recommendations dealt with six topics: "(a) widespread interchange of scientific information with other countries; (b) increased interchange of scientific personnel; (c) fundamental research, including facilities for such research; (d) applied research and development; (e) a build-up in the scientific manpower potential of friendly and neutral nations; and (f) scientific representation and liaison." While most recommendations could be classified as "good for science," others, such as the proposed establishment of a new scientific attaché program backed by a civilian agency of the government, related as well to clear foreign-policy objectives.

Among the criteria suggested to guide U.S. international science activities, the report discussed the advantage of using

multilateral channels, such as international organizations, where feasible. It is especially important that activities of the U.S. Government in the area of science not be tagged internationally as another weapon in our cold war arsenal (although in fact, the activities proposed herein, ostensibly divorced from cold war objectives, would constitute effective weapons indeed.) The use of multilateral channels would minimize such a possibility.

In general, the collaboration of scientists from several countries would yield larger returns than a single country's efforts. While governmental roles in science should be held to a minimum, in some instances formal bilateral agreements would be necessary because most countries were so "sovereignty-conscious" that they would reject attempts to bypass their governing institutions.

Rather than increase the science components of existing programs of economic and military aid, despite the ease of channeling more money into foreign science in this way, the report suggested the screening out of science projects that were incidental to the missions of the supporting agencies and their placement "under the aegis of a general international science program." Support for science "as an end in itself" should be experimental at first and "never more than 'modest.' "

Before anything could be done to implement "an expanded and more unified Federal program in international science," Waterman told the board, he would have to discuss the report's recommendations with the heads of other agencies. But in his and Sunderlin's talks with the State Department, where their efforts focused on the appointment of science attachés in American embassies, movement was discouragingly slow. In October 1956 Waterman reported to the board that although there was general agreement that science attachés should be appointed to the principal foreign capitals, with one to Tokyo being most urgently needed, progress had been delayed because of Under Secretary Herbert Hoover, Jr.'s preoccupation with the Suez crisis. Bronk and Stratton warned against allowing science attachés to become identified in any way with American military or intelligence activities. Waterman said that NSF would staff the attaché offices, thus ensuring their scientific integrity, and he gave the encouraging news that State would add a new top staff official, having direct access to the Secretary and Under Secretary, with responsibility for the department's activities in research and development.[83] But three months later he had no progress to report on the attaché matter. By May 1957 consideration was "being given to the appointment of a limited number of attachés on an area rather than a country basis," with State handling the administrative arrangement, NSF the scientific program.[84]

The board spent a good deal of time discussing international science at its June 1957 meeting. Bronk's summary reveals the members' unhappiness over the low priority given to science by the State Department:

> Responsible officials who guide the destiny of America at times fail to recognize the contribution in international relations which scientists and scholars can make. America frequently sends ambassadors abroad who are concerned chiefly with the material aspects of our culture.
> The Foundation has as one of its highest objectives the interpretation of the advantages of science to a better way of life, not only to America but to the peoples

of the entire world. It is hoped that the Foundation can move toward playing a more active role in such matters. It cannot be done quickly and simply. . . .

The Board recognized the great importance of the military aspects of science. But our present apparent superiority is giving America time only. We must work much more vigorously and far-sightedly during this time we have been given. More than that, we must develop and present to the world ideological and spiritual objectives which are more challenging than those of competing civilizations.[85]

Meantime, Rockefeller's committee still had the aging NSF report on its "list of subjects," though "it was not up for immediate consideration" since the Budget Bureau did not believe that international science matters "were particularly urgent" with respect to government organization. This was essentially the same answer that Rockefeller gave Waterman at the end of the year, though by then the Interdepartmental Committee on Scientific Research and Development had at least endorsed the report's recommendations and the shock of Sputnik was causing some unwonted attention to be given to international science.[86]

* * *

It would be tedious to examine all of NSF's starts in bigger science during the mid-1950s, among them support for university computing centers, reactors for nuclear research, controlled-environment laboratories, and marine biological stations. Yet, one more example of the way the Foundation received and acted on ideas welling up from the scientific community may be in order. At least it will illustrate how an outside force—in this instance, congressional intervention—could affect the course through which a suggestion deemed by NSF staff members to have merit moved toward realization, discard, or temporary shelving.

The establishment by congressional action of a geophysical institute in Alaska, which proved to be a boon both to science and to the quality and reputation of the territory's public university, inspired a plea for a sister institute in the territory of Hawaii, where there were equally strong geographic advantages for the observation of geophysical phenomena. At length this move resulted in a mandate from Congress in 1956 for NSF to study "the need for and the feasibility and usefulness of a geophysical institute" in Hawaii and to report its recommendations within nine months.[87]

Meantime, Lloyd Berkner, always quick to grasp opportunities for promising new ventures in his fields of science, had suggested the need for a national geophysical institute to analyze the torrents of raw data that would flow in during the International Geophysical Year. Meeting one night with Waterman, Kaplan, Seeger, J. Wallace Joyce, the head of the Foundation's IGY office, and H. Kirk Stephenson, director of NSF's earth sciences program, Berkner outlined his concept and named Princeton University as an appropriate location where qualified scientists would have the computer facilities required to interrelate geophysical problems and develop a theoretical framework for understanding "the unity of the earth." Following up the group's suggestion of a conference to discuss the idea and a committee to steer the deliberations, Waterman soon met with John von Neumann, a brilliant Hungarian-born mathematician who had recently been appointed to the Atomic Energy Commission, and persuaded him to chair the committee.[88]

Several months later NSF and the Carnegie Institution of Washington sponsored the proposed conference, whose 70-80 participants emphasized the need for more theoretical work in geophysics and recommended the establishment of "at least one major institute which may devote its primary attention to the theoretical and mathematical aspects of geophysics." The conference's committee on sites listed eleven universities and technical institutes that had expressed an interest in being chosen as the location of the center.[89]

The Foundation rejected the conference's recommendation that a new advisory panel be created for geophysics research but did think about establishing an ad hoc group to consider whether a new institute was feasible and desirable. Stephenson and his assistant, William E. Benson, asked the advice of their program's advisory panel and then recommended against creating a special committee.[90] Harry H. Hess, in a vigorous unofficial reply, said he feared that any likely representative from his university, Princeton, would be ill-matched "as a geopolitician" with certain prominent geophysicists from other institutions. If they were on the committee, Hess wanted to be on it too. He expected that the committee would be "political" in nature and that "some gimmicks" that had been inserted into the conference recommendations would favor state universities over private ones like his own. And he had serious reservations about establishing independent institutes within universities; those responsible for this proposal did not understand what "highly complex social institutions" universities were.[91]

This robust reminder of institutional rivalries and of differing values of scientists in academic settings and those in independent laboratories posted a warning of the hazards inherent in selecting an institution to embody Berkner's idea. And, in fact, his notion was quickly brushed aside by the committee appointed to consider the desirability of an institute in Hawaii in the light of the general needs and opportunities for geophysical research and training. In assessing national needs the hard-working committee concluded that there were serious inadequacies in the educational programs of most existing centers—located mainly in Atlantic and Pacific coastal states—and that there was overemphasis on applied research. Those handicaps would hinder the expansion of the small number of doctorates in the field, and any sudden increase in the number of centers would cause pirating of existing staffs and a loss of their effectiveness. The needs could be best met, the committee believed, by establishing, not a theoretical institute, but four "centers of fundamental inquiry and instruction"—one each in the East, the Midwest, the South, and the West—affiliated with universities of the first rank. The manpower shortage dictated that serial rather than simultaneous establishment of the centers might be sensible.[92]

With respect to the congressional mandate, the committee found, apparently somewhat to its surprise, that conditions were remarkably favorable for the creation of a geophysical institute in the University of Hawaii. Excellent leaders, active research interest and support, good cooperation with local industry and federal installations, and important geophysical problems in the insular environment were among the several arguments for a positive recommendation. Although some physical and mathematical science departments were weak and the legislature had shown little interest in providing research money, the visiting committee thought these shortcomings were being remedied. In addition to four continental centers, therefore, the committee recommended the establishment of a geophysical institute under the control of the University of Hawaii and suggested an appropriation to NSF of about $2 million for its construction and equipment.[93]

The Foundation's earth sciences advisory panel endorsed the report, and all nine members favored establishing a geophysical institute in the University of Hawaii. But the MPE divisional committee, voicing the same doubts originally held but then resolved by the visitors to Hawaii, gave the recommendation a cool response—two for, three neutral, three against. Nonetheless Waterman followed Benson's advice by proposing to the board a recommendation to Congress to establish the Hawaiian institute, though its funding of course should come from a special appropriation. In the board, however, doubters again swayed the outcome of the debate. They insisted that the report to Congress, while acknowledging the reasons for establishing the institute, should recommend that there first be assurance that local funds would guarantee its continuing support and that several physical and mathematical science departments be strengthened.[94] However, the scientists who had visited Hawaii had made a strong case for the establishment of an institute there, and Waterman took Sunderlin's advice to convey that favorable attitude in the report to Congress. Although the board's stipulations were included in the Foundation's report to Congress, they were muted, as some board members complained at their next session. The general tone of the report, Warren Weaver lectured Waterman, was "one of out-and-out endorsement."[95]

Robert W. Hiatt, dean of the graduate school and director of research at the University of Hawaii, with the backing of his president and territorial—

and later, state—officials, kept trying to get NSF support for the institute. Waterman and his staff continued to show sympathy and eventually managed to obtain $300,000 in the Foundation's fiscal 1961 appropriation specifically for the institute, essentially as a facilities planning grant. A grant for construction followed later.[96]

The Hawaiian episode suggests the new kinds of institutional needs growing out of the increasingly global and interdisciplinary character of science in the International Geophysical Year. It is also instructive in that it foreshadows the rise of the Foundation's institutional programs of the 1960s. It seems clear that the special committee's visitors to the University of Hawaii caught the infectious enthusiasm of the institution's planners, administrators, and research-minded faculty. They saw a promise of development that would spread through several departments and inspire a general rise in standards of quality in research and instruction. The Foundation's director, who had always resisted pressure from some of his staff to move toward broader forms of research support than grants for individual projects, had begun to respond favorably to their arguments.

15
Policy for Science

The National Science Foundation hoped that President Eisenhower's executive order of March 17, 1954 would make the agency the principal federal sponsor of basic research. Instead, in encouraging other agencies to sponsor basic research that was "closely related to their missions," the order sanctioned a pluralistic system of federal support in which NSF was not even first among equals. The order neither emboldened the Foundation to develop a national science policy nor gave the Bureau of the Budget the control it wanted over federal science programs.

Pluralism in federal research support, coupled with a relative decline in support from other sources, carried several hazards to the maintenance of good relations between the government and higher education. Cutoffs in the flow of funds, when mission agencies chose to interpret narrowly the order's words "closely related," sometimes disrupted university research programs. Varying government policies on the payment of indirect costs and faculty salaries led to disputes between faculty members and their business offices, between the business offices and federal agencies, and between the agencies themselves. While the executive order was intended to safeguard universities' independence and integrity—values especially important to NSF—the opportunity to shop around for support encouraged the growth of "grantsmanship" practices that endangered the traditional academic ethos. As a self-appointed guardian of university autonomy, the National Science Board established an advisory committee on government-university relationships, which argued for several years about apparently insoluble problems. Finally the Foundation picked up what pieces it could from the rubble and recommended some general principles and practices for federally sponsored research.

Although the Foundation took on most policy chores reluctantly when they threatened to agitate its rivals—for example, an examination of the medical-research programs of the Department of Health, Education, and Welfare (HEW)—it moved quickly and decisively to forestall a governmental threat to scientific freedom. The Foundation's stand against the denial of support for unclassified research on the basis of unsubstantiated charges of an individual's disloyalty challenged and helped bring to an end a practice that might have spread throughout a security-conscious federal establishment.

The Foundation continued to resist the Budget Bureau's efforts to enlist its help in evaluating and coordinating federal research. NSF sought to satisfy the Bureau's demand by expanding its series of valuable but relatively innocuous fact-finding studies of research funds and manpower. Using this mass of information as its source material, NSF also undertook to make a comprehensive study of the government's role in the support of science, which was intended to update the Bush and Steelman reports of a decade before; in the long run this ambitious project culminated in something quite different from the prospectus—a relatively short, clear defense of basic research, which was published just after the first Soviet Sputnik guaranteed that it would have attentive readers.

NSF may have shown too little concern about bringing science to bear on the government's problems, but it earnestly worked to ensure that federal policies and practices served the best interests of science.

* * *

The government's desire to use universities' resources for national purposes and the universities' eagerness to cooperate if they suffered no loss of either money or control over their research and instructional programs led to a troubled partnership. Late in 1953 NSF established an advisory committee to define the mutual responsibilities of the federal agencies and the universities and thus perform an increasingly needed service, one that became a formal charge with the issuance of Executive Order 10521. Section 5 of the order instructed the Foundation to

study the effects upon educational institutions of Federal policies and administration of contracts and grants for scientific research and development, and . . . recommend policies and procedures which will promote the attainment of general national research objectives and realization of the research needs of Federal agencies while safeguarding the strength and independence of the Nation's institutions of learning.[1]

Few tasks were ever started with less hope of success or with more belief that they had to be tried. One of the participants, Vannevar Bush, well shows the conflict between a sense of duty to serve and a feeling that the effort was bound to fail.

Paul Klopsteg complained to Bush that an American Council on Education (ACE) committee's preliminary report on sponsored research policy showed university presidents acting like moneygrubbers rather than intellectual custodians. Klopsteg thought the presidents' concern to get full payment for government-sponsored basic research—one of a university's normal functions—as well as for applied research and "procured development services" was "degrading to the scholarly and intellectual activity of the faculty member" and potentially destructive of university independence. Bush responded that "if the federal government wishes to subsidize the universities of the country"—an idea abhorrent to Klopsteg—"it should do so directly and not by some strange method of bookkeeping. I fear the latter," he wrote, "for it would inevitably lead to bureaucratic control of our university policies, in the field of research and possibly more generally." In addition to suggesting that NSF set up a more representative group than ACE's to study government-university relations, Bush encouraged Klopsteg to publish his plan to change tax laws to stimulate personal contributions to higher education and thus "keep government bureaucracy out of the picture."[2]

Although Bush urged NSF to establish a committee, he worried that it would bog down in arguments over indirect costs and other "minutiae." A compromise report avoiding the real issues "might do far more harm than good," he wrote the board chairman, Chester Barnard, in accepting committee membership, which he did "with great reluctance and the distinct feeling that I may regret having gotten into the matter at all." To other correspondents Bush lamented that his "bright remarks" in favor of an NSF study left him little excuse for declining to serve.[3]

The advisory committee's membership increased Bush's qualms, as it did those of his fellow member and former MIT colleague J. A. Stratton. Like the ACE committee under the chairmanship of Virgil M. Hancher, president of the State University of Iowa—a member of the NSF committee too—the group consisted almost entirely of educational administrators. Their university bias would make their report suspect to Congress, Stratton commented, and would likely lead to duplication of the ACE committee's work "unless we set our sights higher and attack problems of more fundamental difficulty." To Stratton, as to Bush, "the root of this matter is the question of the true purpose of Federal support for research in universities. Is the object to broaden the base and to improve the quality of research, or are Federal funds to be viewed primarily as a disguised subsidy of universities and higher education?" Rather than "convert our universities into research factories," Stratton believed, the government should foster "a variety of patterns of basic research"—national laboratories like Brookhaven and independent research institutions, on the one hand, for organized "power attacks" on unsolved problems, "and the academic community dedicated to the cultivation of creative and imaginative powers of men and women as individuals on the other." Such variety ought to be a main aim of the committee since it would help preserve the character of universities while encouraging research growth.[4]

The exchange of views between Bush and Stratton was intended to clarify the committee's goals so that it would not become preoccupied with procedural details about government grants and contracts. Bush liked Stratton's ideas so much that he wanted them sent to all the committee. And it happened that Bush was also reading the draft lectures of another committee member, Don Price, soon to be published under the title *Government and Science*. Although sharply critical of Price's "New Dealer" attitude in defending President Truman's stand on organization and control of NSF and the Atomic Energy Commission, Bush knew that Price's "good thinking" in his following chapter, "Federalism by Contract," would help the committee get started right and he hoped that at least Stratton and Barnard could read the manuscript.[5]

Barnard's fellow board members subjected him to "an almost indecent amount of heat" to head the committee. Since the board was convinced that the job was of great importance, Barnard took on "this rather intangible and uncertain" task, though he knew that the committeemen would not be able to "write q.e.d. at the end and go home with specific accomplishments very much in mind." But even if they could not answer some questions, he thought that "the mere framing of the problems in the right terms and the statement of the pros and cons ought to be of influence in preventing half-baked and extremely political and emotional treatments." He realized that the committee was pushing into an unknown area, but it had to be explored.[6]

Waterman wanted the committee to begin work quickly, even before selecting an executive director, and Barnard decided that "a little floundering" would do no harm. But Bush thought the first meeting was a disaster. Instead of looking at fundamental questions, the university-dominated group seemed likely simply to repeat the ACE committee's work, and largely from the same point of view. He had "become so highly pessimistic" about the committee's performing a useful service that he saw no "way out of the morass in which we are now embedded." His negativism grew with the issuance of Executive Order 10521, since the committee's limited assignment was insignificant in the light of the board's broad new responsibility. Although Bush continued on the committee until 1955, when his retirement from the presidency of the Carnegie Institution of Washington and his return to Massachusetts gave him an excuse to resign, he seems to have lost interest in its work.[7]

Barnard—getting old, suffering from a lame back and dimming sight, and discouraged by poor attendance at committee meetings and by what he considered members' inability "to divorce themselves from their official academic positions"—conscientiously stuck to a disagreeable chore, even after resigning from the National Science Board. Only once in a series of meetings stretching over two and a half years did a simple majority of the fourteen committeemen convene, and one or two, as Barnard remembered, never came at all.[8]

The main burden fell on the committee's executive secretary, J. W. Buchta, the University of Minnesota physicist who was active in promoting NSF's support of teachers' institutes. Buchta's task, as outlined by Waterman, was to assist the committee "to make an intensive study of the current situation with respect to support furnished by the Federal Government to science in our colleges and universities, having due regard for the mutual interests involved. The study should include consideration of the justification of federal support for these purposes, the effects of present modes of support of science and what role the Federal Government should play in this type of support."[9]

Besides attending all committee meetings and trying to derive a consensus from tape recordings of the discussions, Buchta interviewed more than five hundred faculty members and administrators in colleges and universities. He gained his information on government activities largely from studies by NSF staff members. Although Buchta asked questions suggested by the committee, his heavy reliance on the information he had gathered gave the report he wrote the appearance of a personal more than a committee statement. Answering committee members' complaints that the report was his rather than theirs, Buchta said that a document agreeable to all would have been meaningless. It was not even possible to append a minority report because of the differing views of the several dissenters. So, at length, Buchta's draft was simply thrown in the board's lap with various letters of comment, including his own.[10]

Far from a sparkling piece of writing, as Princeton president Harold W. Dodds remarked, Buchta's draft nevertheless dealt with important questions and clarified issues.[11] It thus served one purpose that Barnard had hoped it would. But it bared irreconcilable beliefs and provoked rather than staved off emotional arguments. These are shown in committee members' comments transmitted to the board along with the draft report. First, some objected to the "gratuitous" statement in Barnard's draft transmittal memorandum that they could not view problems apart from their academic positions, and the offending sentence was deleted. But the bulk of the dissents related to "Buchta's" report, and especially to what Stratton described as the "judgment as to how far an agency of the Federal Government should go in an endeavor to protect a university from the effects of its own bad management." While a few members readily endorsed and even praised Buchta's draft, others, upholding the complete independence of colleges and universities, saw in it an implication that the government was presuming to give advice and recommend policies to institutions. As Arthur S. Adams, president of the American Council on Education, phrased the fundamental objection: "If the policies for the management of [government-sponsored] research are established by the Government for its purposes or even recommended by Governmentally sponsored committees, the university's right and responsibility to manage its own affairs are then invaded. This is the issue which lies at the root of all of the debates our Committee has had...."[12]

The center of the critics' target was a section entitled "Independence of Schools—Relevant Policies." Here Buchta had highlighted dangers arising from federal research support. "The old adage, 'He who pays the fiddler calls the tune', has not become obsolete and its warning cannot be ignored," he wrote. While alluding to committee members' differing views as to whether federal sponsors should pay all research costs, direct and indirect, the report held that cost-sharing of some kind by the institution would enable it to "retain an equity" in a sponsored project. "When Federal agencies, in seeking their own objectives, take over the entire support of projects or programs within a school, including the salaries of all staff members involved, the independence of the institutions, the freedom they have in carrying out their traditional functions, may be lost." The section suggested, not as a general prescription but "as an ideal," that agencies, acting in concert, begin to stop paying any part of the academic-year salaries of tenured faculty members doing research on federal grants or contracts. (The suggestion did not apply to research during the summer months.) The senior faculty member's allegiance would thus remain with his institution, not shift to an outside sponsor, nor would he be selling his services and the use of his university's facilities to the government. The salaries of untenured faculty and technical staff, however, could be borne completely by the sponsoring agency, and indirect costs should "be paid when the institution requested such payments."[13]

In small colleges and universities where instruction overshadowed research, the report suggested that federal grants or contracts might allow for the payment of salaries of substitute teachers for senior faculty members engaged in sponsored research; senior professors should continue to get their salaries solely from the institution.[14]

The committee had not found an increase in tenured faculty owing to federal grants and contracts, but the report nevertheless warned of a threat to institutional solvency if government research support should be withdrawn. "A ten percent cut in budget for the Department of Defense," the draft report said, "could result in a ninety percent cut in funds going to universities." Hence, Buchta implied, institutions should beware of shifting salaries of tenured faculty members to "soft" government money.[15] To Dodds these suggestions constituted "an ill-informed and gratuitous injection of a personal point of view into the philosophy of administration which the universities have developed over the centuries." To him and some other committee members the making of a distinction between tenured and untenured faculty with respect to payment of salaries made no sense and "would hobble" university administrators. President Hancher, recovering from a heart attack and restricted by his doctor from expressing his disagreements fully, took aim at the recommendation that agencies "pay essentially all accountable indirect costs of the sponsored research," and he was especially irritated by the words "when requested by the educational institutions." Hancher saw no reason why the government should not pay full costs, and a university should not have to grovel by asking for them. Here and elsewhere, he said, the report recommended on matters that were internal concerns of universities. Although many of the report's recommendations were sound, Hancher wrote, "I do not agree that it is the function of the National Science Foundation to make such recommendations to the educational institutions."[16]

Other committeemen were less querulous than Dodds and Hancher, even when agreeing with them. T. Keith Glennan, president of Case Institute of Technology, endorsed Hancher's views but complimented Buchta for his diligent work. Don Price did not think that eliminating salaries of tenured faculty members as a direct charge against government contracts was a necessary or particularly useful step toward securing university independence. He subscribed to most of Buchta's diagnosis but regretted the report's failure to deal with two broad subjects: "first, the issues involved in developing a national policy for the support of science, from the point of view of the total national interest and of federal agencies as well as that of universities; and second, the positive benefits that American universities have received from the performance of research with federal aid." Price thought it would have been unfortunate, both for the universities and for the country, if the greatly increased flow of federal research money since 1940 had been channeled only to government laboratories and industry.[17]

Clark Kerr, chancellor of the University of California at Berkeley, liked the "report's general attitude regarding governmental control of universities," but he pointed out some "hidden controls" that posted warning signs to higher education. Trouble could come from allowing academic-year salaries of even junior (untenured) faculty to be charged against federal contracts; and he thought that too many scientists were allowing their research interests to be swayed by the availability or unavailability of government money. Kerr and Berkeley's graduate dean,

M. A. Stewart, enthusiastically endorsed a "proposed departure from 'projects' for fundamental research in favor of 'block' grants."[18]

In a temperate and generous letter, Stratton commented that Buchta had "been saddled ... with an almost impossible task: that of attempting to reconcile the conflicting views of a rather articulate and strong-minded group of committee members on matters that go very deep in principle and that in practice could have a grave import on the conduct of university research in this country for years to come." Stratton said that he and Buchta had the same purpose, the avoidance of "a slow growth of governmental meddling in university affairs." But while Buchta sought to avert bureaucratic incursion by establishing "a set of official federal practices," Stratton believed that "universities, like individuals, will grow in strength only as they are allowed to exercise judgment and take responsibility." Perhaps the committee should have foreseen the impossibility of reaching a consensus, but it had performed an important function, Stratton assured Barnard, in opening the discussion of what would continue to be vital matters.[19]

It was Stratton who suggested a way out of the committee's dilemma: simply declare its work done and turn Buchta's draft and members' comments over to the board. Unchanged from the document completed eight months before except for "somewhat less abrupt" concluding recommendations, the draft report was referred to an ad hoc board committee chaired by Frederick A. Middlebush. Encouraged by Waterman "to find a core of agreement which would constitute a report," Middlebush found how difficult this assignment was when he delved into the problem.[20]

William G. Colman, a special assistant to Waterman who had guided the work of an NSF special commission on rubber research, skillfully helped bring the board committee's work to an early and satisfactory conclusion. He perceived that a report acceptable to the board was feasible if it discussed but avoided a recommendation on the issue of charging salaries of tenured faculty against federal grants or contracts. And since he knew that it was impossible to get full, quick concurrence from all other interested agencies on any controversial document, he proposed to touch base informally with key people in Defense, AEC, NIH, and the Office of Education to see if they had any strong objections to the draft he offered to write.[21]

The board committee gladly accepted Colman's advice. He drew freely on Buchta's draft, and what he saved was clear and flowing. He also incorporated material, prepared by NSF staff member Harold Orlans, which gave a succinct account of the evolution of federal research support since 1940 and provided a context for the discussion of issues in government-university relations. In his conversations with other agencies' representatives Colman met few objections, and he readily handled these and agency suggestions by making slight modifications in his draft and without having to submit it for formal clearance. Within less than three months he had completed his draft, and the board gratefully approved the report in January 1958.[22]

Government-University Relationships in Federally Sponsored Scientific Research and Development, published by NSF in April 1958, recommended to government agencies several principles and practices for their future dealings with universities. First came a fundamental distinction. In a statement remindful of the Bush-Stratton discussion of the advisory committee's purpose, the report told both partners, agency and institution, that the government's goals in supporting research in universities "should be explicitly and completely dissociated from the budgetary needs and crises of the institutions and from the general issue of Federal aid to higher education. . . . there should be no implication that Federal sponsorship of research is a convenient subterfuge for Federal financial aid to institutions of higher learning." Agencies should continue to use the unique resources of universities but not divert them from their primary functions. As stated in Executive Order 10521, basic research support should come from various sources, not be channeled through one agency in the interest of simplification. Simplicity was desirable, however, in grant and contract procedures, as were promptness in negotiations and payments and avoidance of harmful unilateral actions; federal procurement officers should not irritate a delicate relationship by treating academic institutions as ordinary suppliers of "hardware." Since continuity of support was essential for effective basic research, agencies should be permitted to make grants or contracts of more than a year's duration.[23]

The report mentioned the differing views about using federal funds for faculty salary payments but omitted the recommendation in Buchta's draft which had drawn a heavy barrage. Instead, the board report recommended against the use of government money for payment of "incremental salary rates"—that is, bonuses or higher rates than an institution's regular schedules—unless to faculty members on leave at research centers. Luckily the Middlebush committee was able to bypass the related emotional issue—indirect costs—that had upset some of Barnard's committee, since NSF had already made a recommendation to the Budget Bureau on the subject.[24]

Reflecting NSF's protective attitude toward the university as the ideal environment for basic research, the report warned against establishing large applied research and development projects on campus. And because secrecy was "incompatible with educational and research pursuits traditional to the universities," federal agencies should not ask educational institutions to do classified work except "in cases of acute need or unusual circumstances." More suitable for such work would be a separately organized research center, but when located on campus it might result in a "two-headed monster"; the report suggested criteria that federal agencies and universities should consider before creating centers not linked to academic departments.[25]

Although legally a research contract might have the same effect as a research grant, the report said, the two words had different overtones and made a difference psychologically in the government-university partnership; in addition, the grant mechanism might make it easier to transfer title of research equipment to the university. The report recommended extending grant-making authority—like that enjoyed by NSF and NIH—to other government agencies and also giving them the right to vest in the institution ownership of research equipment purchased with government money.[26]

The Buchta draft had cautiously suggested some broadening of the typical project grant, and even the allocation of a small fraction of the research funds as block or departmental grants when the institution so requested.[27] The board report, however, simply described the various forms research sponsorship might take, ranging from narrowly defined projects to institutional grants for general research support. Agencies should use whatever forms seemed appropriate to their needs.[28] The board and director were not quite ready to adopt, or to recommend, the more flexible kind of institutional support advocated by some NSF staff members.

In sum, the report aimed at achieving greater understanding by government business and research-program officers of the need to uphold university autonomy and integrity. Carefully avoiding the appearance of telling universities how to manage their affairs—in fact, not even discussing their responsibility to account for the use of federal money—the report sought to prevent, or stop, what were evidently regarded as growing federal abuses. The recommendations as summarized here, stripped of their explanatory remarks, may appear merely to be powerless pleas to be good. Certainly they did not solve a problem that Chester Barnard, looking back on his committee's experience, concluded "will be a perpetual one."[29] But the report's advice was cogent and it was necessary.

* * *

In its continuing battle to instill order into government research programs, the Budget Bureau in September 1954 asked NSF to recommend a uniform policy on allowances for indirect costs in federal research grants. The report was to be submitted by June 30, 1955.[30] Since the subject was on the agenda of the advisory committee on government-university relationships, NSF expected that Barnard's group would provide the answer to the Bureau's request. Despite the committee's wrangling over the complicated issue of institutional cost-sharing, it seemed after a meeting on April 27, 1955 that there was substantial agreement on the indirect-costs question, and Buchta drafted an interim report for submission to the National Science Board.[31]

NSF staff members felt as intensely about the matter as did the advisory committee, and somewhat differently. Though more knowledgeable than the typical faculty member about the reality of indirect costs, an NSF program director was apt to resent just as keenly the diversion of research money to the payment of university utility bills or administrators' salaries. Too many good proposals had to be turned down already, and any increase in overhead payments would tighten the pinch on his budget. When Waterman got staff reactions to Buchta's draft, he decided it would be impossible to give the Bureau anything more than a recommendation of broad principles. He asked the board to allow him to submit to the Bureau an endorsement of the committee's "basic policy" along with such procedures as seemed appropriate after consultation with other agencies.[32]

The committee's "basic policy" was that federal agencies should, if requested by educational institutions, "pay essentially all accountable indirect costs." But only half of the members had attended the April meeting which had reached this agreement. It dissolved in the acid of critical letters and the "intense feelings" shown three weeks later in a session the evening before the board assembled.[33]

Adding to Waterman's problem were objections—including a threat of resignation—from his associate director. Klopsteg protested the advisory committee's "capitulation to the philosophy" of the ACE committee headed by Hancher, the Budget Bureau's forcing NSF to propose a uniform federal policy, and the wiping-out of "the clear distinction between basic research and applied and developmental research" that would result from a uniform policy. If the final recommendation to the Bureau should be to "pay essentially all accountable indirect costs," Klopsteg told Waterman, "I shall feel compelled to take up a one-man campaign of protest," though not of course as a Foundation employee.[34]

Klopsteg did not resign, but he weakened Waterman's presentation to the board by writing out his views and giving them to like-minded William Houston, who in turn proposed them "as guidance to the Director." Klopsteg's first suggestion was that federal agencies should pay "full accountable costs" in development contracts. The second, dealing with large facilities such as national centers, said that agencies should "be prepared to pay up to full accountable costs," though institutional participation would be welcomed. The third, intended to cover basic research of the kind universities "are supposed to do anyway," did not mention overhead but gave agencies leeway to provide research support "within their statutory authority."[35]

Klopsteg's ideas would have permitted the continuance of widely divergent practices, ranging from full payment of overhead by the

Department of Defense to as little as 8 percent of the total direct costs by the Public Health Service, including its principal component, the National Institutes of Health. Since the Bureau wanted to end this muddle, NSF could not get away with recommending Klopsteg's hands-off principle. And the deadline was near. The board, after hearing Waterman's assurance that he would take its suggestions into account, resolved its dilemma by approving the advisory committee's policy—though deleting the words "essentially all"—and authorizing the director to recommend it and any appropriate procedures he decided on in consultation with the board chairman and the advisory committee.[36]

Waterman had to come up with an expedient policy quickly, but he feared that it would compromise the principles that should be embodied in a long-term policy. "The fundamental question," Waterman believed, "is whether in the long run our universities, both State and private, should continue to remain as independent as possible of the Federal Government, or whether we should modify our traditional policy and admit that direct Federal support is necessary." He was evidently groping toward some system like the British University Grants Committee to preserve the strength of institutions through federal subsidies. The vexations of indirect costs would become "a trivial detail" under either his or Klopsteg's solution.[37]

It was fruitless to try for unanimity of the advisory committee, and though Waterman polled the members, he took Barnard's advice not to worry about their inability to agree. He and Sunderlin met with AEC representatives to learn about that agency's practices, but then decided that the easiest way to get agreement within the government was to discuss general principles informally in a meeting of the Interdepartmental Committee for Scientific Research and Development. Thus NSF completed its report to the Bureau approximately on time.[38]

The main recommendation to the Bureau was the one approved by the board. To implement it Waterman recommended, in general, that all federal agencies be prepared to pay, at an institution's request, indirect costs at a rate determined by government "Blue Book" principles or, at the institution's option, a flat rate of 25 percent of the salaries included in a grant's budget.[39] Only NSF and the Public Health Service would have to pay significantly larger amounts—about $6 million for PHS and under $1 million for NSF on the basis of fiscal 1956 appropriations. Naturally Waterman said that the increased costs should be covered by larger appropriations, not met by cutting the volume of supported research.[40]

Both in his covering letter to the Bureau and in the attached report, Waterman alluded to his "fundamental question." The demands of national security had "merged" government and university interests, and the maintenance of national scientific strength depended on the maintenance of strong universities. But the huge expenditures for research and development threatened to destroy the traditional government-university relationship and to damage the academic environment. Funds earmarked for science increased administrative problems on the campus and resulted in strains on other fields of knowledge. Institutions could get money for special purposes but not general operating funds. Perhaps the long-term answer to the growing problem could be found by "indirect subsidy" through changes in tax laws (Klopsteg's idea) or by "over-all grants in aid of research and education in colleges and universities."[41]

NSF's chore did not end with the submission of the report—the Budget Bureau called for supplementary information on the payment of overhead by private foundations and industries—but the onus now shifted to the Bureau. Nagged by an influential person to put the recommendations into effect quickly, Bureau officials learned how difficult it was to win acceptance of uniform practices on reimbursement of indirect costs.

Robert Cutler, a Boston lawyer, banker, and president of a private teaching hospital (Peter Bent Brigham) affiliated with Harvard's medical school, had recently left his position as special assistant to the President for national security affairs, though he would return to it in 1957. Even before his departure in 1955 he had begun to mediate with federal sponsors of medical research for larger overhead allowances.[42] As soon as the Foundation's report had been delivered, Cutler wrote the Budget Director, Rowland Hughes, that the recommendations would help private teaching hospitals to do a greater public service; and he added in a postscript: "I told Sherm [Sherman Adams, assistant to the President] about these recommendations while we were driving up to Gettysburg (driving and *frying* in an open car) last Friday." Soon Cutler, accompanied by the assistant dean of the Harvard medical school, visited Hughes, Carey, and Waterman, and then wrote Hughes that he "was glad to report to Sherm Friday of the good progress" they were making. Cutler eased off while the Bureau was getting agency reactions to the NSF proposals, but before the end of 1955 he renewed his pressure, reporting to Hughes on a Sunday lunch with President Eisenhower during which his explanation of the need for "a more realistic policy for reimbursing research expenditures" of medical teaching institutions drew a sympathetic response.[43]

As a way "to get General Cutler off our back" and to give Sherman Adams the "conclusive answers" he expected from the Bureau, Hugh F. Loweth and Carey proposed accepting the Foundation's general policy, with the addition of some emphasis on institutional cost-sharing. Agency reactions to the NSF recommendations had been generally favorable, but because questions had been raised about the soundness of the Blue Book method of determining overhead, the matter was to be studied by an accounting group from the Bureau, the Treasury, and the General

Accounting Office (GAO) before the issuance of specific regulations. Hughes told Adams that Cutler, Waterman, and a representative of Marion B. Folsom, Secretary of Health, Education, and Welfare, had agreed to this procedure.[44]

Adams, who had asked the Bureau for a progress report by May 1, 1956, got one from Cutler, who said that his understanding of the slow movement of government machinery had enabled him to keep his composure; but now the Bureau needed "a warm-hearted, encouraging shove or nudge" from the President's chief assistant. September 1 would be a good target date for putting the new policy into effect.[45] Bureau officials would have liked to dispose of the issue quickly too, but they had trouble with GAO, which took, in Loweth's view, "a rather narrow and legalistic approach to the solution of the problem." While concurring in NSF's policy and agreeing with the Bureau's wish to stress cost-participation, GAO suggested ways of determining reimbursable indirect costs which would rule out a simple system. And NSF, no doubt mindful of the strong views of some of Barnard's committee members, seemed unwilling to emphasize cost-sharing.[46]

Cutler's particular concern was the indirect-cost rate on PHS research grants. Though by now raised from 8 percent of direct costs to match NSF's 15 percent, it was still less desirable than the optional flat rate of 25 percent of salaries recommended by the Foundation. To the Bureau's surprise Secretary Folsom told Cutler—who immediately told Adams—that the time had come for the Department of Health, Education, and Welfare to move to full reimbursement of overhead costs. Carey interpreted the switch as an effort by NIH to use up the annual congressional bounty "by larding it into research grants for overhead."[47]

But once again there were roadblocks. GAO objected to predetermined flat rates. Adams said that Folsom could increase his department's allowance on his own authority but should consult other agencies first. And most important, Congressman John Fogarty, who regarded NIH as his barony, blocked efforts to remove the 15 percent ceiling.[48]

And so the complicated business dragged on and on. In April 1957 the Bureau sent out for comment a draft of principles and practices prepared by a special interagency committee. The National Science Board wanted to put its earlier recommendations into effect, but it hesitated because it did not want to anger NIH or Congress by taking unilateral action. A year later Waterman reported to the board that there had been "little progress" and the congressional limitation on NIH still stood in the way of NSF. Stratton argued that the Foundation should "assume its proper leadership in this matter" without regard to NIH, but Waterman held that NSF could not change its policy until revisions of the Blue Book were agreed to and until Congress removed the limitation on NIH. An ad hoc board committee was appointed, and one of its tasks was to analyze Bureau of the Budget Circular No. A-21, giving instructions on determining indirect costs. The Bureau's proposals started another long series of discussions. By October 1959 the board saw "a glimmer of hope that the end might be near." It was a false glimmer.[49]

* * *

"There seems to be a good deal of enthusiasm for making the maximum utilization of the National Science Foundation," Robert Cutler wrote Vannevar Bush in the early days of the Eisenhower Administration.[50] Certainly during the next few years NSF was asked to take on several policy chores that many staff members considered peripheral to the agency's "real" work of supporting scientific research and education and keeping tabs on changes in manpower and funds for the various fields of science.

Some of the extra duties were mandated by Congress, some by the Bureau of the Budget; one resulted from a report to the President. As discussed in the preceding chapter, Congress assigned to NSF an investigation of the establishment of a geophysical institute in Hawaii. By legislative requirement too, NSF wound up the government's war-inspired program of synthetic rubber research, using for the first time the authority contained in the charter to establish special commissions.[51] A recommendation in the 1952 report of the President's Materials Policy Commission (the Paley Commission) led to the creation by the National Science Board of an advisory committee on minerals research which, after several years of activity, proposed the establishment of a minerals research institute, to be supported by the nation's mining industry—a proposal the industry ignored.[52] Of greater import to the NSF staff as a whole was the agency's report in June 1957, responding to a Budget Bureau request, on *Federal Financial Support of Physical Facilities and Major Equipment for the Conduct of Scientific Research*.[53]

Much more than these, another policy responsibility worried the board, the director, and staff members in the Foundation's life sciences programs. The request this time came from a Cabinet member, Oveta Culp Hobby, Secretary of Health, Education, and Welfare, but apparently at the instigation and certainly with the strong support of Budget Director Hughes. The Foundation's task was to study and make recommendations on the department's medical research programs. The HEW secretary's aim—or more likely that of Under Secretary Nelson A. Rockefeller—was to gain control over the medical research arm of her department, which was becoming increasingly autonomous, thanks to influential lobbyists and congressional champions. Besides establishing firmer departmental discipline, Hughes wanted to stop the annual breaking of the President's budget by appropriations committees and the readiness of NIH witnesses before them to admit that they could use more money than the President had requested. The Bureau was alarmed too about imbalances in the medical research program resulting from emphasis, among interest groups and in Congress, on particular categories of disease.[54]

Hughes and Hobby first telephoned the chairman of the National Science Board. In his conversation with Mrs. Hobby, Barnard said that NSF "could not be a policeman of other departments of the government," no matter what the Bureau and some congressional committees might want. "I take it that she is not a bit dumb about it," Barnard wrote Waterman, adding in a vivid farmyard simile that Mrs. Hobby was "like a chicken running up and down the wire trying to find a hole in the fence."[55]

Before long Waterman and Detlev Bronk, penned in by Hughes, were also trying to find a hole in the fence. Bronk was named chairman of a special board committee to consider what was still an informal, confidential proposal, and like other members was uneasy about NSF's accepting the assignment. Robert F. Loeb, for example, whose Columbia University medical school professorship made him especially sensitive to the dangers of the proposed investigation, warned that it might reduce research support for medical scientists and cause bitterness toward NSF. Bronk and Waterman suggested that Secretary Hobby appoint a special commission to make the review, but Rockefeller would not let them off the hook. A "captive committee" would have little credibility, he said, and the problem was much broader than they conceived it. An HEW-appointed group might help with the Bureau's immediate problem of budget recommendations, but the Foundation's advice was needed for "the larger question of the extent to which the Federal Government should enter into direct or indirect support of medical research." Nevertheless, Rockefeller was unable to sway the board committee to go beyond agreeing to advise on the membership and consult with an HEW-appointed commission.[56]

Hughes was, if not more persuasive, more convincing. Though Mrs. Hobby might appoint a committee whose members were suggested by the Foundation, he said, "the case would be stronger and would appear more objective if this review and appraisal were made by the NSF." Barnard, Bronk, and Waterman argued in vain that any adequate evaluation would have to wait until NSF completed its comprehensive study updating the Steelman report; that it was the secretary's job to put her house in order, perhaps by establishing a top-level body to review the recommendations of advisory councils pleading for their respective areas; and that since the problem involved not only basic research but such applied matters as clinical medicine and hospital care it would be improper for NSF to consider it. To all of which, Waterman recorded, "Carey said that in essence . . . [the Budget Bureau's] position was that the Foundation had a responsibility for evaluation of programs and authority for creating commissions, and that the President in turning to a solution for this administrative problem naturally turned to the NSF." Would NSF rather have the President ask it to do the job or have the request come from the HEW secretary? The Foundation representatives preferred that the letter come from HEW, and Hughes asked Waterman to draft a letter to himself from Mrs. Hobby.[57]

Some members of the board committee continued to complain. Loeb thought the request for NSF to perform the distasteful job ought to come from the Budget Director "if he is the one who really wants it." But when Waterman said he did not want "to allow a precedent to start" which would cause more evaluation chores to emanate from the Bureau, Loeb shifted to favoring a presidential request. George W. Merck, however, thought a letter from the President would focus too much attention on a single department; any NSF study of medical research should encompass all agencies' activities, not just those of HEW. There would be a board hearing of these and other objections later, but meantime Waterman sent his draft letter to HEW.[58]

Secretary Hobby's letter, little changed from the draft, asked for a "critical review" of the medical research program of her department, "particularly with regard to its scope and the distribution of support" among the seven categorical-disease institutes of NIH. Recognizing that NSF's comprehensive studies of research by the government, universities, and industry would in the long run furnish a much sounder basis for recommendations, she said that HEW was "most desirous of receiving an early interim appraisal from the Foundation." She suggested that it include:

consideration of the rate of growth of the programs of the Institutes of Health and other research units of the Public Health Service in the light of the responsibilities of the Federal Government with respect to health, medical and related research; a general appraisal of the present level of support of medical research by this Department; careful consideration of the proper balance of effort with respect to the support of basic research and research aimed more directly at the prevention, diagnosis, care and cure of diseases, and the relative distribution of effort among the major special fields of health research.[59]

It was really the Budget Bureau that wanted "an early interim appraisal," one completed by the summer of 1955, in time to be useful in determining NIH's budget allowance for fiscal 1957. Hughes was pleased to hear from Waterman, after the board's acceptance of the evaluation task, that NSF could probably "present some satisfactory preliminary conclusions in three to six months." Presumably to preserve good relations between NSF and NIH program officers, Hughes "agreed that the Foundation staff should stay aloof from the study and the formulation of recommendations."[60]

The NSF staff was isolated from the task but would have had to do the work if Waterman's "three to six months" schedule had been met. Summer had already arrived before the appointment of an eight-member special committee, headed by C. N. H. Long of the Yale University School of Medicine, and its executive secretary, Joseph W. Pisani of the State University of New York College of Medicine in New York City. But once appointed the committee did its work quickly and, in the National Science Board's opinion, exceptionally well. The board on December 5, 1955 unanimously accepted the committee's report and directed Waterman to submit it to the secretary of HEW.[61]

The report may have been of little use to the Budget Bureau, especially given the contempt for that office shown by NIH's paladins on Capitol Hill.[62] Nevertheless the document hit hard at the runaway growth of "categorical" research and its ill effects on university medical schools. The schools had about reached the limit of their capacity for effective use of funds to attack major diseases, the committee said, but they badly needed institutional grants for flexible use and money for fundamental research and for construction of laboratories. If such arguments seemed to be special pleading by medical school administrators, they were balanced by recommendations aimed at improving the lot—and quality—of researchers in NIH's intramural programs, through the offering of good salaries and other benefits that would make employment on the Bethesda, Maryland "campus" as attractive as in the best universities.[63]

"An entirely new approach" to federally supported medical research, the New York *Times* said of the report after its release by HEW. The reference was to the recommendation that a new agency be created in the department, an Office of Medical Research and Training, to take over the support of extramural research and education and enter such close "liaison with the National Science Foundation . . . that it can act with full knowledge of pertinent NSF policies and activities."[64]

Secretary Folsom, Mrs. Hobby's successor, to whom the report was delivered, said that it would be studied intensively. No doubt it was, but so far as the National Science Board was concerned, the report was buried. Lowell T. Coggeshall, special assistant to the HEW secretary, told Waterman that the report raised some apprehensions and that the department wanted to establish a committee to consider its organizational and administrative implications. Yet nothing seemed to happen. A year and a half after HEW released the report Bronk told Waterman that Nelson Rockefeller, now out of government, and members of the NIH Health Council had never seen it. The report had been "released" but not distributed. Bronk and other board members expressed irritation that the hard work of the distinguished committee had gone unnoticed and unrewarded. Finally, in October 1957, Waterman told the board that the HEW secretary had appointed still another committee, under the chairmanship of Stanhope Bayne-Jones, former medical dean at Yale, to advise him on medical research and education.[65]

* * *

In February 1954 Robert C. Cowen of the *Christian Science Monitor* asked a number of science administrators about the effects of the Eisenhower Administration's security regulations. Were they undermining scientists' morale or hindering freedom of research? Waterman delayed his reply more than a month, not from negligence, it seems, but because of uncertainty about how to answer. A loyal servant of the Administration, he was also a scientist. He and the staff discussed Cowen's query at length. Their ambivalence is reflected in the qualifications which followed nearly every definite statement in Waterman's response. A tendency to oscillate appears too in a letter from Waterman to Barnard transmitting the proposed reply: "It is clear that we must support the President's policy. At the same time it would seem to be important that the facts are brought out...."[66]

The spring of 1954 was an anxious time. McCarthyism was at its peak, and the televised spectacle of the Wisconsin senator's war with the U.S. Army dominated the news and editorial columns, though the considerable attention given to J. Robert Oppenheimer's hearing before an AEC personnel security board showed that not only foreign service officers and military personnel were being labeled as suspect. Scientists were deeply disturbed by the Oppenheimer hearing, and by accusations made against other scientists based on the "guilt by association" doctrine and on their failure to conform to official views on such matters as building superbombs or testing of nuclear weapons.

Once again Vannevar Bush furnishes a forceful expression of the prevailing opinion in the science establishment on the security issue. His delight in at last having a Republican President had soon turned sour. The Oppenheimer hearing especially troubled him. Writing to AEC Commissioner Lewis L. Strauss, a key figure in deciding Oppenheimer's future and the Administration's security policy, Bush said that "the hunt for subversives" was causing disregard of "the basic principles of our democracy." Only the President could "speak the words which will put the attitude of government in the proper light," and Bush obviously wanted Strauss to carry that message to Eisenhower. A little over a week later, shortly after defending Oppenheimer before the AEC board, Bush wrote Strauss again. "We must not have a situation where the President becomes accused of thought control," he said. Fear was causing the American people to forget the principles of liberty. The President must exert strong leadership in making "it crystal clear that, while he insists on great care on security, he will not tolerate thought control, or the appearance of it, under any guise, throughout his organization."[67]

Almost buried by the massive coverage of the Army-McCarthy hearing, two brief stories in the Washington *Post and Times Herald* late in April referred to matters of greater concern to NSF. An account of Bronk's report to the annual meeting of the National Academy of Sciences alluded to blacklisting of scientists whose loyalty had been questioned. Scientists should fight back against their detractors, Bronk reportedly told his audience. The following day's issue reported on the denial by the Public Health Service of research grants to about thirty scientists.[68] Mrs. Hobby's press release, only briefly quoted in the news story, said that PHS's policy since June 1952 had been as follows:

> We do not require security or loyalty investigations in connection with the award of research grants. When, however, information of a substantial nature reflecting on the loyalty of an individual is brought to our attention, it becomes our duty to give it most serious consideration. In those instances where it is established to the satisfaction of this Department that the individual has engaged or is engaging in subversive activities or that there is a serious question of his loyalty to the United States, it is the practice of the Department to deny support.
>
> If the subject is an applicant the grant is not awarded. If the subject is an investigator responsible for a grant-supported project or is the recipient of salary from the grant, the grant is terminated unless the sponsoring institution desires to appoint an acceptable substitute.[69]

Waterman, who had already talked about the issue with Surgeon General Leonard Scheele, called a special meeting of his senior staff to get their views, to agree on a response to press queries about NSF's policies, and "to avoid any further Government science split." Rough notes on the meeting show the staff's worries. Sunderlin wondered whether the Foundation should look beyond a researcher's scientific ability to his character. Hoff, the general counsel, suggested that NSF would be "in an awkward position" if it made grants without checking to see whether the recipients were on Mrs. Hobby's "list of 30." Was Linus Pauling on the PHS list? A proposed NSF grant to Pauling was to to come before the BMS divisional committee next week.[70] But, Hoff pointed out, Congress when it established the Foundation had decided against requiring loyalty checks for research support.

The director said "that the current atmosphere is a poor one to take steps toward rectifying the loyalty and security situation. After the McCarthy and Oppenheimer Hearings have been completed we may be in a good position to do so; in the meantime we should work toward the right policy, but avoid carefully making the situation worse." The "right policy," as Waterman outlined it, was that NSF did not make security checks on its grantees and did not need to worry about security risks since its grants supported unclassified research. As to an investigator's loyalty, NSF grants went to institutions, "which implicitly are responsible for the backgrounds of the members of their staffs." Peer review of proposals ensured a researcher's scientific integrity, a basis for deciding on an award. NSF would be concerned only if an applicant had been "officially determined to be disloyal to the country."[71]

If the PHS policy was nearly two years old, as Mrs. Hobby said, not many life scientists knew of it before the spring of 1954. Then rumors began to fly. In mid-April Bronk, as president of the Academy, received a letter "from a distinguished scientist of undoubted wisdom and loyalty" who said that several persons had told him that PHS was requiring security clearances and had canceled grants to investigators doing entirely unclassified work. He had to undergo clearance himself as an NSF panelist, and since he was an adviser to the government, he thought the requirement justified, though not necessarily wise. But the only considerations in the award of basic research grants should be the investigator's competence and the importance of his research problem. Bronk's correspondent called on the Academy, of which he was a member, to resist this grave threat to the freedom of science.[72]

About the same time Bronk received a telegram from Philip Handler of Duke University, secretary of the American Society of Biological Chemists, transmitting a resolution that had just been unanimously adopted at the society's annual meeting. The biochemists asked the Academy to investigate reports that "certain government agencies" were denying or revoking grants for unclassified research for reasons other than the investigators' "competence or integrity." If the reports were true, the Academy should "take strong and appropriate action." Bronk's request for information from Mrs. Hobby elicited her press release explaining the departmental policy.[73]

A few days after Mrs. Hobby's announcement NSF's new divisional committee combining the formerly separate biological and medical sciences committees unanimously adopted a statement, drafted by members George Wald of Harvard University and Jackson W. Foster of the University of Texas, approving the Foundation's practice and opposing that of PHS.[74] Later in the month the National Science Board reviewed the issue, the legal aspects of which had been detailed in a memorandum from Hoff.[75] Waterman warned the board of the danger that though only AEC had announced a policy similar to that of Mrs. Hobby's department, HEW's unilateral action might "be regarded as a precedent for general Government policy." He said that he had emphasized to Gabriel Hauge and Arthur Flemming "that if there should be any attempt to generalize this policy so that it should become common to all Federal agencies dealing with basic research, then it is the function of the National Science Foundation to take the lead in the determination of what the proper policy should be." If the Foundation's policy proved unacceptable to the Administration, Waterman said, an alternative might be to require applicants for research grants, like fellowship applicants, to sign loyalty affidavits. This distasteful compromise would at least be better than the HEW practice and would relieve both the federal sponsor and the scientist's institution of responsibility.

The board, cautioned to keep quiet about the matter, omitted from its open-session minutes all reference to the issue except that the members had unanimously agreed in executive session "on a statement of Foundation policy with respect to proposals for grants." That policy was the one proposed in Hoff's memorandum:

> The policy of the National Science Foundation with respect to proposals for unclassified research, not involving considerations of security, is as follows:
>
> In appraising the merit of a proposal for unclassified research submitted by or on behalf of a scientist, his experience, competence and integrity are always taken carefully into account by scientists having a working knowledge of his qualifications. The Foundation does not knowingly give nor continue a grant in support of research for one who is:
> 1. An avowed Communist or anyone established as being a Communist by a judicial proceeding, or by an unappealed determination by the Attorney General or the Subversive Activities Control Board pursuant to the Subversive Activities Control Act of 1950, or
> 2. An individual who has been convicted of sabotage, espionage, sedition, subversive activity under the Smith Act, or a similar crime involving the Nation's security.[76]

Waterman's unusual assertiveness on the loyalty issue showed how seriously he regarded it as a danger to NSF and to science in general. So too did many members of his staff. The "excited" director asked Carey to let him know if the Bureau learned of any formalization of the HEW policy. Waterman was afraid, Carey said, "that if this thing is pushed to the limit we will one day be withholding funds from entire institutions on the grounds that somewhere in their faculty they have a nut"—that is, since NSF grants were made to institutions rather than individuals, a charge of disloyalty against an art instructor might automatically bar a federal award for research in chemistry. Carey, less perturbed about "Mrs. Hobby's cautious policy," thought that if the matter threatened to become critical, an executive order might "agree with the notion of keeping Federal money out of the hands of subversives, but . . . provide for a fair hearing and examination and appeal before withdrawing or denying funds."[77]

General Cutler also got into the act, since Mrs. Hobby asked the National Security Council about the applicability of loyalty criteria, and he could not "fail to help a beautiful woman in distress." Cutler told Sherman Adams that the withholding of grants on the basis of derogatory information had "inflamed the professional and scientific world." To stop criticism of the Administration, Cutler believed there "should be a Government-wide policy, clearly and explicitly established, and the scientific and professional world should be asked to advise about and agree to the final decision." But since the controversy involved *unclassified* research, it fell outside the National Security Council's jurisdiction, and Rowland Hughes had suggested to Cutler that the Sub-Cabinet, chaired by Adams, would be an appropriate body to consider it.[78]

HEW followed the suggestion and asked Adams to place the problem on the Sub-Cabinet's agenda. Discounting the attacks of "a few individual scientists and a few scientific societies" on a practice that by August 1954 had caused the ending or denial of support in only thirty-nine cases, the department had nevertheless concluded that there should be a common government policy. The Sub-Cabinet accepted the job and asked the Justice Department to establish an ad hoc interagency group to study the problem and make recommendations. Hoff was the NSF representative, Carey the Budget Bureau's.[79]

Meanwhile Nelson Rockefeller of HEW tried to shift the onus on his department to NSF. He suggested informally to Waterman and Barnard that the Foundation might create a panel of scientists to decide on the troublesome accusations against applicants to NIH. The National Science Board rejected the idea because it would be unacceptable to the scientific community and was inconsistent with NSF's policy; besides, the matter was now under review by the Sub-Cabinet. Bronk and some other board members thought the time had come for the Foundation to make its policy known, but Waterman said that a public announcement would embarrass him as a member of the Administration. However, the board, unhappy about continuing to remain silent, at least authorized Bronk to state NSF's position at a meeting of the Academy and suggested that the policy be announced to NSF's divisional committees and advisory panels. The board reaffirmed its earlier statement of policy—though now called "practice"—and added to the list of persons barred from support "anyone who avowedly advocates change in the U.S. Government by other than constitutional means." Though the Foundation still did not proclaim its views, they were given in the board's open-session minutes.[80]

Hoff had supporters on the interagency task force. Carey was surprised to find at the group's first meeting "a strong disposition" to oppose HEW's practice and to agree with NSF's view "that the Government is interested only in the integrity and ability of the scientist, rather than his thoughts or associations." While admitting that name checks in FBI records might turn up derogatory information based simply on "malicious or crackpot" notions, Carey nonetheless thought it "incongruous for the Federal Government to wage war on subversion on the one hand, and on the other to have no standards of loyalty for the granting of Government support of individual scientists." To NSF's list of excluded applicants, Carey suggested adding, "an individual against whom substantial derogatory information has been filed and who, after being afforded a statement of the charges against him, has failed to overcome the weight of those charges."[81]

The referral of the issue to the Sub-Cabinet, to be advised by an interagency group organized by the Justice Department, indicated that the decision would likely be a purely governmental one. A further indication of a closed decisional process was that the matter came under the consideration of "a top-level administration group"—an advisory committee on government organization—under Rockefeller's chairmanship.[82] Yet Waterman, true to his doctrine that science policy should not be "masterminded" from Washington, wanted to enlist "a few distinguished scientists and university representatives to assist the Government in arriving at a general policy," and he thought that Rockefeller's rejected proposal might, if followed up, offer a means to that end. Cutler had early suggested to Sherman Adams that the Administration get the advice and consent of scientists, and his argument was now being reinforced by Gordon Gray, the University of North Carolina president who had chaired the Oppenheimer hearing. Gray and Bush had differed about Oppenheimer, but they agreed on the need for a counterpart to a British royal commission to study the whole question of security and advise the President. Gray strongly recommended their idea to Cutler, and he also told Bronk about the effort.[83]

Especially influential probably was Cutler's advice, backed by a recommendation from Rockefeller's committee, that an extragovernmental scientific organization be consulted. On January 11, 1955 Adams wrote Bronk: "It seems to us that these questions relating to loyalty can best be resolved if scientists, through a representative group such as the National Academy of Sciences, can counsel with the Government on its policy in this matter. . . . The President asked me to express to you his strong personal interest in this matter." Bronk replied that the Academy would be glad to help settle "these troublesome issues," and in March he reported to the National Science Board the appointment of a committee, under Julius Stratton's chairmanship, on loyalty in relation to government support of unclassified research. Board member Robert Loeb was one of the seven committeemen.[84]

Not only had the kind of committee Waterman wanted been appointed, but in other ways too, conditions now seemed more favorable for the success of NSF's argument. McCarthy had been condemned by his Senate colleagues in December 1954, and the Eisenhower Administration had begun to breathe a little easier. Later in that month the AAAS recommended adoption by all government agencies of the Foundation's policy on unclassified research. "The tide is turning without doubt," Bush wrote to the president of Tufts College. Hoff, in his contacts with other federal general counsels, found a strong concern for the protection of government employees against unsubstantiated charges.[85]

The Stratton committee began its work in April, and in August Waterman informed the board that its report was finished and awaiting Bronk's return from Europe for approval and submission to Adams. Waterman related confidentially that the report recommended "adoption of virtually the same principles as those under which the Foundation has been operating."[86]

It was not until fall that the report was sent to Adams, and then a long, anxious wait began. In January Waterman heard good but unofficial news that HEW had approved the report, and the same month NSF did at last publish—with Rockefeller's approval—what everyone already knew, the agency's stand on "loyalty and security considerations in making grants for nonclassified research." Early in February Bronk told Waterman that Adams had returned the report "for slight revision." The director also heard definitely that Secretary Folsom had told Adams that "HEW would interpose no objection" to the policy recommended by the Stratton report.[87]

In the absence of any public announcement of a change in PHS practices, Dael Wolfle, executive officer of the AAAS, reminded the U.S. Surgeon General that "another year has gone by" and "scientists of the country would be interested in knowing the present policies." Scheele at length replied that PHS was following the Foundation's practice. Soon thereafter the Academy committee's report was released. In the issue of *Science* in which it appeared, a Wolfle editorial quoted Scheele's reply and saw "encouraging evidence" that the Stratton report would result in government-wide adoption of the sound principles now being followed by PHS as well as NSF.[88]

Still, there was no announcement of a new, uniform policy, and it was reported that some members of Stratton's committee had expected prompt action and were "openly dismayed at the perfunctory way the White House handled the report."[89] Although representatives of government agencies quickly agreed to follow practices similar to NSF's, a letter to that effect from Adams to Bronk required more than three months to clear. The problem was to ensure credit and avoid blame. NSF wanted public recognition of the acceptance of its long-standing policy; HEW wanted an acknowledgement that it was following a similar practice but without any indication that it did so under pressure; and Bronk and Stratton wanted it clearly stated that HEW had fallen into line only after the Academy's report. Negotiations on wording between Waterman for NSF, Bronk for the Academy, Coggeshall for HEW, and Hauge for the White House finally culminated in a letter from Adams to Bronk saying that the principles embodied in the committee's recommendations "have generally been found satisfactory as a basis for actions regarding grants or contracts for unclassified research" and that "these principles are essentially those which support the policy of the National Science Foundation." The squabble over language pertaining to HEW's policy resulted in omission of any reference to that department. The general agreement, Adams said, meant that government departments and agencies would "follow practices consistent with the recommendations contained in the report of the Academy's Committee."[90]

Those recommendations did not simply confirm Foundation policy, Stratton irritatedly pointed out when he received for the third time the same back-patting memo from NSF. He believed that the report's statement of principles and recommended action went beyond the Foundation's published policy, and that the memo emanating from NSF's public-relations office failed to give the credit owed to the Academy, and Bronk especially, for persuading Adams to take administrative action.[91]

Stratton made a valid point, as can be seen by comparing his committee's recommendations with the Foundation's stated policy. The recommendations were:

1. The test in the award of (Government) grants and contracts for unclassified research should be the scientific integrity and competence of the individuals responsible for carrying out the research, and the scientific merits of their program.
2. When an official of the Government comes into possession of evidence which in his opinion indicates the possible existence of disloyalty in violation of law, he should promptly refer that information to the Federal agencies of law enforcement established to deal with such matters.
3. An allegation of disloyalty should not by itself be grounds for adverse administrative action on a grant or contract for unclassified research by scientifically competent investigators; if the indications of disloyalty appear sufficiently serious to warrant any action at all, the Government in the opinion of the Committee has no other course than to bring formal charges and to produce the evidence in open hearing before legally constituted authority.[92]

The National Science Board's statement of guiding principles for NSF awards closely resembled the first of the Stratton committee's recommendations. The Foundation's excluded persons—avowed Communists, persons convicted of sabotage, espionage, etc.—had not, as Stratton said, "practically, . . . ever given us much trouble," and though they were not listed in his committee's recommendations, they were certainly covered. The second of the committee recommendations corresponded to an addition to the original NSF policy statement: "Furthermore, if substantial information coming to the attention of the Foundation indicates that a potential or actual researcher might be guilty of violation of any such law, the information will be forwarded to the Department of Justice for its consideration."[93] It was hardly in the province of NSF to say what kind of consideration the Department of Justice should give to the information referred to it. The

Academy committee could give such advice, as it did in its third recommendation for a general government policy, one which was designed both to ensure "due process" to persons charged with disloyalty and to end the practice of denial or termination of awards on the basis of unsubstantiated allegations of disloyalty.

His complaints aside, Stratton said that he and his fellows "greatly admired the integrity and courage of the Director and the Board in the establishment of such a policy in very difficult times." The times had been difficult indeed, justifying the concern, described in the Stratton committee's report, that "administrative practices that were developed for the handling of sensitive projects might gradually prevail over a larger domain and by slow diffusion from one department or agency to another ultimately affect the activities of all men and women engaged in scientific investigations under Government sponsorship."[94] This deep worry had called forth the Foundation's effort, which was instrumental in freeing government science agencies from the fear of ignoring unsubstantiated allegations and from assuming law-enforcement responsibilities that belonged elsewhere. It was a contribution that staff members of the time rightly remember as their agency's most important policy achievement, for science and for government.

* * *

If NSF expected Executive Order 10521 to stop the cries for it to develop national science policy, it was quickly disappointed. Clifford Grobstein, commenting on Eisenhower's fiscal 1955 research budget, argued as he had for years that the Foundation should furnish policy guidance and leadership. Whatever of policy the research budget contained, Grobstein said, had "arisen without benefit of conscious over-all consideration or public appraisal . . . . In the absence of specific policy formulation to suggest new directions scientific progress in the U.S. apparently will remain more dependent on international developments, and their reflection in military appropriations, than on our own evaluation of the national importance of scientific research."[95]

Grobstein expressed a liberal view, but conservatives similarly longed for a guiding policy that would help bring research and development expenditures under control. The Cold War mentality, which saw a conspiratorial monolithic communism aiming at world domination, spurred those expenditures, creating inflationary pressures that worried budget balancers fearful of another Great Depression—which of course would furnish the ideal conditions for a resurgence of radicalism.

The Budget Bureau continued to want Waterman's assistance in reviewing agencies' requests, and he continued to resist giving the service it sought. Quarrels over NSF's policy responsibilities resulted in a meeting of the antagonists with the President in 1956 and before the Cabinet a year later. The launching of the first Soviet Sputnik at last brought a resolution of the problem with the installation of a science adviser in the White House to provide the kind of guidance the Foundation had chosen not to attempt.

Waterman went through the motions required by the executive order of consulting with top executives of other agencies, but he made almost none of the effort desired by the Bureau to review their budget requests and to shape NSF's budget to fill their gaps or to stimulate special areas. He insisted that "formal clearance or review was undesirable."[96] In the absence of critical budget review by NSF, Carey hoped that at least the Foundation's studies of science support would analyze problem areas "frankly and imaginatively" and fill the policy vacuum. It would be desirable, he thought, to have a special assistant in the White House to supervise NSF's studies and "to strengthen Presidential leadership in the research area of public policy."[97] But the Foundation's deliberate approach to the task and emphasis on the long-term utility of its studies provided no immediate guidelines for the Bureau's own use in reviewing agencies' science budgets.

In March 1956 Carey complained to Waterman about his failure to object strongly to a House Appropriations Committee's cut in the request for NSF's policy studies and its stated intention to make deeper cuts in later years. The Bureau considered the studies important, Carey said, and NSF could expect an inquiry into its actions under the executive order. Waterman was told that this examination resulted from a presidential request for a report on NSF's "coordinating activity."[98] To meet a March 30 deadline Bureau staff members promptly submitted analyses of the Foundation's role in "Programing and Coordinating Basic Research."[99]

A Budget Bureau examiner noted NSF's "passive"—even "submissive"—approach to the coordination of basic research, the only segment of research and development for which the agency accepted responsibility. Occasionally NSF acted as a catalyst by sponsoring conferences in specialized fields, and it made some claim of steering the work of other agencies and of active intervention when it detected "gap areas," though the NSF staff believed that proposal pressure gave the best measure of needs in different fields of science. Basic research, in NSF's view, was self-coordinating; good scientists knew the work of other investigators and did not duplicate it. Nor did NSF believe it "possible or practical" to try to determine how much money should go to specific disciplines. Insofar as the Foundation had a coordinating role it was

> really the bringing together of all those interested in and directly involved in the support of research to create an improved environment for the conduct of research,

providing sufficient data on the extent and nature of current support and the status of research in this country and facilitating the exchange of information so that scientists engaged in basic research can be led through their own efforts and that of their fellow scientists to engage in the most productive areas of basic research. It is within this context that the Foundation approaches not only its day to day contacts with other agencies but also ... its implementation of Executive Order 10521.[100]

Yet if science was self-coordinating, as NSF argued, government science agencies were not. Although Foundation staff members held that their "healthy rivalry" with other agencies was really a harmonious relationship, they admitted that some jurisdictional problems existed, such as NIH's effort to keep the Foundation from dealing with medical schools as distinct institutions as the NSF program providing summer research opportunities for medical students did.[101]

The Bureau's report accurately summarized NSF's position, and Hughes told the President he was "very doubtful if anything like the type of supervision that I believe you had in mind can be effected" by the Foundation. But the new Budget Director, Percival Brundage, and Waterman, meeting with Sherman Adams and Gabriel Hauge, agreed to put the Bureau's recommendations into effect, with the exception of one, considered "not in order at this time," suggesting that Rockefeller's committee on government organization explore the question of installing a science adviser in the Executive Office of the President.[102] The other five recommendations were:

(a) The Foundation, through its Director, should assume more leadership within the Federal Government in bringing into focus the Federal programs for basic research support.
(b) The Foundation should clarify for lay officials of the Executive Branch and the Congress the important feasible goals for the support of basic research.
(c) The Foundation should not be asked to assume formal coordinating responsibilities which it does not believe in and is not prepared to handle, and which would be strongly resisted by Federal agencies and scientists generally.
(d) The Bureau of the Budget should assure that other agencies show evidence of prior consultation with the Foundation in their proposed basic research programs, before funds are recommended to the President.
(e) The Bureau of the Budget, in consultation with the Foundation, should periodically review the adequacy of actions taken by agency heads to strengthen their management of internal research support programs as directed by Section 6 of the Executive Order.[103]

The recommendations focused on basic research, which was hardly the Bureau's main problem. But Hugh Loweth and Carey suggested several specific ways of implementation that would remove some of the uncertainties with which they had to deal and make NSF, if not a control arm of the Bureau, at least an active counselor. These suggestions, made to Brundage to help him argue the Bureau's case in a meeting with Waterman and the President, would have forced the Foundation to abandon its passive role.

For example, the NSF director should each spring call a meeting of the heads of research-support agencies to agree on their budget requests and areas of responsibility for basic science; and NSF should submit annually to the President and heads of science agencies an assessment of the needs, priorities, and imbalances of research support and manpower for each principal field of science. Waterman rejected these suggestions.[104]

The President seems to have been less concerned than the Bureau about coordination. When Waterman and Brundage met with Eisenhower and explained their views, the President was "fairly noncommittal," and since he gave no directive at the end of the session, Hauge told the NSF director that he "could therefore assume that our present method of operation was satisfactory." It was hardly satisfactory to the Bureau. Carey, after hearing Waterman's impressions of the meeting, concluded: "On the whole, the meeting with the President did not add anything particular to the whole situation."[105]

But something of possible importance had occurred in the earlier meeting with Sherman Adams. Waterman had been told to take the initiative in bringing scientific matters to the President's attention and invited to attend White House meetings where they were discussed. In other words, as Carey interpreted Adams's invitation, Waterman was to "be available as the administration's general advisor on matters scientific." In fact, Waterman did attend several meetings of the Cabinet and the National Security Council as an adviser.[106] Obviously pleased by this recognition and by what he interpreted as "warm approval" of the Foundation's policies, he told his senior staff that the Budget Bureau had "confirmed the opinion that the present coordination of basic research in the Government is good." The maintenance of good communications with other agencies through informal contacts of program directors and division directors would enable NSF to meet its responsibility for coordination.[107]

Frustrated Bureau officials, seeing their moves stalemated, looked for some other solution. Loweth told Colman "that the only course left to the Bureau was to undertake the appraisal job itself," and this effort would require NSF to furnish staff both to collect essential information and to interpret it critically; but he supposed—certainly correctly—that Waterman would decline to participate in the critical analysis.[108]

Perhaps it was such persistent pressure on a matter that Waterman regarded as settled that led him to draw up a policy statement based on his previous "understanding" with the Bureau and to ask the board to confirm it. The statement contained three general policy positions:

1. The Foundation is responsible for facilitating the coordination of programs of basic research among the agencies of the Federal Government.

(This facilitation came through the exchange of information, both informally and systematically, between NSF and other agencies; the sharing of knowledge about pending research proposals and the sponsoring of specialized conferences served to prevent duplication and to stimulate needed research.)

2. The National Science Foundation does not attempt to exercise formal coordinating controls over Federal agencies in the planning or administration of basic research programs.

(Each federal science agency should support basic research related to its mission, and since each was the best judge of its needs it "would be inappropriate[,] . . . impractical and unrealistic" to make NSF a central coordinator.)

3. The Foundation is guided by the principle that there should not be centralization of Federal support or direction of basic research in a single agency.

("Centralized responsibility for the administration or direction of all Government-supported basic research would impede progress through restriction of freedom of inquiry by scientists and would impose avoidable difficulties on the agencies that must conduct or support research related to their respective missions.")[109]

Since the board wanted to announce these principles publicly, Waterman asked Brundage if he thought the statement could "be improved to conform to our agreement." Brundage did think so. Conceding that the description of NSF's practices was consistent with their understanding in March, he was afraid that the statement might cause a reader to infer "that there is no overall executive branch judgment applied to individual agency programs." Besides, the statement omitted several major policy responsibilities imposed on NSF by its charter and the executive order. Waterman responded that the statement applied only to coordination, and he agreed that any public announcement should mention NSF's other policy functions. He also told Brundage's deputy, A. R. Jones, that questions raised in a recent NSF budget hearing indicated that some Bureau officials still did not understand the agency's "desirable policy" for dealing with "a delicate subject among scientists."[110]

If the Bureau did not understand the wisdom of NSF's views on coordination, in Waterman's opinion, neither did he think it properly appreciated the need for more money for basic research. Conflicting demands for military security and for economy threatened by 1957 to clap a lid on government spending for uncommitted research. At the same time Cold War budget requests for military applications and development intensified the Administration's longing for guidance on scientific and technical matters. Waterman had agreed to "assume more leadership" on basic research policy and been invited to advise the President on scientific matters. Given these circumstances Waterman should not have been surprised—though he had reason to be alarmed—by the science section of the *Saturday Review* of February 2, 1957.

Not quite everything in the section was repugnant to Waterman. The science editor, John Lear, at least emphasized the enormous disparity between expenditures for military research and those for basic science. But the thrust of the argument—in Lear's editorial, in his account of Waterman's views on science policy as given in an interview, and particularly in an article by Sidney Hyman—was that the President desperately needed clear directions from a new, high-level source to meet the "impending crisis in the relationships between science and American society."[111] Lear and Hyman had learned the substance of the Budget Director's memorandum to the President recommending NSF leadership and also of Sherman Adams's standing invitation to Waterman to advise the President on scientific matters. Yet the Foundation, Hyman said, had done nothing to fulfill its statutory duties or those under the executive order to appraise the impact of science on society or to develop national science policy.[112]

Carey may have smiled to see the accusing finger pointed at Waterman, but the leak of the Budget Director's memo and the reprinting, without Carey's foreknowledge, of an article he had written seven years before were not amusing. And it must have stung to read a question that he and his associates had long tried to answer: ". . . why hasn't the power of the Bureau of the Budget been sternly invoked to require other agencies involved in science to consult with the NSF in the formulation of policy?" Maybe, Hyman concluded, a stronger hand was needed—a Secretary of Science in the Cabinet, or at least a Science Commission on the level of the Budget Bureau, the Council of Economic Advisers, and the National Security Council, and for Congress, a Joint Committee on Science.[113]

Of more immediate concern to Waterman than the threat of centralization of science policy or the creation of a department of science was the danger to NSF's budget owing to the costs of applied research and development. While disclaiming any NSF responsibility for bringing these mounting expenditures under control, he tried to safeguard federal budgets for basic research, and the Foundation's in particular, by urging the use of operations research and systems analysis methods in making budget decisions on development and production, especially as they related to defense hardware. In the spring of 1957 Waterman sought to convince Hauge, Cutler, and Maxwell M. Rabb (secretary to the Cabinet) in the White House, Brundage in the Budget Bureau, Donald Quarles in the Defense Department, and H. Alexander Smith in the Senate of the possibility of making large savings and preventing waste through modern techniques made possible by digital computers. He told Cutler that these new methods would enable the government "to provide in money and effort for the increasingly costly technological developments that appear necessary for national security without endangering the nation's economy." The solution of this problem, he insisted, did not lie in cutting back on basic research, which "should be regarded as an investment, the precise spots where high returns occur being unknown in advance."[114]

Pressure to hold the line on federal research support especially threatened to squeeze basic research out of the defense program. The issue came before the Cabinet early in August 1957 in a discussion, in which Waterman participated, of a paper prepared by the Budget Bureau with the Foundation's collaboration. Waterman had tried, not completely successfully, to influence Brundage to make a strong case for basic research, and he got backing from the Science Advisory Committee. Pleased by modifications of Brundage's recommendations as a result of the Cabinet discussion, Waterman reported to Bronk that the result was "completely satisfactory," and Bronk agreed "that our position vis-a-vis the BOB had been strengthened."[115]

While the Cabinet paper retained Brundage's emphasis on the need for departments and agencies to exercise greater selectivity in their research and development projects, and thus curtail further expansion, it did emphasize that basic research was important "to our national security as well as to our national welfare." Government support of basic research should remain at least at existing levels; increases should be offset when possible by reductions in applied research and development. As NSF wished, the paper held that "Federal support of basic research, outside Government laboratories, should continue to be concentrated in the colleges and universities," and industries and private foundations should "be encouraged to increase their support of basic research, especially in the universities."[116]

Cabinet approval did not necessarily mean implementation. Soon after the August 2 Cabinet meeting an air force cutback in basic research support caused hardships in several universities, including the one, Johns Hopkins, headed by a brother of the President. Waterman promptly reported these departures from the Cabinet-approved recommendations. His intervention perhaps helped to repair some of the damage caused by the sudden termination of research contracts.[117] At least it showed his and the Foundation's continuing championing of the cause of basic science and of its nurturing universities.

* * *

Eleven days after the launching of Sputnik I Waterman submitted a report to President Eisenhower entitled *Basic Research—A National Resource*. This statement of NSF's views on science policy had been long in the making, having its origin in Budget Director Joseph Dodge's request in 1953 for "a comprehensive study of the Nation's present effort and needs in research and development."[118]

The Foundation had assumed from the outset that the report would draw on the planned studies of research and research support by government, industry, and universities and other nonprofit institutions. The gathering of this basic information provoked some quarreling within NSF over the methods and responsibility for direction of the studies, and between NSF and the suppliers of information over reasons for the questions and the work required to answer them. To stop the domestic squabbles Waterman early in 1955 recruited a new assistant, James M. Mitchell, an official for manpower and personnel in the Defense Department, and gave him general oversight of the studies program. Some bending in response to vigorous objections from a few universities and the Defense Department and assurance of confidentiality to industries enabled NSF to gain substantial cooperation from the principal research performers and supporters.[119]

Some early NSF conceptions of the "general report" tended to be monumental, envisioning a publication running to at least 100,000 words, perhaps to a million.[120] In the event, the 64-page report, attractively printed with large type and ample leading between the lines, was about one-fifth the length of the early minimal estimate. It owed its factual base to the thoughtful collection and arrangement of data by NSF's study directors, its attitudes especially to Waterman, and its clarity and readability to a talented science writer, John E. Pfeiffer.

Throughout most of 1956 confidential drafts of a report, prepared within the Foundation, underwent staff criticism. Late in the year Waterman and Mitchell decided to get outside help and arranged with Pfeiffer to put the material into more suitable form. Pfeiffer essentially finished his assignment the following spring, and the manuscript moved unhurriedly toward publication. While its printing before the launching of the Soviet satellite forestalled an even stronger plea for federal funds for basic research, its delayed publication was otherwise fortunate in allowing NSF to profit from that shocking event.[121]

Although Waterman had earlier conceived a fairly limited audience for the report—heads of government agencies primarily, members of Congress secondarily—he was delighted to see the obviously broader appeal of Pfeiffer's product.[122] The main emphasis was on the federal government's unavoidable responsibility to encourage and support basic research, but the report also stressed the need for greater state support of academic science, the desirability of stimulating private patronage through tax incentives, and the importance of larger contributions from industry as unrestricted research funds for universities.[123] The Foundation's concern for traditional academic values was apparent too in a recommendation urging "a minimum of restrictions on the freedom of the scientist and the administration of his institution" and in another calling for a reduction in government contracts with universities for development projects and a corresponding increase in government sponsorship of basic research.[124]

The report's title was well chosen. *Basic Research—A National Resource* was "designed to convey in nontechnical language the meaning of basic research in science and how important it is to the Nation in its concern for its economy, the health of its citizens, and its defense." It recalled, for example, Bush's argument in *Science—The Endless Frontier* that the nation had to develop its own scientific knowledge if its industrial products were to be competitive in world markets. And the report dwelt at length on the formidable challenge to American security posed by Russia's progress in science and technology. The development of new American products and new American weapons alike depended on the establishment of favorable conditions and more funds for the growth of basic research in the United States.[125]

The report did not discuss science education directly or shortages of scientists and engineers; in fact, it insisted that many competent scientists were unable to obtain backing for their good proposals. Still, as a New York *Times* editorial pointed out, the report's objectives implied increased national emphasis on science at all levels of education, both to ensure an adequate supply of trained scientists and engineers and to give laymen an understanding of science as a cultural activity. As a *Times* news story also mentioned, the report seemed likely to serve as a guide to the Administration in drawing up an action program to meet the Soviet challenge.[126] Certainly the report summed up well the views on policy for science the Foundation had accumulated during its formative years and provided a reasoned argument for the agency's rapid growth in the years ahead.

How Firm a Foundation?

In the summer of 1957 a close student of the Foundation's history referred to the agency's early years as a period of "lusty growth."[1] To anyone familiar with the flush times that began a few months later and lasted for a decade, "lusty" surely seems excessive. But while hindsight corrects, it also distorts. Viewed from the perspective of August 1957—a time of government emphasis on economy and practicality—the growth of NSF, dedicated as it was to the support of pure science, had been substantial.

That growth had occurred under conservative leadership. If either Frank Graham (Harry Truman's first choice) or Lloyd Berkner (William Golden's) had been NSF's first director, the agency would have been quite different from the one formed under Alan Waterman's guidance. For despite the part-time National Science Board's authority to determine NSF policy, the founding legislation had endowed the full-time director with substantial power. Graham would have tried to apply knowledge from the social sciences as well as the natural to the nation's problems, and Berkner would have emphasized interdisciplinary "big science" efforts rather than small projects housed in traditional academic settings. Perhaps under such direction the Foundation would not have endured for seven years as an independent agency, but it would have caused some excitement while it lasted.

Waterman lacked their venturesomeness and zeal. He watched for trouble around the corner. His fear of corruption of basic research by applied probably had much to do with the Foundation's exceeding caution in extending support to the social sciences and perhaps to some neglect of engineering relative to the physical and life sciences. He insisted, however, that NSF must have its hand in all important areas of the natural sciences. As a general-purpose science agency it had a duty to support able scientists in all fields even if their research needs were being met rather well by such mission agencies as the Atomic Energy Commission and the National Institutes of Health. Conversely—and this belief did not spring simply from worry about NSF's giving offense to powerful rivals—he held that mission agencies should support fundamental research that seemed to have relevance to their functions.

But while the Foundation championed a plural system of federal research support, the huge growth of expenditures for military science and technology and for the conquest of disease intensified the need for centralized oversight and coordination of that system. NSF might have done more than it did to help the Budget Bureau perform this function; yet it probably could not have done what the Bureau called for without actually being made an arm of the Bureau and being placed in the Executive Office of the President. In any event, someone other than Waterman would have been required for the purpose. Convinced that science policy must come from the scientific community, not from Washington, he was really a spokesman for basic science and its protector in the government, not an instrument serving the short-term goals of a political Administration.

Waterman was determined to keep the Foundation out of partisan politics. While he encouraged board members to influence their friends on Capitol Hill in NSF's behalf, he avoided building close ties with Congress. Not wanting to make enemies, he did not make many powerful congressional friends either, or at least new ones. He likewise avoided partisan entanglements with the White House, though he established direct lines of communication there which helped him deflect Budget Bureau aims for his agency. President Eisenhower showed his satisfaction with Waterman's performance by reappointing him in 1957 for a second six-year term as director.

NSF's two-headed structure was an unusual one for a federal agency, but the director and board worked harmoniously during the Foundation's formative years. Occasionally a board member complained that the so-called policy-making body merely ratified the recommendations of the director and his staff; perhaps the board could do more to develop *national* science policy—not simply *Foundation* policy—if it had a staff of its own.[2] But the board remained generally content to follow Waterman's advice and agreed with him that its main functions were to advocate more support of basic research, to ensure an adequate supply of scientific manpower, and to guard the independence and health of colleges and universities.

NSF program directors—the key persons in the agency's operations—often held academic values different from those of university presidents on the board—professorial rather than institutional and administrative—and they were even more ardent advocates of support for basic research in their disciplines. Science policy to a program director meant most of all more money for his field of science. Even if he were a permanent member of the staff rather than a "rotator" on a year's leave from a university, a research program director maintained close association with working scientists throughout the country and regarded them as his colleagues. He might be inclined to push the development of a particular area of his discipline, rather than react evenhandedly to proposal pressure from all areas, and he might foster a promising interdisciplinary connection with another field; but like Waterman he believed that science policy should respond to scientists' needs.

The professional scientific staff emphasized high-quality science, that which the peer-review system judged most worthy of support. The limited amount of money available for research support during NSF's early years reinforced the emphasis on quality. Although small budgets parcelled out in individual project grants added a seemingly insignificant amount to research money available through other sources, NSF program directors believed that their funds made a large difference through supporting the best science and the best scientists. Unashamed of being called elitists, the program officers cultivated their agency's growing reputation as a *foundation* dedicated to excellence, not unlike such counterparts in the private realm as Ford and Rockefeller.

Respect for academic values and for the scientist's freedom from restraints other than those required by his discipline underlay another Foundation characteristic—belief in simplicity of research administration. There was even some thought at first that NSF scientific program directors could handle the administration of their grants. But the wish to be simple, to give the best scientists the means to work unhampered by outside rules, was of course impossible for a federal agency disbursing taxpayers' money to support research that had no clearly practical use. The spending of the money had to be accounted for, and while nonconforming bureaucrats on NSF's staff resisted the trend, they could only slow the growth of uniform regulatory procedures. The principles that NSF was supporting science rather than the institutions where science was done, and that basic research was a normal function of universities and that they should share in its costs, ruined hopes for simplicity.

Some modifications in the Foundation's dominating ideas and its ways of operating came along with larger budgets and more confidence in the agency's survival. Program officers in the biological sciences group began to advocate broader and more flexible kinds of support than grants for individual projects. The requirements of some areas of science for expensive instruments and facilities brought significant departures from the first patterns of research support, causing worry among partisans of academic little science and among scientists fearful of centralized planning and control. The Foundation's coordinating responsibilities for U.S. participation in the International Geophysical Year gave NSF a strong push into big science and toward greater participation in international cooperative activities. And a force external to science—congressional pressure—impelled the Foundation into a new and much larger role than it wanted in the improvement of precollege science education.

The issues that had dominated the long debate over the Foundation's creation had largely subsided by the end of 1957 or lay dormant. The question of ownership of patents developed through NSF research support had proved to be negligible for an agency sponsoring only basic research. The social sciences had won a recognized place in the Foundation's research and fellowship programs, though still a small and somewhat limited one. The distribution of research funds remained an issue, though more institutional than regional or demographic. The issue of basic research versus applied had been settled by the act of 1950 and by Waterman's determination to restrict NSF support to uncommitted research; support for "engineering *sciences*" and for social sciences that met rigorous standards of "objectivity, verifiability, and generality" exemplified the dedication to scientific purity.

The main issue of the legislative debate, control of the Foundation, had resulted in a compromise which had proved workable. It functioned smoothly because the first director had the confidence and support of his part-time board. Although he served two masters—the Administration of which he was a part and the scientific community—his principal loyalty was to science, especially academic science. Waterman spent long years in government service, but the values that set the course of his direction of the Foundation grew mainly out of his academic life.

NSF's academic connection can hardly be overemphasizied. A staff member who knew the Foundation well wrote that "there is something of the scholarly aura of the campus about it; and the chief fear of its friends and supporters is that as the Foundation becomes larger and more influential, it may slip into the bureaucratic mold."[3] Yet, of Waterman's three goals for NSF—the advancement of science, the development of the individual scientist, and the strengthening of institutions where science is done and taught—only the first two got much attention during the agency's formative years. One need not suspect that the onetime associate professor distrusted university department heads, deans, and presidents; rather, he believed that sound judgments of scientific merit could be made only for individuals, not groups, and that no more than federal officials should campus administrators "mastermind" the creative work on which the progress of science depended. But after seven years as director he was beginning to acknowledge that individual project grants, no matter how effective for supporting the best science, were not a means of securing the health of institutions and in fact sometimes sapped it. In the years just ahead he would accept arguments from the staff and from spokesmen for higher education for new programs of institutional support.

Characteristically, however, Waterman would approve the idea of institutional support with deliberate caution. He would continue, as in his first years at NSF and earlier at ONR, to build slowly and surely. He was content with small gains because his ambition was to establish a *permanent* federal agency for fundamental science. That, more than personal renown, would be his legacy.

As a patron of pure science, NSF had gained valuable experience in its formative years. Its championing of excellence had won the praise of university scientists and administrators, of their professional societies, and of students in training for scientific careers. It had gained a secure place as the only general-purpose federal science agency. Its avoidance of responsibility to develop policy for the application of science to government's problems meant that the Administration would have to look elsewhere for policy guidance after the Soviets stunned the nation and intensified those problems by putting Sputnik I in orbit on October 4, 1957. Otherwise, the Foundation was well prepared to undertake the large tasks of fostering scientific research and education that loomed ahead.

Appendix 1
Executive Order (10521) Concerning Government Scientific Research

Whereas the security and welfare of the United States depend increasingly upon the advancement of knowledge in the sciences; and

Whereas useful applications of science to defense, humanitarian, and other purposes in the Nation require a strong foundation in basic scientific knowledge and trained scientific manpower; and

Whereas the administration of Federal scientific research programs affecting institutions of learning must be consistent with the preservation of the strength, vitality, and independence of higher education in the United States; and

Whereas, in order to conserve fiscal and manpower resources, it is necessary that Federal scientific research programs be administered with all practicable efficiency and economy; and

Whereas the National Science Foundation has been established by law for the purpose, among others, of developing and encouraging the pursuit of an appropriate and effective national policy for the promotion of basic research and education in the sciences:

Now, therefore, by virtue of the authority vested in me as President of the United States, it is hereby ordered as follows:

SECTION 1. The National Science Foundation (hereinafter referred to as the Foundation) shall from time to time recommend to the President policies for the Federal Government which will strengthen the national scientific effort and furnish guidance toward defining the responsibilities of the Federal Government in the conduct and support of scientific research.

SEC. 2. The Foundation shall continue to make comprehensive studies and recommendations regarding the Nation's scientific research effort and its resources for scientific activities, including facilities and scientific personnel, and its foreseeable scientific needs, with particular attention to the extent of the Federal

Government's activities and the resulting effects upon trained scientific personnel. In making such studies, the Foundation shall make full use of existing sources of information and research facilities within the Federal Government.

SEC. 3. The Foundation, in concert with each Federal agency concerned, shall review the scientific research programs and activities of the Federal Government in order, among other purposes, to formulate methods for strengthening the administration of such programs and activities by the responsible agencies, and to study areas of basic research where gaps or undesirable overlapping of support may exist, and shall recommend to the heads of agencies concerning the support given to basic research.

SEC. 4. As now or hereafter authorized or permitted by law, the Foundation shall be increasingly responsible for providing support by the Federal Government for general-purpose basic research through contracts and grants. The conduct and support by other Federal agencies of basic research in areas which are closely related to their missions is recognized as important and desirable, especially in response to current national needs, and shall continue.

SEC. 5. The Foundation, in consultation with educational institutions, the heads of Federal agencies, and the Commissioner of Education of the Department of Health, Education, and Welfare, shall study the effects upon educational institutions of Federal policies and administration of contracts and grants for scientific research and development, and shall recommend policies and procedures which will promote the attainment of general national research objectives and realization of the research needs of Federal agencies while safeguarding the strength and independence of the Nation's institutions of learning.

SEC. 6. The head of each Federal agency engaged in scientific research shall make certain that effective executive, organizational, and fiscal practices exist to ensure (a) that the Foundation is consulted on policies concerning the support of basic research, (b) that approved scientific research programs conducted by the agency are reviewed continuously in order to preserve priorities in research efforts and to adjust programs to meet changing conditions without imposing unnecessary added burdens on budgetary and other resources, (c) that applied research and development shall be undertaken with sufficient consideration of the underlying basic research and such other factors as relative urgency, project costs, and availability of manpower and facilities, and (d) that, subject to considerations of security and applicable law, adequate dissemination shall be made within the Federal Government of reports on the nature and progress of research projects as an aid to the efficiency and economy of the overall Federal scientific research program.

SEC. 7. Federal agencies supporting or engaging in scientific research shall, with the assistance of the Foundation, cooperate in an effort to improve the methods of classification and reporting of scientific research projects and activities, subject to the requirements of security information.

SEC. 8. To facilitate the efficient use of scientific research equipment and facilities held by Federal agencies:

    (a) the head of each such agency engaged in scientific research shall, to the extent practicable, encourage and facilitate the sharing with other Federal agencies of major equipment and facilities;

    (b) a Federal agency shall procure new major equipment or facilities for scientific research purposes only after taking suitable steps to ascertain that the need cannot be met adequately from existing inventories or facilities of its own or of other agencies; and

(c) the Interdepartmental Committee on Scientific Research and Development shall take necessary steps to ensure that each Federal agency engaged directly in scientific research is kept informed of selected major equipment and facilities which could serve the needs of more than one agency. Each Federal agency possessing such equipment and facilities shall maintain appropriate records to assist other agencies in arranging for their joint use or exchange.

SEC. 9. The heads of the respective Federal agencies shall make such reports concerning activities within the purview of this order as may be required by the President.

> DWIGHT D. EISENHOWER.
> THE WHITE HOUSE,
> *March 17, 1954.*

Appendix 2

*Peer Review in the Earth Sciences Program**

BENSON: ... When I came in '56, Earth Sciences included the whole shebang from the core to the top of the ionosphere, solid, liquid, and gaseous, in what are now the three sections of DES [Division of Environmental Sciences]. And we had about $450,000 for the year. And, incidentally, we had about $1.7 million worth of proposals at that time. So we had roughly about one dollar in four requested, just about the same ratio as today. In FY 1975 we will have spent approximately $13 million on solid earth alone (with roughly the same amount for the other two sections). We had between $40 and $45 million worth of proposals—in other words, about one dollar out of every four requested!

JME: The more things change, the more they stay the same in some respects.

BENSON: That fluctuation has not been large. We have never had less than one dollar out of five or more than one dollar out of three. Most of the time in the 19 and a half years I've been here we ... have given out somewhere between 25 and 30 percent of the dollars requested.

....

JME: Peer review, of course, is one of the big topics of conversation around NSF, and has always been. I'd like to find out a little bit about your experience with the peer review system, how it's operated in your programs, and how you think it has operated in some other research programs in the Foundation.

BENSON: O.K. I guess in many respects I'm one of the leading exponents of the peer review system around here, and believe in it, but "peer review" is a term that is used to cover a multitude of actual processes. All it means, of course, is

---

*Excerpts from an interview with William E. Benson, June 12, 1975.

opinion by one's equals or peers. And the peer review system of NIH, for example, is not the same as the peer review system of NSF, not only in details but in one very important aspect in that NIH peer review is not just peer judgment but almost peer decision. The study sections can be overruled but not easily, whereas here in NSF the system is peer advice. Now peer advice in NSF is actually given in four or five ways. We tend to forget that. The two most important are probably the ad hoc mail reviews and the panels. And different programs use a different mix. Which is a long introduction to discussing how do we do it and how did we grow up.

When I came, procedures were still very fluid, and I sat down with King Hubbert, who was chairman of the Earth Sciences Advisory Panel at that time. I did this during the six-month period that I was assistant program director, and Kirk Stephenson [the program director] wasn't involved. Kirk actually was in poor health when I came (although how poor none of us realized). Anyway, King and I sat down and decided that the only way to approach my job was to assume that I was totally incompetent to do it. This was a perfectly reasonable assumption, because remember I told you that Earth Sciences in those days included solid, liquid, and gaseous earth—from the core to the top of the ionosphere. And there wasn't or isn't anybody who could cover all that by himself. And in NSF it is really the program director's decision that counts. Of course, officially he only recommends, but if his recommended decision is not illegal, immoral, or fattening it's going to stick. And we used to fight to establish this right in the old days. Every once in a while somebody from the old Grants Office would say, "Hey, you know, these reviews don't look very good on that proposal," and we'd say, "It's none of your business. It's the professional judgment of the scientist in charge that this grant should be made, and if it has three poor reviews, you don't know whether the others are any good or not." So it was really up to the program director, and to do his job properly he damn well needed the best advice possible. We (King and I) decided there are two primary ways of getting it: the ad hoc mail review and the advisory panel, and we elected to go both routes. Some programs already were leaning to the ad hoc mail review as the main review, and some programs were leaning toward the panel as the primary. But we decided that both were valuable, and that a combination would be the best. Ad hoc mail reviews are very good in getting detached expert opinion, but a mail reviewer is looking only at one proposal. He doesn't know what the total budget is; he doesn't know what it's in competition with; he doesn't know a lot of other factors; and therefore all he can do is give an isolated opinion of that proposal. Also, since we are all human, his rating of that proposal can vary from day to day, unless he is a super-objective guy. (If his breakfast didn't agree with him, or he had a fight with his wife, he's apt to be more critical than if it's a beautiful day and the birds are singing, and everything else is going fine.) So it's not so much what box they check—good, very good, or excellent—but the actual comments that are the most valuable parts of the mail review. Then we have the panel, and if we're wise in choosing a good, broad-gauged panel that covers all of the discipline, it adds a dimension to the mail reviews. These are available at the panel meeting, and the pros and cons are discussed. That's when the mail reviews reach their maximum utility, and everybody who has an input makes it at that time and shame on him if he doesn't! That includes the staff (in the early days just me). For example, one of us may have just made a site visit to that particular university and may say, "Look, the reviewers have raised points that sound rather critical, but I happen to know the guy has already taken care of this objection." Crank that and all other information in and finally the panel takes a quality vote and we establish a relative order of priority, which is their final advice, on the matter. Do we differ from that priority? Sometimes, but only with very good reason. Because I have always figured that if I think that something is good or bad, but that after a complete discussion (including the mail reviews) the panel is still against my opinion, then I'd better re-evaluate that opinion. So it's a gray day in September when we go against that priority order, because it really has been evolved not just by an independent panel vote, but by a vote that has taken into account all of the discussion and all of the mail reviews too. On the other hand, when we do go against it, we always tell the panel at the next meeting—that's one thing that I have always done right from the very beginning.

Some programs have used their panels largely for policy advice, but we concluded early in the game that the Supreme Court has been very wise in refusing to decide an issue *in vacuo* but always demanding a test case. In our experience, the best advice that the panel has provided, other than screening proposals, has been because they *have* screened the proposals. Either the principle came up and was raised in somebody's mind as a result of a particular proposal, or, if a question was raised to the panel by staff, rating the proposals had provided a better baseline for the discussion. In other words, they saw what the bread-and-butter operation of the program actually was.

JME: But at the same time did not try to be program directors themselves.

BENSON: That's right, but they had been involved in the *input* to the decision-making; they had a more intimate knowledge of what we in Earth Sciences were doing, and therefore we felt that there was a better baseline for giving policy advice, as well as for the screening. That is the way we have operated the peer review system in Earth Sciences, essentially from the time I came. There have, of course, been minor modifications because of increase in volume. We tried, for a while, going to the system that some programs or sections have used, namely, referring only the "middle" group of proposals to the panel, but the panel preferred to see the whole spectrum. Instead, we have split into sub-panels so that all members don't see all proposals, but each sees the entire range within a sub-discipline. Again, this was largely the panel's own choice—to provide a proper kind of a baseline.

To go back to the one dollar granted out of four requested, not only has it stayed pretty constant, but so has the quality. If you had a quality graph—a graph of the quality of proposals—you would get a Gaussian curve with a peak near the middle and tapering on either end. About 10 or 15 percent of the proposals are gold-plated—you would almost steal the money to fund them—and about 10 or 15 percent are dogs, and you wouldn't fund them no matter how much money you had; and the rest sort of peak in the middle. If you had about two-thirds of the dollars requested you wouldn't be ashamed at anything you would support. More than about two-thirds of the dollars requested you'd start getting into things that intellectually you'd feel pretty leery about defending. Now I said only 10 or 15 percent are "dogs"; the difference between that and the "two-thirds" we'd like to support is involved in budget fat and a few things like that, and proposals that might be all right but that you'd really hate to defend on a real quality basis.

JME: Did geographic distribution play much part in your decisions on those borderline cases?

BENSON: Oh, yes. On borderline cases, certainly. But of course we were never very low in the quality scale. But to go back for a moment to the panel operations. It turned out that it doesn't waste the panel's time very much to see all the proposals as opposed to just the "middle" ones. Because you don't spend much time at the meetings discussing either extreme. If a proposal comes through with all very good to excellent reviews and the budget looks all right—i.e., the "gold-plated" proposals—we often don't even bother reading the mail reviews.

JME: But at least they have seen the first-rate proposals.

BENSON: They have seen the spectrum; they have a much better basis for judgment; and it doesn't waste that much time to do the whole thing. It's the same way with the very bad ones. As a matter of fact, some of the very bad ones are kind of fun to read. Especially the very few—and it's *surprisingly* few—crackpot proposals that do come in. Randal Robertson* used to like to see the crackpots. I think secretly he enjoyed writing letters to them and sparring with them, and we always used to encourage him to so we wouldn't have to. But every once in a while a real oddball would come in because the fellow had sent it through his Congressman. It would usually come over with the "Hey, what'll I tell this guy?" type of letter—the Congressman's office knew it was crackpot, too. But sometimes it was a proposal as well as just a letter. I remember one that came in and Randal said, "What are we going to do with this?" And I said, "Look, Randal, you have already replied to this and said we will evaluate it in the normal manner of the Science Foundation." He said, "Well, can't we just decline it by staff review?" I said, "Your letter went back through Congressman so-and-so's office, saying we were going to review it, so we're going to review it." "Oh, they'll think we're crazy sending the proposal out." I said, "No, Randal, I'll send it out." "Who are you going to send it to?" Well, I named four people, such as Bob Sharp and Harry Hess, all ex-chairmen of our advisory panel. Randal said, "But those people! They'll think you're crazy!" I said, "No, they won't. They'll get a big bang out of it." So we always used to do that. The only hazard was that every once in a while, just for the hell of it, one of them would take a crackpot proposal and give it an "excellent" rating and write a humorous review.

BENSON: . . . But, back to the geographic distribution—I'm sure that in delving into the burrows of the past you have found Alan Waterman's stated policy on this, namely, that quality comes first, and then other things being equal, geographic distribution would come in. Certainly that played a significant role when we were in the cut-off area, and, remember, the cut-off area was still high quality. The cut-off area in the early days was around 40-45 percent of the pro-

---

*Assistant Director for Mathematical, Physical, and Engineering Sciences, 1958-61; Associate Director for Research, 1961-70.

posals by number. (That is not inconsistent with my one dollar out of four ratio, because you can fund more small proposals than you can large proposals.) So we were funding maybe 40 percent of the proposals by number that came in. And when there was money enough, say, for one more proposal and there was a choice of proposals of equal quality, one was from M.I.T. and one from Jonesboro Teachers College, to coin a name, we always gave it to Jonesboro Teachers College.

JME: I suppose there probably is a somewhat better geographic distribution of strength in earth sciences than there is in some other fields.

BENSON: Yes, and also quite a difference from program to program. For example, there's a much wider geographic distribution in straight geology than there is in geophysics. There are good reasons for this. Modern geophysics is newer, is not taught in as many schools. It's spreading out more, but it's never going to spread as far as geology, because it's more expensive, and the small schools aren't going to be able to afford a lot of the sophisticated types of gear that are needed. But there's a lot of good geology that can be done relatively cheaply. So we get more geology proposals from small schools. You know, some of the critics of the peer review system are really criticizing *in vacuo*. They've never seen the system in operation and the accusations that they throw are about 180 degrees out of phase with reality. For example, from the very first we have always had someone on our advisory panel who is the defender of the young guy getting a start, and he doesn't usually have to fight very hard. A decent proposal from a young investigator starting out in an obscure or small school has a better than average chance of getting funded. It always happens that way. In the geology program (where it's easiest to have that kind of a distribution) about 15 percent of our proposals by number come from small schools, small colleges, and about 30 percent of our grants go there.

JME: I think there's an enormous amount of sympathy for the young unsupported investigator.

BENSON: That's right! Far from being self-congratulatory and back-slapping the panel is always harder on the top people in the profession. "Why, this is from so-and-so who—"

JME: "He ought to do better than that!"

BENSON: "He ought to do *much* better than that, and by God if he can't do better than that you better send it back to him and tell him to rewrite it!" It's just the reverse of what some of the critics are saying.

JME: How have you gone about picking members of your advisory panel?

BENSON: That was another thing that King Hubbert and I discussed early in the game. We felt that there should be two things that the panel ought to have: It ought to have an independent mind (i.e. not be a "captive committee"), and it ought to have continuity without being a self-perpetuating body. So we evolved a system whereby the continuity was provided by rotating a third of the members off each year. Then at the fall meeting, the second meeting of each year, we would pick a nominating committee from people who know the Foundation— either panel alumni or divisional committee alumni. And either the chairman or I would write to them and say, "O.K., the following people are going off the panel. Here's a list of all people who've been on the panel, and here's the current panel. Keeping in mind such things as geographic distribution, representation from industry, small schools, etc., give us a slate of nominees of three guys for each vacancy." Then at the spring panel meeting the panel and the staff would establish a priority order of these nominations for new members. After about six or seven years we finally had to abandon the nominating committee business, because it was getting a little too complicated. So we shortcut it to a discussion by both panel and staff as to who should replace "graduating" members. In other words, the panel does not choose its own successors but they do have a strong voice in recommending who those successors will be. And, conversely, I couldn't put somebody on the panel that everybody else thought was a dog. In other words, it can't be a captive committee nor can it be self-perpetuating. We think those two things are very important.

Now, over the years, especially in the earlier days, the Earth Sciences panel had a reputation of being one of the hardest working, most obstreperous, most annoying panels around, and undoubtedly the one that had the highest esprit de corps. And I'm sure it's because they have always felt they were doing a real job.

Appendix 3
NSF Organizational Structure, 1950-57

NATIONAL SCIENCE FOUNDATION
Organization Prescribed in the Enabling Act

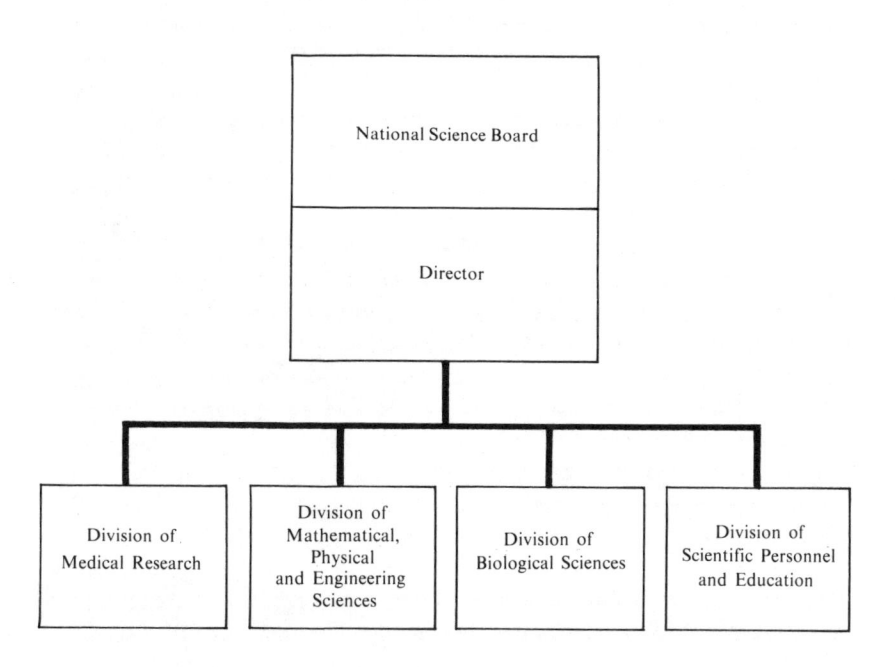

```
                    ┌─────────────────────────┐
                    │ National Science Board  │
                    ├─────────────────────────┤
                    │        Director         │
                    └────────────┬────────────┘
        ┌──────────────┬─────────┼─────────┬──────────────┐
┌───────┴──────┐ ┌─────┴──────┐ ┌┴─────────┐ ┌────────────┴──┐
│  Division of │ │Division of │ │Division of│ │  Division of  │
│   Medical    │ │Mathematical│ │Biological │ │  Scientific   │
│   Research   │ │ Physical   │ │ Sciences  │ │  Personnel    │
│              │ │and Engineer│ │           │ │ and Education │
│              │ │ing Sciences│ │           │ │               │
└──────────────┘ └────────────┘ └───────────┘ └───────────────┘
```

NATIONAL SCIENCE FOUNDATION
ORGANIZATION AS OF JUNE 30, 1957

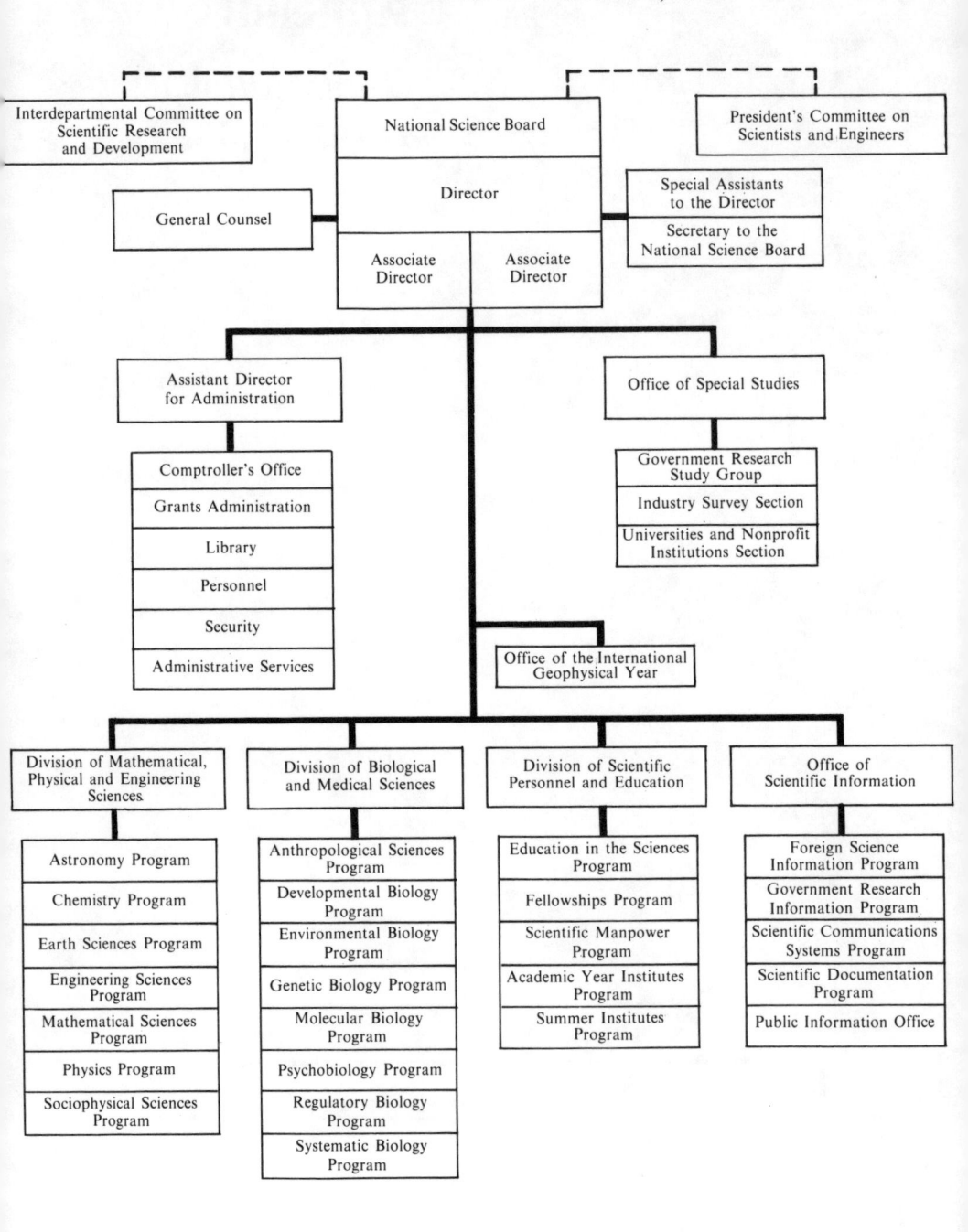

- Interdepartmental Committee on Scientific Research and Development
- National Science Board
  - Director
    - Associate Director
    - Associate Director
  - Special Assistants to the Director
  - Secretary to the National Science Board
- President's Committee on Scientists and Engineers
- General Counsel

Assistant Director for Administration
- Comptroller's Office
- Grants Administration
- Library
- Personnel
- Security
- Administrative Services

Office of Special Studies
- Government Research Study Group
- Industry Survey Section
- Universities and Nonprofit Institutions Section

Office of the International Geophysical Year

Division of Mathematical, Physical and Engineering Sciences
- Astronomy Program
- Chemistry Program
- Earth Sciences Program
- Engineering Sciences Program
- Mathematical Sciences Program
- Physics Program
- Sociophysical Sciences Program

Division of Biological and Medical Sciences
- Anthropological Sciences Program
- Developmental Biology Program
- Environmental Biology Program
- Genetic Biology Program
- Molecular Biology Program
- Psychobiology Program
- Regulatory Biology Program
- Systematic Biology Program

Division of Scientific Personnel and Education
- Education in the Sciences Program
- Fellowships Program
- Scientific Manpower Program
- Academic Year Institutes Program
- Summer Institutes Program

Office of Scientific Information
- Foreign Science Information Program
- Government Research Information Program
- Scientific Communications Systems Program
- Scientific Documentation Program
- Public Information Office

NATIONAL SCIENCE FOUNDATION
ORGANIZATION AS OF JUNE 30, 1954

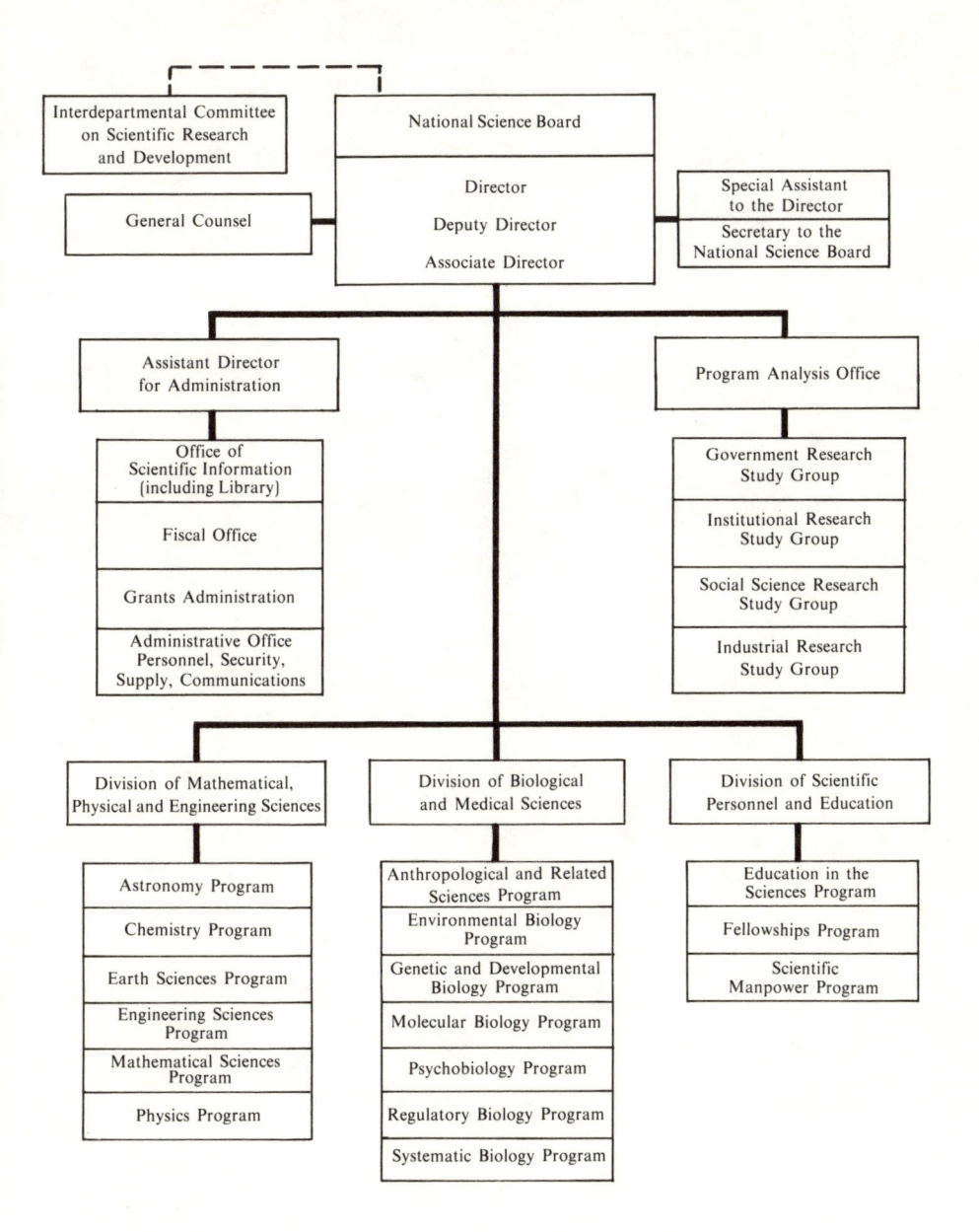

- **Interdepartmental Committee on Scientific Research and Development**
- **General Counsel**
- **National Science Board**
  - Director
  - Deputy Director
  - Associate Director
- **Special Assistant to the Director**
- **Secretary to the National Science Board**

Assistant Director for Administration
- Office of Scientific Information (including Library)
- Fiscal Office
- Grants Administration
- Administrative Office Personnel, Security, Supply, Communications

Program Analysis Office
- Government Research Study Group
- Institutional Research Study Group
- Social Science Research Study Group
- Industrial Research Study Group

Division of Mathematical, Physical and Engineering Sciences
- Astronomy Program
- Chemistry Program
- Earth Sciences Program
- Engineering Sciences Program
- Mathematical Sciences Program
- Physics Program

Division of Biological and Medical Sciences
- Anthropological and Related Sciences Program
- Environmental Biology Program
- Genetic and Developmental Biology Program
- Molecular Biology Program
- Psychobiology Program
- Regulatory Biology Program
- Systematic Biology Program

Division of Scientific Personnel and Education
- Education in the Sciences Program
- Fellowships Program
- Scientific Manpower Program

Notes

Introduction

[1] Robert F. Maddox, "The Politics of World War II Science: Senator Harley M. Kilgore and the Legislative Origins of the National Science Foundation," *West Virginia History*, Vol. 41, No. 1 (Fall 1979), pp. 20-39; Lyman Chalkley, "Prologue to the U.S. National Science Foundation (1942-1951)," typescript in NSF History files (hereafter NSF HF). Chalkley's manuscript, written in 1951, is now available through University Microfilms.

[2] James Phinney Baxter 3rd, *Scientists Against Time* (Boston, 1950), p. 14; James B. Conant, *My Several Lives: Memoirs of a Social Inventor* (New York, 1970), p. 234; Bethuel M. Webster, "Lunch at the Century" (June 1948), mimeographed paper, NSF HF.

[3] Vannevar Bush, *Pieces of the Action* (New York, 1970), especially ch. 2; Irvin Stewart, *Organizing Scientific Research for War: The Administrative History of the Office of Scientific Research and Development* (Boston, 1948), ch. 2.

[4] Stewart, *Organizing Scientific Research for War*, ch. 3; Bush, *Pieces of the Action*, pp. 42-50.

[5] Bush, *Pieces of the Action*, pp. 52-56, and ch. 3, *passim*; Baxter, *Scientists Against Time*.

[6] Daniel J. Kevles, "Scientists, the Military, and the Control of Postwar Defense Research: The Case of the Research Board for National Security, 1944-46," *Technology and Culture*, Vol. 16, No. 1 (Jan. 1975), pp. 20-47.

[7] Daniel J. Kevles, "The National Science Foundation and the Debate over Postwar Research Policy, 1942-1945," *Isis*, Vol. 68 (March 1977), pp. 5-26, especially pp. 10-15.

Chapter 1

[1] Palmer C. Putnam to Carroll L. Wilson, Dec. 7, 1944, in OSRD Records, Record Group 227, National Archives, Item 1, Box 11. Unless otherwise indicated, all unpublished documents cited in this chapter are in the OSRD Records. Concise biographical notes on Putnam, Wilson, and several other persons mentioned here may be found in Vannevar Bush, *Pieces of the Action* (New York, 1970), pp. 318, 330-31, and *passim*.

This chapter appeared in substantially the same form in *Science*, Vol. 191 (Jan. 9, 1976), pp. 41-47, copyright 1976 by the American Association for the Advancement of Science. I am grateful for permission to reprint it.

[2] Wilson to Putnam, Dec. 12, 1944, Item 1, Box 11.

[3] Franklin D. Roosevelt to Vannevar Bush, Nov. 17, 1944, quoted in Bush, *Science—The Endless Frontier: A Report to the President* (Washington, 1945), pp. vii-viii.

[4] Daniel J. Kevles describes the origins of FDR's request in a letter to the editor of *Science*, Vol. 183 (March 1, 1974), pp. 798, 800. Cox's draft is attached to Oscar S. Cox to Irvin Stewart, Oct. 18, 1944, Item 13, Box 224.

[5] Oscar M. Ruebhausen to Cox, Oct. 26, 1944, Legal Div. chron. files (6/1/44-11/30/44—tray 5366); Ruebhausen to Bush, Oct. 26, 1944, and attached draft, Item 13, Box 238; Kevles, *Science* (March 1, 1974), p. 800.

[6] Robert F. Maddox, "The Politics of World War II Science: Senator Harley M. Kilgore and the Legislative Origins of the National Science Foundation," *West Virginia History*, Vol. 41, No. 1 (Fall 1979), pp. 20-39.

[7] Bush to Frank B. Jewett, Aug. 21, 1943, Item 13, Box 224; Bush to Harley M. Kilgore, Aug. 27, 1943, Item 13, Box 185. Bush's letter to Kilgore was printed in *Science*, Vol. 98 (Dec. 31, 1943). pp. 571-77.

[8] Bush to Thomas Barbour, Jan. 17, 1944, Item 13, Box 185.

[9] For Schimmel's part, see Maddox,"The Politics of World War II Science," pp. 22-23, 25; Lyman Chalkley, "Prologue to the U.S. National Science Foundation (1942-1951)," NSF HF; Detlev W. Bronk, "The National Science Foundation: Origins, Hopes, and Aspirations," *Science*, Vol. 188 (May 2, 1975), pp. 409-10.

[10] Jewett to Bush, June 8, 1944, enclosing copies of letters from George B. Pegram and William J. Robbins, both dated June 2, 1944, Item 13, Box 185.

[11] Memo by Lyman Chalkley, June 5, 1944; Karl T. Compton to Chalkley, June 9, 1944; Wilson to Chalkley, June 21, 1944; Bush to Kilgore, June 20, 22, 1944; [Chalkley], statement of comments phoned to C. Theodore Larson of Kilgore's staff, June 9, 1944, Item 13, Box 185.

[12] Kevles, *Science* (March 1, 1974), p. 800.

[13] Though Kilgore's bill had been much improved, it was still faulty, Bush thought. In a note to Chalkley (n.d., Item 13, Box 185) Bush commented on Kilgore's proposed revision of S. 702 in a Senate Subcommittee Print dated Nov. 10, 1944:

"Except for the pat[ent] section this is not bad—on the other hand I don't believe such a setup will do much good & it certainly will do strange things.

"I ought to accumulate some criticisms—for use when called to testify."

[14] Bush to J. A. Furer, Dec. 12, 1944, Item 2, Box 48.

[15] Bush to files, Dec. 19, 1944, Item 13, Box 224; Bush to Robert E. Wilson, Jan. 1, 1945; Bush to Isaiah Bowman, Jan. 10, 1945; Bush to C. L. Wilson, Jan. 15, 1945, Item 2, Box 48.

[16] Bush *Science—The Endless Frontier*, pp. 178-84.

[17] *Ibid.*, pp. 128-77.

[18] *Ibid.*, pp. 130-34, 142-45.

[19] *Ibid.*, pp. 150-54. The overseas technical training idea appealed to the veteran artillery captain in the White House. When Bush discussed the report with the President on June 14, Truman asked about any special plans to make up the wartime deficit in trained scientific personnel. Bush said: "I . . . told him about my proposal that selected men might be sent back from overseas, under orders, to acquire the latest information in many fields, to return to instruct those remaining on the other side in such matter, and gave the illustration of a sergeant who has put in good performance on maintaining tanks who might spend some time with the automobile industry and return to give his buddies the latest information. The President said he thought this sounded like an excellent idea and asked me if I had taken it up with the Army, and I told him of my contacts thus far on the subject. He said he thought I ought to follow the matter up, and that I could quote him as of the opinion that this was a good idea that ought to be followed up." Bush, memorandum of conference with the President, June 15, 1945, Item 2, Box 48.

[20] Bush, *Science—The Endless Frontier*, pp. 154-57.

[21] Bush to Bowman, Jan. 10, 1945, Item 2, Box 48.

²² Bush to C. L. Wilson, Jan. 15, 1945, Item 2, Box 48.
²³ Bush to Bowman, Jan. 29, 1945, Item 2, Box 48; Bush to Bowman, Feb. 19, 1945, Item 2, Box 49; Bush to Conway P. Coe, Dec. 26, 1944, Item 13, Box 224; Bush to Delos G. Haynes, Feb. 21, 1945, Item 2, Box 49.
²⁴ C. L. Wilson to W. Rupert Maclaurin, April 5, 14, 1945, Item 2, Box 48; Henry A. Wallace to Bush, April 24, 1945; Bush to Bruce Brown, April 26, 1945; Bush to Bradley Dewey, April 26, 1945, Item 2, Box 49.
²⁵ Kilgore to Bush, Feb. 5, 1945; Bush to Kilgore, Feb. 10, 1945; Bush to Bowman, Feb. 10, 17, 1945; Bowman to Bush, Feb. 28, 1945; Bush to Sanford E. Thompson, March 24, 1945, Item 2, Box 49; Kilgore to Bush, Feb. 15, 1949; Chalkley to Bush, Feb. 24, 1945, Item 3, Box 85.
²⁶ Jewett to Bush, March 20, 1945; Bush to Jewett, March 22, 1945, Item 2, Box 48.
²⁷ Robert A. Millikan to Bush, April 2, 1945, Item 2, Box 48.
²⁸ Bush to Millikan, April 5, 1945, Item 2, Box 48.
²⁹ Bowman to Bush, April 11, 1945, Item 2, Box 49.
³⁰ Bush, *Science—The Endless Frontier*, pp. 71-74.
³¹ *Ibid.*, pp. 69, 109-10.
³² Notes on Meeting of the Chairmen and Secretaries of the Four Committees . . . on March 8, 1945, Item 2, Box 48.
³³ Homer W. Smith to C. L. Wilson, March 11, 1945, Item 2, Box 49.
³⁴ C. L. Wilson to Smith, March 14, 1945, and attached note, Item 2, Box 49.
³⁵ Walter W. Palmer to Bush, April 25, 1945, Item 2, Box 47.
³⁶ L. K. F[rank] [to C.L. Wilson], n.d.(about May 10, 1945), note attached to typed comments on draft report of Palmer committee dated April 25, 1945, Item 2, Box 49.
³⁷ Bush to Jewett, June 7, 1945, Item 2, Box 48.
³⁸ C. L. Wilson to Palmer, June 15, 1945, Item 2, Box 48.
³⁹ Smith to C. L. Wilson, June 21, 1945, Item 2, Box 49.
⁴⁰ Bush, *Science—The Endless Frontier*, pp. vi, 7, 26.
⁴¹ *Ibid.*, pp. 45, 53-54, 59-63.
⁴² *Ibid.*, p. viii.
⁴³ C. L. Wilson to Richardson Wood, May 21, 1945, Item 2, Box 47, and related correspondence in same file; interview with Don K. Price, April 18, 1975.
⁴⁴ Bush, *Science—The Endless Frontier*, p. 109.
⁴⁵ *Ibid.*, pp. 26-27; C.L. Wilson, Notes in Connection with Bush Report to President, May 22, 1945, Item 2, Box 47.
⁴⁶ Bush, penciled notes on draft report, May 23, 1945, Item 2, Box 47.
⁴⁷ Bush to Palmer *et al.*, May 31, 1945, Item 2, Box 48.
⁴⁸ Smith to Bush, June 5, 1945; Maclaurin to Bush, June 4, 1945; Harlow Shapley to Bush, June 4, 1945, Item 2, Box 48.
⁴⁹ "Master Copy" attached to Bush's mimeographed letter of May 31, 1945, to Palmer *et al.*, Item 2, Box 48.
⁵⁰ Bush to Jewett, June 2, 1945: Jewett to Bush, June 5, 1945, Item 2, Box 48.
⁵¹ Bush to Jewett, June 7, 1945, Item 2, Box 48.
⁵² Jewett to Bush, June 8, 1945, Item 2, Box 48.
⁵³ "Master Copy" (see n. 49, above).
⁵⁴ Carbon copy (with intermixed mimeographed sheets) dated "June, 1945" of the overall report, *ibid.*; the carbons are pages retyped to incorporate the changes resulting from comments elicited from committee members and others following the May 31 mailing. This copy contains marginal comments and changes in Bush's hand, and thus, he obviously approved the change.

Bush or his assistants may have sounded out some committee members on this change—perhaps by telephone, since I have found no evidence on this matter in the OSRD files. But since there were bound to be violent objections, he may have decided on his own to return to the earlier wording.

⁵⁵ Bush, memorandum of conference with the President, June 14, 1945, Item 2, Box 48.
⁵⁶ On the arrangements for printing and releasing the report, see Ruebhausen's memorandum to files, June 16, 1945; C.L. Wilson to Webster, June 30, 1945, Item 2, Box 48;

and Bush to Cleveland Norcross, July 14, 1945, Item 13, Box 225.
⁵⁷ Bush, *Science—The Endless Frontier*, pp. v-vi.
⁵⁸ *Ibid.*, pp. 4, 28.
⁵⁹ *Ibid.*, pp. 28-29.
⁶⁰ *Ibid.*, pp. 29, 31.
⁶¹ *Ibid.*, pp. 31-32.
⁶² *Ibid.*, pp. 32-33.
⁶³ *Ibid.*, p. 33.
⁶⁴ *Ibid.*, p. 34.

Chapter 2

¹ Carroll L. Wilson to Wilbur D. Mills, July 13, 1945, OSRD Records, Item 2, Box 48; Mills to Wilson, July 13, 1945, Item 2, Box 50.
² H. M. Kilgore to Vannevar Bush, May 14, 1945, OSRD, Item 1, Box 12; C. L. Wilson to Bethuel M. Webster, June 11, 1945, OSRD, Item 2, Box 48; Don K. Price to [Arnold] Miles, July 20, 1945, Bureau of the Budget Records, Record Group 51, National Archives (hereafter BOB), Series 39.32, file E8-2/44.2.
³ A partisan of the Bush report later wrote that discussions between Kilgore's and Magnuson's staffs broke down when "it was realized that differences in concept between the two groups were fundamental and that further collaboration was impossible. When a bill was drafted embodying the recommendations of the Bush Report, the aid of Senator Magnuson was enlisted. However, before he accepted the Bush bill, Senator Magnuson conferred with Senator Kilgore and urged a more careful consideration of the viewpoint represented by Doctor Bush . . . ." Magnuson then introduced the Bush bill "when Senator Kilgore refused to subscribe to the principles therein." [W. Parker Anslow, Jr.], "Brief History of National Science Legislation," n.d., attached to Homer W. Smith to Bush, Feb. 18, 1947, in Vannevar Bush Papers, Manuscript Division, Library of Congress (hereafter Bush MSS), Box 104, file 2465.
⁴ *Public Papers of the Presidents of the United States. Harry S. Truman . . . April 12 to December 31, 1945* (Washington, 1961), pp. 292-94.
⁵ Irvin Stewart to A. P. Brogan, Sept. 24, 1945, OSRD, Item 13, Box 225; Wilson to Smith, Oct. 4, 1945, OSRD, Item 2, Box 49; Price to Miles, Sept. 20, 1945, BOB, Series 39.1.
  Kilgore said that he first questioned the inclusion of the social sciences but later concluded "that their omission from the bill is unthinkable." Kilgore to Paul O. Summers, Nov. 26, 1945, Kilgore Papers, West Virginia University Library, Series 8, Box 1, file 8; Kilgore to N. M. Perrins, May 2, 1946, Series 4, Box 1, War Mobilization and Reconversion file.
⁶ Harold D. Smith to Bush, Oct. 1, 1945, BOB, Series 39.1.
⁷ Bush to Smith, Aug. 13, 1945, BOB, Series 39.1.
⁸ Paul H. Appleby to John W. Snyder, Sept. 27, 1945; Smith to Bush, Oct. 1, 1945, BOB, Series 39.1.
⁹ Price to Miles, Sept. 20, 1945, BOB, Series 39.1; Price to Director, Sept. 21, 1945, BOB, Series 39.32—E8-2/44.2.
¹⁰ [Anslow], "Brief History of National Science Legislation."
¹¹ Harold D. Smith, Diary, Oct. 5, 1945, copy, in Harry S. Truman Library.
¹² U. S. Senate, Subcommittee of the Committee on Military Affairs, *Hearings on Science Legislation (S. 1297 and Related Bills)*, 79th Cong., 1st Sess., pp. 2-8.
¹³ *Ibid.*, p. 9.
¹⁴ *Ibid.*, pp. 10-14.
¹⁵ *Ibid.*, pp. 368-69, 381. Although the printed hearings say "abrogating" rather than "arrogating," it seems safe to assume that this was a stenographic or printing error.

[16] *Ibid.*, pp. 25-26, 34-35, 38-40.
[17] *Ibid.*, pp. 52-54, 65-66.
[18] *Ibid.*, pp. 91-93.
[19] *Ibid.*, p. 104.
[20] *Ibid.*, p. 97.
[21] *Ibid.*, pp. 99-101.
[22] *Ibid.*, pp. 97-98, 101-02.
[23] *Ibid.*, pp. 98-99, 102.
[24] *Ibid.*, p. 102.
[25] *Ibid.*, pp. 137-41.
[26] Bush to Gordon S. Rentschler, Oct. 20, 1945, Bush MSS, Box 95, file 2206; Bush to James E. Webb, Dec. 27, 1946, Box 85, file 1912.

James R. Newman pointed out to John W. Snyder that Bush had arranged for the drafting and introduction of his foundation bill without prior clearance on its policies, which were out of line with the President's recommendations. Newman wanted Bush told that he must support the Administration's stand, or discuss the matter with the President. Newman to Snyder, Dec. 4, 1945, and draft (11/30/45) of letter for Snyder to Bush, in Byron S. Miller Papers, Manuscript Division, Library of Congress, Box 3.

[27] *Hearings*, pp. 200, 203-05.
[28] *Ibid.*, p. 205.
[29] *Ibid.*, pp. 228-31, 237, 240-41.
[30] *Ibid.*, p. 280. Smith's Daily Record (copy in Truman Library), Oct. 15, 1945, says that he telephoned Schimmel "that he considered our letter of October 1 to Dr. Bush . . . had been cleared with the President and had his approval."
[31] *Ibid.*, p. 291.
[32] *Ibid.*, pp. 737-38.
[33] Alice Kimball Smith, *A Peril and a Hope: The Scientists' Movement in America: 1945-47* (Chicago, 1965), p. 152.
[34] *Hearings*, pp. 303-04.
[35] *Ibid.*, pp. 300-01, 308.
[36] *Ibid.*, pp. 320-22. 330-33.
[37] *Ibid.*, p. 1032.
[38] *Ibid.*, pp. 455-510; Smith's poll appears on pp. 506-09 and the exchange with Schimmel on pp. 509-10.
[39] *Ibid.*, pp. 552-53, 560-61, 564-65.
[40] *Ibid.*, pp. 593-97.
[41] *Ibid.*, pp. 738-86, *passim*; see especially pp. 744, 760-61.
[42] *Ibid.*, p. 928.
[43] *Ibid.*, pp. 707, 715.
[44] *Ibid.*, pp. 664-70.
[45] *Ibid.*, p. 629.
[46] *Ibid.*, pp. 786-87.
[47] E. E. Day to Howard L. Bevis, Nov. 6, 1945, in NSF Bills, Correspondence file, National Association of State Universities and Land-Grant Colleges, Washington, D.C. (hereafter NASULGC).
[48] *Hearings*, p. 714.
[49] *Ibid.*, pp. 1042-46, 1065-66.
[50] *Ibid.*, pp. 428-29. Similarly, I. I. Rabi, Nobel prizewinning physicist of Columbia University, asserted that "Scientists will not be happy to operate under even a benevolent czar in times of peace." *Ibid.*, p. 991.
[51] *Ibid.*, pp. 429-30.
[52] *Ibid.*, p. 448.
[53] J. Robert Oppenheimer, *The Open Mind* (New York. 1955), p. 88.
[54] Solly Zuckerman, *Scientists and War: The Impact of Science on Military and Civil Affairs* (New York, 1967), pp. 140-41.
[55] *Hearings*, p. 1002.
[56] *Ibid.*, pp. 977-78.

[57] *Science*, Vol 102 (Nov. 30, 1945), pp. 545-48. James Newman said he was "certain that the Bowman group does *not* speak for even a majority of scientists," let alone "the great majority" that Bowman claimed. Newman to Snyder, Dec. 4, 1945, Miller MSS, Box 3.

[58] Bowman to Charles Ross (telegram), Nov. 23, 1945, Bowman Papers, Johns Hopkins University Library, NSF 1945-47 file.

[59] Bowman to C. L. Wilson, Nov. 26, 1945, Bowman Papers, NSF 1945-47 file.

[60] Smith Diary (copy), Nov. 28, 1945, Truman Library.

[61] *Public Papers of... Harry S. Truman... April 12 to December 31, 1945*, pp. 570-71.

[62] Frank B. Jewett to Bowman, Dec. 3, 1945, Bowman Papers, NSF 1945-47 file.

[63] *Science*, Vol. 102 (Dec. 21, 1945), p. 644.

[64] *Ibid.*, Vol. 103 (Jan. 4, 1946), p. 11. For a comment on Shapley's and Urey's activity in the Independent Citizens Committee see Bush to Jewett, May 7, 1946, Bush MSS, Box 56, file 1377.

[65] Price to Director, Dec. 19, 1945, BOB, Series 39.32—E8-2/44.2; Smith's handwritten comment appears on a copy of the memo.

[66] I. B[owman], memorandum of telephone conversation with Day, Dec. 14, 1945, Bowman Papers, NSF 1945-47 file.

[67] Bowman to Shapley, Dec. 22, 1945, Bowman Papers, NSF 1945-47 file.

[68] Howard A. Meyerhoff, "Science Legislation and the Holiday Recess," *Science*, Vol. 103 (Jan. 4, 1946), pp. 10-11.

[69] *Ibid.*, p. 11.

[70] Homer Smith to Bowman, Jan. 12, 1946, Bowman Papers, NSF 1945-47 file. Smith enclosed the memorandum, "unread and unedited," which presumably was endorsed by the steering committee at a meeting on January 14.

[71] I. B[owman], memorandum on S. 1720, Jan. 17, 1946, Bowman Papers, NSF 1945-47 file.

[72] *Ibid*. A partisan of the Bush bill reacted just as strongly as Kilgore to Smith's "Emergency Memorandum of Utmost Importance." Father O'Donnell of Notre Dame asked whether the memorandum meant that "the good Doctor [Bush] and Senator Magnuson are about to make an obeisance to expediency" with respect to the organization of the board. "Personally, I shall never subscribe to any measure that gives the government administrator the power of policy making with the help of an advisory board, as Mr. Smith outlines it in his report. In my opinion, this simply means adding another tentacle to the growing octopus of federal bureaucracy." J. Hugh O'Donnell to Bowman, Jan. 29, 1946, Bowman Papers, NSF 1945-47 file. Bowman sought to mollify Father O'Donnell in his reply. Bowman to O'Donnell, Feb. 8, 1946, Bowman Papers, NSF 1945-47 file.

[73] Bowman to Homer Smith, Jan. 24, 1946, Bowman Papers, NSF 1945-47 file.

[74] Price to Mr. Hoelscher, Feb. 1, 1946, BOB, Series 39.32—E8-2/44.2.

Kilgore agreed that the changes were "primarily 'face-saving' amendments by which they may gradually retire from their formerly extreme position on the major issues." As a price for the support of the Bush-Bowman group, Kilgore was willing to allow an addition to the bill providing for consultation of the board with the President before his appointment of the agency's administrator, though the provision would be "in no way binding on the President." But Kilgore intended to tell Truman that "I would be absolutely against such a compromise if I were not sure that you are fully aware of the nefarious pressure which the Bush-Bowman group have and will probably continue to exert to gain the control of the Foundation." Memorandum for conference with the President, Feb. 8, 1946, Kilgore Papers, Series 1, Box 4, S. 1720 file.

[75] [Samuel Callaway] to Bradley Dewey, Jan. 28, 1946, Bush MSS, Box 32, file 740.

[76] Howard A. Meyerhoff, "S. 1720 vs. S. 1777," *Science*, Vol. 103 (Feb. 8, 1946), pp. 161-62.

[77] Meyerhoff, "Compromise Bill for a National Science Foundation," *ibid.* (Feb. 15, 1946), p. 192.

[78] Meyerhoff, "S. 1720 vs. S. 1777," *ibid.* (Feb. 8, 1946), p. 162; "The National Science Foundation: S. 1850, Final Senate Bill," *ibid.* (March 1, 1946), pp. 270-73. On Jewett's role in instigating S. 1777, see Price to Hoelscher, Feb. 1, 1946, BOB, Series 39.32—E8-2/44.2.

Chapter 3

[1] Howard A. Meyerhoff, "The National Science Foundation: S. 1850, Final Senate Bill," *Science*, Vol. 103 (March 1, 1946), p. 271.

[2] Isaiah Bowman to Homer W. Smith, March 4, June 7, 1946, Bowman Papers, NSF 1945-47 file.

[3] Frank B. Jewett to Vannevar Bush, March 29, 1946, Bush MSS, Box 56, file 1377.

[4] Jewett to Bush, May 3, 1946, Bush MSS, Box 57, file 1377.

[5] Bush to Jewett, May 7, 1946, Bush MSS, Box 57, file 1377.

[6] Some had similar thoughts about Bush: "Bush ... was temperamentally something of an autocrat. In consulting a few key scientists whose opinions he respected, he felt that he was adequately tapping those of the scientific community." Alice Kimball Smith, *A Peril and a Hope: The Scientists' Movement in America: 1945-47* (Chicago, 1965), p. 33.

[7] Bush to Jewett, April 2, 1946, Bush MSS, Box 56, file 1377.

[8] U. S. Senate, *National Science Foundation. Report on Science Legislation from the Subcommittee on War Mobilization to the Committee on Military Affairs* .... Subcommittee Report No. 8, 79th Cong., 2d Sess., Feb. 27, 1946; U.S. Senate, *National Science Foundation. Report from the Committee on Military Affairs ... Pursuant to S. 1850 ...* , Report No. 1136, 79th Cong., 2nd Sess., April 9, 1946.

[9] John H. Teeter to Bush, April 24, 25, 1946, Bush MSS, Box 110, file 2617; Meyerhoff, "The Senate and S. 1850," *Science*, Vol. 103 (May 10, 1946), p. 590.

[10] Meyerhoff, "The Senate and S. 1850," p. 589; Committee Supporting the Bush Report, "Statement Concerning S. 1850," *Science*, Vol. 103 (May 3, 1946), p. 558. The NAM opposition to the bill was announced on April 7. New York *Times*, April 8, 1946, p. 33.

[11] Teeter to Bush, April 11, 24, 25, May 11, 14, 17, 24, 1946, Bush MSS, Box 110, file 2617.

[12] Bush to Jewett, May 7, 1946, Bush MSS, Box 56, file 1377.

[13] U.S. Senate, *National Science Foundation*, 79th Cong., 2d Sess., Rept. No. 1136, Pt. 2, May 24, 1946, pp. 1, 3, 7-15.

[14] Belatedly, on June 4, Emanuel Celler (D., New York) introduced a companion bill (H. R. 6672) to S. 1850, and it was referred to the same subcommittee.

[15] Howard A. Meyerhoff, "H. R. 6448," *Science*, Vol. 103 (June 7, 1946), pp. 687-88.

[16] Watson Davis, "Scientists Divided," *ibid.*, p. 688.

[17] Bowman to Edmund E. Day, June 5, 1946, Bowman Papers, NSF 1945-47 file. See also Bowman to Smith, June 7, 1946, Bowman Papers, NSF 1945-47 file; Teeter to Peter Edson, June 4, 1946, Bush MSS, Box 110, file 2617.

[18] Bowman to Day, June 5, 1946.
Just after the introduction of the Mills bill, Teeter invited members of the House subcommittee to a buffet luncheon on May 22, where they could meet Bush and "discuss this important legislation." All of the subcommittee members seem to have accepted the invitation, as did John W. McCormack (D., Massachusetts), the majority leader, John J. Sparkman (D., Alabama), the majority whip, and Eugene E. Cox (D., Georgia) of the Rules Committee. Teeter to Bush, May 17, 22, 1946, Bush MSS, Box 110, file 2617.

[19] House of Representatives, *Hearings before Subcommittee of the Committee on Interstate and Foreign Commerce ... H. R. 6448,* 79th Cong., 2d Sess., May 28-29, 1946, p. 84.

[20] *Ibid.*, p. 50.

[21] *Ibid.*, p. 72.

[22] *Ibid.*, p. 92.

[23] *Ibid.*, p. 13.

[24] Bowman to Smith, June 7, 1946, Bowman Papers, NSF 1945-47 file. See also Bowman to Bush, June 7, 1946, Bush MSS, Box 13, file 315.

[25] Bush to Conant, June 7, 1946, Bush MSS, Box 27, file 614; Bush to Bowman, June 18, 1946, Bush MSS, Box 13, file 315.

[26] Teeter to Bush, June 10, 1946, Bush MSS, Box 110, file 2617.

[27] Washington *Daily News*, June 5, 1946.

[28] Teeter to Bush, June 10, 1946, Bush MSS, Box 110, file 2617.

[29] *Ibid.*
[30] Teeter to Bush *et al.*, June 18, 1946, Bush MSS, Box 110, file 2617.
[31] Bowman to Day, June 21, 1946, Bowman Papers, NSF 1945-47 file.
[32] Teeter to Bush, June 24, 1946, Bush MSS, Box 110, file 2617.
[33] The debate appears in *Congressional Record*, 79th Cong., 2d Sess., pp. 8026-53 (July 1, 1946), 8097-8107, 8112-22, 8123-28, 8136-48 (July 2, 1946), 8208-16, 8218-28, 8229-32, 8233-35, 8236-42 (July 3, 1946). Smith's amendment in the nature of a substitute appears on pp. 8105-07.
[34] *Ibid.*, pp. 8241 (Smith's "quandary"), 8125-28 (Willis), 8147 (McKellar), 8145 (Taft).
[35] *Ibid.*, pp. 8030-31, 8047, 8103-04, 8211, 8214.
[36] *Ibid.*, pp. 8114-15, 8120-21, 8211.
[37] *Ibid.*, p. 8214.
[38] *Ibid.*, p. 8146.
[39] *Ibid.*, pp. 8114, 8119. For Hart's "pork-barrel" reference, *ibid.*, p. 8100.
[40] *Ibid.*, p. 8140.
[41] *Ibid.*, pp. 8142-44.
[42] *Ibid.*, p. 8147.
[43] *Ibid.*, pp. 8208-16. Actually, one negative vote was not recorded, and the corrected count was 35-34 against the amendments. A later attempt to get a reconsideration of the amendments resulted in another 35-34 rejection. *Ibid.*, pp. 8229-30.
[44] *Ibid.*, pp. 8218-20.
[45] *Ibid.*, p. 8228.
[46] *Ibid.*, p. 8230.
[47] *Ibid.*, p. 8145.
[48] *Ibid.*, pp. 8230-31.
[49] *Ibid.*, pp. 8233-35.
[50] *Ibid.*, pp. 8237-39.
[51] *Ibid.*, pp. 8239-40.
[52] *Ibid.*, pp. 8240-41.
[53] *Ibid.*, p. 8241.
[54] *Ibid.*, pp. 8241-42.
[55] Miller to Steelman, July 9, 1946, Papers of Harry S. Truman, Truman Library, Official File, 192-E (1945-47), Box 681.
[56] Teeter to Bush *et al.*, July 16, 1946, Bush MSS, Box 110, file 2617.
[57] Meyerhoff, "S. 1850 in the House," *Science*, Vol. 104 (July 19, 1946), p. 48.
[58] [W. Parker Anslow, Jr.], "Brief History of National Science Legislation," Bush MSS, Box 104, file 2465.
[59] Jack Merritt to Patterson French, July 19, 1946, BOB, Series 39.32—E8-2/44.2; *Science*, Vol. 104 (July 26, 1946), p. 79.
[60] Miller to Steelman, July 22, 1946, Truman Papers, Official File, 192-E (1945-47), Box 681.
[61] Bowman to Teeter, July 30, 1946, Bowman Papers, NSF 1945-47 file; *Science*, Vol. 104 (July 26, 1946), p. 79.
[62] *Science*, Vol. 104 (Aug. 2, 1946), p. 97.
[63] *Ibid.*
[64] *Ibid.*, pp. 97-98.
[65] Jewett to Bush, Aug. 7, 1946, Bush MSS, Box 56, file 1377.
[66] Smith, *A Peril and a Hope*, p. 171.

Chapter 4

[1] Talcott Parsons, "National Science Legislation: Part I, An Historical Review," *Bulletin of the Atomic Scientists*, Vol. 2, Nos. 9-10 (Nov. 1, 1946), pp. 7-9.

[2] Day to Bowman, Sept. 16, 1946, Bowman Papers, NSF 1945-47 file.
[3] Bowman to Day, Sept. 27, 1946, Bowman Papers, NSF 1945-47 file.
[4] Bowman to Teeter, Sept. 25, 1946; Teeter to Bowman, Oct. 1, 1946, Bowman Papers, NSF 1945-47 file.
[5] Bowman to Day, Sept. 27, 1946; Bowman to Conant, Sept. 27, 1946, Bowman Papers, NSF 1945-47 file.
[6] M. C. Latta to Bush, Oct. 18, 1946; Bush to Paul Scherer, n.d., Bush MSS, Box 93, file 2144.
[7] William A. W. Krebs, Jr. to John T. Connor, Oct. 22, 1946; W. John Kenney to Bush, Oct. 29, 1946, and attached memo, Kenney to Secretary of Navy, Oct. 24, 1946, Bush MSS, Box 93, file 2144.
[8] Jack Merritt to William D. Carey and Charles B. Stauffacher, July 3, 1947, BOB, Series 47.1—NSF Act of 1947. In an earlier report on PSRB Merritt wrote: "The original purpose of the PSRB was largely political. The PSRB was to counter-balance the effect of the military on research, it was to influence legislation to establish a National Science Foundation and, lastly, it was to do a pinch-hitting job for the NSF in coordinating Federal research. The PSRB was actually established without consulting the Federal agencies involved." Expecting the PSRB report to be superficial, Merritt was afraid it would "give Bush real ammunition" for board control of the foundation. Merritt to Elmer Staats, Feb. 13, 1947, BOB, Series 47.3, E6-2 (1950-52).
[9] J. H. Teeter, Memorandum on NSF Legislation, Oct. 29, 1946, Bowman Papers, NSF 1945-47 file.
[10] Conant to Bush, Oct. 31, 1946; Bush to Conant, Nov. 4, 1946, Bush MSS, Box 27, file 614. To counter the charges that the military was trying to control university research, Bush suggested to the secretaries of the army and navy that they speak out in favor of a foundation "to take over at least the bulk of federal support of basic research, so that the Services can benefit therefrom, and also so that the Services can pay more complete attention to the applied military aspects which is their more natural field of operation." Bush to James Forrestal, Dec. 11, 1946, Bush MSS, Box 85, file 1912.
[11] Shapley to Bowman, Nov. 6, 1946, Bush MSS, Box 13, file 315.
[12] Bowman to Shapley, Nov. 9, 1946, Bush MSS, Box 13, file 315. Bowman sent copies of this exchange of correspondence with Shapley to Bush and Homer Smith and asked that it be kept confidential. Bowman to Bush, Nov. 13, 1946, Bush MSS, Box 13, file 315.
[13] Bowman to Day, Jan. 16, 1947, Bowman Papers, NSF 1945-47 file.
[14] Telegram, Conant to Bowman, Oct. 5, 1946, Bowman Papers, NSF 1945-47 file; Conant to Bush, Oct. 31, 1946, Bush MSS, Box 27, file 614; Dael Wolfle, "The Inter-Society Committee for a National Science Foundation: Report for 1947," *Science*, Vol. 106 (Dec. 5, 1947), pp. 529-30.
[15] Wolfle, "The Inter-Society Committee... Report for 1947," pp. 530-31.
[16] Stewart to Smith, March 1, 1947; Smith to Stewart, March 13, 1947, H. Alexander Smith Papers (hereafter Smith MSS), Princeton University Library, Box 132; Bush to J. R. Killian, Jr., March 26, 1947, Bush MSS, Box 62, file 1471.
[17] Wolfle, "The Inter-Society Committee... Report for 1947," p. 530.
[18] Smith to Bush, Dec. 18, 1946; Bush to Smith, Dec. 23, 1946, Bush MSS, Box 85, file 1912.
[19] Bush to Webb, Dec. 27, 1946, BOB, Series 47.1—NSF Act of 1947.
[20] *Ibid*.
[21] Bush to Smith, Dec. 31, 1946, Bush MSS, Box 85, file 1912.
[22] Kingsley to Steelman, Dec. 31, 1946, Truman Papers, Official File, 192-E, Box 681.
[23] FJB[ailey] to Director, Jan. 6, 1947, and attached memorandum for the President from the Director, n.d., written by Bailey on Jan. 16, 1947, BOB, Series 39.1—NSF Act of 1947 (E9-1/47.1). A handwritten note on the copy of the memorandum to the President says that it was taken to the White House by the Director about January 30, 1947. Steelman's copy of the memorandum, also undated, is in Truman Papers, Official File, 192-E, Box 682.
[24] Bush to Conant, Jan. 29, 1947, Bush MSS, Box 85, file 1912.
[25] Bush to Bowman, Jan. 31, 1947, Bush MSS, Box 13, file 315. For other optimistic assessments of the conference and legislative prospects, see Bush to Warren Weaver,

Jan. 28, 1947, Bush MSS, Box 117, file 2801, and Bush to Gordon S. Rentschler, Jan. 28, 1947, Bush MSS, Box 59, file 1403.

[26] Bush to Conant, Jan. 29, 1947, Bush MSS, Box 85, file 1912. I have found no evidence that the meeting with the President occurred.

[27] Bush to Baruch, Feb. 14, 1947, Bush MSS, Box 10, file 209.

[28] Teeter, memorandum on National Science Foundation Legislation, Jan. 15, 1947; Teeter to Bush, Jan. 16, 1947; Teeter to Bush, n.d. (about Jan. 16, 1947), Bush MSS, Box 85, file 1812; Homer Smith to Bowman, Feb. 26, 1947, Bowman Papers, NSF 1945-47 file.

[29] Bush to Smith, Dec. 23, 31, 1946, Jan. 28, Feb. 14, 1947; John Q. Stewart to Smith, Dec. 21, 1946, Jan. 4, 1947; H. D. Smyth to Smith, Jan. 4, 1947; Conant to Smith, Jan. 2, 1947; Smith to Conant, Jan. 6, 1947; Teeter to Smith, Jan. 16, 1947; Merck to Smith (telegram), Feb. 3, 1947; Smith to Merck, Feb. 11, 1947; Smith to Teeter, Feb. 11, 1947, Smith MSS, Box 132; Teeter to Bush, n.d. (about Jan. 16, 1947); Bush to Conant, Jan. 29, 1947, Bush MSS, Box 85, file 1912.

[30] E. E. Day to Oscar Ruebhausen, April 9, 1947; Ruebhausen to Day, April 10, 1947, Bush MSS, Box 100, file 2309.

[31] Warren G. Magnuson to Arthur A. Hauck, March 26, 1947; Day to Hauck, April 7, 1947, NASULGC, NSF 1947 file. This file contains many copies of letters from members of Congress to presidents of land-grant colleges and universities in response to their arguments for a geographic-distribution formula.

[32] Donald C. Stone to Director, March 19, 1947; Elmer B. Staats to Director, May 1, 1947, BOB, Series 47.1—NSF Act of 1947.

[33] *Cong. Record*, 80th Cong., 1st Sess., 5471 (May 19, 1947).

[34] *Senate Report No. 78*, 80th Cong., 1st Sess.

[35] Kingsley to Steelman, April 1, 1947, Truman Papers, Official File, 192-E, Box 681.

[36] Carey to Staats, Feb. 20, 1947, BOB, Series 47.1—NSF Act of 1947.

[37] Staats and Stauffacher to Bailey and Stone, March 28, 1947; Webb to Bush, April 10, 1947, BOB, Series 47.1—NSF Act of 1947.

[38] Stone to Director, May 15, 1947, and attached draft memorandum to President, May 14, 1947, BOB, Series 47.1—NSF Act of 1947.

[39] Ida to Staats, May 6, 1947, BOB, Series 47.1—NSF Act of 1947. This note indicates that Conant and Saltonstall may have influenced Smith. See also Conant to Smith, April 12, 1947, Smith MSS, Box 132.

[40] Webb to Bush, May 9, 1947, Charles S. Murphy Files, Box 24, Truman Library.

[41] Bush to Webb, May 13, 1947, Bush MSS, Box 85, file 1912.

[42] Stone to Charles S. Murphy, May 21, 1947, Murphy Files, Box 24.

[43] Smyth to Smith, Feb. 4, 1947; Randolph T. Major to Smith, Feb. 21, 1947; Smith to Smyth, Feb. 11, 1947, Smith MSS, Box 132.

[44] George H. E. Smith to Smith, April 24, 1947, Smith MSS, Box 132.

[45] Harry S. Truman, *Memoirs* (2 vols., Garden City, N.Y., 1955-56), I, *Year of Decisions*, p. 330.

[46] L. D. to Murphy, May 12, 1947, Murphy Files, Box 24.

[47] Stone to Director, May 15, 1947, and attached draft memorandum for the President, by C. B. S[tauffacher], May 14, 1947, BOB, Series 47.1—NSF Act of 1947.

[48] *Cong. Record*, 80th Cong., 1st Sess., p. 5251 (May 14, 1947), p. 5508 (May 20, 1947); Carey to Staats, July 23, 1947, BOB, Series 47.1—NSF Act of 1947.

[49] For the full Senate debate on S. 526: *Cong. Record*, 80th Cong. 1st Sess., pp. 5230, 5246, 5248-60, 5264-65 (May 14, 1947), 5320-22, 5324-45 (May 15, 1947), 5398-5404, 5412, 5413-27, 5430-39 (May 16, 1947), 5445, 5447-81 (May 19, 1947), 5494, 5498-5515 (May 20, 1947), 5564-65 (May 21, 1947), 5635 (May 22, 1947); for the votes on Kilgore's amendments: pp. 5404, 5480, 5506; for the vote on Fulbright's amendment: p. 5512.

[50] For the debate on Morse's amendment: *ibid.*, pp. 5412, 5413-27, 5430-39, 5445, 5447-71. For Morse's appeal for support from presidents of state universities and land-grant colleges, Morse to Day (night letter), (May 16, 1947), NASULGC, NSF 1947 file.

One land-grant president got "a lot of satisfaction" from the vote "because of some of the things that were said to me over the long distance phone last Sunday by one John H. Teeter, who claimed to represent the 'interests really behind the Science Foundation movement.' Teeter threatened all manner of dire misfortunes to the Land-Grant colleges if we did not call Senator Morse off at once. He insisted that if we did not, the bill would be killed in the Senate and that the terrible deed would be laid at the doors of the Land-Grant institutions. He also threatened that if the Land-Grant colleges persisted in their position, it meant that the present Federal grants to these institutions would be seriously jeopardized." R. D. Hetzel to Day (copy), May 20, 1947, NASULGC, NSF 1947 file.

[51] Thackrey to Day, March 31, April 14, 1947; Thackrey to Hauck, April 3, 1947; Thackrey to C. E. Brehm, April 5, 17, 1947; Thackrey to Thomas Cooper, April 10, 1947; Thackrey to Wilson Compton, April 10, 1947; Thackrey to R. G. Gustavson, April 17, 1947; Thackrey to Carl R. Woodward, April 23, 1947; Thackrey to Milton S. Eisenhower (telegram), May 17, 1947; Thackrey to Hetzel and Cooper, May 20, 1947, and attached draft memorandum to presidents of land-grant colleges and universities, NASULGC, NSF 1947 file.

Eight years later, in a letter to an NSF official, Thackrey wrote: "At the time of this argument [over geographical distribution] most of us from the hinterland were still a little bitter over the fact that during the war the Federal government plowed millions of dollars into large research efforts of a half dozen universities, giving them the money to strip us of our best mathematical and physical talent. This was probably a war necessity, but the people did not come back and it took years to replace them. We felt that the war and postwar research funds of the Federal government in fields other than agriculture were used to make the strongest research institutions stronger, and the pretty good and average, weaker." Thackrey to William Colman, Aug. 30, 1955, NSF HF.

[52] Discussion of Magnuson's amendment appears in *Cong. Record*, 80th Cong., 1st Sess., pp. 5249, 5321-22, 5331, 5506-11.

[53] *Ibid.*, pp. 5564-65, 5635. At the White House, J. Donald Kingsley had "the impression that when Senator Smith agreed to withdraw his motion for recommital of S. 526 it was on the basis of a deal with the House Committee that the House would kill the amendment providing for presidential appointment of the Executive Director." If that happened, Kingsley doubted that Truman would sign the bill. Carey to Staats, May 26, 1947, BOB, Series 47.3, file E6-2.

[54] A good brief account is Don C. Swain, "The Rise of a Research Empire: NIH, 1930 to 1950," *Science*, Vol. 138 (Dec. 14, 1962), pp. 1233-37; a lively longer study is Stephen P. Strickland, *Politics, Science, and Dread Disease: A Short History of United States Medical Research Policy* (Cambridge, Mass., 1972).

[55] *Cong. Record*, 80th Cong., 1st Sess., 5249-50, 5345; H. R. 4102 (July 7, 1947).

[56] *Cong. Record*, 80th Cong., 1st Sess., p. 5512.

[57] New York *Times*, May 21, 1947, p. 26.

[58] *Hearings before the Committee on Interstate and Foreign Commerce, House of Representatives, 80th Congress, First Session, on H. R. 942, H. R. 1815, H. R. 1830, H. R. 1834, and H. R. 2027, Bills Relating to the National Science Foundation. March 6 and 7, 1947* (Washington, 1947). Jewett's testimony appears on pp. 73-94, and supplementary documents on pp. 94-110; Bush's testimony, pp. 231-38; Jewett to Bush, March 12, 1947; Bush to Jewett, March 17, 1947, Bush MSS, Box 56, file 1377.

[59] Bush to Jewett, March 17, 1947, Bush MSS, Box 56, file 1377. For Foster's testimony, see *Hearings*, pp. 171-77; for that of Robert M. Yerkes representing SSRC, pp. 182-91.

[60] *Hearings*, pp. 49-68 (poll and questionnaire on pp. 64-68).

[61] Carey, memo to files, May 1, 1947, BOB, Series 47.1—NSF Act of 1947.

[62] Carey to Staats, May 23, 1947, BOB, Series 47.1—NSF Act of 1947.

[63] *Ibid.*

[64] Carey to McCandless, June 11, 1947, BOB, Series 47.1—NSF Act of 1947. A committee print of the bill dated June 27, 1947 contains the added language. Senator Smith, when he learned that the House committee had eliminated the geographic distribution formula but increased the director's power, wrote to a colleague: "I hope in conference we can get both these objectionable features removed from the final legislation." Smith to Guy Cordon, July 2, 1947, Smith MSS, Box 132.

[65] Brown to Bush, June 15, 1947, Bush MSS, Box 85, file 1912.

[66] Paul A. Scherer to Bush, June 12, 1947, Bush MSS, Box 21, file 475.

[67] Scherer to Bush, June 17, 1947, Bush MSS, Box 21, file 475.
[68] Washington *Post*, June 25, 1947.
[69] *House Report No. 864*, 80th Cong., 1st Sess., July 10, 1947.
[70] The full debate appears in *Cong. Record*, 80th Cong., 1st Sess., pp. 9060-94 (July 16, 1947); Scott's amendment, pp. 9079-80.
[71] *Ibid.*, pp. 9061-64, 9068-69.
[72] *Ibid.*, p. 9073.
[73] *Ibid.*, p. 9069.
[74] *Ibid.*, p. 9080.
[75] *Ibid.*, pp. 9065-67, 9068, 9068-69.
[76] *Ibid.*, pp. 9089-93.
[77] *House Report No. 102*, 80th Cong., 1st Sess. (July 21, 1947).
[78] *Cong. Record*, 80th Cong., 1st Sess., pp. 9670-81 (July 22, 1947).
[79] Thackrey to Day (telegram), July 23, 1947; Thackrey to Executive Committee, ALGCU, July 23, 1947; Thackrey to J. L. Morrill (telegram), Aug. 6, 1947, NASULGC, NSF 1947 file; Wolfle, "The Inter-Society Committee . . . Report for 1947," p. 532.
[80] Graham to the President (telegram), July 26, 1947, Truman Papers, Official File, 192-E, Box 682.
[81] *Ibid.*
[82] Morse to the President, July 23, 1947, Truman Papers, Official File, 192-E, Box 81.
[83] O'Connor to Murphy, July 27, 1947, Murphy Files, Box 24.
[84] Condon to Steelman, July 28, 1947, Truman Papers, Official File, 192-E, Box 81.
[85] Webb to M. C. Latta, Aug. 1, 1947, BOB, Series 47.1—NSF Act of 1947.
[86] Carey to Staats, July 23, 1947, and attachments, BOB, Series 47.1—NSF Act of 1947.
[87] Carey to McCandless (route slip), July 23, 1947, BOB, Series 47.1—NSF Act of 1947.
[88] *Cong. Record*, 80th Cong., 1st Sess., pp. A4442-43 (Aug. 15, 1947).
[89] Copy in Bush MSS, Box 85, file 1912.
[90] Truman to Smith, Aug. 7, 1947, Smith MSS, Box 132.
Recalling the episode several years later, Truman wrote that he had told a senator (Smith) that "unless legislation was drawn up in such a manner as not to infringe in any way on the powers of the President, the bill would never be signed. He made the statement that I didn't have the education to know anything about science. 'Well,' I said, 'I think I know a little more about the Constitution than you do, Senator, and as long as I am here I am going to support it as I have sworn to do.' I got the bill in the form I wanted, and then I signed it, but it took a long time." *Year of Decisions*, p. 330.
[91] Bush to Connor, Sept. 5, 1947, Bush MSS, Box 27, file 620.

Chapter 5

[1] Washington *Sunday Star*, Aug. 10, 1947, clipping, Bush MSS, Box 85, file 1912.
[2] San Francisco *Chronicle*, Aug. 8, 1947, clipping, Bush MSS, Box 85, file 1912.
[3] Paul Scherer to Bush, n.d. (about Aug. 30, 1947); John H. Teeter to Bush, Sept. 18, 1947, Bush MSS, Box 110, file 2617.
[4] E.g., John T. Connor to Bush, Aug. 7, 1947, Bush MSS, Box 27, file 620; Bethuel M. Webster to Bush, Sept. 12, 1947, Bush MSS, Box 117, file 2806.
[5] Howard A. Meyerhoff, "The Truman Veto," *Science*, Vol. 106 (Sept. 12, 1947), p. 237.
[6] Webster to Editor, New York *Times*, Aug. 7, 1947, clipping; Webster to Bush, Sept. 12, 1947, Bush MSS, Box 117, file 2806. Webster's letter was published in the *Times* on Aug. 11, 1947.
[7] *Science*, Vol. 106 (Nov. 7, 1947), pp. 444-45.
[8] Meyerhoff to Webster (copy), Dec. 2, 1947, Bush MSS, Box 117, file 2806. This file also contains correspondence between Bush and Webster on the *Science* statement and copies of letters Webster received from a number of its readers.

⁹ Webster to Bush, Nov. 10, 1947; Case to Webster (copy), Nov. 18, 1947, Bush MSS, Box 117, file 2806.
¹⁰ Memorandum of Conference with the President on Sept. 24, 1947, Bush MSS, Box 119, file 2856.
¹¹ Dael Wolfle, "The Inter-Society Committee for a National Science Foundation: Report for 1947," *Science*, Vol. 106 (Dec. 5, 1947), p. 532.
¹² Shapley to Bush, Nov. 5, 12, 25, 1947, Bush MSS, Box 102, file 2403; Shapley to H. Alexander Smith, Nov. 12, 20, 1947, Smith MSS, Box 132; Shapley to Willis H. Shapley Nov. 5, 1947; W. H. Shapley to [Elmer B.] Staats, Nov. 7, 1947; Charles B. Stauffacher to Director, Nov. 21, 1947; Harlow Shapley to James E. Webb, Nov. 25, 1947; Staats to Director, Nov. 28, 1947; Harlow Shapley to Staats, Dec. 7, 1947, BOB, Series 47.1—NSF Act of 1948; *Science and Public Policy: A Report to the President*, Vol. I, *A Program for the Nation* (Washington, Aug. 27, 1947), p. 35.
¹³ Stauffacher to Director, Nov. 21, 1947; Harlow Shapley to Staats, Dec. 7, 1947, BOB, Series 47.1—NSF Act of 1948; Shapley to Bush, Dec. 7, 1947; Shapley, Memorandum on Morse Amendment to S. 526, Dec. 7, 1947, Bush MSS, Box 85, file 1912.
¹⁴ Harlow Shapley, *Through Rugged Ways to the Stars* (New York, 1969).
¹⁵ Dael Wolfle, "Inter-Society Committee for a National Science Foundation: Report of the Meeting of December 28, 1947," *Science*, Vol. 107 (March 5, 1948), pp. 235-36.
¹⁶ Bush to Shapley, Dec. 10, 1947, Bush MSS, Box 102, file 2403.
¹⁷ Teeter to Bush, Sept. 18, 1947, Bush MSS, Box 110, file 2617; Charles F. Brown to Bush, Nov. 18, Dec. 17, 23, 1947, Bush MSS, Box 16, file 358; Shapley to Bush, Nov. 25, 1947, Bush MSS, Box 102, file 2403; Stauffacher to Brown, Dec. 15, 1947, Bush MSS, Box 16, file 358; Stauffacher to Donald C. Stone and Staats, Dec. 17, 1947; Stone to Director, Dec. 17, 1947, BOB, Series 47.1—NSF Act of 1948.
¹⁸ Shapley to Bush, Dec. 7, 1947, Bush MSS, Box 102, file 2403; Stauffacher to Director, Nov. 21, 1947; Harlow Shapley to Staats, Dec. 7, 1947; Stauffacher to Stone and Staats, Dec. 18, 1947; Staats to Director, Dec. 19, 1947, BOB, Series 47.1—NSF Act of 1948.
¹⁹ Clipping, BOB, Series 47.1—NSF Act of 1947; Bush to Conant, Sept. 5, 1947, Bush MSS, Box 27, file 614.
²⁰ Bush, Memorandum of Conference with the President on Sept. 24, 1947, Bush MSS, Box 119, file 2856; Truman to Bush, Oct. 1, 1947, Bush MSS, Box 112, file 2675; Bush to James Forrestal, Sept. 10, 1947, Bush MSS, Box 59, file 1403; Bush to Webster, Nov. 13, 1947, Bush MSS, Box 117, file 2806; P[aul] S[cherer] to Bush, Aug. 28, 1947, Bush MSS, Box 93, file 2144; Teeter to Bush, Aug. 29, 1947, Bush MSS, Box 110, file 2617.
²¹ "Controversial Points, Science Foundation Bills," Nov. 25, 1947; Carey to Staats, Oct. 31, 1947, BOB, Series 47.1—NSF Act of 1948; Teeter to Bush *et al.*, Dec. 24, 1947, quoting *Washington Report on the Medical Sciences*, Dec. 15, 1947, p. 4, Bush MSS, Box 110, file 2617.
²² Staats to Director, Nov. 28, 1947, BOB, Series 47.1—NSF Act of 1948.
²³ *Science*, Vol. 106 (Oct. 24, 1947), pp. 385-87; *Bulletin of the Atomic Scientists*, Vol. 3 (Dec. 1947), pp. 357 ff.
²⁴ Teeter to Bush, Nov. 12, 1947, Bush MSS, Box 110, file 2617.
²⁵ Conant to Harriman (photostat), Nov. 5, 1947, BOB, Series 47.1—NSF Act of 1948.
²⁶ Teeter to Bush, Aug. 29, Sept. 18, Nov. 12, Dec. 29, 1947, Jan. 21, 1948; [Samuel Callaway to Bush], Nov. 28, 1947, Bush MSS, Box 110, file 2617; Teeter to [Thomas P.] Cooper, Nov. 5, 1947, NASULGC, NSF 1947 file; Teeter to A. B. Herman, Nov. 26, 1947, Smith MSS, Box 131.
²⁷ Webster to Bush, Dec. 3, 1947; Meyerhoff to Webster, Dec. 2, 1947, Bush MSS, Box 117, file 2806.
²⁸ Homer Smith to Bush, Dec. 4, 1947; Bush to Smith, Dec. 8, 1947, Bush MSS, Box 104, file 2465.
²⁹ Teeter to Bush, Dec. 29, 1947, Bush MSS, Box 110, file 2617.
³⁰ On Teeter and land-grant officials, see Thackrey to Day, May 3, 12, 1948; Day to Thackrey, May 10, 1948, NASULGC, NSF 1948 file.
³¹ On negotiations between executive and legislative branches, see Smith to Charles A. Wolverton, Dec. 5, 1947; Wolverton to Smith, Dec. 9, 20, 1947; A. B. Herman to Smith,

Dec. 22, 23, 1947, Smith MSS, Box 132; Stone to Director, Dec. 17, 1947; Carey to Staats, Jan. 22, 1948; Staats to Director, Dec. 19, 1947, Jan. 27, 1948; Webb to Smith, March 15, 1948; Smith to Webb, March 24, 1948, BOB, Series 47.1—NSF Act of 1948; Teeter to Bush, Dec. 24, 1947, Jan. 21, March 17, 1948, Bush MSS, Box 110, file 2617; David H. Stowe to Steelman, Jan. 6, March 8, 1948; Staats to Steelman, Jan. 27, 1948; Webb to Steelman, n.d. (Jan. 29, 1948 stamp on memorandum, but it was written earlier), Truman Papers, Official File, 192-E (1948), Box 681.

[32] *Cong. Record*, 80th Cong., 2d Sess., pp. 5176-81 (May 3, 1948), 5301-03 (May 5, 1948); Webb to Smith, May 5, 1948, *ibid.*, p. 5434.

[33] Day to Thackrey, Dec. 11, 1947, Feb. 14, March 29, 1948; Thackrey to Day, Feb. 18, April 5, 1948; H. P. Hammond to Day, Feb. 19, 1948; Hammond to Thackrey, Feb. 24, 1948; Thackrey to Hammond, Feb. 25, 1948; Thackrey to Thomas Cooper, March 3, 1948; Day to Morse, March 29 (telegram), March 31, 1948; Morse to Day (telegram), March 30, 1948; Day to Smith, March 31, May 3, 1948; Day to Shapley, April 13, 1948; J. L. Morrill to Thackrey, May 4, 1948, NASULGC, NSF 1948 file.

[34] *Hearing before the Committee on Interstate and Foreign Commerce, House of Representatives, Eightieth Congress, Second Session on H. R. 6007 and S. 2385* (Washington, 1948), pp. 35-37; Carey to Staats, June 1, 1948, BOB, Series 47.1—NSF Act of 1948.

[35] Condon to Solicitor, Department of Commerce, May 25, 1948, BOB, Series 47.1—NSF Act of 1948.

[36] Carey to Elmer [Staats], June 1, 1948, BOB, Series 47.1—NSF Act of 1948.

[37] Carey to Virgil [L. Almond], June 8, 1948, BOB, Series 47.1—NSF Act of 1948.

[38] *House Report No. 2233*, 80th Cong., 2d Sess., June 4, 1948.

[39] Day to Morrill (telegram), June 3, 1948, NASULGC, NSF 1948 file.

[40] Charles A. MacQuigg to Day, June 5, 1948, NASULGC, NSF 1948 file.

[41] Carey to Staats, June 8, 1948, BOB, Series 47.1—NSF Act of 1948.

[42] W.D.C[arey], brief statement of information from Wolfle, June 17, 1948, and attached papers on National Science Foundation Legislative Status, June 14, 1948, and Notes on Current Developments, June 15, 1948, BOB, Series 47.1—NSF Act of 1948; Thackrey to National Science Foundation Committee, June 9, 1948, NASULGC, NSF 1948 file.

[43] Carey statement and attachments cited in n. 42.

[44] Memorandum of phone call to Bush, June 17, 1948, Bush MSS, Box 85, file 1912.

[45] Carey to Staats, Jan. 12, 1949, BOB, Series 47.1b—NSF Act of 1949.

[46] Day to Smith (copy), Aug. 24, 1948, NASULGC, NSF 1948 file.

[47] Day to Steelman, Nov. 13, 1948; Steelman to Day, Dec. 16, 1948, Truman Papers, Official File, 192-E (1948), Box 681.

[48] *Public Papers of the Presidents . . . Harry S. Truman . . . 1949* (Washington, 1964), p. 78.

[49] Staats to Director, Dec. 3, 1948, BOB, Series 47.1b—NSF Act of 1949.

[50] Carey to Staats, Jan. 10, 1949, BOB, Series 47.1b—NSF Act of 1949.

[51] Carey to Staats, Jan. 11, 1949, BOB, Series 47.1b—NSF Act of 1949.

[52] Frederick C. Schuldt, Jr. to Carey, Jan. 12, 1949, BOB, Series 47.1b—NSF Act of 1949.

[53] Carey to Staats, Jan. 12, 1949, BOB, Series 47.1b—NSF Act of 1949.

[54] Schuldt to files, Jan. 25, 1949, BOB, Series 47.1b—NSF Act of 1949.

[55] *Ibid.*

[56] Carey to Staats, Jan. 26, 1949; Rufus Miles and E. E. Ferebee to Staats, Jan. 27, 1949, BOB, Series 47.1b—NSF Act of 1949. In using Condon's term "fat cats," Carey was apparently referring to a few institutions of higher education, not federal science agencies.

[57] Frank Pace, Jr. to Elbert Thomas, Feb. 7, 1949, and attached "Suggested Drafting Revisions in S. 247," Feb. 4, 1949, BOB, Series 47.1b—NSF Act of 1949.

[58] Carey to Staats, March 7, 1949, BOB, Series 47.1b—NSF Act of 1949.

[59] *Senate Report No. 90*, 81st Cong., 1st Sess., March 3, 1949; *Cong. Record*, 81st Cong., 1st Sess., p. 2767 (March 18, 1949).

[60] *Hearings before a Subcommittee of the Committee on Interstate and Foreign Commerce . . . Eighty-first Congress, First Session on H. R. 12, S. 247, and H. R. 359* (Washington, 1949), pp. 151-55.

[61] *Ibid.*, pp. 170, 171, 175-79, 188.

[62] Carey to Staats (route slip), March 25, 1949; Pace to Priest, March 29, 1949, BOB, Series 47.1b—NSF Act of 1949; Charles S. Murphy to John W. McCormack, April 5, 1949; McCormack to Murphy, April 9, 1949, Murphy Files, Box 24, Truman Library.

[63] *House Report No. 796*, 81st Cong., 1st Sess., June 14, 1949.

The Senate concurrently wrote into an appropriation bill a requirement that all applicants for AEC fellowships be investigated by the FBI. Jewett wrote Bush that he did not object to loyalty oaths for fellowship recipients but he did oppose clearance of applicants. "If Congress sets such a pattern it will also inevitably crop up in Science Foundation fellowship awards if such a Foundation as you favor is established and then we will be in the race started by the Nazis and Moscow." Jewett to Bush, June 3, 1949, Bush MSS, Box 56, file 1377.

[64] Teeter to Bush, June 3, 1949, Bush MSS, Box 110, file 2617; Scherer to Bush, June 24, 1949, Bush MSS, Box 21, file 475; Bush to Wadsworth, June 27, 1949, Bush MSS, Box 116, file 2752; Lloyd N. Cutler to Bush, July 29, 1949, Bush MSS, Box 30, file 677; Staats to Murphy, July 13, 1949; Murphy to Sabath, July 23, 1949; LD to Murphy, Aug. 3, 1949, Murphy Files, Box 24.

[65] Carey to Murphy, Aug. 8, 1949, Murphy Files, Box 24; RPA to Steelman, Aug. 8, 1949, Truman Papers, Official File, 192-E, Box 682; Carey to files, Aug. 10, 1949, BOB, Series 47.1b—NSF Act of 1949; Martin L. Fausold, *James W. Wadsworth, Jr.: The Gentleman from New York* (Syracuse, N.Y., 1975), pp. 377-78.

[66] Staats to William F. McCandless, Sept. 6, 1949, Murphy Files, Box 24.

[67] Wadsworth to Bush, Oct. 12, 1949; Bush to Wadsworth, Oct. 13, 1949, Bush MSS, Box 116, file 2752.

[68] Bush to Pace, Oct. 13, 1949, BOB, Series 47.1b—NSF Act of 1949.

[69] Pace to Bush, Nov. 21, 1949, BOB, Series 47.1b—NSF Act of 1949.

[70] Carey to Staats, Oct. 20, 1949, BOB, Series 47.1b—NSF Act of 1949.

[71] *Ibid.*

[72] C. Spencer Platt to Ralph J. Burton, Oct. 24, 1949, BOB, Series 47.1b—NSF Act of 1949.

[73] Pace to Wadsworth, Nov. 21, 1949, and enclosure, Pace to Priest, May 24, 1949, BOB, Series 47.1b—NSF Act of 1949.

[74] Wadsworth to Bush, Dec. 21, 1949, Bush MSS, Box 116, file 2752.

[75] Bush to Wadsworth, Oct. 27, Dec. 28, 1949, Bush MSS, Box 116, file 2752.

[76] Bush to Wadsworth, Dec. 28, 1949, Bush MSS, Box 116, file 2752.

[77] *Ibid.*

[78] *Ibid.*

[79] Fausold, *Wadsworth*, p. 394; *Cong. Record*, 81st Cong., 2d Sess., pp. 2406, 2410 (Feb. 27, 1950).

[80] *Public Papers of the Presidents... Truman... 1950*, pp. 9, 84.

[81] Staats to Steelman, Jan. 25, 1950, Truman Papers, Official File, 192-E, Box 682; Cutler to Murphy, Feb. 6, 1950; Charles Maylon to Murphy, Feb. 8, 1950, Murphy Files, Box 24.

A delegation from the Engineers' Joint Council, after consultation with members of the Rules Committee and other congressmen, told Staats that Crosser seemed to be waiting for the White House to give him a signal to get the bill to the floor, and they urged prompt action. A. A. Potter to Steelman, Feb. 13, 1950; Schuldt to Staats, Feb. 15, 1950, BOB, Series 47.1b—NSF Act of 1949.

[82] Dael Wolfle, "A National Science Foundation: 1950 Prospects," *Science*, Vol. 111 (Jan. 27, 1950), pp. 79-81; *ibid.*, Vol. 111 (Feb. 24, 1950), pp. 208-10. Charles Brown suggested to Priest that the Inter-Society Committee's statement might be helpful in the House debate, and Lloyd Cutler sent Priest several reprints. Cutler to Priest (copy), Feb. 24, 1950, Murphy Files, Box 24.

[83] *Cong. Record*, 81st Cong., 2d Sess. pp. 2516-25 (Feb. 28, 1950); Schuldt to Carey, March 1, 1950, BOB, Series 47.1b—NSF Act of 1949.

[84] *Cong. Record*, 81st Cong., 2d Sess., pp. 2444-49 (Feb. 27, 1950).

[85] *Ibid.*, pp. 2442-44.

[86] *Ibid.*, pp. 2426, 2428, 2436-40. Hinshaw's quoted remark appears on p. 2439.

[87] *Ibid.*, p. 2529 (Feb. 28, 1950).
[88] Carey to Staats, March 3, 1950, BOB, Series 47.1b—NSF Act of 1949.
[89] *Cong. Record*, 81st Cong., 2d Sess., pp. 2578, 2581 (March 1, 1950).
[90] *Ibid.*, p. 2598.
[91] *Ibid.*, pp. 2602-03.
[92] Schuldt to Staats, March 1, 1950; Carey to Staats, March 2, 1950, BOB, Series 47.1b—NSF Act of 1949.
[93] Goudsmit to Bush, March 2, 1950; Bush to Goudsmit, March 3, 1950, Bush MSS, Box 85, file 1913.
[94] Alfred N. Richards to the President, March 9, 1950, Truman Papers, Official File, 192-E, Box 682. Richards's letter and the council statement were published in *Science*, Vol. 111 (March 24, 1950), p. 315.
[95] O. Oldenberg to Bush, April 3, 1950, and attached copy of telegram to Thomas and Priest, March 28, 1950, Bush MSS, Box 85, file 1913. Alexander Smith said he had "had blasts from a number of different people on this subject, including President [Harold W.] Dodds of Princeton, who feels that the House bill has gone much too far in requiring F.B.I. loyalty checks." He asked Bush for specific language to correct the flaws. Smith to Bush, March 13, 1950, Bush MSS, Box 85, file 1913.
[96] Penciled note, J.T.S[teelman] [to Murphy?], March 1, 1950, Murphy Files, Box 24.
[97] Carey to Staats, March 2, 3, 1950, BOB, Series 47.1b—NSF Act of 1949.
[98] Brown to Bush, March 2, 1950; Cutler to Bush, March 3, 1950; Bush to McCormack, March 3, 1950; McCormack to Bush, March 6, 1950; Priest to Bush, March 8, 1950; Smith to Bush, March 13, 1950; Bush to Smith, March 14, 1950, Bush MSS, Box 85, file 1913; Smith to Bush, April 1, 1950; Bush to Smith, April 3, 1950, Bush MSS, Box 104, file 2462.
[99] Brown to Bush, March 2, 1950, and attached copy of Brown's memo to Felix Larkin, March 2, 1950, Bush MSS, Box 85, file 1913; Carey to Staats, March 3, 1950, BOB, Series 47.1b—NSF Act of 1949. Ford's letter to the conference committee, dated March 6, 1950, appears in the conference report on S. 247, *Cong. Record*, 81st Cong., 2d Sess., pp. 5903-04; the Defense Department's comments on the draft security provisions, *ibid.*, p. 5904 (April 27, 1950). The security provisions agreed on in conference appear *ibid.*, p. 5901.
[100] Bush to O. Oldenberg, April 5, 1950, Bush MSS, Box 85, file 1913.
[101] *House Report No. 1958*, and statement by House managers, published in *Cong. Record*, 81st Cong., 2d Sess., pp. 5899-5906 (April 27, 1950). The House acceptance appears *ibid.*, p. 5908, and the Senate, p. 5968.
[102] Schuldt and James L. Grahl to Carey, April 27, 1950; Roger W. Jones to William J. Hopkins, May 5, 1950, BOB, Series 47.1b—NSF Act of 1949.
[103] *Public Papers... Truman... 1950*, pp. 338-39, 340.

Looking Backward, 1950-1945

[1] Vannevar Bush, *Pieces of the Action* (New York, 1970), p. 65.

Chapter 6

[1] Bush to Jewett, May 20, 1947; Jewett to Bush, May 25, June 5, 1947, Bush MSS, Box 56, file 1377; Ruebhausen to Richards (copy), May 20, 1947; Bush to Ruebhausen, May 23, 1947; Ruebhausen to Bush, May 26, June 5, 1947; Jewett to Ruebhausen (copy), June 2, 1947; Ruebhausen to Jewett (copy), June 5, 1947, Bush MSS, Box 100, file 2309; Bush to Richards, May 23, 1947, Bush MSS, Box 97, file 2225; Homer W. Smith to Bush, June 9, 1947, Bush MSS, Box 104, file 2465.
[2] Bush to Paul Scherer and Fred Fassett, July 2, 1947, Bush MSS, Box 85, file 1912; Bush to Richards, July 7, 1947; Richards to Bush, July 14, 1947, Bush MSS, Box 97, file 2225.

[3] Mimeographed sheet dated Nov. 18, 1945, showing nominees agreed on by the NAS council on June 10, 1948, and April 24, 1949, which the council, on Oct. 23, 1949, agreed to review. (Bush MSS, Box 85, file 1912.) All of the nominees were men, as were Bush's suggested additions. Six on the Academy list were later among the first appointees to the National Science Board as was one of Bush's "public affairs" additions. Despite Bush's suggestions, the Academy list submitted to the President in April 1950 contained the names of all twenty-six scientists agreed on by the council the year before and no other persons. The council decided to drop its "public affairs" nominees but offered to make them available if the President desired. Richards to President (copy), April 4, 1950, Truman Papers, Official File, 192-E, Box 682.
[4] Bush to President, March 3, 1950, Bush MSS, Box 119, file 2856. Bush had made a similar proposal in 1947. (Bush to James E. Webb, April 1, 1947, BOB, Series 47.1—NSF Act of 1947.) This brought a laugh from J. Donald Kingsley who told visitors from the Budget Bureau "that the President had already said he wouldn't appoint anybody recommended by Bush. Kingsley added, however, that the President probably wouldn't stick to that position." (WDC[arey], "Science Foundation Bill," April 10, 1947, BOB, Series 39.33, file unit 93—NSF Preliminary Planning.)
[5] Truman to Bush, March 6, 1950, Bush MSS, Box 119, file 2856. In his autobiography Bush tells of a dinner-table conversation with Truman shortly after the passage of the NSF act. "The subject of the science board came up, and I said, 'Mr. President, I wish you would leave me off that board. I know my name is on the list, but I wish you would leave me off.' He said, 'Why?' and I said, 'Well, I have been running about everything scientific during the war, and somewhat since, and I think people are getting tired of seeing this guy Bush run things around here. I think this outfit would do better if it had some new leadership. If you put me on the board, they will elect me chairman, and I do not think that body of scientists are going to like this continuation of one man in the top post. So I think you would do better to let somebody else do it.' Well, after a bit more talk, he agreed to leave me off the board. Then he said, 'Well, Van, you are not looking for a job, are you?' And I said, 'No, Mr. President, I am not looking for a job.' He said, 'You cannot say I went looking for this job that I am in.' And I said, 'No, Mr. President, not the first time,' which tickled him a bit. He poked me in the ribs and said, 'Van, you should be a politician. You have some of the instincts.' I said, 'Mr. President, what the hell do you think I was doing around this town for five or six years?' " Bush, *Pieces of the Action*, p. 302.
[6] Staats to McCandless, J. Weldon Jones, and Stauffacher, March 27, 1950, BOB, Series 39.33, file unit 95—NSF Personnel.
[7] Carey to S. R. Broadbent, April 3, 1950, BOB, Series 39.33, file unit 95—NSF Personnel. A month later Carey endorsed a suggestion from Mary Switzer of the Federal Security Agency "that the Board be leavened with some young people, and not loaded with eminent greybeards." Carey to Staats, May 10, 1950, BOB, Series 39.33, file unit 95—NSF Personnel.
[8] Platt to Stauffacher, April 25, 1950; James L. Grahl to Carey, April 7, 1950, BOB, Series 39.33, file unit 95—NSF Personnel; Condon to Steelman, May 9, 1950, Truman Papers, Official File, 192-E, Box 682.
[9] Lawrence R. Hafstad to Steelman, May 16, 1950, Martin L. Friedman Papers, Box 42, NSF Multiple Endorsements File, Truman Library. The black scientist was Percy L. Julian.
[10] Friedman Papers, Box 42, NSF Multiple Endorsements File.
[11] Staats to Donald Dawson, May 8, 1950, Friedman Papers, Box 42, Multiple Endorsements File.
[12] Bush to John A. Dienner, May 23, 1950, Bush MSS, Box 33, file 748; Smith to Bush, May 1, 8, 1950; Bush to Smith, May 3, 1950, Bush MSS, Box 104, file 2462; Bush to Webster, May 15, 1950; Webster to Bush, May 16, 1950, Bush MSS, Box 117, file 2806. Some of the names on the FAS list probably would have disturbed Webster—Howard Meyerhoff's, for example—but none of the fifteen persons suggested received an appointment. Three of the fifteen nominees of the Inter-Society Committee, however, were chosen. The FAS and Inter-Society nominees are listed on: William D. Hassett to W. A. Higinbotham (copy), June 6, 1950, Truman Papers, Official File, 192-E, Box 683; Truman to Dael Wolfle (copy), May 16, 1950, Official File, 192-E, Box 682.

[13] See especially Truman Papers, Official File, 192-E—Endorsements, Boxes 682 and 683, and Friedman Papers, Box 42, Multiple Endorsements File.

[14] Weaver to Bush, June 16, 1950; Bush to Weaver, July 10, 1950, Bush MSS, Box 117, file 2801; Bush to Guy Martin, Oct. 2, 1950, Bush MSS, Box 69, file 1705.

[15] The names of Budget Bureau and Civil Service Commission candidates are listed under the following headings: Physical Sciences and Mathematics; Engineering; Medicine and Biology; Social Science; Agriculture; Education; Public Affairs and Industry; Negro; Women; Labor; Catholic; Jewish; South; Farwest; Midwest; East. Friedman Papers, Box 42, NSF (Misc., etc.).

[16] Philleo Nash to Charles Maylon, June 22, July 6, 1950, Files of Philleo Nash, General Correspondence, Box 10, Truman Library; interview with Nash, March 9, 1977.

[17] For example, Frederick A. Middlebush, president of the University of Missouri, wrote President Truman on May 31, 1950, urging him to "make certain that public institutions, especially Land-Grant Colleges and State Universities, receive representation [on the board] in accordance with their importance. If this is not done, I have little doubt that the usual inequitable distribution of funds will result." He enclosed a copy of this letter to his friend Charles Ross, Truman's press secretary, who in turn passed it along to Donald Dawson. If Middlebush's own name appeared on any of the voluminous recommendations of board possibilities, I failed to spot it (though it could easily have been overlooked). It seems highly probable that he was appointed to the board because the President and others on the White House staff knew him. (Both Ross and Dawson were Missourians with ties to the university.) Although Middlebush was not a nominee of the land-grant association, two of the five persons agreed on by that organization as early as May 1949 were appointed to the first board, A. A. Potter and Elvin C. Stakman. Summary of Actions of the ALGCU Executive Committee Meeting in Washington, D.C., May 2-3, 1949, May 27, 1949, NASULGC files.

[18] Steelman to Kenneth McKellar, Aug. 29, 1950; McKellar to Steelman, Aug. 29, 1950, Truman Papers, Official File, 192-E, Box 682; Staats, memorandum for the record, Sept. 6, 1950, Papers of Frederick J. Lawton, Box 6, Truman Library; *House Rept. No. 2987*, 81st Cong., 2d Sess. (Aug. 24, 1950), p. 28.

[19] DuBridge to Steelman, Sept. 5, 1950, Truman Papers, Official File, 192-E, Box 682.

[20] *Senate Rept. No. 2567*, 81st Cong., 2d Sess. (Sept. 13, 1950), p. 16; Schuldt to Staats, Sept. 15, 1950; Schuldt to Carey, Sept. 14, 1950, BOB, Series 39.33, file unit 97—NSF Supplementals; *House Rept. No. 3096* (Conference Report), 81st Cong., 2d Sess. (Sept. 18, 1950), p. 8; P.L. 81-843, Supplemental Appropriation Act of 1951 (approved Sept. 27, 1950).

[21] Copies of the presidential letters dated Sept. 30, 1950, to those who were later nominated are in the files of the National Science Board.

[22] Harley M. Kilgore to John W. Davis, May 8, 1950, Kilgore Papers, Franklin D. Roosevelt Library. (I am indebted to Robert F. Maddox for a copy of this letter.)

[23] Morris had campaigned for the appointment of one of his colleagues, Fred C. Cole, a Tulane historian and dean, and probably stimulated some of the many other recommendations for Cole, including one from the Rice president, Houston, whose name was replaced by Morris's. (These recommendations—from presidents of several southern universities and of historical associations—are in Truman Papers, Official File, 192-E, Box 682. See also, Morris to Bush, May 24, 1950, BOB, Series 39.33, file unit 95—NSF Personnel.)

[24] Ford to President, Oct. 17, 1950; Julian to President, Oct. 20, 1950, Truman Papers, Official File, 192-E, Box 682. Letters indicating willingness to accept appointment are also in this file.

[25] The positions of the nominees are in nearly all instances those shown in NSF's *First Annual Report, 1950-51*, pp. 23-24, rather than in the White House listing.

[26] For a similar analysis, see *Science*, Vol. 112 (Nov. 17, 1950), p. 607.

[27] DuBridge to Steelman, Nov. 13, 1950; Steelman to DuBridge, Nov 17, 1950; Dawson to DuBridge *et al.*, Nov. 18, 1950, Truman Papers, Official File, 192-E, Box 682.

[28] Dollard to Bush, Nov. 17, 1950, Bush MSS, Box 33, file 767.

[29] Graham to Truman, Nov. 7, 1950; Truman to Graham, Nov. 13, 1950, Truman Papers, Official File, 192-E, Box 682.

[30] A longhand note on Graham's letter to Truman of Nov. 7 says "Nothing prev[ious] in

file offering this post."

[31] New York *Times*, Nov. 25, 1950, p. 8.

[32] Golden, memorandum for the file, Nov. 20, 1950, in Golden's possession.

[33] DuBridge to Members of the National Science Foundation Board, Dec. 1, 1950, Truman Papers, Official File, 192-E, Box 682.

[34] Dawson to President, Dec. 11, 1950, Truman Papers, Official File, 192-E, Box 682.

[35] Charles S. Murphy to James E. Webb, Dec. 29, 1950, Webb Papers, alphabetical name file, Box 50, Truman Library.

[36] This procedure, rather than moving directly to nominations at the first meeting, seems to have been agreed on in advance. Golden suggested it to Bronk, who conferred with several other members on the best way of conducting business at the first session. Golden, memorandums for the file, Dec. 4, 8, 1950.

[37] Minutes of Organizational Meeting of the National Science Board, Dec. 12, 1950; Detlev W. Bronk, "Science Advice in the White House," *Science*, Vol. 186 (Oct. 11, 1974), p. 117; Schuldt to files, Dec. 18, 1950, BOB, Series 39.33, file unit 94—NSF General Administration. National Science Board Minutes (hereafter cited NSB Minutes) are on file in the board office in the Foundation and in the NSF Library.

[38] "The 'Pattern' of Qualifications for the Job," appended to NSB Minutes, 2d Meeting, Jan. 3, 1951.

[39] NSB Minutes, 2d Meeting, Jan. 3, 1951, pp. 2-4.

[40] *Ibid.*, p. 5. According to a Budget Bureau staff member, Conant took the names to the White House during the meeting. Schuldt to files, Jan. 9, 1951, BOB, Series 39.33, file unit 94—NSF General Administration.

[41] Golden, memorandum for the file, Jan. 8, 1951.

[42] F. M. [Florence Mahoney] to Donald [Dawson], [Jan. 10, 1951], Truman Papers, Official File, 192-E, Box 682; telephone conversation with Mrs. Mahoney, Nov. 18, 1977. For her work in behalf of medical research see Stephen P. Strickland, *Politics, Science, and Dread Disease: A Short History of United States Medical Research Policy* (Cambridge, Mass., 1972), pp. 33-34 and *passim*.

[43] Teeter to Dawson, Feb. 19, 1951, Truman Papers, Official File, 192-E, Box 682.

[44] Golden, memorandums for the file, Nov. 8, 14, 21, 1950.

[45] Golden, memorandums for the file, Jan. 5, 8, 1951.

[46] Golden, memorandum for the file, Nov. 22, 1950.

[47] Golden, memorandums for the file, Jan. 4, 5, 1951. Later Bronk made the "interesting comment" to Golden "that he was glad that it had been possible to bring the Board around to recognizing that it should stay out of defense or other applied research matters and stick to basic research interests." Golden, memorandum for the file, Feb. 27, 1951.

[48] Golden, Memorandum on Program for the National Science Foundation, Feb. 13, 1951, attached to F. J. Lawton to Chairman of the National Science Foundation, Feb. 15, 1951, BOB, Series 39.33, file unit 94; Golden, memorandums for the file, Jan. 26, 30, 1951.

[49] NSB Minutes, 3d Meeting, Feb. 13-14, 1951, p. 2.

[50] Golden, memorandums for the file, Jan. 26, 30, Feb. 6, 1951.

[51] Bush to Charles S. Garland, April 1, 1948, Bush MSS, Box 57, file 1382; Bush to William Webster, May 25, 1950, Bush MSS, Box 117, file 2809; Condon to Steelman, May 9, 1950, Truman Papers, Official File, 192-E, Box 682; Harlow Shapley, *Through Rugged Ways to the Stars* (New York, 1969), p. 146.

[52] Edward L. Moreland to Waterman, Dec. 5, 1950; Waterman to Moreland, Dec. 8, 1950, Alan T. Waterman Papers, Manuscript Division, Library of Congress (hereafter ATW MSS), Box 22. Waterman gave a similar reply to DuBridge, Dec. 7, 1950, ATW MSS, Box 17.

[53] Schuldt to Carey, March 8, 1951, BOB, Series 39.33, file unit 94—NSF General Administration; Golden to Waterman, Feb. 27, 1951, ATW MSS, Box 24.

[54] Bush to Garland, April 1, 1948, Bush MSS, Box 57, file 1382.

[55] James B. Conant, *My Several Lives: Memoirs of a Social Inventor* (New York, 1970), p. 562.

[56] NSB Minutes, 4th Meeting, March 8-9, 1951, p. 5; Schuldt to Carey, March 12, 1951, BOB, Series 39.33, file unit 97—NSF Supplementals.

Chapter 7

[1] Moreland to Waterman (hereafter ATW), March 13, 1951; Compton to ATW, March 12, 1951; Stratton to ATW, March 12, 1951; Sherwood to ATW, March 12, 1951; Killian to ATW, March 12, 1951, ATW MSS, Box 24. Compton also wrote John Steelman praising the appointment of the man "almost unanimously mentioned as first choice." Compton to Steelman, March 12, 1951, Truman Papers, Official File, 192-E, Box 682.

[2] Ginny [Virginia] Sides to ATW, March 14, 1951, ATW MSS, Box 24.

[3] ATW and Robert D. Conrad, "The Office of Naval Research," *American Scholar*, Vol. 15 (Summer 1947), pp. 354-56.

[4] K. Lark-Horovitz to ATW, March 19, 1951; Kelly to ATW, March 14, 1951; Suits to ATW, March 21, 1951, ATW MSS, Box 24; Golden, memorandums for the file, 1950-51, *passim*. The weekly news magazine *Time* (March 19, 1951), p. 73, said that "Dr. Waterman was largely responsible for the extraordinary respect which non-Government scientists felt toward ONR."

[5] Lawrence R. Hafstad to Steelman, March 1, 1950, Truman Papers, Official File, 192-D, Box 681.

[6] Carey to Staats, March 2, 1950, BOB, Series 47.1b—NSF Act of 1949; Staats to Steelman, April 11, 1950; Steelman to Hafstad, April 17, 1950, Truman Papers, Official File, 192-D, Box 681.

[7] Undated paper evidently prepared by Waterman in March 1951 for his Senate confirmation hearing, ATW MSS, Box 24; ATW, Notes on Harold Orlans MS., Nov. 1965, ATW MSS, Box 30.

[8] Bronk to ATW, Dec. 22, 1963, ATW MSS, Box 29. Waterman said he did "not feel at all competent to judge the painting as a likeness, but Mary really likes it and that is enough from my standpoint. My impression is that the portrait looks like a real person but whether he is the one I have been living with all this time is a puzzle. I could not help a feeling of confusion at the 'ceremony' as to whether he was supposed to look like me or I like him." ATW to Bronk, Nov. 11, 1963, ATW MSS, Box 29.

[9] Sophie D. Aberle to ATW, Dec. 29, 1952, NSB files; ATW to Peter van de Kamp, April 5, 1956, in Waterman Daily File (hereafter ATW DF), NSF files; interview with Dorothy Lang, Dec. 17, 1975; Milton Lomask, *A Minor Miracle: An Informal History of the National Science Foundation* (Washington, 1976), pp. 71-72, 77-78.

In 1949 George W. Carr saw Waterman's picture in a magazine, and though about thirty years had passed, he recalled his pleasure in hearing Waterman play Irish melodies from a book checked out of the District's public library. "The thing I recall most distinctly is your playing the piano in the technique of the harp, sweeping chords, the beauty of which remains in my memory to this day." He wanted the name of the music book, and Waterman informed him that it was " 'A Cycle of Old Irish Melodies,' arranged by Arthur Whiting and published by G. Schirmer." Carr to ATW, Feb. 14, 1949; ATW to Carr, March 25, 1949, ATW MSS, Box 17.

[10] ATW to Douglas, July 9, 1965, ATW MSS, Box 17; Compton to Steelman, March 12, 1951, Truman Papers, Official File, 192-E, Box 682.

[11] Schuldt to Staats, Feb. 12, 1951, BOB, Series 39.33, file unit 98; Schuldt to files, Feb. 16, 1951, BOB, Series 39.33, file unit 94.

[12] Schuldt to Carey, April 24, 1951, BOB, Series 39.33, file unit 94.

[13] *Ibid.*; ATW to Sunderlin, Dec. 13, 1950; Sunderlin to ATW, Feb. 7, 1951, ATW MSS, Box 36; ATW, Diary Note, March 23, 1951, ATW MSS, Box 2; ATW to P. D. Lohmann, April 9, 1951, ATW DF; NSF Press Release (hereafter cited PR) No. 3, May 4, 1951.

[14] ATW, Diary Note, March 26, 1951, ATW DF; ATW, Diary Note, March 27, 1951, ATW MSS, Box 2; ATW to Connor, April 19, 1951, ATW DF; NSB Minutes, 5th Meeting, April 6, 1951, pp. 2, 3.

[15] NSF PR-3, May 4, 1951.

[16] ATW, Diary Notes, April 12, 13, 1951; ATW to NSB, April 14, 1951; ATW to Kelly, April 17, 1951, ATW DF; NSF PR-6, July 19, 1951.

[17] ATW, Diary Note, April 16, 1951, ATW DF; NSF PR-4, June 19, 1951.
[18] ATW, Diary Note, April 23, 1951, ATW MSS, Box 2; ATW to Brode, July 13, 1951, ATW MSS, Box 1; ATW to Brode, May 28, 1951, ATW DF. Brode was an associate director of NSF in 1958-59.
[19] ATW, Diary Note, July 30, 1951, ATW MSS, Box 2; ATW to E.B. Fred, Aug. 14, 1951, ATW DF; NSF PR-10, Oct. 10, 1951; NSF PR-43, Dec. 31, 1952.

Kloptsteg's diary (in his possession) contains interesting personal information on his joining NSF and his off-duty socializing with the Watermans and other NSF families.

[20] Schuldt to Carey, April 24, 1951, BOB, Series 39.33, file unit 94; NSB Minutes, 6th Meeting, May 11, 1951, pp. 5-6; 7th Meeting, July 27, 1951, p. 2.
[21] NSB Minutes, 2d Meeting, Jan. 3, 1951, pp. 3-4; 15th Meeting, Aug. 8, 1952, p. 12; 24th Meeting, Dec. 7, 1953, p. 8; 25th Meeting, Jan. 29, 1954, p. 6; ATW, Diary Notes, July 30, Dec. 4, 13, 1951, ATW MSS, Box 2; ATW to Loeb, July 13, 1951; ATW, Diary Notes, Jan. 15, 16, March 10, June 24, Aug. 4, 1952; ATW to Goodpasture, June 30, July 15, 18, Aug. 4, 1952; ATW to Sunderlin et al., July 16, 1952; ATW to senior staff, July 22, 1952, ATW DF.
[22] Dollard to Bush, Aug. 6, 1951, Bush MSS, Box 33, file 767.
[23] NSB Minutes, 5th Meeting, April 6, 1951, pp. 3-4. Schuldt cautioned Waterman against overuse of the authority to make appointments without regard to Civil Service and Classification Act regulations. Schuldt pointed out that the AEC's liberal use of a similar authority had resulted in an appropriation act rider. Schuldt to Carey, April 24, 1951, BOB, Series 39.33, file unit 94.
[24] ATW, Diary Note, March 28, 1951, ATW MSS, Box 2; ATW to Condon, April 4, 1951; ATW to Sunderlin, April 17, 1951, ATW DF; Schuldt to Carey, April 24, 1951, BOB, Series 39.33, file unit 94; NSF PR-5, July 5, 1951; Harwood interview (1968), Columbia University Oral History Collection.
[25] NSB Minutes, 6th Meeting, May 11, 1951, p. 3; Schuldt to files, Jan. 9, 1951, BOB, Series 39.33, file unit 94; ATW, Diary Notes, March 26, 28, 1951, ATW MSS, Box 2. Waterman mentioned to Conant the possibility of a large Georgetown house, possibly Dumbarton Oaks. Conant said that the space in Dumbarton Oaks "was fully occupied."
[26] ATW, "The Beginnings of the National Science Foundation," Speeches of the Director (1951), p. 8, NSF Library; Lomask, *A Minor Miracle*, p. 78.
[27] ATW to William E. Reynolds, May 18, 1951, ATW DF.
[28] ATW, Diary Note, April 10, 1951, ATW DF.
[29] ATW to Reynolds, May 18, 1951, ATW DF.
[30] ATW to Reynolds, May 19, 1951; Sunderlin to Ferdinand Kaufholz, Jr., June 26, 1951, ATW DF.
[31] Sunderlin to Kaufholz, June 26, 1951; ATW to Reynolds, May 2, 1952; Sunderlin to F. Moran McConihe, Sept. 27, 1956, ATW DF.
[32] ATW to NSB, Aug. 5, 1952; ATW to L. A. Ziernicki, Sept. 17, 1952; ATW, Diary Note, Sept. 24, 1952; ATW to Ruth E. Jenkins, May 30, 1953; ATW to Mrs. Edward L. Moreland, Nov. 5, 1953, ATW DF. The Dolley Madison and Ogle Tayloe houses are described and their histories discussed in Harold D. Eberlein and Courtlandt Van Dyke Hubbard, *Historic Houses of George-Town & Washington City* (Richmond, 1958), pp. 275-91. The Ogle Tayloe House came to be referred to as the "Little White House" during William McKinley's presidency because of his many visits to consult his political mentor, Senator Mark Hanna, who lived there. *Ibid.*, p. 291.
[33] Sunderlin to McConihe, Sept. 27, 1956, ATW DF; NSF Organizational Directory, Dec. 2, 1957, NSF HF.
[34] ATW to Assistant Director for Administration, Aug. 5, 1958, ATW DF.
[35] Interview with Dorothy Lang, Dec. 17, 1975; interview with Virginia Sides by Milton Lomask, May 7, 1973.
[36] ATW to William W. Edwards, May 10, 1951, ATW DF.
[37] ATW, Diary Notes, March 14, April 2, 1951; ATW to Condon, May 7, 1951, ATW DF; ATW, Diary Note, March 26, 1951, ATW MSS, Box 2.
[38] Interview with John T. Wilson, May 21, 1974.

Chapter 8

[1] F. J. Lawton to the President, Oct. 19, 1950; Golden to the President, Dec. 18, 1950, NSF HF. For a good account of Golden's review and its aftermath, see Detlev W. Bronk, "Science Advice in the White House," *Science*, Vol. 186 (Oct. 11, 1974), pp. 116-21; also, Golden, "What Can You Scientists and Engineers Do for Me: or, Why Should the President Want a Science Adviser?" a lecture given at Duke University, April 2, 1975, NSF HF.

[2] Golden, Memorandum on Program for the National Science Foundation, Feb. 13, 1951, attached to Lawton to Chairman of the National Science Foundation, Feb. 15, 1951, BOB, Series 39.33, file unit 94. An earlier draft version of this memorandum, in the same file, was dated Dec. 12, 1950, the date of the board's first meeting.

[3] Golden to the President, Dec. 18, 1950; Bronk, "Science Advice in the White House," p. 117; Schuldt to files, Jan. 9, 1951, BOB, Series 39.33, file unit 94. A Defense Department committee chaired by Irvin Stewart had recommended the prompt reestablishment of OSRD, a proposal which Golden opposed.

[4] Schuldt to files, Jan. 9, 1951.

[5] Golden, memorandums to the file, Nov. 22, Dec. 13, 1950, Jan. 2, 4, 5, 8, 1951.

[6] Schuldt to files, Jan. 9, 1951.

[7] NSB Minutes, 2d Meeting, Jan. 3, 1951, pp. 10-11; 3d Meeting, Feb. 13-14, 1951, p. 3; Schuldt to files, Feb. 16, 1951, BOB, Series 39.33, file unit 94.

[8] ATW, Diary Note, March 9, 1951, ATW DF. In a telephone conversation a month later, board member Charles Dollard told Waterman "that there was some fear of domination of the NSF by military interests and others outside, and it would be well for [Waterman] to uphold its independence." ATW, Diary Note, April 9 (?), 1951, ATW DF.

[9] Bronk, "Science Advice in the White House," pp. 118-19; Golden, "What Can Scientists and Engineers Do for Me . . .?"; ATW, Diary Note, May 22, 1952, ATW MSS, Box 2.

[10] NSB Minutes, 2d Meeting, Jan. 3, 1951, pp. 6-7; Schuldt to files, Jan. 9, 1951; Golden to Staats, Carey, and Schuldt, Feb. 8, 1951, BOB, Series 39.33, file unit 98.

[11] Schuldt to Staats, Feb. 12, 1951, BOB, Series 39.33, file unit 98.

[12] NSB Minutes, 3d Meeting, Feb. 13-14, 1951, pp. 2, 3; 4th Meeting, March 8-9, 1951, p. 2, and appendix.

[13] NSB Minutes, 4th Meeting, March 8-9, 1951, p. 5; Schuldt to Staats, March 9, 1951, BOB, Series 39.33, file unit 94.

[14] One possible problem was a legislative requirement of FBI investigation of applicants for the AEC awards, as opposed to the less stringent requirement of an affidavit of loyalty for recipients of NSF fellowships, but the Bureau thought that this could be solved.

[15] ATW, Diary Notes, March 27, April 3, 10, 19, 1951; ATW to Harry C. Kelly, April 17, 1951, ATW DF; E. C. Wine to Schuldt, April 30, 1951; Schuldt to Carey, May 1, 1951, BOB, Series 39.33, file unit 97; Golden to Schuldt, May 15, 1951; Schuldt to Staats, May 16, 1951, BOB, Series 39.33, file unit 98.

[16] ATW, Diary Note, April 23, 1951, ATW DF; Schuldt to Carey, April 24, 1951, BOB, Series 39.33, file unit 94.

[17] ATW, Diary Note, May 9, 1951, ATW DF; NSB Minutes, 6th Meeting, May 11, 1951. p. 7.

[18] NSB Minutes, 6th Meeting, May 11, 1951, pp. 7-8.

[19] ATW, Diary Notes, June 18, July 5, 1951, ATW DF; NSB Minutes, 7th Meeting, July 27-28, 1951, pp. 11-12.

[20] ATW, Diary Notes, June 25, July 5, 1951, ATW DF; NSB Minutes, 6th Meeting, May 11, 1951, pp. 10-11.

[21] NSB Minutes, 7th Meeting, July 27-28, 1951. pp. 8-9.

[22] See ch. 7, p. 131.

[23] ATW to NSB, May 25, 1951, ATW DF.

[24] ATW, Diary Note, May 10, 1951, ATW DF; Schuldt to BOB Director, May 15, 1951, BOB, Series 47.3, file G1-143.

[25] NSB Minutes, 6th Meeting, May 11, 1951, pp. 5-6.

[26] Schuldt to BOB Director, May 15, 1951; Schuldt to Staats, May 16, 1951, BOB, Series 47.3, file G1-143.

[27] Schuldt to files, May 17, 1951, BOB, Series 39.33, file unit 97; ATW to Lawton, May 15, 1951; ATW to NSB, May 25, 1951, ATW DF. The budget submitted to Congress on May 23 requested $1.3 million for medical research, $2.6 for biological, and $3.9 for mathematical, physical, and engineering.

[28] NSB Minutes, 6th Meeting, May 11, 1951, p. 9. For fuller discussions of these ideas, see memos by C. E. S[underlin] in Waterman's Board Book, 6th NSB Meeting, NSB Records, Record Group 307, Federal Records Center, Suitland, Maryland, Box 1 (hereafter NSB Records).

[29] Schuldt to Carey, May 1, 1951, BOB, Series 39.33, file unit 97. This memorandum set forth policies for the Bureau's review of NSF's 1952 budget estimates. Carey and Staats indicated their approval.

[30] NSB Minutes, 3d Meeting, Feb. 13-14, 1951, p. 5; 4th Meeting, March 8-9, 1951, p. 5; 5th Meeting, April 6, 1951, p. 10; NSF PR-2, April 7, 1951.

[31] NSB Minutes, 6th Meeting, May 11, 1951, pp. 8, 9.

[32] ATW to NSB, May 25, 1951, ATW DF; NSF, Justification of Estimates on Appropriations, Fiscal Year 1952, p. 4, Office of the NSF Director Subject Files (hereafter OD SF), Record Group 307, National Archives, 1952 Budget file.

[33] *First Annual Report of the National Science Foundation, 1950-51*, p. 13.

[34] A national roster of scientific personnel had been established during World War II as an aid for locating persons with special skills, and it was continued after the war by the National Research Council with financial support from several federal agencies. A recommendation in 1949 by the National Security Resources Board for a broadly based roster as an element of mobilization readiness led to the incorporation of the Register in the science foundation legislation, but pending passage of the NSF act the Register was transferred to the Office of Education. NSF, Justification of Estimates . . . Fiscal Year 1952, p. 15, OD SF, 1952 Budget file.

[35] NSB Minutes, 3d Meeting, Feb. 13-14, 1951, pp. 4-5.

[36] NSB Minutes, 4th Meeting, March 8-9, 1951, p. 5; 5th Meeting, April 6, 1951, pp. 9, 10; Justification of Estimates . . . Fiscal Year 1952, p. 15.

[37] Justification of Estimates . . . Fiscal Year 1952, pp. 16-17; Harry S. Truman to James B. Conant, June 5, 1951; Conant to the President, June 12, 1951, Truman Papers, Official File, 192-D, Box 81.

[38] ATW, Diary Notes, April 24, 27, 1951, ATW DF.

[39] Questions raised during an informal budget hearing on May 1 and NSF answers are in OD SF, 1952 Budget file.

[40] Schuldt to BOB Director, May 29, 1951, BOB, Series 47.3, file G1-143.

[41] Justification of Estimates . . . Fiscal Year 1952, p. 18. Compare Waterman's view with that expressed by William D. Nordhaus of the Council of Economic Advisers in a speech of June 15, 1977 before a AAAS colloquium on Research and Development in the Federal Budget: "In this age of scarcity, it is comforting to know that, unlike other scarce goods, knowledge is not a depletable resource. No matter how many times the second law of thermodynamics is used or abused, it will remain for future generations to use and abuse."

Waterman was, however, stating a view held by many scientists. As Don Price says, "They were inclined to look on the startling technical achievements of World War II not as a kind of progress that could be carried on indefinitely, but as the rapid consumption of a stock pile of basic knowledge. To them our scientific resources had been depleted just as we had depleted our basic reserves of iron ore and oil." Price, *Government and Science: Their Dynamic Relation in American Democracy* (New York, 1954), p. 32.

A better analysis than Waterman's of what occurred in World War II is I. I. Rabi's: ". . . let me attempt to distinguish two aspects of physics. There is, first, the creative intellectual activity which constantly pushes back the boundaries of our understanding of natural phenomena; second, there is an industrial activity which applies the results of scientific knowledge and understanding to satisfy material human needs and whimsies. Only the first is what I call the 'science of physics' proper; the second is only the side of physics which has been called 'the inheritance of technology.' If the science of physics lags, the inheritance of technology is soon spent. In the war years, our inheritance of technology was exploited to the point where further substantial progress could come only from a new advance in the science of physics." I. I. Rabi, *Science: The Center of Culture* (New York, 1970), p. 5.

[42] House of Representatives, *Hearings . . . on the Supplemental Appropriation Bill for 1952*, Pt. 2, 82d Cong., 1st Sess., pp. 543-49, 557. Schuldt was surprised to learn "that Thomas went out of the way to compliment the Foundation on the quality of its written budget justification." Schuldt to Carey, June 8, 1951, BOB, Series 39.33, file unit 97.

[43] *Hearings*, p. 562.

[44] Schuldt to Carey, June 8, 1951, relaying Waterman's impressions of the hearing.

[45] *Hearings*, pp. 567-70.

[46] Schuldt to Carey, June 8, 1951; ATW to Brode, July 13, 1951, ATW MSS, Box 1; *Hearings*, p. 571.

[47] *House Report No. 890*, 82d Cong., 1st Sess., Aug. 17, 1951, p. 28.

[48] *Cong. Record*, 82d Cong., 1st Sess., pp. 10379-80, 10396-97 (Aug. 20, 1951).

[49] ATW to NSB, Aug. 18, 1951, ATW DF. Bronk advised against calling the board into an emergency meeting, since it could do nothing but pass an ineffective resolution. Individual members, however, should get in touch with their senators. ATW, Diary Note, Aug. 20, 1951, ATW DF.

[50] NSF PR-7, Aug. 19, 1951.

[51] ATW, Diary Notes, Aug. 18, 20, 1951; ATW, memo for files, Aug. 28, 1951, ATW DF; Steelman to McKellar, Aug. 22, 1951, Truman Papers, Official File, 192-E, Box 682; Senate, *Hearings before the Committee on Appropriations . . . on H. R. 2215*, 82d Cong., 1st Sess., pp. 1118-19, 1152-55.

[52] ATW, Diary Notes, Aug. 28, 29, 1951, ATW MSS, Box 2; ATW, Diary Note, Aug. 29, 1951, ATW DF. At a strategy-mapping conference at the Budget Bureau, "Staats felt that the strongest case would be made if the DOD called the committee and asked to produce a statement or testify. Failing this, the Committee might ask the DOD and then [RDB Chairman Walter G.] Whitman either to produce a statement or testify. Both these cases would be weaker if the NSF requested the witnesses." ATW, Diary Note, Aug. 29, 1951, ATW MSS, Box 2.

[53] *Hearings*, pp. 1166-67. Waterman also sent a copy of the RDB letter to Senator Alexander Smith, at his request, and Smith testified for NSF at the Senate hearing. ATW to Miss Wherry, Aug. 29, 1951, ATW DF; *Hearings*, pp. 1145-50.

[54] See, for example, the lists of persons to whom Waterman wrote on Aug. 18, in ATW DF, and of those who wrote supporting NSF's request, in OD SF, 1952 Budget file.

[55] ATW to NSB, Aug. 18, 1951; ATW, Diary Note, Aug. 31, 1951, ATW DF; Bush to McKellar, Aug. 31, 1951; Bush to Kilgore, Aug. 31, 1951, Bush MSS, Box 85, file 1913. A copy of Bush's letter to McKellar went to Leverett Saltonstall, like Kilgore a member of McKellar's committee.

[56] ATW, Diary Note, Aug. 29, 1951, ATW MSS, Box 2; ATW, Diary Note, Aug. 30, 1951, OD SF, 1952 Budget file; ATW to Cordon, Sept. 28, 1951, ATW DF; *Hearings*, pp. 1094-1104.

Other board members also wrote their senators. For example, Dollard wrote to his two New York senators, and one of them, Herbert H. Lehman, wrote a strong letter to Kilgore which became a part of the hearing record. Joseph Morris of Tulane wrote Allen Ellender (D., Louisiana), a member of the committee, E. B. Fred wrote the senators from Wisconsin, and John W. Davis wrote Kilgore. ATW to Dollard, Nov. 5, 1951; ATW to Morris, Nov. 5, 1951; ATW to Fred, Nov. 6, 1951; ATW to Davis, Nov. 6, 1951, ATW DF; *Hearings*, p. 1119.

[57] ATW, Diary Note, Aug. 30, 1951, OD SF, 1952 Budget file.

[58] New York *Times*, Aug. 19, 1951, Sec. 4, p. 9. Copies of this and other newspaper stories and editorials are filed in OD SF, 1952 Budget file.

[59] Washington *Post*, Aug. 22, 1951.

[60] *Ibid.*, Aug. 24, 1951.

[61] Philadelphia *Bulletin*, Aug. 27, 1951. The Washington *Star*, which on August 21

commented on the Foundation's "modest" budget request, suggested that the National Science Board needed to master "what is becoming the basic science in America today—the science of obtaining money from Congress." Similarly a brief story in *Newsweek*, Aug. 27, 1951, was headed "Pin Money for NSF."

[62] Washington *Post*, Aug. 22, 1951.

[63] The quotations from Winchell's column of Sept. 23, 1951, appear in a memorandum by John H. Teeter, Sept. 28, 1951, Bush MSS, Box 110, file 2617. Teeter probably supplied the item for Winchell's column. In a letter to Teeter on Oct. 8, 1951 (ATW DF), Waterman wrote: "I am sure it has been helpful to us to have this problem brought to the attention of so wide an audience as Mr. Winchell enjoys."

[64] Meyerhoff to members of AAAS Council, Aug. 24, 1951, copy, OD SF, 1952 Budget file.

[65] *Higher Education and National Affairs*, Aug. 23, 1951.

[66] ATW, "The National Science Foundation Program," *Science*, Vol. 114 (Aug. 31, 1951), pp. 251-52.

[67] *Chemical & Engineering News*, Aug. 27, 1951.

[68] *Bulletin of the Atomic Scientists*, Vol. 7, No. 10 (Oct. 1951), pp. 290-91.

[69] ATW to McKellar, Aug. 24, 1951, and enclosure, Salaries and Expenses, National Science Foundation, OD SF, 1952 Budget file.

[70] Salaries and Expenses, *passim*. The program of general research support for medicine is much like that suggested in 1945 by Bush's Medical Advisory Committee. See above, ch. 1, p. 18. Robert Loeb, chairman of the Natinal Science Board's medical research committee, strongly suggested the use of this form in the budget document as "the only way a quick presentation could be given without the danger of running into conflict with other agencies operating in the same field"—that is, to avoid an appearance of duplicating NIH research support. ATW to NSB, Aug. 27, 1951, ATW DF.

[71] Potter to ATW, Aug. 30, 1951, NSB files; ATW, Diary Note, Sept. 5, 1951, ATW DF. The board endorsed Waterman's budget document at its meeting in September but agreed that the proposed program "might be modified as further study indicates desirable." NSB Minutes, 8th Meeting, Sept. 7, 1951, p. 4.

[72] ATW DF, Aug. 24-Sept. 19, 1951, contains numerous diary notes detailing the preparation for the hearings.

[73] ATW to Everard H. Smith, Sept. 18, 1951, ATW DF.

[74] Senate, *Hearings*, pp. 1104-09, 1114.

[75] Schuldt to Staats, Sept. 20, 1951, BOB, Series 39.33, file unit 97; *Hearings*, pp. 1114-15, 1144-45, 1150.

[76] *Hearings, passim*; Schuldt to Staats, Sept. 20, 1951. Sunderlin had not been present at the hearing since, according to Schuldt, "Waterman had made it a point to minimize staff representation."

[77] *Senate Report No. 891* (Oct. 6, 1951), 82d Cong., 1st Sess., p. 17.

[78] ATW, Diary Note, Oct. 2, 1951, ATW DF.

[79] ATW, Diary Note, Sept. 25, 1951; ATW to Saltonstall, Oct. 15, 1951; ATW to Kenneth McKellar *et al.*, Oct. 12, 1951, ATW DF.

[80] ATW, Diary Note, Sept. 25, 1951, ATW DF.

[81] *Cong. Record*, 82d Cong., 1st Sess., pp. 13706-07, 13755-58 (Oct. 20, 1951).

[82] NSB Minutes, 9th Meeting, Oct. 13, 1951, p. 3.

[83] ATW, Diary Note, Oct. 23, 1951, ATW DF.

Chapter 9

[1] Working Paper on Techniques of Fostering Research, July 23, 1951; NSF Staff Meeting Notes, July 5, 10, 16, 20, 1951, NSF HF.

[2] ATW's notes on Working Paper on Techniques of Fostering Research, in ATW's

Board Book, 7th NSB Meeting, NSB Records, Box 1; NSB Minutes, 7th Meeting, July 27-28, 1951, p. 10.

³ATW to NSB, Oct. 3, 1951, and attached staff paper, Administrative Aspects of Research Support, Sept. 28, 1951, in ATW's Board Book, 9th NSB Meeting, NSB Records, Box 1.

⁴NSB Minutes, 9th Meeting, Oct. 13, 1951, p. 5.

⁵In addition, the "typical grant" should cover a 2-5 year period; be payable in advance on an installment basis; allow the grantee to obtain a patent but require a royalty-free license for the government; provide for progress reports; be administered, both in substantive and business aspects, by a single NSF staff member; contain a termination clause; and require the return of unused funds unless the grant should be renewed. The paper presented in some detail the reasons for each of these characteristics. Administrative Aspects of Research Support, pp. 7-22.

⁶Working Paper on Techniques of Fostering Research, pp. 13-16. Lee DuBridge, perhaps the strongest advocate on the board for full payment of indirect costs, told Waterman that NSF should find means of "defraying the actual total cost of the project to the institutions." Disliking the uniform 8 percent rate, he hoped "that the interminable arguments on overhead can be eliminated." (ATW, Diary Note, June 30 (?), 1951, ATW DF.) During the board discussion of the question in July, someone pointed out the danger of setting a rate "which would prejudice the attitude" of AEC and the military services. (A. A. Potter to ATW, Aug. 1, 1951, NSB files.) In October Waterman informed AEC and PHS officials of NSF's intention of paying indirect costs on research grants at the rate of 15 percent, which was perhaps "on the low side" judging from ONR experience. The AEC officials said they thought this was a good policy, and NIH administrators told NSF staff members that they had been considering a substantial increase in their allowance, possibly to 20 percent. (ATW, Diary Note, Oct. 22, 1951; ATW to Leonard A. Scheele, Oct. 30, 1951; ATW to Gordon Dean, Nov. 13, 1951, ATW DF.)

Although the Budget Bureau did not stop NSF from instituting the 15 percent rate, Schuldt told Sunderlin that the board should not have acted without first consulting the Bureau and the other agencies concerned. "Sunderlin was very contrite about the whole affair, saying that NSF was simply not aware of the implications for other agencies of its decisions and assuring me that NSF would be careful in the future to avoid any repetition of this incident." Schuldt to files, April 7, 1952, and attached draft memo, 10/18/51, BOB, Series 51.10, Box 21, NSF Indirect Costs, 1953-56 file.

⁷A number of university business officers promptly challenged some of these ideas and met with Waterman and NSF staff members on Feb. 2, 1952 to discuss their differing views. See ATW to NSB, Feb. 22, 1952, and attachments, NSB Records, Box 1, Book 3.

⁸Administrative Aspects of Research Support, pp. 7-11.

⁹ATW to Howard A. Meyerhoff, Dec. 11, 1951, ATW DF; Grants for Scientific Research: A Guide for the Submission of Research Proposals (Dec. 1951), NSF HF. The guide, without an attached sample grant letter, is printed in *Second Annual Report of the National Science Foundation, Fiscal Year 1952*, pp. 50-52.

¹⁰Grants for Scientific Research: Administrative Aspects of Research Support, pp. 23-24.

¹¹NSB Minutes, 11th Meeting, Feb. 1, 1952, pp. 4-5, and Appendix II.

¹²NSB Minutes, 11th Meeting, Feb. 1, 1952, Appendix II.

¹³NSB Minutes, 11th Meeting, Feb. 1, 1952, pp. 6-7; ATW's Board Book, 11th Meeting, Tab 4, p. 28, NSB Records, Box 1.

¹⁴NSB Minutes, 11th Meeting, Feb. 1, 1952, pp. 4, 6-7; ATW's Board Book, 11th Meeting, Tab 3.

¹⁵"A Proposed Fellowship Program," attached to NSB Minutes, 4th Meeting, March 8-9, 1951.

¹⁶*Ibid.*, p. 6.

¹⁷*Ibid.*, pp. 4, 5; NSB Minutes, 8th Meeting, Sept. 7, 1951, p. 6; Plans for the Foundation's Fellowship Program (as of 5 September 1951), ATW's Board Book, 8th Meeting, NSB Records, Box 1. Another unsuccessful effort to reduce fellowship stipends was made at the October board meeting. NSB Minutes, 9th Meeting, Oct. 13, 1951, p. 6.

[18] Plans for the Foundation's Fellowship Program; NSB Minutes, 8th Meeting, Sept. 7, 1951, p. 6; 9th Meeting, Oct. 13, 1951, pp. 6-7.

[19] Copies of the pre- and postdoctoral announcements are in Book 2, Tab 48, NSB Records, Box 1.

[20] The elaborate review and selection processes are described in NSB Minutes, 12th Meeting, Feb. 29, 1952, pp. 9-10; 13th Meeting, April 4-5, 1952, pp. 4-7.

[21] ATW, Diary Notes, Dec. 17, 1951, Jan. 5, Feb. 6, 1952; ATW to Commanding General, Air Research and Development Command, April 1, 1952; ATW to O. G. Haywood, Jr., May 15, 1952, ATW DF; Nick A. Komons, *Science and the Air Force: A History of the Air Force Office of Scientific Research* (Arlington, Va., 1966), pp. 41-42.

[22] "A Proposed Fellowship Program," p. 3; NSB Minutes, 12th Meeting, Feb. 29, 1952, p. 9; NSF PR-20, April 9, 1952.

[23] NSF PR-20, April 9, 1952; NSF, *Second Annual Report* (FY 1952), pp. 22, 55.

[24] NSB Minutes, 13th Meeting, April 4-5, 1952, pp. 5, 6.

[25] "A Proposed Fellowship Program," p. 7.

[26] NSB Minutes, 2d Meeting, Jan. 3, 1951, pp. 3-4; 3d Meeting, Feb. 13-14, 1951, pp. 3-4; 11th Meeting, Feb. 1, 1952, pp. 5-6.

[27] NSB Minutes, 5th Meeting, April 6, 1951, pp. 6-7.

[28] ATW to NSB, Sept. 6, 1951, in ATW's Board Book, 8th Meeting, NSB Records, Box 1.

[29] NSB Minutes, 8th Meeting, Sept. 7, 1951, pp. 7-8.

[30] *Ibid.*; NSB Minutes, 10th Meeting, Dec. 3, 1951, p. 7; 12th Meeting, Feb. 29, 1952, p. 2; 15th Meeting, Aug. 7-8, 1952, pp. 11-12; 16th Meeting, Oct. 3, 1952, pp. 8, 9; 24th Meeting, Dec. 7, 1953, p. 8; Staff Notes, Fourth Meeting of the Biological Sciences Divisional Committee, Oct. 1, 1952; Minutes, First Meeting of the Divisional Committee for Medical Research, May 23, 1953; Minutes of the Meetings of the Divisional Committees for Biological Sciences and Medical Research, Nov. 19-20, 1953, NSF HF.

[31] The members of the first four divisional committees are listed in NSF, *Second Annual Report* (FY 1952), pp. 37-39. One person, Douglas M. Whitaker, provost of Stanford University, was a member of two committees.

[32] ATW to NSB, July 29, 1952, in ATW's Board Book, 15th Meeting, NSB Records, Box 1.

[33] *Ibid.*

[34] NSF, *Second Annual Report* (FY 1952), pp. 13, 16, 44. The following analysis is based on the list of grants in *ibid.*, pp. 44-50.

[35] A Harvard professor asked Waterman whether he could file a proposal through another agency with which he had a connection, "since Harvard's policy is to endorse no proposals to the Foundation. He says he understands the reason for this but is concerned that this policy decision on Harvard's part is very much misunderstood. He hopes that it will not remain a permanent policy. I assured him," Waterman recorded, "that while I could not speak for Harvard's policy, it did not seem likely that Harvard would continue in this." The reason for the policy was Conant's reluctance "to have projects from Harvard appear prominently in the first award of grants" because of his chairmanship of the National Science Board. ATW, Diary Note, Jan. 24, 1952, ATW DF; ATW, Diary Note, Jan. 5, 1952, ATW MSS, Box 2.

[36] ATW to Goudsmit, Dec. 19, 1951, Jan. 21, 1952; ATW, Diary Note, Jan. 31, 1952, ATW DF; NSF, *Second Annual Report* (FY 1952), pp. 32, 53; NSB Minutes, 11th Meeting, Feb. 1, 1952, pp. 7-8.

[37] NSB Minutes, 11th Meeting, Feb. 1, 1952, p. 8; 15th Meeting, Aug. 7-8, 1952, p. 5; ATW to Sunderlin, Aug. 8, 1951, ATW DF.

[38] Progress Report on Program for Dissemination of Scientific Information, Jan. 30, 1952, in ATW's Board Book, 11th Meeting, NSB Records, Box 1.

[39] ATW, Diary Notes, Oct. 9, Nov. 1, 1951, March 4, Oct. 30, 1952, ATW DF.

[40] ATW, memo to files, June 13, 1951, ATW DF.

[41] ATW to Raymond P. Whearty, Aug. 15, 1951, ATW DF.

[42] Progress Report on Program for Dissemination of Scientific Information, Jan. 30, 1952; NSF, *Second Annual Report* (FY 1952), pp. 33-34.

The Central Intelligence Agency connection was disclosed in the *Columbia* [University] *Daily Spectator*, April 17, 1980, on the basis of CIA documents obtained under the Freedom of Information Act.

[43] ATW to Richard H. Barnes, May 13, 1952, ATW DF; NSF, *Second Annual Report* (FY 1952), pp. 34, 53-54.

[44] ATW to Earl J. McGrath, May 31, July 13, Nov. 6, 1951, July 15, 1952, ATW DF.

[45] ATW to NSB, June 5, 1952, and attached report by Dael Wolfle, Responsibility of the National Science Foundation for a Scientific Register and Clearinghouse of Information on Scientific Personnel, May 5, 1952, in ATW's Board Book, 14th Meeting, NSB Records, Box 1.

[46] *Ibid.*; NSB Minutes, 14th Meeting, June 13, 1952, pp. 14-15.

[47] For the matters treated summarily in this and the following paragraph, see ATW, Diary Notes, July 9, 10, 11, 15, 1952; William J. Hoff to ATW, June 28, 1956; ATW to Arthur S. Flemming, June 29, 1956, ATW DF; Minutes of Divisional Committee for SPE, 1952-53, *passim*, NSF HF. The consultant referred to was Philip N. Powers.

Chapter 10

[1] ATW, Diary Note, March 9, 1951, ATW DF.

[2] National Science Foundation, Agenda—1952 Budget, May 1, 1951, OD SF, 1952 Budget file.

[3] Draft memo, May 11, 1951, BOB, Series 39.33, file unit 98. At the bottom of the memo someone penciled three target figures: Defense $4 million, AEC $3 million, and PHS $1 million.

[4] ATW, Diary Note, March 12, 1951, ATW DF.

[5] ATW, Diary Note, July 18, 1951, ATW DF; conversation with Emanuel Haynes, Aug. 26, 1977.

[6] Kidd to Schuldt, May 29, 1951, BOB, Series 39.33, file unit 98. Kidd enclosed a number of questions which PHS thought NSF should try to answer.

Several months earlier Kidd had told William Golden that NSF "should not undertake to supervise specific research projects by operating agencies but should rather consider and recommend broad research policies for the national interest and, particularly, study and recommend the weights or proportions of funds to be spent in each of the several major areas." Golden, memorandum for the file, Oct. 20, 1950.

[7] Schuldt and Shapley to Director, Aug. 3, 1951, BOB, Series 47.3, file E6-2.

[8] *Ibid.*

[9] Draft statement, Aug. 9, 1951, BOB, Series 47.3, file E6-2.

[10] Carey to Staats, Sept. 27, 1951, BOB, Series 39.33, file unit 94.

[11] ATW, Diary Note, Oct. 5, 1951, ATW DF; Agenda—Meeting with Dr. Waterman, Oct. 9, 1951; Staats to ATW, Oct. 12, 1951, BOB, Series 39.33, file unit 94.

[12] NSB Minutes, 9th Meeting, Oct. 13, 1951, p. 7.

[13] ATW to Frederick J. Lawton, Nov. 30, 1951, ATW DF.

[14] Carey to Schuldt, Jan. 4, 1952, BOB, Series 39.33, file unit 94. The resulting transmittal message reflected the Bureau's effort to mold NSF into an evaluative and policy-developing agency and said that it "will ultimately assume major responsibility for the Federal Government's support of basic research through grant or contract." *Public Papers of the Presidents... Harry S. Truman... 1952-53* (Washington, 1966), p. 34.

[15] Schuldt to S. R. Broadbent, March 14, 1952, BOB, Series 39.33, file unit 98.

[16] Milton Lomask, *A Minor Miracle: An Informal History of the National Science Foundation* (Washington, 1976), p. 91.

[17] Draft, Director, BOB to ATW, May 14, 1952, BOB, Series 39.33, file unit 98.

[18] Carey to Staats, June 5, 1952, BOB, Series 39.33, file unit 98. Lee DuBridge was one board member with whom Waterman talked. DuBridge thought the letter should say that

NSF "would proceed on this matter immediately but with the exception that a thorough job could be done only after consolidation of the office and some years of experience." ATW, Diary Note, May 22, 1952, ATW DF.

[19] Carey to Staats, June 11, 1952, BOB, Series 39.33, file unit 98. There had already been some friction between NSF and the Office of Education over a Foundation contract with the National Research Council to collect information on college enrollments in science courses. James Grahl to Carey, Oct. 2, 1951; Schuldt to Staats, Oct. 5, 1951, BOB, Series 39.33, file unit 98.

[20] NSB Minutes, 14th Meeting, June 13, 1952, pp. 6-8.

[21] *Public Papers of . . . Harry S. Truman . . . 1952-53*, p. 103.

[22] ATW, Diary Note, June 20, 1952, ATW MSS, Box 2; Staats to Carey, June 23, 1952, BOB, Series 39.33, file unit 98.

[23] ATW to John T. Wilson and Charles G. Gant, June 25, 1952; ATW, Diary Notes, June 26, July 2, 7, 10, 19, 1952; ATW to NSB, July 30, 1952, ATW DF.

[24] ATW to Lawton, Oct. 2, 1952, ATW DF; NSB Minutes, 15th Meeting, Aug. 7-8, 1952, p. 13. At the August board meeting Waterman distributed a draft of his letter to Lawton which did not differ in essential matters from the one finally sent two months later. Draft letter dated Aug. 4, 1952, Tab 124, Book 5, NSB Records, Box 2.

[25] ATW to Lawton, Oct. 2, 1952; ATW to Barnard, Oct. 7, 1952, ATW DF.

[26] Carey to William F. Finan, Oct. 16, 1952, and attached paper, "Organization and Management of Federal Scientific Research and Development," Sept. 29, 1952, BOB, Series 52.6, file E8-20/52.1.

[27] "Organization and Management of Federal Scientific Research and Development," pp. 1-21, *passim*, especially pp. 13, 15, 16, 18, 20.

[28] *Ibid.*, pp. 22-25.

[29] *Ibid.*, pp. 25-32.

[30] *Ibid.*, pp. 33-34.

[31] *Ibid.*, pp. 34-40.

[32] *Ibid.*, pp. 33-40.

[33] *Ibid.*, pp. 41-43.

[34] *Ibid.*, pp. 43-44, 46-48.

[35] *Ibid.*, pp. 48-50.

[36] *Ibid.*, pp. 52-53.

[37] ATW to Wilson and Gant, June 25, 1952, ATW DF.

[38] Interview with Wilson, May 21, 1974.

[39] ATW to Ewell, July 25, Sept. 26, 1952, April 9, 10, June 16, 23, 1953; ATW to Sunderlin, Aug. 11, 1952, ATW DF; NSF PR-67, Aug. 10, 1953.

[40] Interview with Wilson; Wilson "National Science Policy and the Evaluation of the Federal Government's Research Programs," July 1, 1952, Program Analysis file, NSF HF.

[41] These activities are discussed in NSF's *Third Annual Report*, FY 1953, pp. 1-10. Waterman described the Foundation's plans for studies to Bush and received his approval. Bush, he said, "was particularly enthusiastic about photosynthesis and solar energy, this being an area in which he has always been interested and in which the Carnegie Institution has carried on active work." ATW, Diary Note, July 8, ATW MSS, Box 2.

[42] House, *Hearings, Independent Offices Appropriations for 1953*, Pt. 1, 82d Cong., 2d Sess., pp. 177, 204-05, 208-09.

[43] Dodge to ATW, March 19, 1953, in Senate, *Hearings . . . on H. R. 4663, First Independent Offices Appropriations, 1954*, 83d Cong., 1st Sess., p. 317. A few days before receiving Dodge's letter Waterman had been told by Phillips that NSF "was not yet furnishing the answers to the questions which the [Independent Offices subcommittee] desired." The government was spending $2.4 billion a year on research, Phillips said, and he wanted to know "how can the Foundation assist them in reducing this." (ATW, Diary Note, March 11, 1953, ATW MSS, Box 2.) It seemed to NSF's associate director that the "enigmatic" Phillips meant "well but I suspect that his ability to comprehend is limited and his desire to comprehend is not notable. He labors under the illusion that NSF is supposed to 'coordinate' all research supported by the government and he confuses development with research." (Klopsteg to Bush, July 30, 1953, Bush MSS, Box 63, file 1489.)

⁴⁴ Acting Head, PAO to Director, March 24, 1953, Program Analysis file, NSF HF.
⁴⁵ ATW to NSB, May 22, 1953; ATW to NSB, July 2, 1953, ATW's Board Book, 21st Meeting, NSB Records, Box 3.
⁴⁶ "The major functions of such a Foundation should be (a) to examine the total scientific research effort of the Nation, (b) to assess the proper role of the Federal Government in this effort, (c) to evaluate the division of research effort among the scientific disciplines and among fields of applied research, and (d) to evaluate the key factors that impede the development of an effective national research effort." ATW to NSB, July 9, 1953, ATW's Board Book, 21st Meeting, NSB Records, Box 3. Soon after the change of Administration, Waterman had quoted these words to President Eisenhower's National Security Adviser as the clearest statement of NSF's "policy-making function." ATW to Robert Cutler, Feb. 4, 1953, ATW DF.
⁴⁷ ATW to NSB, July 9, 1953.
⁴⁸ Ibid.; NSB Minutes, 21st Meeting, July 10, 1953, pp. 4-5.
⁴⁹ See Program Analysis file, NSF HF, especially Wilson to H. Burr Steinbach, Oct. 21, 1953; William V. Consolazio to Steinbach, Oct. 21, 1953; Louis Levin to Steinbach, Oct. 27, 1953; John C. Honey to Gant, Oct. 29, 1953; Steinbach to Director, Nov. 19, 1953; R. H. Ewell to Director, Dec. 7, 1953.
⁵⁰ Sherman Adams, *Firsthand Report: The Story of the Eisenhower Administration* (New York, 1961), pp. 20-21.
⁵¹ Dodge to ATW, May 12, 1953, BOB, Series 52, file E4-1.

Robert R. McMath, a friend of Paul Klopsteg, came to NSF's aid in its budget troubles with Dodge. McMath arranged an interview between Waterman and Walker L. Cisler, president of the Detroit Edison Company, who intervened with Dodge on the Foundation's behalf for the fiscal 1953 budget. The following year, when the NSF officials again wanted Cisler's help, he was willing to give it if McMath thought he should, but he was irritated—and McMath more so—because Klopsteg and Waterman had been "too busy" to visit with him and thank him personally for his earlier help. Since they had failed to do the proper thing, McMath said that Cisler should not bail them out. (McMath to Klopsteg, May 27, June 11, Aug. 8, Dec. 15, 22, 1953; Klopsteg to McMath, June 8, Aug. 5, Dec. 19, 1953; McMath to Otto Struve, Jan. 6, 1954, McMath Collection, Michigan Historical Collections, Bentley Historical Library, University of Michigan. I am indebted to Frank K. Edmondson of Indiana University for calling my attention to these documents.)

⁵² ATW, Diary Note, May 15, 1953, ATW MSS, Box 2; ATW to Dodge, May 28, 1953, ATW DF.

Lee DuBridge had suggested having a scientific adviser on the National Security Council staff. Bush thought there should be someone on the staff "who at least knows the individuals in science and understands their language," though he need not be a specialist. "There is nothing more dangerous," he warned, "than to have scientific opinions interpreted by utter laymen." And to have scientific consultants available, it might be sensible to attach the Science Advisory Committee of ODM to the National Security Council. (Bush to Robert Cutler, April 14, 1953, Bush MSS, Box 30, file 678.)

⁵³ ATW, Diary Note, June 9, 1953, ATW MSS, Box 2. There was some discussion too of the ineffectiveness of the Science Advisory Committee, which Cutler thought might as well be abolished. He had already made arrangements to get science advice informally from Douglas Cornell of the National Research Council. Waterman, who was establishing direct lines of communication with the White House, especially with Hauge, asked for a chance to discuss the science advisory arrangements further with Cutler. *Ibid.*

Dryden and Waterman talked about the meeting a few days later. Waterman recorded that "Dryden felt that the NSF position was sound, namely: assignment of responsibility to each agency for its developmental program, assignment of responsibility (in the sense understood by NSF) for basic research, and understanding between the Bureau of the Budget and other agencies of the NSF functions of evaluation and advice to the Bureau. Dryden felt that . . . it would be helpful to consider [a] carefully prepared statement or agreement with the Bureau of the Budget on the part NSF should play. It was his opinion that the Bureau of the Budget felt some such statement was due to the Congress. We both felt that any such agreement should be understood by the other research agencies. I agreed to explore the matter personally and informally with key members of the ICSRD and Dryden said he would likewise talk with them informally. We agreed to keep in touch on this matter." ATW, Diary Note, June 18, 1953, ATW MSS, Box 2.

[54] Piore to DuBridge, June 5, 1953, OD SF, ONR file. Piore sent a copy of his letter to Waterman, as he had his earlier letter of May 27, 1953 to J. A. Stratton, provost of MIT, expressing similar worries and hoping that Stratton would persuade the Ford Foundation to help avert the "degradation of American science."

[55] DuBridge to ATW, June 26, July 6, 1953, NSB files.

[56] ATW to DuBridge, July 20, 1953, ATW DF.

[57] ATW, Diary Notes, July 9, 15, Aug. 12, 1953, ATW MSS, Box 2; ATW, Diary Note, July 15, 1953, ATW DF.

[58] ATW to DuBridge, Aug. 12, 1953, ATW DF.

[59] ATW, Diary Note, Aug. 13, 1953, ATW DF; Carey to Director, Aug. 18, 1953, BOB, Series 53.2, E9-1/53.2.

[60] DuBridge to Flemming, Aug. 12, 1953, BOB, Series 53.2, E9-1/53.2.

[61] ATW to DuBridge, Aug. 18, 1953, ATW DF. Waterman sent copies of the letter to Carey and Barnard.

[62] ATW, Diary Note, Aug. 19, 1953, ATW MSS, Box 2; Hauge to Acting Director, BOB, Aug. 20, 1953, BOB, Series 53.2e, E9-1/53.2.

The officials recommended by Waterman were: Killian, DuBridge, Barnard, Bronk, Virgil M. Hancher (president of the State University of Iowa and chairman of an American Council on Education committee considering government-university relations), and Franklin D. Murphy (chancellor of the University of Kansas). ATW to Rowland R. Hughes, Aug. 24, 1953, ATW DF.

[63] ATW, Diary Note, Aug. 20-21, 1953, ATW MSS, Box 2; Flemming to Roger W. Jones, Sept. 3, 1953, BOB, Series 53.2e, E9-1/53.2.

[64] ATW to Dodge, Aug. 28, 1953, ATW DF.

[65] Strauss to Dodge, Sept. 16, 1953, BOB, Series 53.2e, E9-1/53.2. This Budget Bureau file contains all of the agencies' comments on the orders.

[66] Deputy General Counsel, Office of Secretary of Defense to Dodge, Sept. 11, 1953, BOB, Series 53.2e, E9-1/53.2; ATW, Diary Note, Oct. 2, 1953, ATW DF.

[67] Carey to Belcher, Oct. 29, 1953, BOB, Series 53.2e, E9-1/53.2.

[68] ATW, Diary Note, Nov. 3, 1953, ATW MSS, Box 2; ATW, Diary Note, Nov. 3, 1953, ATW DF; Carey to Belcher, Jan. 16, 1954, BOB, Series 53.2e, E9-1/53.2.

At a meeting in the Bureau on January 26, attended by Waterman and Klopsteg, Quarles acquiesced in the issuance of the order though he still thought it unnecessary. He said that Defense "had decided it would no longer support basic scientific research which had for its aims (1) the general increase of the Nation's knowledge, unrelated to Defense matters, and (2) general support of educational institutions." Waterman said he could not guarantee that NSF would pick up all of the estimated $3 million of basic research which Defense proposed to drop. (Carey to files, Feb. 2, 1954, BOB, Series 52.1, E4-3.)

[69] Carey to Belcher, Jan. 16, 1954; Dodge to Attorney General, Feb. 10, 1954; Dodge to the President, Feb. 10, 1954, BOB, Series 53.2e, E9-1/53.2.

[70] *Public Papers of the Presidents . . . Dwight D. Eisenhower, 1954* (Washington, 1960), pp. 320, 335-36.

[71] ATW to DuBridge, March 19, 1954, ATW DF.

End of the Beginning

[1] A tabulation in the *Fourth Annual Report*, FY 1954, p. 41, shows a total of $6.6 million; the $6.7 figure comes from the addition—to determine institutional, state, and regional totals—of the individual grants listed in the appendixes of the annual reports for 1952-54.

Chapter 11

[1] This appropriate term comes from the subtitle of Daniel Yergin's *Shattered Peace: The Origins of the Cold War and the National Security State* (Boston, 1977). The information on staff and budgets in the above two paragraphs was derived from NSF telephone directories (NSF HF) and annual reports.

[2] ATW to Bates, March 9, 1954, ATW DF; Bates to ATW, March 11, 1954, OD SF, Prospective Personnel file.

[3] Blinks to ATW, March 27, 1954, OD SF, Prospective Personnel file.

[4] Blinks to ATW, April 3, 1954, OD SF, Prospective Personnel file.

[5] Interview with John T. Wilson, May 21, 1974; Louis Levin to JME, Jan. 10, 1978.

[6] ATW to Frederick Seitz, Aug. 14, 21, Nov. 17, 1953, Feb. 20, Dec. 2, 1954; ATW to Street, Jan. 14, Feb. 2, 1954; ATW to Brode, Dec. 2, 1954, ATW DF; ATW, Diary Note, Oct. 7, 1954, ATW MSS, Box 2; Street to ATW, Jan. 25, 1954, OD SF, Prospective Personnel file.

[7] NSF PR-57-121, June 19, 1957; ATW to NSF staff, June 5, 1958, ATW DF.

[8] Changes in NSF's internal organization may be traced in NSF Manual No. 10, "Organizational Development of the National Science Foundation."

[9] Interview with William E. Benson, June 25, 1975.

[10] Interview with Wayne R. Gruner, Feb. 15, 1978; Edward Creutz, "Some Concerns of the Professional Staff of the Research Directorate," Sept. 13, 1972, NSF HF.

[11] ATW, Speeches, May 8, 1951, May 18, 1956, Dec. 28, 1959, June 2, 1963, NSF Library.

[12] Interview with Virginia Sides by Milton Lomask, May 7, 1973.

[13] NSF *Fourth Annual Report*, FY 1954, pp. 62-69; FY 1958, pp. 110-15.

[14] S[amuel] C[allaway] to Bush, March 10, 1954; Teeter to Bush, March 22, 1954; Bush to Teeter, March 24, 1954, Bush MSS, Box 110, file 2617. In thanking Waterman for a copy of Executive Order 10521, Bush made a similar judgment: "It seems to me that this sets the stage, and that the Foundation will either take a position of strong leadership, or it will cease to be an effective agency.... The job cannot be done without antagonizing some of the other agencies, ... and an attempt to do it by general agreement and compromise would, I think, now fail." Bush to ATW, March 24, 1954, Bush MSS, Box 117, file 2790.

Teeter tried to get on the National Science Board a few years later. Warren Weaver thought his appointment would be "a national disaster," to which Waterman replied "Amen.³" Weaver to ATW, Jan. 6, 1958; ATW to Weaver, Jan. 18, 1958, NSB files.

[15] House of Representatives, *Hearings before the Subcommittee [on Independent Offices] of the Committee on Appropriations*, Pt. 1, 83d Cong., 2d Sess., pp. 788-92.

[16] ATW, Diary Notes, Oct. 12, Nov. 24, Dec. 1, 1954; ATW to Rowland R. Hughes, Nov. 26, 1954, ATW DF.

[17] ATW, Diary Note, Dec. 1, 1954, ATW DF.

[18] ATW to NSB, May 21, 1956; ATW to Percival F. Brundage, May 29, June 28, 1956, ATW DF. Waterman's letter of June 28 to Brundage also stressed the economic returns from scientific research. One NSF study showed that of the $22 billion income from sales in chemical industries since 1955, about half was from products that basic research since 1930 had made possible.

[19] Brundage's first impulse was to slash $10 million, but he changed $50 to $55 in pen, perhaps in a display of magnanimity. Brundage to ATW, July 14, 1956, OD SF, 1958 Budget file.

[20] ATW, Diary Note, July 18, 1956, ATW DF; ATW, Diary Notes, July 20, Nov. 5, 8, 1956, ATW MSS, Box 1; ATW to NSB, July 26, 1956; ATW to assistant directors and office heads, Sept. 5, 1956; ATW to Brundage, Oct. 18, 1956; ATW, office memo, Nov. 30, 1956, ATW DF.

[21] House *Hearings*, Pt. 1, 83d Cong., 2d Sess., pp. 792-94; House, *Hearings before the Subcommittee [on Independent Offices]*, Pt. 2, 85th Cong., 1st Sess., pp. 1283-85.

[22] House *Hearings [on Independent Offices]*, 82d Cong., 2d Sess., p. 194; House *Hearings [on Independent Offices]*, 84th Cong., 1st Sess., pp. 230-34; House *Hearings [on Independent Offices]*, Pt. 1, 84th Cong., 2d Sess., pp. 522-28, 532-33, 543, 545-47, 551, 596; House *Hear-*

ings [on Independent Offices], 85th Cong., 1st Sess., pp. 1276-79.

[23] House *Hearings*, 84th Cong., 2d Sess., pp. 522-23, 528, 551; Hillier Krieghbaum and Hugh Rawson, *An Investment in Knowledge* (New York, 1969), pp. 185-92.

[24] ATW to Thomas, Aug. 29, Dec. 7, 12, 1956, ATW DF; ATW, Diary Note, Nov. 9, 1956, ATW MSS, Box 1.

[25] House *Hearings*, 85th Cong., 1st Sess., p. 1303; *House Report No. 197*, 85th Cong., 1st Sess., p. 11; ATW, Diary Note, June 20, 1956, ATW DF.

[26] ATW, Diary Notes, April 9, Nov. 11, Dec. 31, 1957, March 16, 1958, Nov. 12, 1959; Thomas to ATW, March 17, 1958; Paul E. Klopsteg to Thomas, March 21, 1958; ATW to Thomas, June 3, 1958, ATW DF; Thomas to ATW, Jan. 9, 1959; ATW to Thomas, Jan. 14, 21, 1959, OD SF, Congressional Contacts file.

[27] Two examples will illustrate this point:

(1) A Houston medical doctor sought support for a research project which was primarily in clinical medicine. Louis Levin in BMS thought the proposal's chances were slim, but since it contained some basic science elements, he sent it to a panel for review. The panel's decision would not come until it met five months later, he informed Waterman. "This won't do for Thomas," Waterman noted, and Klopsteg asked Wilson to "look over the file once more and suggest what Dr. Waterman might say to Mr. Thomas in the event of a telephone call. Thomas calls so frequently that we need to pay special attention to being prepared in advance to give him information and make comments which, if they do not satisfy him, will at least not injure his dignity."

Later Thomas called Levin directly, who told the congressman that while the proposal seemed to him too clinical for NSF, the final decision would depend on the advice of reviewers and the panel. Three weeks later Thomas needled the director's office and "said that after all the amount is fairly small, and this might induce some of the rich oil people in Texas to come through." Klopsteg doubted that result but immediately wrote Levin: "If you can see merit in the basic part and can conscientiously recommend support, it would both achieve the objectives of the Foundation in supporting research and as a by-product help to make Congressman Thomas more happy." Levin then called the Texas doctor, explaining the program's procedures and telling him that no decision could be made until at least after the panel meeting in mid-March.

"I suggested to him," Levin wrote, "that there was no need to waste his telephone tolls in contacting Mr. Thomas because we cannot provide an answer even to Mr. Thomas until the above schedule has been accomplished. I also pointed out that we attempt to arrive at our decisions on the basis of the scientific merit of the proposals submitted and I called his attention to the fact that an agency would be in fairly sad shape if it had to respond to pressure from 435 Congressmen and 96 Senators. He quickly stated that it is not he who has been pushing Mr. Thomas but, rather, members of his Board of Trustees. I asked if he would not inform them of the situation so that they could utilize their efforts for other purposes."

The day after the panel meeting Thomas phoned Waterman asking him about the proposal and another he was encouraging NSF to support. (In addition, Thomas mentioned three or four other research proposals that would be coming from Baylor Medical School.) A few days later Klopsteg, writing as acting director, informed Thomas that the panel had unanimously recommended against NSF support of the proposal because of its clinical orientation.

(ATW, Diary Notes, Nov. 11, 1957, March 16, 1958; V[ernice] A[nderson] to ATW, Nov. 12, 1957; Klopsteg to Wilson, Nov. 26, 1957; Klopsteg to Levin, Feb. 19, 1958; Levin, Diary Note, Feb. 20, 1958; Klopsteg to Thomas, March 21, 1958, OD SF, Congressional Contacts file.)

(2) Thomas's doctor friend from a medical school in Iowa submitted a proposal somewhat more basic in nature. Thomas began asking what NSF was doing about it even before its formal submission. Since a letter from Klopsteg to Thomas incorrectly indicated that the Foundation might be able to reach a decision within less than two months, Levin set matters straight in a phone conversation with the proposer. He "appeared to understand and was very nice about the whole thing," Levin recorded. (Waterman commented that the doctor would understand, but not Thomas.) "I pointed out," Levin continued, "that

the fate of the proposal depends on its evaluation on the basis of scientific merit. He replied by saying that he understands this and mentioned that he figures that dealing with a congressman with reference to a proposal may even be of negative value. He told me that he had not contacted Mr. Thomas about the matter but rather that Mr. Thomas has a particular interest in their work and has urged him from time to time to submit a proposal to the Foundation. I responded by telling him that I would wish that Mr. Thomas would appropriate the funds we seek for research without juggling our budget rather than soliciting proposals for us. [He] told me that he will be in Washington next week and will be seeing Mr. Thomas at that time and that if I wish he can tell Thomas something to that effect. I told him he can use his judgment and do so if an opportunity presents itself."

Levin's blunt advice to the doctor was hardly balm for Waterman's anxiety about giving offense to Thomas, and the director and Klopsteg evidently decided to intervene personally. After they attended a luncheon for the doctor given by Thomas, Klopsteg wrote their host that he had been "much impressed" by the Iowa researcher and thoroughly understood the congressman's "enthusiasm for the work he is doing." Waterman soon wrote Thomas that Klopsteg was going to visit the doctor's laboratory "in order to expedite consideration" of his request. Klopsteg reported favorably on the doctor's "strong investigative streak" and his research facilities and associates, though his work was in part "necessarily clinical." "Unfortunately," Klopsteg wrote in an earlier note to Waterman, "the Reviewing Panel considers the . . . proposal to have too low a level of merit to receive support. This requires making a difficult decision." Klopsteg offered three options to the director: (1) "We might make the grant notwithstanding the low rating and receive the approbation of the Chairman of our Subcommittee on Appropriations." (2) Decline the proposal and send a copy of the declination to Thomas. (3) Ask the doctor "to withdraw the proposal, which I think he would be glad to do if requested; and see whether he would communicate with Mr. Thomas and tell him that he had withdrawn it because he has adequate support from other sources." Klopsteg believed the Foundation would have to choose either the second or third option, and his choice was the third. Waterman evidently then got members of the board BMS committee to look at the proposal, and penciled at the bottom of Klopsteg's note: "Accept, subject to inclusion of a competent immunologist or immunochemist on the project (based on appraisal by reviewers listed, Dr. Loeb, Dr. Tatum & Dr. Bronk & Director's staff)." Modified in this way the proposal was recommended to the board and approved. Even before the board's action (obviously a foregone conclusion) Klopsteg had phoned the news of the favorable decision to Representative Sidney R. Yates, a member of the appropriations subcommittee, who "said he would transmit the message to Congressman Thomas. He remarked . . . that this is a good time to tell him."

(Klopsteg to Thomas, March 21, April 3, 15, 1958; Levin, Diary Note, April 9, 1958; ATW to Thomas, May 3, 1958; Klopsteg to ATW, June 6, 1958, with ATW's penciled note, June 18, 1958; Klopsteg, memorandum for the files, June 20, 1958; Klopsteg, Diary Note, June 25, 1958; abstract of proposal for NSB action, June 19, 1958, OD SF, Congressional Contacts file; NSB Minutes, 54th Meeting, June 28-30, 1958, p. 3 and Appendix I.)

[28] House *Hearings*, 83d Cong., 1st Sess., p. 93; House *Hearings*, 83d Cong., 2d Sess., pp. 792-94; *House Report No. 1428*, 83d Cong., 2d Sess., p. 23; *House Report No. 304*, 84th Cong., 1st Sess., p. 13; *House Report No. 1847*, 84th Cong., 2d Sess., p. 15.

[29] House *Hearings*, 85th Cong., 1st Sess., pp. 1283-86.

[30] House *Hearings*, 84th Cong., 1st Sess., pp. 234-37, 241, 244-46; ATW, Diary Note, April 18, 1955, ATW DF; *Chemical Week*, April 2, 1955, p. 45 (clipping in Bush MSS, Box 75, file 1749).

[31] The term is Michael Polyani's. See his "The Republic of Science: Its Political and Economic Theory," in *Criteria for Scientific Development: Public Policy and National Goals. A Selection of Articles from* Minerva, ed. by Edward Shils (Cambridge, Mass., 1968), pp. 1-20.

[32] NSF History files contain a nearly complete set of divisional committee minutes. Most of the material in this section is based on these minutes for the years 1954-57.

[33] House *Hearings*, 83d Cong., 2d Sess., p. 753; ATW to NSB, Aug. 17, 1955, ATW DF; MPE Divisional Committee minutes, 8th meeting, March 24-25, 1955, p. 5.

[34] MPE Divisional Committee minutes, 6th meeting, Feb. 4, 1954.

³⁵ *Ibid.*, 9th meeting, Oct. 27-28, 1955, Appendix B, p. 2. What Seeger called "a noncooperative spirit of competition" was not new in the MPE division, nor did he manage to overcome it. It was due in part to unhappiness of some program directors with his administrative methods, but also to related feelings of the program officers—and their advisory panels, and members of their field generally—that their disciplines were not getting their "share" of NSF's budget. Also program panels, made up of members of the program director's discipline, often sought to protect him from what they regarded as unfair treatment. For example, see the files on Mathematical Sciences, MPE Division, OD SF, 1952-57; and M. King Hubbert to ATW, Feb. 23, Aug. 10, 1956, NSF HF.

³⁶ MPE Divisional Committee minutes, 8th meeting, p. 10; 10th meeting, March 8-9, 1956, p. 6.

³⁷ Thomas K. Sherwood to Bronk and ATW, Jan. 21, 1957, MPE Divisional Committee minutes, 12th meeting, Appendix C.

³⁸ "We call it a gold-plated greenhouse, Mr. Phillips." Bronk, in House *Hearings*, 84th Cong., 2d Sess., p. 621.

Chapter 12

[1] NSF, *First Annual Report*, 1950-51 p. vi; Vannevar Bush, *Science—The Endless Frontier*, p. 137.

[2] Richard Hofstadter, *Anti-intellectualism in American Life* (New York, Vintage ed., 1968), p. 345.

[3] NSB Minutes, 26th Meeting, March 12, 1954, pp. 5-7; NSF, *Fourth Annual Report*, FY 1954, pp. 52-53, 96-97; Bowen C. Dees, "The Fellowship Program of the National Science Foundation," *American Journal of Physics*, Vol. 22 (Nov. 1954), pp. 559-62.

[4] Interview with Virginia Sides by Milton Lomask, May 7, 1973; ATW to NSB, March 11, 1954, ATW DF.

[5] ATW to Kelly, May 6, 1953, ATW DF.

[6] SPE Divisional Committee minutes, 8th meeting, Feb. 4-5, 1954; 17th meeting, Feb. 9-10, 1956. Renewals were by no means automatic. In 1954, for example, 306 fellows submitted renewal applications, and 304 of these were included in the list of finalists; but only 185 were recommended for fellowships. ATW to NSB, March 11, 1954, ATW DF.

[7] SPE Divisional Committee minutes, 18th meeting, May 23-24, 1956; 19th Meeting, Sept. 6-7, 1956; 20th meeting, Dec. 16-18, 1956; 21st meeting, Feb. 7-8, 1957.

[8] ATW to Marston Morse, Nov. 25, 1953, ATW DF.

[9] ATW to Arthur S. Adams, March 28, 1957, ATW DF.

[10] Kelly to ATW, Sept. 5, 1957, OD SF, Support to Small Institutions file; SPE Divisional Committee minutes, 16th meeting, Nov. 18, 1955.

[11] SPE Division, Annual Report, FY 1957, Appendix C, pp. 22-25, OD SF, Annual Reports 1957 file.

[12] ATW to W. J. Moore, Dec. 30, 1957, ATW DF.

[13] NSF *Annual Report*, FY 1956, pp. 72-73; Staff Study on a Senior Postdoctoral Fellowship Program, April 30, 1954, OD SF, Staff Meeting Notes; SPE Divisional Committee minutes, 9th meeting, May 19-20, 1954; 13th meeting, May 18-19, 1955.

[14] NSF *Annual Report*, FY 1957, pp. 68-69; SPE Divisional Committee minutes, 13th meeting, May 18-19, 1955; 23d meeting, Aug. 4-5, 1957.

[15] SPE Divisional Committee minutes, 8th meeting, Feb. 4-5, 1954; 9th meeting, May 19-20, 1954; 13th meeting, May 18-19, 1955; 14th meeting, July 6, 1955; 17th meeting, Feb. 9-10, 1956 (McBride quotation); 18th meeting, May 23-24, 1956; 19th meeting, Sept. 6-7, 1956; 20th meeting, Dec. 16-18, 1956; 21st meeting, Feb. 7-8, 1957.

[16] When John Teeter saw that NSF intended to award fellowships in "convergent" fields, he warned Waterman: "I have in mind how firm the Congress was in regard to excluding the social sciences when the bill was written—and the recent criticism I received on the 'hill'

because of the violence of social science projects in the Foundation proposals." Bush, to whom Teeter sent a copy of his letter, saw no "great danger" in the Foundation's move. "The danger comes only when one gets into sociology and the like." Teeter to ATW, Oct. 17, 1955; Bush to Teeter, Oct. 25 (?), 1955, Bush MSS, Box 110, file 2617.

[17] Fellowship announcements in NSF HF; Alpert to Director, June 14, 1957, OD SF, Social Science Research Program file.

[18] SPE Divisional Committee minutes, 9th meeting, May 19-20, 1954; 12th meeting, Feb.17-18, 1955; Associate Director (Research) to Deputy Assistant Director, SPE, Dec. 19, 1957; Klopsteg to Kelly, Jan. 6, 1958; J. E. Luton to Director, Jan. 10, April 7, 1958; Kelly to Director, Jan. 13, March 31, 1958; Klopsteg to ATW, Jan. 13, 1958; William J. Hoff to ATW, March 27, 1958; draft statement for fellowship announcement on eligible fields of science, n.d., OD SF, Social Science Research Program file.

[19] Dees to Kelly, March 19, 25, 1954; ATW, memo for files, Sept. 15, 1954; Kelly to ATW, July 13, 1956; Kelly, Diary Note, July 16, 1956, OD SF, Div. of SPE—Fellowships file.

[20] Kelly to ATW, Feb. 19, 1953; Dees, memos to files, Oct. 2, 12, 15, 1953, OD SF, Div. of SPE—Fellowships file; ATW, Diary Notes, Oct. 22, 23, 1953; ATW to John T. Edsall, Dec. 11, 1953, ATW DF.

[21] Kelly, Diary Note, May 5, 1954; ATW, note to Harwood, n.d.; F. C. Sheppard to ATW, May 10, 1954, OD SF, Div. of SPE—Fellowships file.

[22] ATW, Diary Note, Oct. 12, 1954, ATW DF. NSF constantly worried about what it considered NIH's imperial ambitions. For example, Louis Levin warned that NIH was about to move into support of college and high school education "with both feet and we will have lost a possibility for a major program which might be very constructive." Levin to file, Jan. 18, 1957, OD SF, Coordinating Committee on Education in the Sciences file.

[23] ATW, Diary Note, Jan. 3, 1956; ATW to Lewis Strauss, Feb. 9, 1956, ATW DF.

[24] ATW, Diary Note, March 2, 1956, ATW DF.

[25] ATW to Roger W. Jones, March 8, 1956, ATW DF.

[26] ATW to A. Tammaro, March 16, 1956, ATW DF.

[27] Dees to Kelly, May 16, 1956, OD SF, Div. of SPE—Fellowships file.

[28] Hoff to Kelly, June 1, 1956, OD SF, Div. of SPE—Fellowships file. When AEC voted to award graduate fellowships in nuclear engineering, it got NSF's approval on the proposed stipend. ATW, Diary Note, Oct. 4, 1956, ATW DF.

[29] Dees to Kelly, Jan. 22, 1957; Kelly to ATW, Jan. 23, 1957, OD SF, SPE Div.—Fellowships file; NSB Minutes, 44th Meeting, Jan. 25, 1957, pp. 8-10.

[30] Not surprisingly, there were several instances in which internal NSF jurisdiction over proposals or projects came into question. For several years the BMS division made awards for summer or short-term research training of medical students, and BMS also made some rather broad grants to liberal arts colleges especially to support undergraduate research training. Such grants raised jurisdictional and policy questions in the minds of some NSF officials and advisers. The grants for medical students' research training, besides being a possible affront to NIH, might be an infringement of SPE's area of responsibility. Which purpose was predominant, research or training? The broad grants to undergraduate colleges not only might be considered as mainly educational in nature, but they seemed to breach the Foundation's policy against departmental or institutional block grants. In the spring of 1957 Waterman appointed a committee, consisting of representatives from SPE, MPE, and BMS, "to consider and, insofar as possible, decide questions of jurisdiction and coordination as need arises." If they were unable to decide, he would. ATW to Assistant Directors for BMS, MPE, and SPE, March 5, April 26, 1957; ATW to Donald B. Anderson, April 23, 1957, OD SF, Coordinating Committee on Education in the Sciences file.

[31] Staff Study on a Possible National Science Foundation Scholarship Program, April 30, 1954, OD SF, Staff Meeting Notes.

[32] See above, p. 147.

[33] ATW, Diary Note, July 1, 1953, ATW DF; Consideration of a National Science Foundation Scholarship Program—1955, n.d., OD SF, Div. of SPE file.

[34] [Lee Anna Embrey], National Science Foundation Conference on Scholarship Support, Aug. 17-18, 1953, OD SF, Div. of SPE file; SPE Divisional Committee minutes, 6th

meeting, Sept. 10-11, 1953; Charles F. Phillips to ATW, Aug. 26, 1953; ATW to Phillips, Oct. 5, 1953, OD SF, 1955 Budget file.

[35] Staff Study on a Possible National Science Foundation Scholarship Program, April 30, 1954.

[36] NSF Staff Meeting Notes, May 10, 1954, OD SF, Staff Meeting Notes.

[37] SPE Divisional Committee minutes, 10th meeting, Sept. 10, 1954; 11th meeting, Nov. 10, 1954.

[38] ATW to Roger W. Jones, Feb. 28, 1955; ATW to NSB, March 9, May 17, 1955; ATW to Wilson Compton, March 18, 1955, ATW DF.

[39] SPE Divisional Committee minutes, 13th meeting, May 18-19, 1955; Kelly to ATW, June 2, 1955, and attached letters from members of the divisional committee (Harry Winne, Ralph W. Tyler, George W. Thorn, Frank J. Welch, and Harold W. Stoke), OD SF, Div. of SPE file.

[40] ATW to NSB, May 21, 1956; ATW to Percival F. Brundage, May 29, 1956, ATW DF; SPE Divisional Committee minutes, 18th meeting, May 23-24, 1956.

[41] "Distribution of Talent," *Science*, Vol. 122 (Dec. 9, 1955), p. 1125. Wolfle's editorial mentioned the recent inauguration of the National Merit Scholarship Program under Ford Foundation sponsorship. C. E. Sunderlin believed that this new program may have prevented NSF from sponsoring scholarships. Interview with Sunderlin, March 20, 1978.

[42] SPE Divisional Staff Memorandum, Dec. 13, 1956, OD SF, Div. of SPE file; ATW to Earle E. Bailey, Nov. 29, 1956, ATW DF.

[43] SPE Divisional Committee minutes, 24th meeting, Nov. 14-15, 1957; Doris McCarn, Diary Note, Nov. 15, 1957, ATW DF; Kelly to Director, Oct. 25, 1957, OD SF, 1959 Budget file.

[44] Kelly to Director, Oct. 25, Dec. 8, 1957, OD SF, Div. of SPE file.

[45] ATW to Killian, Nov. 22, Dec. 5, 1957; ATW to NSB, Dec. 18, 1957, ATW DF; Klopsteg to ATW, Nov. 21, 1957, OD SF, Bureau of the Budget file.

[46] Hillier Krieghbaum and Hugh Rawson, *An Investment in Knowledge* (New York, 1969), p. 97. This book, written under contract with NSF, gives a detailed account of NSF's institutes programs to 1965.

[47] *Ibid.*, pp. 100, 102-03, 113-22.

[48] *Ibid.*, pp. 90-104.

[49] Kelly to ATW, July 7, 1953, OD SF, Div. of SPE—RES file.

[50] Klopsteg to ATW, Aug. 3, 1953, OD SF, Div. of SPE—RES file.

[51] SPE Divisional Committee minutes, 7th meeting, Nov. 15-16, 1953.

[52] [Embrey], National Science Foundation Conference on Scholarship Support.

[53] Krieghbaum and Rawson, *Investment in Knowledge*, pp. 6-8.

[54] *Ibid.*, pp. 141-57.

[55] *Ibid.*, pp. 159-68.

[56] *Ibid.*, pp. 169-73; "Evaluation Measures for National Science Foundation Programs in Basic Research and Education in the Sciences" (NSF, January 1957), Appendixes A and B.

[57] Hoff to ATW, July 12, 1955, OD SF, Div. of SPE—RES file.

[58] Barnard to ATW, Aug. 9, 1955, NSB files. Barnard's letter caused Hoff to argue the case for NSF to emphasize "experimental programs" as a way of providing "leadership and assistance" to other agencies and of carrying out the charter's mandate to develop national science policy. Hoff to ATW, Aug. 12, 1955, NSF HF.

[59] Kelly to ATW, Oct. 25, 1955; Comments and Questions of Bureau of Budget Personnel at NSF Hearings, Nov. 14, 1955, OD SF, 1957 Budget file.

[60] ATW to NSB, Jan. 26, 1956, NSB Records, Box 7; ATW, "The Crisis in Science Education," Dec. 29, 1955, NSB Records, Box 6.

[61] NSF FY 1957 Justification of Estimations of Appropriations, NSB Records, Box 7.

[62] House, *Hearings [on Independent Offices]*, 84th Cong., 1st Sess., pp. 522, 551, 596, 611-12, 613-15; Krieghbaum and Rawson, *Investment in Knowledge,* pp. 185-94.

[63] Kelly to ATW, Jan. 31, 1956, OD SF, 1957 Budget file.

[64] Rowland Hughes to ATW, Feb. 2, 1956; Comptroller to Director, Feb. 2, 1956, OD SF, 1957 Budget file.

[65] ATW, Notes for Conference with Mr. Lewis L. Strauss, Feb. 2, 1956, OD SF, 1957

Budget file. It seems doubtful that the conference occurred, since there is no subsequent reference to it in Waterman's files.

[66] ATW, Diary Note, Feb. 3, 1956, ATW DF.
[67] ATW to Thomas, Feb. 3, 1956, ATW DF.
[68] ATW to NSB, March 8, 1956, ATW DF.
[69] ATW to Warren Magnuson, March 16, 1956, ATW DF.
[70] ATW to Middlebush, May 24, 1956, ATW DF.
[71] Krieghbaum and Rawson, *Investment in Knowledge*, pp. 202-03.
[72] SPE Divisional Committee minutes, 10th meeting, Sept. 10, 1954.
[73] Krieghbaum and Rawson, *Investment in Knowledge*, pp. 313-15.
[74] *Ibid.*, pp. 203-04; NSF *Annual Report*, FY 1957, pp 163-67.
[75] Unless otherwise indicated, the following discussion of the institutes and integration is based on Krieghbaum and Rawson, *Investment in Knowledge*, ch. 14, pp. 259-86.
[76] ATW, Diary Note, Oct. 22, 1956, ATW DF.
[77] See above, ch. 11, p. 220. In a memorandum to Waterman, Nov. 8, 1956 (OD SF, Div. of SPE—RES file), Kelly wrote: "In your call to Mr. Thomas you might point out that the only real difficulty with the segregation issue is with Stephen F. Austin State Teachers College. . . ." Waterman noted on the memorandum that there was "No problem."
[78] Krieghbaum and Rawson, *Investment in Knowledge*, pp. 266-73. In a letter to Senator Strom Thurmond (D., South Carolina), Dec. 26, 1956 (ATW DF), responding to his question about NSF grant policy "with reference to segregation or non-segregation according to the race of students in applicant institutions," Waterman wrote that "while the Foundation is following its established practice of selecting grantees on the basis of the relative merits of the undertakings proposed, taking geographic need into account, it is also requesting that the institutes select their participants primarily on the basis of academic competence and capacity to develop as teachers. Therefore, the selection of institutes is based on many factors and the matter of segregation is not isolated." In a letter to the University of Florida Waterman wrote: With respect to your question as to whether your application [for an institute grant] was found wanting because you do not yet have any negroes at your institution, I can say that this fact did not enter into the decision." ATW to N. E. Bingham, March 1, 1957, ATW DF.
[79] Krieghbaum and Rawson, *Investment in Knowledge*, pp. 206-07.
[80] *Ibid.*, pp. 216-17.
[81] *Ibid.*, pp. 313-22, *passim*.
[82] A quite different group—"institute bums," who spent their summers at institutes in pleasant climes—did not become numerous before the 1960s. They are reminiscent of "winter Shakers" a century before, tramps who became converts and found lodging in Shaker communities when cold weather set in, then drifted away in the spring.
[83] Krieghbaum and Rawson, *Investment in Knowledge*, pp. 213-33, *passim*. Because of the importance of the post-Sputnik mood for the implementation of the new curricula a discussion of their development will be deferred for the next volume of this history.
[84] Flemming to ATW, May 24, 1954, OD SF, ODM—Interdepartmental Committee file; ATW, Diary Note, July 21, 1954, ATW DF.
[85] "The Development and Maintenance of an Adequate Supply of Scientific and Engineering Manpower" (ODM-7800), May 19, 1954, OD SF, ODM—Interdepartmental Committee file. Someone at NSF thought that the figure of 42 percent "looks a little high from our data."
[86] ATW, Diary Note, July 21, 1954, ATW DF.
[87] SPE Divisional Committee minutes, 10th meeting, Sept. 10, 1954.
[88] Kelly to ATW, Sept. 7, 1954, OD SF, ODM—Interdepartmental Committee file; ATW to Taylor, Sept. 8, 1954, ATW DF.
[89] SPE Divisional Committee minutes, 10th meeting, Sept. 10, 1954.
[90] Kelly to ATW, Sept. 20, 1954, and attached draft comments by Hoff, OD SF, ODM—Interdepartmental Committee file.
[91] NSB Minutes, 29th Meeting, Oct. 15, 1954, p. 8.
[92] ATW, Diary Note, Oct. 21, 1954, ATW DF.
[93] SPE Divisional Committee minutes, 11th meeting, Nov. 10, 1954.

[94] ATW to Flemming, Dec. 17,1954, ATW DF.
[95] Kelly, Diary Note, Jan. 5, 1955, OD SF, ODM—Interdepartmental Committee file.
[96] Kelly to ATW, Dec. 27, 1954, Jan. 4, 1955; Maxwell M. Rabb to ATW, May 3, 1955, OD SF, ODM—Interdepartmental Committee file; ATW, Diary Note, Aug. 26, 1955, ATW MSS, Box 2; ATW to Sproul, Sept. 24, 1955; ATW, Diary Note, Dec. 7, 1955; ATW to Bevis, Feb. 4, 1956, ATW DF.
[97] *Public Papers of the Presidents . . . Dwight D. Eisenhower, 1956* (Washington, 1958), pp. 365-81.
[98] NSF PR-144, April 6, 1954.
[99] NSF PR-145, April 12, 1954.
[100] New York *Times*, April 8, 1956, Sec. 4, p. 9; *ibid*., Dec. 1, 1957, pp. 1, 58.
[101] *Ibid*., April 26, 1956, p. 67; *ibid*., June 22, 1956, p. 25.
[102] *Ibid*., April 5, 1956, p. 28; *ibid*., Dec. 2, 1957, p. 26.
[103] James R. Killian, Jr. told Waterman of his distress at seeing a newspaper column and other accounts about a book (David M. Blank and George J. Stigler, *The Demand and Supply of Scientific Personnel* [New York, 1957]) which made it look as if there were no manpower shortage. The study had been made under an NSF grant. Killian said he "felt compelled to make a public statement on the subject." Waterman promptly tried to offset any impression among his colleagues on the Interdepartmental Committee on Scientific Research and Development that NSF was responsible for the book's conclusions; it would be unfortunate if "an erroneous impression [were] created on the basis of insufficient evidence that there is no shortage of scientists and engineers—a premise which, in my judgment, would be injurious to the best economic and defense interests of the United States." He told Killian that NSF would wait to see if the book made a stir before making any public statement about it. No statement was issued. ATW, Diary Notes, July 8, 11, 1957; ATW to Byron T. Shaw, July 18, 1957; ATW to Killian, July 22, 1957, ATW DF.
[104] SPE Divisional Committee minutes, 1953-57, *passim*.
[105] "Manpower Statistics,"*Science*, Vol. 123 (Jan. 13, 1956), p. 45.

Chapter 13

[1] ATW, Diary Note, March 17, 1954, ATW DF.
[2] The apt description of the relationship comes from the title of a study by Gene M. Lyons, *The Uneasy Partnership: Social Science and the Federal Government in the Twentieth Century* (New York, 1969).
[3] *Grants for Scientific Research* (April 1955), pp. 1, 9.
[4] NSF *Annual Report*, FY 1955, pp. 47-48.
[5] NSF *Annual Report*, FY 1955, p. 49; FY 1956, pp. 46-47; FY 1957, p. 48.
[6] NSF *Annual Report*, FY 1957, p. 54; FY 1958, p. 47.
[7] NSF *Annual Report*, FY 1953, p. 35; FY 1954, p. 41; FY 1955, p. 45; FY 1956, pp. 44-45; FY 1957, p. 54; FY 1958, p. 47.
[8] For fiscal years 1952-54 see above, pp. 203-07. The following information on geographic and institutional distribution of research funds has been derived from NSF *Annual Reports*, FY 1952-58 (especially FY 1956, pp. 45-46), and annual *Hearings* before the Independent Offices Subcommittee of the House of Representatives Committee on Appropriations (especially on fiscal 1959 appropriations, 85th Cong., 2d Sess., pp. 275-92, and fiscal 1960 appropriations, 86th Cong., 1st Sess., pp. 534-51).
[9] NSF *Annual Report*, FY 1956, pp. 45-46.
[10] The NSF *Annual Report* for fiscal 1957 (p. 53) gives the figure of 350 institutions; that for fiscal 1958 (p. 47) says 293. There are difficulties in determining what are separate "institutions," but the lists in NSF's House budget hearings show that the *Annual Report* figures are too high, especially for 1957.

[11] This section is based on the annual reports of Louis Levin, as program director for the regulatory biology program, to the Assistant Director for Biological and Medical Sciences, April 6, 1954, June 1, 1955, June 20, 1956, June 17, 1957, and as program director for metabolic biology, June 10, 1958, all in NSF History files.

[12] William D. McElroy, a member of the regulatory biology advisory panel and the Hopkins biologist in charge of the grant, when he became the Foundation director a dozen years later championed NSF support of undergraduate research.

[13] NSB Minutes (Executive Session), 47th Meeting, June 18-19, 1957.

[14] ATW, "National Science Foundation Program in the Social Sciences," July 8, 1958, OD SF, Social Science Research Program file.

[15] Harry Alpert (with the assistance of Bertha W. Rubinstein), "The Role of the Foundation With Respect to Social Science Research," April 15, 1954, pp. 1-2, NSF HF.

[16] Bush to D. C. Josephs, Sept. 19, 1946, Bush MSS, Box 60, file 1416; Bush to Albert J. Engel, Dec. 16, 1947, Bush MSS, Box 36, file 855.

[17] Quoted in Alpert, "The Role of the Foundation With Respect to Social Science Research," p. 5.

[18] A series of Alpert's position papers and progress reports is in NSF History files.

[19] Alpert to ATW, May 22, 1953, OD SF, Social Science Research Program file.

[20] A review of NSF's legislative history by William Krebs, the general counsel, concluded that while the agency clearly had the right to make research and fellowship awards in the social sciences, "Congress intended the Foundation to exercise a fair amount of restraint in the use of this authority." (Krebs to Harry C. Kelly, March 17, 1953, in Alpert, "The Role of the Foundation With Respect to Social Science Research," pp. 36-40.) The loose linking of social science with radicalism manifested in congressional hearings and statements in 1953-54 showed that distrust of social scientists continued to be intense among conservatives on the Hill.

[21] Alpert, "The Role of the Foundation With Respect to Social Science Research," p. 33.

[22] *Ibid.*, pp. 14-20.

[23] *Ibid.*, pp. 19-20.

[24] *Ibid.*, pp. 7, 8-11, 12-14.

[25] *Ibid.*, pp. 10-11.

[26] *Ibid.*, pp. 27-28, 31.

[27] *Ibid.*, pp. 23-26. Several studies in the sociology, history, and philosophy of science had already been made through the Program Analysis Office. For example, a two-year award to the American Academy of Arts and Sciences resulted in a valuable book by A. Hunter Dupree, *Science in the Federal Government: A History of Policies and Activities to 1940* (Cambridge, Mass., 1957).

[28] Alpert, "The Role of the Foundation With Respect to Social Science Research," pp. 34-35. The proposed budget included $75,000 for support of research in anthropological and related science, $75,000 for support of research in statistical and related sciences, $50,000 for surveys of specialized areas in the social sciences, $50,000 for studies in sociology of science and history and philosophy of science, and $8,000 for printing, international travel grants, staff and consultant travel, and consultant expenses. *Ibid.*, pp. 29-30.

[29] NSF Staff Meeting Notes, April 19, 1954, NSF HF.

[30] ATW to NSB, May 12, 1954, ATW's Board Book, 27th Meeting, Tab 7, NSB Records, Box 4.

[31] NSB Minutes, 27th Meeting, May 21, 1954, p. 8.

[32] Alpert to Director, July 2, 1954, OD SF, Social Science Research Program file; Alpert to Director, July 27, 1954, in ATW's Special Board Book, 28th Meeting, Tab X, NSB Records, Box 4. Bush's statement was quoted from the July 1954 Quarterly Report of the Carnegie Corporation.

[33] NSB Minutes, 28th Meeting, Aug. 13, 1954, p. 7. Clark Kerr, chancellor of the university's Berkeley campus, was a member of Alpert's advisory panel, and Alpert suggested to Waterman that it might be worth while for Kerr to participate in the discussion of social science research. (Alpert to Director, June 4, 1954, ATW's Special Board Book, 28th Meeting, Tab XII.) The board minutes do not mention Kerr's attendance.

[34] Alpert to ATW, July 1, 1955, and attached Progress Report No. 4, "The Social

Sciences and the National Science Foundation, 1945-1955," pp. 9-10, NSF HF; Seeger to Director, April 20, 1954; Alpert to Director, June 4, 1954; Seeger to Director, May 29, 1956, OD SF, Social Science Research Program file.

[35] Alpert, "Social Science, Social Psychology, and the National Science Foundation," *American Psychologist*, Vol. 12, No. 2 (Feb. 1957), pp. 95-98.

[36] ATW to Clark Goodman, March 21, 1955, ATW DF.

[37] Alpert, "The Sociological Research Program of the National Science Foundation," *American Sociological Review*, Vol. 22, No. 5 (Oct. 1957), pp. 584-85.

[38] ATW to Kefauver, Feb. 24, 1956, ATW DF; NSB Minutes (Executive Session), 39th Meeting, March 12, 1956.

[39] Alpert to Director, March 1, 1956, ATW's Special Board Book, 39th Meeting, March 12, 1956, NSB Records, Box 7.

[40] "The Role of the National Science Foundation With Respect to Social Science Research: Recommendations for Fiscal Year 1958" (Progress Report No. 5 [Revised]), Feb. 1, 1956, p. 5; ATW to NSB, Aug. 13, 1956, NSF HF.

[41] There was no separate line item for social science research in the fiscal 1958 budget submitted to Congress. One Republican member of the House subcommittee examining the NSF budget did question the necessity of an anthropology grant, though not because it was social science. House of Representatives, *Hearings on Independent Offices Appropriations for 1958*, Pt. 2, 85th Cong., 1st Sess., pp. 1405-06.

The apparent failure of the board to question the extension is surprising, especially since a full-scale discussion of the social sciences program had been scheduled.

[42] Alpert to Director, June 14, 1957, OD SF, Social Science Research Program file; Lyons, *The Uneasy Partnership*, p. 281.

[43] Hall, an earnest and animated former newsman, told Waterman and James M. Mitchell, an associate director in charge of NSF's congressional relations, that as a taxpayer he "would be pleased . . . to know that some of my money was being invested in basic research to support investigations into the causes of juvenile delinquency." He wondered, in view of the subcommittee's strong recommendations, if the Foundation was not "overlooking an opportunity to gain much public goodwill by failing to support more research in the behavioral sciences. Our research in the 'true' sciences now impinges upon DHEW and DOD in the chemical and biological areas. Thus, I see no very strong reason for hesitating to move more vigorously into these social science areas when a number of Senators feel we should."

Waterman's reply—more than two months later—betrays his irritation at Hall's suggestion. Juvenile delinquency was a subject of applied research and belonged to HEW. Of course basic research bearing on the topic would be valuable, but NSF's policy was "not deliberately to stress one area above another"; instead it responded to unsolicited proposals. "If we were to do otherwise, we should be beset by local and temporary pressures, as well as permanent ones, which would in time distort our primary function." Hall to Mitchell and ATW, May 22, 1957; ATW to Hall, July 29, 1957, OD SF, Social Science Research Program file.

[44] Alpert to Director, July 1, 1958 (Annual Review of the Social Science Research Program, Fiscal Year 1958), p. 1, NSF HF. Appendix C of this annual report (pp. 24-28) summarizes congressional expressions of interest in NSF's social science activities.

[45] *Ibid.*, p. 26. Nixon's interest in the behavioral sciences led to the issuance of a statement from a group of social scientists, organized by James G. Miller of the University of Michigan, calling for greater national support for behavioral science. See Lyons, *The Uneasy Partnership*, pp. 282-84; and for Alpert's part in this activity, Alpert to Director, Jan. 21, 1958, describing a meeting in James R. Killian's office, OD SF, Social Science Research Program file.

[46] ATW to Alpert, July 24, 1957, OD SF, Social Science Research Program file.

[47] The specific disciplines included in the program's scope by the end of fiscal 1958 were: physical anthropology, functional archeology, cultural anthropology, psycholinguistics, human ecology, demography, sociology, social psychology, economic and social geography, economics, history of science, and philosophy of science. Alpert to Director, July 1, 1958, p. 2, NSF HF.

[48] *Ibid.*, p. 3. Alpert relied both on mail reviews (an average of three per proposal) and the advisory panel to evaluate proposals.

[49] See above, pp. 232-33.

[50] I. Bernard Cohen *et al.* to ATW, March 7, 1958; S. L. Washburn to ATW, March 15, 1958, and attached recommendations and resolutions, OD SF, Social Science Research Program file.

[51] *Cong. Record*, 85th Cong., 2nd Sess. pp. 7850-51 (May 1, 1958), 18591-94 (Aug. 19, 1958). Porter's speech was carefully researched, presumably with the aid of the Library of Congress. A few days before he gave it, a staff member of the Library of Congress phoned Waterman's secretary to inquire if any of the new board members were social scientists. DMc [Doris McCarn] to ATW, Aug. 15, 1958, OD SF, Social Science Research Program file.

[52] NSB Minutes, 51st Meeting, Jan. 20, 1958, pp. 13-14; 52d Meeting, March 14, 1958, p. 12.

[53] McCann to Middlebush, Aug. 12, 1958, NSB files.

[54] Alpert to Director, July 1, 1958, Appendix B, pp. 18-23, OD SF, Social Science Research Program file.

[55] Vernice Anderson to NSB, June 24, 1958, and attached report, OD SF, Social Science Research Program file; NSB Minutes, 54th Meeting, June 28-30, 1958, p. 19.

[56] NSB Minutes, 57th Meeting, Dec. 1, 1958, pp. 3-4, and executive session minutes, pp. 3-5; NSB Minutes, 58th Meeting, Jan. 23, 1959, Appendix VII (text of final report as approved by NSB), and executive session minutes, p. 3; interview with the Very Reverend Theodore M Hesburgh by Frank K. Edmondson, Nov. 1, 1979.

[57] Assistant Director for BMS to Director, June 30, 1957, NSF HF.

Hoff had similarly advised emphasis on experimental programs two years before. Hoff to ATW, Aug. 12, 1955, NSF HF.

[58] Assistant Director for BMS to Director, Oct. 22, 1957, OD SF, 1959 Budget file.

[59] Staff Notes on 9th meeting of BMS Divisional Committee, Oct. 11-12, 1957, NSF HF.

[60] M. King Hubbert to ATW, Oct. 23, 1956, OD SF, Division of MPE—Earth Sciences file.

[61] Annual Report, MPE Division, FY 1957, p. 24; MPE Divisional Committee minutes, 11th meeting, Oct. 25-26, 1956; MPE Divisional Committee minutes, 13th meeting, Oct. 24-25, 1957, Appendix B, Mathematics Panel Report, NSF HF.

[62] Ralph A. Morgen to ATW, July 31, 1956, NSF HF; Earl P. Stevenson to ATW, July 16, 1956, NSB files.

[63] Annual Report, MPE Division, FY 1958, p. 1.

[64] NSB Minutes (Executive Session), 47th Meeting, June 18-19, 1957.

[65] ATW to T. Keith Glennan, Aug. 31, 1957, ATW DF.

[66] Consolazio to Blinks, Dec. 4, 1952; Blinks to Consolazio, Dec. 10, 1952, NSF HF. Others whose replies are in this Consolazio file were: Elvin A. Kabat, David R. Goddard, Manfred M. Mayer, Jackson W. Foster, John D. Ferry, I. C. Gunsalus, and John T. Edsall.

[67] ATW, Diary Note, June 9, 1956; ATW to Wilson, Jan. 15, 1957, ATW DF; Staff Notes on 8th meeting of BMS Divisional Committee, April 5-6, 1957, NSF HF.

[68] Stevenson to ATW, Jan. 7, 1955; Seeger to ATW, Jan. 14, 1955, NSB files; ATW to Stevenson, Jan. 18, 1955, ATW DF.

[69] Annual Report, MPE Division, FY 1958, p. 1.

Chapter 14

[1] ATW, Diary Notes, Feb. 12, 14, 15, 1954, ATW DF.

[2] Otto Struve "Cooperation in Astronomy,"*Scientific Monthly*, Vol. 50 (Feb. 1940), pp. 142-47; Struve to Frank K. Edmondson, March 19, 1940, NSF HF.

[3] Helen S. Hogg, Development of National Astronomical Observatory and Needs of

Astronomy Program, Nov. 25, 1955; "Kitt Peak National Observatory: Historical Record—Outline," Oct. 17, 1962, *NSB-602*, Attachment No. 2, NSF HF.

Frank K. Edmondson of Indiana University is making a detailed study of the development of the national observatories at Kitt Peak in Arizona and at Cerro Tololo in Chile and of the Association of Universities for Research in Astronomy, which operates the observatories under contract with NSF.

[4] "Kitt Peak National Observatory: Historical Record—Outline"; A. E. Whitford, "The Plan for a New American Observatory" (draft for dinner meeting of American Astronomical Society, Nov. 10, 1955), NSF HF.

[5] R. J. Seeger, Diary Notes, June 4, 6, 1956; ATW to Robert R. McMath, June 25, Oct. 16, 1956; draft letters for ATW's signature, Sept. 21, 28, 1956; Program Director for Astronomy to Director, Sept. 28, 1956; Edmondson to Seeger, Oct. 16, 1956; McMath to ATW, July 3, 1956, NSF HF; interview with Edmondson, June 28, 1979.

[6] "National Radio Astronomy Observatory: Historical Record—Outline," Oct. 17, 1962, *NSB-602*, Attachment No. 1; NSF Conference on Radio Astronomy Facility, July 11, 1956, pp. 41-42, 51, NSF HF.

For a good discussion of the origin and early development of the observatory, see Richard M. Emberson, "National Radio Astronomy Observatory," *Science*, Vol. 130 (Nov. 13, 1959), pp. 307-18.

[7] "National Radio Astronomy Observatory: Historical Record—Outline."

[8] NSB Minutes, 34th Meeting, May 20, 1955, p. 10.

[9] ATW to Hauge, Aug. 29, 1955, ATW DF.

[10] ATW, Diary Notes, Jan. 18, 19, 1956, ATW DF; ATW, Diary Note, May 3, 1956, ATW MSS, Box 1; NSB MPE Sciences Committee Minutes, May 24, 1956; Seeger, Diary Notes, June 5, 6, 13, 1956, OD SF, Radio Astronomy Facility file.

[11] ATW, Diary Note, Sept. 7, 1954, ATW DF; interview with Edmondson.

[12] ATW, Diary Notes, Jan. 18, 19, 1956; NSF Conference on Radio Astronomy Facility, July 11, 1956, p. 7; Hogg, Diary Note (and addendum), March 29, 1956, OD SF, Radio Astronomy Facility file.

[13] NSB MPE Sciences Committee Minutes, May 24, 1956.

[14] Seeger, Diary Notes, June 1, 5, 6, 11, 13, 1956, OD SF, Radio Astronomy Facility file; ATW, Diary Note, June 8, 1956, ATW DF; C. E. Sunderlin, Diary Note, Jan. 12, 1956, in Earl P. Stevenson file, NSB files; interview with Edmondson.

[15] NSF Conference on Radio Astronomy Facility, July 11, 1956; J. C. Morris to J. A. Stratton, July 18, 1956, NSB files; interview with Edmondson. The following discussion is based on the 70-page transcript of the conference and on Edmondson's recollections of the meeting, which he observed as NSF's program director for astronomy.

[16] This sort of alarm may have helped bring the two branches of the discipline closer together. Edmondson believes that the original split was being healed during this period. Interview with Edmondson.

[17] Interview with Edmondson; Seeger, Diary Note, July 12, 1956; Minutes, Joint Meeting of NSF Advisory Panel for Astronomical Observatory and NSF Advisory Panel on Radio Astronomy, July 23, 1956; Paul Klopsteg to ATW, July 24, 1956, and attachments; McMath to ATW, July 24, 1956, NSF HF.

[18] ATW, Diary Notes, July 13, 21, 1956; ATW to William C. Marland, July 23, 1956 (and other letters of same date to West Virginia senators and representatives in Congress); Sunderlin, Diary Note, July 23, 1956; Vernice Anderson, Diary Note, July 20, 1956; Lee Anna Embrey to ATW, July 23, 1956; C. B. Ruttenberg to files, July 18, 1956; NSF PR-154, July 26, 1956, NSF HF.

[19] William G. Pollard to Howard L. Bevis *et al.*, July 16, 1956; Edmondson, Diary Note, July 18, 1956, OD SF, Radio Astronomy Facility file.

[20] Menzel to ATW *et al.*, July 18, 1956; Edmondson, Diary Note, July 18, 1956; Seeger, Diary Note, July 18, 1956, OD SF, Radio Astronomy Facility file.

[21] Menzel to Tuve, July 19, 1956, OD SF, Radio Astronomy Facility file.

[22] Pollard to ATW, Aug. 2, 1956; Berkner to ATW, July 20, 1956, NSF HF; ATW, Diary Note, July 30, 1956, ATW MSS, Box 1; ATW to Berkner, July 31, 1956, ATW DF.

[23] ATW, Diary Notes, July 20, 24, 27, 28, Aug. 7, 1956, ATW MSS, Box 1; ATW, Diary

Notes, July 27, Aug. 6, 10, 1956, ATW DF; Morris to Stratton, July 18, 1956; Stratton to Morris, Aug. 3, 1956, NSB files; Stewart to ATW, Aug. 2, 1956, NSF HF.

[24] ATW, Diary Note, Aug. 20, 1956, ATW DF; J. W. Beams to ATW, Aug. 20, 1956, NSF HF.

[25] ATW to NSB, Aug. 2, 1956, ATW DF; ATW to NSB, Aug. 18, 1956, OD SF, National Radio Astronomy (NRAO) file; ATW, Diary Note, Aug. 7, 1956, ATW MSS, Box 1; ATW, draft diary notes, Dec. 21, 22, 1955, ATW MSS, Box 26.

[26] NSB Minutes, 41st Meeting, Aug. 24, 1956, pp, 4-5, and minutes of executive session.

[27] ATW to Berkner, Sept. 4, Oct. 23, 1956, ATW DF; Assistant Director for Administration to Director, Oct. 5, 1956; Berkner to ATW, Oct. 8, 1956; Waterman to Paul M. Gross, Oct. 9, 1956; William J. Hoff, Diary Note, Oct. 22, 1956, OD SF, NRAO file; NSB Minutes, 43d Meeting, Dec. 3, 1956, pp. 5-6.

[28] Berkner to Menzel, Sept. 21, 1956, and attached memo of telephone conversation between Berkner and Sunderlin, Sept. 24, 1956; Edmondson, Diary Note, Oct. 16-17, 1956; Edmondson to Director, Oct. 30, 1956; Goldberg to Berkner, Nov. 30, 1956, NSF HF.

[29] Interview with Edmondson; "National Radio Astronomy Observatory: Historical Record—Outline."

[30] Milton Lomask, *A Minor Miracle* (Washington, 1976), pp. 142-47.

[31] NSB Minutes, 80th Meeting, Oct. 19-20, 1962, p. 4.

[32] "Kitt Peak National Observatory: Historical Record—Outline"; NSF Staff Meeting Notes, Jan. 24, 1955; MPE Divisional Committee minutes, 7th meeting, Nov. 12, 1954; 8th meeting, March 24-25, 1955, p. 5; 9th meeting, Oct. 27-28, 1955, Appendix, NSF HF; interview with Edmondson.

[33] "Kitt Peak National Observatory: Historical Record—Outline"; *Kitt Peak National Observatory* (Tucson, March 1960).

[34] Seeger, Diary Notes, March 14, 1957; Edmondson to ATW (draft), Feb. 19, 1957; Geoffrey Keller to Goldberg, Feb. 20, 1957; Minutes of Advisory Panel for Astronomical Observatory, 5th meeting, Feb. 25-26, 1957; Goldberg to Waterman, April 3, May 3, 1957, NSF HF.

[35] Edmondson to Bart J: Bok, June 15, 1957, NSF HF; *Kitt Peak National Observatory*.

[36] NSB Minutes, 46th Meeting, May 20, 1957, pp. 10-11; 48th Meeting, Sept. 6, 1957, pp. 5-6; 49th Meeting, Oct. 14, 1957, p. 4; 50th Meeting, Dec. 2, 1957, pp. 5-6; E. A. Eckhardt to Goldberg, July 17, 1957, and attached minutes of meeting with Goldberg, June 27, 1957; Goldberg to Eckhardt, July 24, 1957; Eckhardt to Goldberg, n.d. [about Aug. 1, 1957], Aug. 16, 1957; Goldberg to Eckhardt, Aug. 28, Sept. 12, 1957; ATW to Goldberg, Sept. 19, 1957; Hoff to Goldberg, Oct. 8, 1957, NSF HF.

Despite the board's concern over "user participation" fees, Waterman thought "that the scientific soundness and the democratic character of the operation can best be safeguarded by making the facility available on scientific criteria alone without requiring the payment of fees for participation in the research." ATW to NSB, May 9, 1957, NSF HF.

[37] ATW to McMath, Nov. 12, Dec. 10, 31, 1957, Jan. 8, 1958, ATW DF; ATW, Diary Note, Dec. 26, 1957; Keller to Assistant Director for MPE Sciences, Dec. 18, 1957, NSF HF.

[38] Seeger, Diary Note, Oct. 19, 1953, OD SF, MPE Div.—Physics file.

Daniel S. Greenberg gives an interesting account of the MURA struggle up to 1964 to develop an accelerator in *The Politics of Pure Science* (New York, 1971), chs. 10 and 11.

[39] J. Howard McMillen, Diary Note, Dec. 21, 1953, OD SF, MPE Div.—Physics file.

[40] ATW, Diary Notes, Oct. 5, 1955, Jan. 5, Nov. 5, 14, 1956, ATW DF; ATW, Diary Note, Nov. 14, 1956, ATW MSS, Box 1; Seeger to ATW, Nov. 7, 1955, OD SF, MPE Div. file; ATW to Willard F. Libby, April 3, 1957, ATW DF; Senate, *Hearings, Independent Offices Appropriations, 1958*, pp. 273-75.

[41] ATW, Diary Note, March 8, 1954, ATW DF.

[42] ATW, Diary Notes, Feb. 12, 15, July 20, 1954, ATW DF; Seeger, Diary Note, Dec, 5, 1955; Klopsteg to ATW, June 1, 1956; Lee Anna Embrey, Diary Note, Nov. 14, 1957; Libby to Alexander Wiley, Dec. 2, 1957 (with marginal comments by Klopsteg), OD SF, MURA file.

[43] ATW, Diary Note, Feb. 15, 1954; ATW to E. R. Piore, March 19, 1954, ATW DF;

McMillen to Director, March 8, 1957; [E. A. Eckhardt], Position Paper—High-Energy Accelerators, Jan. 17, 1958, OD SF, Accelerators file; [NSF], *Federal Financial Support of Physical Facilities and Major Equipment for the Conduct of Scientific Research: A Report to the Bureau of the Budget* (June 1957), Appendix B, p. 71; NSF *Annual Report, FY 1957*, pp. 14-18.

[44] NSB Minutes, 32d Meeting, Jan. 21, 1955, p. 6; 35th Meeting, Aug. 19, 1955, p. 6; 36th Meeting, Oct. 17-18, 1955, p. 7; 50th Meeting, Dec. 2, 1957, p. 4; [Eckhardt], Position Paper—High-Energy Accelerators, Jan. 17, 1958; ATW, Diary Note, Aug. 30, 1955, ATW DF; Klopsteg to ATW, Sept. 18, 1957, OD SF, MURA file.

[45] ATW, Diary Notes, June 9, Sept. 7, 1954, Aug. 24, Nov. 25, 1955, March 2, 1956, July 15, 1957; ATW to E. B. Fred, Nov. 15, 1954, ATW DF; Seeger, Diary Note, Feb. 12, 1954, OD SF, MPE Div.—Physics file; Seeger, Diary Note, Aug. 16, 1955; McMillen to Director, April 22, 1957, OD SF, MURA file.

[46] Klopsteg to ATW, June 1, 1956, March 14, 1957, OD SF, MURA file.

[47] Klopsteg to ATW, April 22, 1957; Seeger, Summary of MURA Discussion, April 18, 1957, OD SF, MURA file.

[48] McMillen, Diary Note, April 22, 1957; McMillen, Memorandum on Future Accelerator Building, July 31, 1957; McMillen to Director, Oct. 10, 1957; [Eckhardt], Position Paper—High-Energy Accelerators, Jan, 17, 1958, OD SF, Accelerators file; ATW, Diary Note, July 20, 1957, ATW MSS, Box 1; McMillen, Diary Note, Aug. 29, 1957; Klopsteg to ATW, Sept. 18, 1957; Klopsteg, Diary Note, Oct. 23, 1957, OD SF, MURA file.

[49] McMillen to Director, Oct. 10, 1957; Klopsteg, Diary Note, Dec. 17, 1957; J. E. Luton to Director, Dec. 27, 1957; Seeger, Diary Note, Jan. 16, 1958; Klopsteg to Director, April 24, 1958, OD SF, Accelerators file; Klopsteg to ATW, Nov. 14, 1957, OD SF, Bureau of the Budget file; ATW to James B. Fisk, Dec. 20, 1957; ATW, Diary Note, Dec. 27, 1957, ATW DF.

[50] [Eckhardt], Position Paper—High-Energy Accelerators, Jan. 17, 1958, OD SF, Accelerators file.

[51] Robert B. Brode to ATW, Feb. 8, 1956, and attached minutes; Wolfgang K. H. Panofsky to ATW, Feb. 14, 1956, OD SF, MPE Div.—Physics file.

[52] Frederick Seitz to McMillen, Dec. 10, 1957, and attachment, Seitz to Fisk, Nov. 30, 1957, OD SF, Accelerators file.

[53] ATW to NSB, Nov. 25, 1953, ATW DF; Walter Sullivan, *Assault on the Unknown: The International Geophysical Year* (New York, 1961), chs. 2-3; Harold Bullis, *The Political Legacy of the International Geophysical Year* (Washington, 1973), pp. 4-6.

[54] Bullis, *Political Legacy*, pp. 6-8, 10-13; J. Tuzo Wilson, *IGY: The Year of the New Moons* (New York, 1961), p. vii.

[55] ATW to NSB, Nov. 25, 1953, ATW DF; NSB Minutes, 24th Meeting, Dec. 7, 1953, p. 7; 25th Meeting, Jan. 29, 1954, pp. 4-5; House *Hearings, Supplemental Appropriation Bill, 1955*, pt. 2, 83d Cong., 2d Sess., p. 901.

[56] ATW to Joseph Dodge, Feb. 26, 1954; ATW, Diary Notes, March 2, 10, 11, April 7, May 28, 1954; ATW to NSB Budget Committee, May 20, 1954, ATW DF; House *Hearings, Supplemental Appropriation Bill, 1955*, pt. 2, pp. 900-01.

[57] House *Hearings, Supplemental Appropriation Bill, 1955*, pt. 2, pp. 895-938; Senate *Hearings, Supplemental Offices Appropriations, 1956*, pt. 1, pp. 541-61; House *Hearings, Independent Offices Appropriations, 1956*, pt. 1, pp. 311-43; Senate *Hearings, Independent Offices Appropriations, 1956*, pp. 438-52; House *Hearings, Second Supplemental Appropriation Bill, 1956*, pp. 426-528; Senate *Hearings, Second Supplemental Appropriation Bill, 1956*, pp. 201-40; House, Committee on Appropriations, Subcommittee on Independent Offices, *Hearings, National Science Foundation, Report on International Geophysical Year*, 85th Cong., 1st Sess., pp. 1-126; House, Committee on Appropriations, Subcommittee on Independent Offices, *Hearings, National Science Foundation, National Academy of Sciences, Report on the International Geophysical Year (February 1959)*, 86th Cong., 1st Sess., pp. 1-197.

[58] House *Hearings, Second Supplemental Appropriation Bill, 1956*, pp. 440-42.

[59] House *Hearings, Supplemental Appropriation Bill, 1955*, pp. 904, 906, 915, 937; Senate *Hearings, Supplemental Appropriations Bill, 1955*, pp. 553, 557-60; House *Hearings, Independent Offices Appropriations, 1956*, pt. 1, p. 318; House *Hearings, Second Supple-*

mental Appropriation Bill, 1956, pp. 429, 430, 433-34, 435, 471, 482, 483-84; Senate *Hearings, Second Supplemental Appropriation Bill, 1956*, pp. 215, 219-20, 223.

[60] ATW to Styles Bridges, July 19, 1954; ATW to NSB, Aug. 3, 1954; ATW, Diary Notes, July 19, Nov. 9, 24, 1954, ATW DF.

[61] House *Hearings, Independent Offices Appropriations, 1956*, pt. 1, pp. 310-11, 312-13; House *Hearings, Second Supplemental Appropriation Bill, 1956*, pp. 426, 443-44; Senate *Hearings, Second Supplemental Appropriation Bill, 1956*, pp. 202, 206; NSF *Annual Report*, FY 1956, p. 186.

[62] For a full account of the satellite program see Constance M. Green and Milton Lomask, *Vanguard—A History* (Washington, 1970).

[63] ATW, Diary Notes, Feb. 19, March 12, April 29, 1954, ATW DF.

[64] ATW, Diary Notes, June 3, Aug. 16, 1954, ATW MSS, Box 2; ATW, Diary Note, June 4, 1954, ATW DF. Defense estimated that a "major effort" would cost $50-60 million. The department did not think its scientific interest could justify "a logistic expense several times the cost of the science itself," but it encouraged NSF to advance "national interest" reasons for the expedition which would warrant a request for special funds. Donald A. Quarles to Rowland R. Hughes, May 29, 1954, OD SF, IGY file.

[65] Robert Murphy to ATW, June 23, 1954, OD SF, IGY file; *Public Papers of the President . . . Eisenhower, 1955*, p. 308n.

[66] *Public Papers . . . Eisenhower, 1955*, p. 308n. The White House announcement followed immediately one by the international committee (CSAGI).

[67] ATW, Diary Notes, May 9, 19, 21, June 8, 1956, ATW MSS, Box 1; Green and Lomask, *Vanguard*, pp. 108-09. The long and difficult negotiations leading to the transfer are detailed in William G. Colman, Diary Notes, May 23-June 8, June 11-15, 1956, OD SF, IGY file.

[68] ATW, Diary Notes, Feb. 16, April 24, 26, 29, 30, May 1, 2, 17, 1957, ATW MSS, Box 1; Laurence M. Gould to ATW, May 8, 1957, NSB files.

[69] Kaplan to ATW, July 24, 1956; ATW to Kaplan, Sept. 6, 1956, ATW DF.

[70] ATW, Diary Note, July 20, 1957, ATW MSS, Box 1.

[71] NSB Minutes (Executive Session), 44th Meeting, Jan. 25, 1957; Weaver to NSB, Oct. 18, 1957; Hesburgh to ATW, Oct. 8, 1957, NSB files.

[72] Weaver to NSB, Oct. 18, 1957; Stevenson to ATW, Aug. 16, 25, Oct. 5, 1955, NSB files; NSB Minutes, 35th Meeting, Aug. 19, 1955, pp. 7-8. For Barnard's full statement, quoted by Stevenson, see ATW's Special Book, 36th NSB Meeting, Oct. 17-18, 1955, NSB Records, Box 6.

[73] ATW to Stevenson, Sept. 13, 1955, ATW DF; NSB Minutes, 36th Meeting, Oct. 17-18, 1955, pp. 13-19.

[74] ATW, memorandum for files, Dec. 12, 1955, ATW DF.

[75] House, Committee on Appropriations, Subcommittee on Independent Offices, *National Science Foundation, Report on International Geophysical Year*, 85th Cong., 1st Sess., p. 111.

[76] ATW, Diary Notes, Feb. 18, March 5, 1954, ATW DF.

[77] Gould to ATW, Aug. 26, 1955, NSB files. Gould's correspondence in the NSB files contains several of his letters to Thye and Humphrey and copies of some replies.

[78] Gould to ATW, Sept. 11, Oct. 2, Nov. 26, 1957, NSB files.

[79] ATW, Diary Note, Sept. 12, 1958; Gould to ATW, Jan. 30, 1959, ATW MSS, Box 2.

[80] Bullis, *Political Legacy*, pp. 55-57.

[81] "The State Department's Opportunity in Science," *Science*, Vol. 123 (Feb. 10, 1956), p. 205; Eugene B. Skolnikoff, *Science, Technology, and American Foreign Policy* (Cambridge, Mass., 1967), pp. 254-57. The Berkner report (*Science and Foreign Relations: International Flow of Scientific Technological Information*, Department of State Publication 3860, May 1950) resulted from a request of Under Secretary of State James E. Webb to the National Academy of Sciences.

Before State established the office recommended by Berkner a science attaché in the American embassy in London complained forlornly to Vannevar Bush about not having any authoritative person to report to or from whom he should receive instructions. His letters to State, he said, "seem to disappear into the blue." He felt like the Cheshire cat. "I am reduced now to merely the grin, with no body whatever left behind it. I wonder if the grin will not soon disappear." He was convinced that science attachés could "be really useful," but not "without authoritative high level support in the Department." C. S. Piggot to Bush, Sept. 13, 1950, Bush MSS, Box 92, file 2095.

[82] Senior Staff Notes, Dec. 27, 1955, NSF HF; ATW to NSB, Feb. 28, 1956, and attached "Preliminary Report on Role of the Federal Government in International Science" (December 1955), in Board Members' Book, Tab G, 39th Meeting, NSB Records, Box 7; ATW, Diary Note, Dec. 31, 1957, ATW DF.

[83] ATW to NSB, Feb. 28, Aug. 21, 1956; NSB Minutes (Executive Session), 42d Meeting, Oct. 15, 1956. An article by John Lear in the *Saturday Review* of May 29, 1956, quoted in part in *Science*, Vol. 123 (June 15, 1956), p. 1067, discussed the inadequate scientific representation in American embassies and the efforts of Bronk and the Academy to get attachés appointed.

[84] NSB Minutes (Executive Session), 44th Meeting, Jan. 25, 1957; NSB Minutes (Executive Session), 46th Meeting, May 20, 1957.

[85] NSB Minutes (Executive Session), 47th Meeting, June 18-19, 1957. NSF's efforts to get State to appoint a science adviser, including suggestions of persons to fill the position, and to provide for attachés in major embassies are detailed in ATW, Diary Notes, June 8, 1956, March 15, 1957; ATW to Herbert Hoover, Jr. (2 memos), Nov. 2, 1956; ATW to Christian Herter, Feb. 12, Aug. 8, Nov. 21, 1957; ATW to James R. Killian, Jr., Nov. 20, 1957, ATW DF; ATW, Diary Note, Aug. 8, 1957, ATW MSS, Box 1.

[86] William G. Colman, Diary Note, May 8, 1957; Colman to ATW, Dec. 17, 1957; Colman to Arthur Kimball, Dec. 27, 1957; ATW, Diary Note, Dec. 31, 1957, NSF HF; Skolnikoff, *Science, Technology, and American Foreign Policy*, pp. 257 ff.

[87] P. L. 909, 84th Cong., ch. 685, H.J. Res. 643, approved Aug. 1, 1956; comments by William E. Benson, Oct. 1, 1980, NSF HF.

[88] H. K. Stephenson, Diary Note, n.d. [about March 9, 1955]; Berkner to ATW, April 21, 1955, OD SF, MPE Div.—Earth Sciences file; ATW, Diary Note, March 28, 1955, ATW DF.

[89] Stephenson to Director, April 24, 1956, and attached resolutions and recommendations, Conference on Theoretical Physics, Feb. 1-3, 1956, OD SF, MPE Div.—Earth Sciences file.

[90] Stephenson to Director, April 24, 1956.

[91] H. H. Hess to Benson, March 5, 1956, in Benson's possession.

[92] ATW to NSB, Feb. 26, 1957, and attached Report of the Advisory Committee on the Hawaiian Geophysical Institute, Jan. 8, 1957, ATW's Board Book, Vol. I, 45th Meeting, Tab G, NSB Records, Box 9; comments by Benson.

[93] Report of the Advisory Committee, Jan. 8, 1957; comments by Benson.

[94] Benson to Director, Feb. 21, 1957, ATW's Special Book, 45th Meeting, NSB Records, Box 9; ATW to NSB, Feb. 26, 1957; NSB Minutes, 45th Meeting, March 11-15, 1957, pp. 11-12, 15-16.

[95] Report . . . to the Congress . . . concerning a Geophysical Institute in the Territory of Hawaii [May 1, 1957], ATW's Board Book, Vol. I, 46th Meeting, Tab B, NSB Records, Box 9; NSB Minutes, 46th Meeting, May 20, 1957, p. 3; Weaver to ATW, June 20, 1957, NSB files; comments by Benson.

[96] ATW to Phillip S. Hughes, June 9, 1958; ATW to Hiatt, Sept. 24, 1958, Jan. 9, 1959; ATW to R. M. Robertson, Dec. 14, 1959, ATW DF; William F. Quinn to ATW, Dec. 22, 1959; ATW to Quinn, Jan. 20, 1960; Daniel K. Inouye to ATW, Feb. 2, 16, 1960; ATW to Inouye, Feb. 11, 1960, NSF HF; NSF *Annual Report*, FY 1961, p. 58.

Chapter 15

[1] NSF *Annual Report*, FY 1954, p. 119.

[2] Paul Klopsteg to Paul Scherer, May 7, 1953; Klopsteg to Vannevar Bush, May 25,

July 30, 1953; Klopsteg to Virgil Hancher, May 15, 1953; Bush to Klopsteg, May 27, Oct. 1, 1953, Bush MSS, Box 63, file 1489.

Klopsteg's views, which he said were "at variance with one aspect of foundation policy," were later published in *Science*: "Role of Government in Basic Research," Vol. 121 (June 3, 1955), pp. 781-84; "University Responsibilities and Government Money," Vol. 124 (Nov. 9, 1956), pp. 919-22; "How Shall We Pay for Research and Education?" Vol. 124 (Nov. 16, 1956), pp. 965-68.

[3] Bush to Chester Barnard, Oct. 28, 30, Nov. 13, 1953, Bush MSS, Box 85, file 1913; Bush to J. A. Stratton, Nov. 13, 1953, Box 109, file 2562; Bush to Lowell J. Reed, Oct. 28, 1953, Box 58, file 1385; Bush to Charles Dollard, Oct. 29, 1953, Box 34, file 767; Bush to Don K. Price, Nov. 16, 1953, Box 94, file 2147.

[4] Bush to Barnard, Nov. 13, 1953, Bush MSS, Box 85, file 1913; Stratton to Bush, Dec. 1, 1953, Box 109, file 2562.

[5] Bush to Price, Nov. 16, 30, Dec. 3, 1953, Bush MSS, Box 94, file 2147; Bush to Stratton, Dec. 3, 1953, Box 109, file 2562; Bush to Barnard, Dec. 3, 1953, Box 85, file 1913.

[6] Barnard to Bush, Oct. 26, Nov. 9, 18, 1953, Bush MSS, Box 85, file 1913; Dollard to Bush, Oct. 27, Nov. 4, 1953, Box 34, file 767.

[7] Barnard to Bush, Dec. 2, 1953, Bush MSS, Box 85, file 1913; Bush to Price, Feb. 9, 1954, Box 94, file 2147; Bush to Klopsteg, Feb. 18, 1954, Box 85, file 1913-14; Bush to ATW, March 24, 1954, Box 117, file 2790; Bush to J. W. Buchta, March 31, 1954, Sept. 22, 1955, Box 85, file 1913-14.

[8] Barnard to ATW, Oct. 31, 1956, Feb. 26, 1957, and attached draft letter to NSB, Feb. 26, 1957, NSB files.

[9] ATW to Buchta, Feb. 3, 1954, ATW DF.

[10] Barnard to NSB, March 12, 1956; comments by J. W. Buchta, n.d., NSB Records, 45th Meeting, Box 9. Despite Buchta's justified excuse, he probably did regard the report as his own more than the committee's. Because of the members' irreconcilable views, he proposed to Waterman and Barnard in 1955 "that, for the present, I do not attempt to write a preliminary report of the Committee but rather that I submit my report to the Committee." Buchta to Barnard, June 27, 1955, NSB files.

[11] The scope of the 89-page draft is indicated by the titles of its twenty sections: Organization of the Committee; Preamble; Objectives of Colleges and Universities Compared with Those of Federal Agencies Sponsoring Research; Direction to Research—Sponsorship of Basic Research; Research vs. Development; Imbalance Produced by Federal Programs; Sharing of Costs of Sponsored Research at Universities and Colleges—Indirect Cost; Independence of Schools—Relevant Policies; Project System of Support of Research vs. Other Methods; Staff Without Normal Academic Status; Incremental Salary Rates; Managerial Functions. Classified Laboratories on Campus; Continuity of Support; Level of Support; Equipment; Graduate Students—Graduate Instruction; Liberal Arts Colleges; Fellowship and Scholarship Program; Security Clearance and Loyalty Evaluation—Classified Work; Recommendations—Comments.

The draft Report of the Advisory Committee on Government-University Relationships to the National Science Board, dated July 25, 1956, and the accompanying comments are in NSB Records, 45th Meeting, Box 9, and in NSF HF.

[12] Harold W. Dodds to Detlev W. Bronk, Nov. 8, 1956; Stratton to Barnard, Dec. 21, 1956; Arthur S. Adams to Barnard, Jan. 28, 1957, Report of the Advisory Committee, Tab D. Adams's views are also given in ATW, Diary Note, Jan. 18, 1957, ATW MSS, Box 1. Those who said they were willing to sign the report were James S. Coles, president, Bowdoin College; C. A. Elvehjem, graduate dean, University of Wisconsin; William V. Houston, president, Rice Institute; Clark Kerr, chancellor, University of California, Berkeley; and Harry A. Winne, retired vice president, General Electric Company.

[13] Report of the Advisory Committee, pp. 38-44.

[14] *Ibid.*, pp. 42-43.

[15] *Ibid.*, p. 42.

[16] Dodds to Bronk, Nov. 8, 1956; Hancher to Barnard, Jan. 4, 1957, *ibid.*, Tab D.

[17] T. Keith Glennan to Barnard, Jan. 9, 1957; Price to Buchta, Nov. 2, 1956, and Supplementary Statement, Nov. 1, 1956, *ibid.*, Tab D.

[18] Kerr to Buchta, Nov. 15, 1956, Jan. 4, 1957, *ibid.*, Tab D.
[19] Stratton to Barnard, Dec. 21, 1956, *ibid.*, Tab D.
[20] Stratton to Barnard, Dec. 21, 1956, *ibid.*, Tab D; Barnard, draft memo to NSB, Feb. 22, 1957, NSB files; ATW, Diary Notes, Jan. 11, Feb. 11, May 29, Sept. 25, 1957, ATW DF.
[21] William G. Colman to ATW, Oct. 11, 15, 1957, NSF HF; Middlebush, "Government-University Relationships: Progress Report," Oct. 14, 1957, ATW's Board Book, 49th Meeting, NSB Records, Box 9. Colman suggested the same method of clearance of an NSF report to the Budget Bureau on federal financial support of facilities for research. Colman to C. E. Sunderlin, Nov. 2, 1956, NSF HF.
[22] Colman to Middlebush, Oct. 22, Nov. 12, 1957; Colman to Members of NSB Ad Hoc Committee, Dec. 23, 1957, NSF HF; Colman to Warren Weaver, Jan. 8, 1958, NSB files; ATW to Middlebush, Oct. 23, 1957, ATW DF; NSB Minutes, 51st Meeting, Jan. 20, 1958, pp. 10-11.
[23] *Government-University Relationships in Federally Sponsored Scientific Research and Development* (NSF 58-10; Washington, April 1958), pp. 21-24, 32-33.
[24] *Ibid.*, pp. 24-27.
[25] *Ibid.*, pp. 27-30.
[26] *Ibid.*, pp. 30-31, 33.
[27] Report of the Advisory Committee, pp. 45-49, 85.
[28] *Government-University Relationships*, pp. 34-35.
[29] Barnard to ATW, April 6, 1957, NSF HF.
[30] Rowland R. Hughes to ATW, Sept. 15, 1954, BOB, Series 51.10, Box 21, NSF Indirect Costs file.
[31] ATW to Buchta, March 8, 19, 1955, ATW DF; Barnard to Members of Advisory Committee on Government-University Relationships, May 5, 1955, and attached "Report on the Sharing of Costs Done at Colleges and Universities under Federal Grants and Contracts," May 1955, NSF HF.
[32] ATW, Notes on Staff Consideration of the Buchta Report, May 11, 1955, NSF HF; ATW, Diary Note, May 11, 1955; ATW to NSB, May 14, 1955, ATW DF.
[33] ATW to NSB, May 14, 1955; Buchta to Barnard and ATW, May 20, 1955, NSB files.
[34] Klopsteg to ATW, May 26, 1955, ATW MSS, Box 29.
[35] *Ibid.*; NSB Minutes, 34th Meeting, May 20, 1955, pp. 5-7.
[36] NSB Minutes, 34th Meeting, May 20, 1955, p. 7.
[37] ATW, draft memo for NSB, May 19, 1955, ATW's Special Book, 34th NSB Meeting, NSB Records, Box 5.
[38] ATW, Diary Notes, June 3, 10, 15, July 13, 1955; ATW to Barnard, June 22, 1955; ATW to Norman T. Ball, June 25, 1955; ATW to Hughes, July 1, 1955, ATW DF; NSF Staff Meeting Notes, July 7, 1955, NSF HF. Although dated July 1, the report to the Bureau was sent July 6.
[39] The NSF recommendations are greatly simplified here. They are detailed in "Recommendations for a Uniform Policy for Paying the Indirect Costs of Research Supported by the Federal Government at Universities and Colleges," June 1955, in Waterman's Special Book, 35th Meeting, NSB Records, Box 6. The recommendations and explanatory information are presented in NSF *Annual Report*, FY 1955, pp. 28-32.
[40] "Recommendations for a Uniform Policy" p. 15.
[41] *Ibid.*, pp. 8-10; ATW to Hughes, July 1, 1955, ATW DF.
[42] Robert Cutler to ATW, Feb. 16, 1955, NSF HF; ATW to Cutler, March 30, 1955; ATW to George P. Berry, July 5, 1955, ATW DF.
[43] Cutler to Hughes, July 8, 25, Dec. 21, 1955, BOB, Series 51.10, Box 21, NSF Indirect Costs file.
[44] Hugh F. Loweth to Carey, Jan. 16, 1956; Carey to Director [BOB], Jan. 17, 1956; Hughes to Sherman Adams, Jan. 19, 1956, BOB, Series 51.10, Box 21, NSF Indirect Costs file.
[45] Adams to Hughes, Jan. 30, 1956; Cutler to Adams, April 30, 1956, BOB, Series 51.10, Box 21, NSF Indirect Costs file.
[46] Loweth to Carey, May 31, 1956, BOB, Series 51.10, Box 21, NSF Indirect Costs file.

[47] Cutler to Adams, June 6, 1956; Carey to Percy Rappaport, June 7, 1956, BOB, Series 51.10, Box 21, NSF Indirect Costs file. Carey's guess was right. Lowell T. Coggeshall of HEW told Waterman that since Congress had increased the NIH appropriation considerably above the request, Folsom thought it was a good time to raise the overhead allowance. ATW, Diary Note, June 7, 1956, ATW MSS, Box 1.

[48] Carey to Rappaport, June 7, 1956; Adams to Cutler, June 13, 1956, BOB, Series 51.10, Box 21, NSF Indirect Costs file; F. J. Callender to Director [Waterman], May 17, 1957, ATW's Special Book, 46th Meeting, NSB Records, Box 9. Coggeshall told Waterman that Lister Hill, NIH's champion in the Senate, had agreed to lift this ceiling. Coggeshall thought the unenthusiastic Fogarty had been "persuaded to go along," but if so, he changed his mind. ATW, Diary Note, July 20, 1956, ATW DF.

[49] NSB Minutes, 46th Meeting, May 20, 1957, pp. 3-4; 47th Meeting, June 18-19, 1957, p. 3; 53d Meeting, May 18-19, 1958, pp. 23-24; 54th Meeting, June 28-30, 1958, p. 18; 55th Meeting, Sept. 16-17, 1958, p. 20; 62d Meeting, Oct. 12-13, 1959, p. 22.

[50] Cutler to Bush, May 6, 1953, Bush MSS, Box 30, file 678.

[51] NSF *Annual Report*, FY 1955, pp. 26-27; *ibid.*, FY 1956, pp. 28-30.

[52] *Ibid.*, FY 1953, pp. 9-10; *ibid.*, FY 1957, pp. 19-21.

[53] The report's recommendations are briefly summarized in NSF *Annual Report*, FY 1957, pp. 12-13.

[54] For an excellent and lively discussion, see Stephen P. Strickland, *Politics, Science, and Dread Disease* (Cambridge, Mass., 1972), ch. 5.

[55] Barnard to ATW, Aug 20, 1954, NSB files.

[56] ATW to Barnard, Oct. 25, 1954, NSB files; NSB Minutes (Executive Session), 30th Meeting, Nov. 5, 1954; ATW to Hughes, Nov. 10, 1954; ATW to Bronk *et al.*, Nov. 23, 1954; telegram, ATW to Hesburgh *et al.*, Nov. 29, 1954, ATW DF; ATW, Diary Note, Nov. 29, 1954, ATW MSS, Box 2; NSB Minutes (Executive Session), 31st Meeting, Dec. 6, 1954.

[57] ATW, Diary Note, Dec. 15, 1954, ATW DF.

[58] ATW, Diary Notes, Dec. 16, 17, 1954, Jan. 18, 20, 1955, ATW MSS, Box 2; ATW to NSB, Dec. 23, 1954; ATW to Hesburgh, Dec. 30, 1954; ATW to Barnard, Dec. 30, 1954, ATW DF.

[59] Telegram, ATW to Loeb *et al.*, Jan. 14, 1955, ATW DF; Oveta Culp Hobby to ATW, Jan. 14, 1955, copy in "Medical Research Activities of the Department of Health, Education and Welfare: Report of the Special Committee on Medical Research...," December 1955, Appendix I, NSB Minutes, 37th Meeting, Dec. 5, 1955, pp. 66-68.

[60] ATW, Diary Notes, Jan. 20, 24, 1955, ATW MSS, Box 2.

[61] NSF PR-123, Aug. 12, 1955; NSB Minutes, 37th Meeting, Dec. 5, 1955, p. 3. The problems of recruiting the committee chairman and executive secretary are detailed in Waterman's diary notes, NSF HF.

[62] Strickland, *Politics, Science, and Dread Disease*, p. 305, n. 43. For William Carey's recollection of the Budget Bureau's low regard for the report, see Lomask, *A Minor Miracle*, p. 107.

[63] "Medical Research Activities of the Department of Health, Education and Welfare," *passim*.

[64] *Ibid.*, pp. 50-52; New York *Times*, Feb. 28, 1956, p. 16.

[65] ATW, Diary Note, Jan. 5, 1956; ATW to C. N. H. Long, Feb. 6, 1956; ATW to Hancher, June 28, 1956, ATW DF; ATW, Diary Notes, Feb. 6, 1956, Sept. 4, 1957, ATW MSS, Box 1; NSB Minutes, 48th Meeting, Sept. 6, 1957, p. 12; NSB Minutes (Executive Session), 49th Meeting, Oct. 14, 1957.

[66] Robert C. Cowen to ATW, Feb. 19, 1954, NSF HF; ATW to Cowen, March 26, 1954; ATW to Barnard, March 22, 1954, ATW DF.

[67] Bush to Lewis L. Strauss, April 19, 28, 1954, Bush MSS, Box 109, file 2563; U.S. Atomic Energy Commission, *In the Matter of J. Robert Oppenheimer; Transcript of Hearing before Personnel Security Board, Washington, D.C., April 12, 1954, through May 6, 1954*, pp. 500-08, 909-15.

At a press conference in October, George E. Herman asked Eisenhower to comment on Bush's view "that the morale among our scientists, especially those working for Government in military installations, is dangerously low, and . . . that we may be a year or so behind where we should be in continental defense for that reason." Eisenhower answered: "Dr. Bush is entitled to his opinion. But I must say this, the scientists who have come to see me exhibit no such attitude." (*Public Papers of the Presidents of the United States, Dwight D. Eisenhower, 1954* [Washington, 1960], p. 972.)

Klopsteg wondered who those scientists were. He wrote Bush: "I agree with your surmise that there may have been only one and that he was not a scientist"—presumably referring to Strauss, whom Eisenhower had defended at the news conference. (Klopsteg to Bush, Nov. 1, 1954, Bush MSS, Box 63, file 1489.)

[68] Washington *Post and Times Herald*, April 28, 1954, p. 25; *ibid.*, April 29, 1954, p. 54.

[69] Copy of Secretary Hobby's statement, April 28, 1954, NSF HF.

[70] The BMS committee evidently did not question the grant to Linus Pauling, which received the board's approval at its next meeting. It was reported later that the PHS policy had obviously caused the cancellation of two grants to Pauling. NSB Minutes, 27th Meeting, May 21, 1954, Appendix I, p. iii; "Loyalty and U.S. Public Health Service Grants," *Bulletin of the Atomic Scientists*, Vol. 11, No. 5 (May 1955), p. 197.

[71] Leonard [Scheele] to ATW, April 27, 1954; draft Special NSF Staff Meeting Notes, April 29, 1954, NSF HF.

[72] Excerpt from letter of April 12, 1954, attached to Leonard [Scheele] to ATW, April 27, 1954, NSF HF.

[73] Philip Handler to Bronk, April 15, 1954; Bronk to Hobby, April 22, 1954, attached to Leonard [Scheele] to ATW, April 27, 1954, NSF HF.

[74] BMS Divisional Committee minutes, 1st meeting, May 3, 1954, NSF HF.

[75] Hoff to ATW, May 18, 1954, NSF HF.

[76] NSB Minutes (Executive Session), 27th Meeting, May 21, 1954; NSB Minutes, 27th Meeting, May 21, 1954, p. 8.

[77] Carey to Mark Alger, Aug. 6, 1954; Carey to Director, Aug. 12, 1954, BOB, Series 51.10, Box 21, Federal Scientific Research at Colleges and Universities file.

[78] Cutler to Adams, Aug. 4, 1954; James S. Lay, Jr. to Hobby, Aug. 3, 1954, BOB, Series 51.10, Box 21, Federal Scientific Research at Colleges and Universities file. Carey preferred putting the problem before the Science Advisory Committee, of which Waterman was a member. "This would be consistent," Carey said, "with Cutler's belief that the scientific community should be asked to give some help with the problem." Carey to Director, Aug. 12, 1954, same file.

[79] Russell R. Larmon to Adams, Aug. 30, 1954; William F. Tompkins to Hughes, Oct. 18, 1954; Percival F. Brundage to Tompkins, Oct. 30, 1954, BOB, Series 52.1, E4-1 (1952-56); ATW to Tompkins, Oct. 20, 1954, ATW DF.

Besides NSF and the Budget Bureau, the interagency group had representatives from the departments of Agriculture, Defense, HEW, and Justice, AEC, the National Advisory Committee for Aeronautics, and the Office of Defense Mobilization.

[80] NSB Minutes (Executive Session), 29th Meeting, Oct. 15, 1954; NSB Minutes (Executive Session), 30th Meeting, Nov. 5, 1954; NSB Minutes, 30th Meeting, Nov. 5, 1954, pp. 2-3.

[81] Carey to Director, Nov. 4, 1954; Carey to Rockefeller, Nov. 9, 1954, BOB, Series 52.1, E4-1 (1952-56).

[82] This group included the executive secretary of the National Security Council, the Budget Director, the secretary of HEW, the U.S. Surgeon General, the chairman of AEC, the Assistant Secretary of Defense for Research, and Waterman. NSB Minutes (Executive Session), 31st Meeting, Dec. 6, 1954.

[83] ATW to E. B. Fred, Nov. 15, 1954, ATW DF; Cutler to Adams, Aug. 4, 1954, BOB, Series 51.10, Box 21, Federal Scientific Research at Colleges and Universities file; Gordon Gray to Bush, Dec. 4, 1954, Jan. 3, 10, 1955; Bush to Gray, Dec. 6, 1954, Jan. 7, 1955; Gray to Cutler, Jan. 10, 1955, Bush MSS, Box 44, file 1076.

[84] Hughes and Rockefeller to Adams, Dec. 16, 1954, BOB, Series 52.6, file E8-35/54.1; NSB Minutes (Executive Session), 32d Meeting, Jan. 21, 1955; NSB Minutes (Executive Session), 33d Meeting, March 14, 1955; ATW to Rockefeller, Jan. 26, 1955, ATW DF; Adams to Bronk, Jan. 11, 1955, BOB, Series 52.1, E4-1 (1952-56); Bronk to Adams, Jan. 28,

1955, quoted in Federation of American Scientists, Information Bulletin No. 58, Feb. 15, 1955.

The members of the Academy committee, in addition to Stratton and Loeb, were: Robert F. Bacher of Caltech; Laird Bell, a Chicago lawyer; Wallace O. Fenn of the University of Rochester; E. Bright Wilson, Jr. of Harvard University; and Henry M. Wriston, president of Brown University.

[85] Charles C. Alexander, *Holding the Line: The Eisenhower Era, 1952-1961* (Bloomington, Indiana, 1975), pp. 60-61; *Bulletin of the Atomic Scientists*, Vol. 11, No. 2 (Feb. 1955), p. 71; Bush to Nils Y. Wessell, Feb. 1, 1955, Bush MSS, Box 113, file 2682; Hoff to ATW, Jan. 27, 1955; Hoff, Diary Note, Feb. 15, 1955, NSF HF.

[86] NSB Minutes (Executive Session), 34th Meeting, May 20, 1955; NSB Minutes (Executive Session), 35th Meeting, Aug. 18, 1955.

[87] NSB Minutes (Executive Session), 36th Meeting, Oct. 17, 1955; NSB Minutes (Executive Session), 38th Meeting, Jan. 27, 1956; ATW, Diary Notes, Jan. 12, Feb. 3, 1956, NSF HF; ATW, Diary Note, Feb. 3, 1956, ATW MSS, Box 1.

[88] Dael Wolfle to Scheele, Feb. 14, 1956; Scheele to Wolfle, March 21, 1956, OD SF, PHS file; "Science and Loyalty," *Science*, Vol. 123 (April 20, 1956), p. 651; "Loyalty and Research: Report of the Committee on Loyalty in Relation to Government Support of Unclassified Research," *ibid.*, pp. 660-62.

[89] Washington *Post and Times Herald*, April 9, 1956.

[90] M. B. Folsom to ATW, May 8, 1956, NSF HF; ATW to Folsom, May 10, 1956; ATW, Diary Notes, July 20, 26, Aug. 10, 1956; ATW to Hauge, Aug. 13, 1956, ATW DF; ATW, Diary Notes, July 20, 25, Aug. 2, 7, 1956, ATW MSS, Box 1; White House Press Release (Adams to Bronk), Aug. 14, 1956, attached to Clyde C. Hall to Friends of the National Science Foundation, Aug. 24, 1956, NSF HF.

[91] Stratton to Bronk, Sept. 11, 1956, NSB files. Stratton was complaining about the memo from Hall to Friends of NSF, Aug. 24, 1956, NSF HF.

[92] NSF *Annual Report*, FY 1956, p. 10.

[93] *Ibid.*, p. 9.

[94] Stratton to Bronk, Sept. 11, 1956, NSB files; "Loyalty and Research," *Science*, Vol. 123 (April 20, 1956), p. 661.

[95] Clifford Grobstein, "Washington Listening Post," *Bulletin of the Atomic Scientists*, Vol. 10, No. 3 (March 1954), pp. 103-04. See also, Grobstein, "Washington Listening Post," *ibid.*, Vol. 10, No. 5 (May 1954), pp. 169-70.

[96] ATW, Diary Note, Oct. 12, 1954, NSF HF.

[97] [Carey], Organization of the Federal Research Program, May 18, 1955, BOB, Series 52.6, E8-36/53.1a; Comments and Questions of Bureau of Budget Personnel at NSF Hearings, Nov. 14, 1955, OD SF, 1957 Budget file.

[98] ATW, Diary Notes, March 9, 1956, ATW DF; [Budget] Director to President, March 30, 1956, BOB, Series 51.10, Box 21, NSF Programing and Coordination file.

[99] Notes on Role of the NSF in Programing and Coordinating Basic Research, n.d. [March (?) 1956], BOB, Series 51.10, Box 21, NSF Programing and Coordination file. Other papers in the same file discuss NSF's relations with other science agencies.

[100] Notes on Role of the NSF in Programing and Coordinating Basic Research.

[101] *Ibid.*

[102] ATW, Diary Note, March 30, 1956, ATW MSS, Box 1; [Budget] Director to the President, March 30, 1956; Director [Brundage] to Carey, April 25, 1956, BOB, Series 51.10, Box 21, NSF Programing and Coordination file; L. A. Minnich, Jr. to Brundage and ATW, May 8, 1956, and attachment, OD SF, Coordination of Basic Research file.

[103] ATW to NSB, Aug. 21, 1956, OD SF, Coordination of Basic Research file.

[104] Carey to [Budget] Director, May 7, 1956, BOB, Series 51.10, Box 21, NSF Programing and Coordination file.

"Too specific—not accepted by ATW at meeting w. Brundage, Carey *et al*," Waterman wrote on his copy of the memo. (OD SF, Coordination of Basic Research file.) Carey said that "Waterman ran like a rabbit" on seeing the annual report suggestion. "Director told him to go away and think up something different." (Carey to Alger and Loweth, n.d., attached to Carey to Director, May 7, 1956.)

[105] ATW, Diary Note, May 21, 1956, ATW MSS, Box 1; Carey to Alger, May 28, 1956, BOB, Series 51.10, Box 23, NSF Scientific and Technical Manpower file.

[106] Minnich to Brundage and ATW, May 8, 1956, and attachment; Carey to Alger, May 28, 1956, BOB, Series 51.10, Box 23, NSF Scientific and Technical Manpower file; NSB Minutes (Executive Session), 40th Meeting, May 25, 1956.

[107] ATW to NSB, Aug. 21, 1956; NSF Senior Staff Meeting Notes, Sept. 4, 1956, NSF HF.

[108] Colman, Diary Note, July 6, 1956, NSF HF.

[109] ATW to NSB, Oct. 12, 1956, NSF HF.

[110] NSB Minutes, 42d Meeting, Oct. 15, 1956, pp. 3-4; ATW to Brundage, Oct. 17, 30, 1956, ATW DF; Brundage to ATW, Oct. 25, 1956, OD SF, Coordination of Basic Research file; ATW, Diary Note, Oct. 30, 1956, ATW MSS, Box 1.

[111] The "impending crisis" quotation came from a recent committee report to the AAAS Council. "Notes on the Crisis Between Science and Society," *Saturday Review*, Feb. 2, 1957, p. 39.

[112] Sidney Hyman, "Science: The President's New Power," *ibid.*, pp. 40-44; J[ohn] L[ear], "Another Side of the Story," *ibid.*, pp. 42-43.

[113] Carey, "Science Administrators," *ibid.*, pp. 45-46; Hyman, "Science," pp. 43-44.

Carey and Waterman expressed their concerns about the articles to one another but agreed that a rebuttal would not be worth making. Similarly Loeb and Bronk thought that a response would be fruitless. ATW, Diary Notes, Jan. 29, Feb. 13, 1957, ATW MSS, Box 1.

[114] ATW to Hauge, March 27, June 12, 1957; ATW to Cutler, April 26, 1957; ATW to Maxwell M. Rabb, July 3, 1957; Notes for Use at Conference with Senator H. Alexander Smith, May 16, 1957; ATW, Diary Notes, April 3, June 12, ATW DF.

[115] ATW, Diary Notes, May 4, June 27, July 12, 15, 16, 18, 22, 1957, ATW DF; ATW, Diary Notes, July 26, Aug. 8, Sept. 4, 1957, ATW MSS, Box 1.

[116] NSB Minutes (Executive Session), 48th Meeting, Sept. 6, 1957.

[117] ATW to Milton S. Eisenhower, Sept. 24, 1957; ATW, Diary Notes, Sept. 27, Oct. 4, 1957, ATW DF; NSB Minutes (Executive Session), 49th Meeting, Oct. 14, 1957.

The causes and effects of the air force cutback, and the continuing danger of such abrupt action, were discussed in a *Science* editorial, "Ups and Downs in Research Support." *Science*, Vol. 126 (Oct. 18, 1957), p. 723.

[118] See ch. 10, pp. 194-95.

[119] ATW, Diary Notes, Dec. 21, 1954, March 17, June 8, 1955; ATW to Carter L. Burgess, Feb. 23, 1955; ATW to J. M. Mitchell, April 15, 1955; ATW to K. T. Keller, April 21, 1955; ATW to J. Roscoe Miller, May 4, 1955; ATW to Edgar S. Furniss, May 5, 1955; ATW to Logan Wilson, May 25, 1955; ATW to R. J. Cordiner, Aug. 3, 1955; ATW to Clarence H. Linden, Aug. 16, 1955; ATW to Wilson F. Harwood, Oct. 3, 1955, ATW DF; L. A. DuBridge to ATW, March 26, 1955; Richard G. Axt to Director, April 13, June 16, 1955; Klopsteg to ATW, April 14, 1955; Axt to DuBridge, April 21, 1955, OD SF, Program Analysis Office: Institutional Research file; Donald A. Quarles to ATW, May 26, 1955; ATW to Quarles, June 30, 1955, NSF HF.

[120] R. H. Ewell to ATW, Jan. 20, Feb. 15, 18, 1955, OD SF, Program Analysis Office file.

[121] NSF Senior Staff Meeting Notes, March 8, Oct. 1, 1956, NSF HF; ATW, Diary Notes, Aug. 13, 1956, Jan. 9, May 17, 1957; ATW to John E. Pfeiffer, [Oct. 16, 1956], April 9, 1957; ATW to Mervin J. Kelly, Nov. 21, 1957, ATW DF.

[122] ATW, Diary Notes, Aug. 13, 1956, Jan. 9, May 17, 1957; ATW to Pfeiffer, April 9, 1957, ATW DF.

[123] In the summer of 1957 Waterman queried heads of several large industries and presidents of five important universities about their attitudes toward increasing industrial support of basic research and conditions that should be placed on the use of the funds. For this correspondence and Waterman's analyses of the replies, see OD SF, Letters to Selected Industries Regarding Increased Support of Basic Research file.

[124] *Basic Research—A National Resource* (NSF, 1957), pp. 5-7, and *passim*.

[125] *Ibid.*, pp. vii, 4, 6, 44-46.

[126] *Ibid.*, p. 21; New York *Times*, Oct. 28, 1957, pp. 1, 17; Oct. 29, 1957, p. 30.

How Firm a Foundation?

[1] Dael Wolfle, "National Science Foundation: the First Six Years," *Science*, Vol. 126 (Aug. 23, 1957), p. 335. Wolfle's article (pp. 335-43) is an excellent appraisal of NSF's achievements and problems through fiscal year 1957. For Waterman's defense of NSF's stand on the science policy role, in response to a draft of the article, see ATW to Wolfle, May 4, 1957, NSF HF.

[2] Sophie D. Aberle to Chester I. Barnard, July 23, 1954, Bush MSS, Box 9, file 198.

[3] Lee Anna Embrey, "The Lengthened Shadow: The National Science Foundation," *The Graduate Journal*, Vol. 5, No. 2 (Winter 1963), p. 305.

Glossary of Abbreviations

AAAS	American Association for the Advancement of Science
ACE	American Council on Education
AEC	Atomic Energy Commission
AUI	Associated Universities, Incorporated
AURA	Association of Universities for Research in Astronomy
BMS	Division of Biological and Medical Sciences
BOB	Bureau of the Budget
FAS	Federation of American Scientists
FBI	Federal Bureau of Investigation
FSA	Federal Security Agency
FY	Fiscal Year
GAO	General Accounting Office
GSA	General Services Administration
HEW	Department of Health, Education, and Welfare
ICSRD	Interdepartmental Committee on Scientific Research and Development
IGY	International Geophysical Year
MIT	Massachusetts Institute of Technology
MPE	Division of Mathematical, Physical, and Engineering Sciences
MURA	Midwestern Universities Research Association
NACA	National Advisory Committee for Aeronautics
NAS	National Academy of Sciences
NDRC	National Defense Research Committee
NIH	National Institutes of Health
NRC	National Research Council
NSB	National Science Board

NSF	National Science Foundation
ODM	Office of Defense Mobilization
OE	Office of Education
ONR	Office of Naval Research
ORINS	Oak Ridge Institute of Nuclear Studies
OSRD	Office of Scientific Research and Development
OWMR	Office of War Mobilization and Reconversion
PHS	Public Health Service
PSRB	President's Scientific Research Board
R&D	research and development
RBNS	Research Board for National Security
SAC	Science Advisory Committee
SPE	Division of Scientific Personnel and Education

Note on Unpublished Source Materials

This volume is based mainly on unpublished materials, most of them in Washington, D.C. Two collections in the Manuscript Division of the Library of Congress were especially useful: the papers of Vannevar Bush (cited: Bush MSS) for the years of his presidency of the Carnegie Institution of Washington (1939-55); and the papers of Alan T. Waterman (cited: ATW MSS), which include many personal and confidential items that he kept out of his files as director of the National Science Foundation. Other papers in the Manuscript Division of slight usefulness were those of Byron S. Miller.

In the National Archives the records of the Office of Scientific Research and Development (OSRD) furnished most of the source material for Chapter 1. Records of the Bureau of the Budget (cited: BOB) were essential for all parts of the study. Also housed in the National Archives, since their recent transfer from the Federal Records Center in Suitland, Maryland, are the Subject Files of the Office of the Director, National Science Foundation (cited: OD SF).

The National Archives and Records Service Federal Records Center at Suitland, Maryland contains the bulk of the Foundation's retired records. Important for this study were records of the National Science Board (cited: NSB Records), especially the books used by the director at board meetings and documents sent to board members.

Much of the source material remains in the Foundation's headquarters at 1800 G Street, N.W., Washington, D.C. Of great value was Alan Waterman's daily, or chronological, file (cited: ATW DF). Correspondence of National Science Board members (cited: NSB files) is in storage in the building. During the research for this study many other

NSF documents were collected or photocopied and are filed in the office of the Foundation's historian (cited: NSF HF).

Another Washington collection, useful for the story of NSF's establishment, is the correspondence on science foundation legislation in the records of the National Association of State Universities and Land-Grant Colleges (cited: NASULGC).

Papers in the Harry S. Truman Library in Independence, Missouri—Martin L. Friedman, Frederick J. Lawton, Charles S. Murphy, Harold D. Smith's diary, James E. Webb, and Truman's Official File—provided much of the documentation on the establishment of the Foundation and the appointment of its first board and director.

William T. Golden's memoranda for the files (in his possession) furnished fascinating glimpses into the process of selecting NSF's first director and conditions affecting the National Science Board's early decisions on the Foundation's program.

Paul E. Klopsteg's diaries (in his possession) are rich in detail on his activities before joining the Foundation staff, but he stopped keeping his diary shortly thereafter.

Papers of two United States senators—Harley M. Kilgore and H. Alexander Smith—provided information on the legislative history in Part I. Kilgore's papers are in the West Virginia Collection, West Virginia University Library, Morgantown; Smith's are in the Princeton University Library, Princeton, New Jersey.

Isaiah Bowman's papers in the Johns Hopkins University Library, Baltimore, Maryland, helped fill out the story of the campaign he led for the enactment of legislation in accord with the Bush report, *Science—The Endless Frontier*.

Interviews supplemented the documentary record. Milton Lomask provided notes and transcripts of some interviews he conducted during his research for *A Minor Miracle: An Informal History of the National Science Foundation* (Washington, 1976). Other interviews, not all of them cited, furnished valuable anecdotal information and flavorful reminiscences.

Index

Aberle, Sophie D., 119
academic institutions:
   subsidies to, 15, 63, 145, 146, 191, 323
   and Smith bill, 70, 80, 376-77 n. 50
   on nomination of NSF board members, 73
   tax-supported vs. private, 79
   federal support, 100, 275
   NSB representation, 114, 120-21
   grants to, 166, 203-07, 259-61
   problems, 190
   research support, 198-201
   fellowships, 203-07, 231
   studies of, 207
   summer institutes, 220
   departmental support, 235
   and NSF, 255
   observatory control by, 284
   and independent institutes, 308, 319-20
   independence, 313, 316-18, 322
   relationships with government, 311-20, 322-23. *See also* fellowships; grants; scholarships; *and individual colleges and universities*
accelerator development, 292-97
Adams, Arthur S., 316
Adams, Roger, 124
Adams, Sherman, 295
   and indirect costs, 323, 324
   and security issue, 332-36, 339, 340
Agriculture, Department of, 34, 191, 199
air force, fellowships for, 169-70
Alaska:
   research fund allocation, 55
   geophysical institute, 307
Allen, Leo, 92

Alpert, Harry, and social science program, 232, 267-72
American Association for the Advancement of Science (AAAS):
   on Kilgore and Magnuson bills, 29
   on Kilgore-Magnuson bill, 47, 48
   and scientific unity effort, 63, 64
   mailing list use, 165
   grants to, 177
   and security policy, 334
American Astronomical Society, 280, 290
American Chemical Society, 38, 263
American Council on Education (ACE), 157, 165, 313
American Men of Science, 177, 178
American Philosophical Society, 269
American Physiological Society, 187, 264
American Society of Biological Chemists, 263, 331
Amherst College, 205, 260
Anderson, John W., 96
Anslow, W. Parker, Jr., 47
Antarctic expedition, 299-300, 303-04, 412 n. 64
Antioch College, 205, 260
applied research. *See* research, basic vs. applied
Argonne National Laboratory, 292-93
Arizona, 284
Arkansas, 204
Armed Forces Institute, U.S., 13
Army Ordnance Department, 182
Associated Universities, Incorporated (AUI), and radio astronomy observatory, 281-89
Association of American Colleges, 70, 233

425

Association of Land-Grant Colleges and Universities, 34, 70
Association of Los Alamos Scientists, 33
Association of Oak Ridge Scientists, 33
Association of Universities for Research in Astronomy (AURA), 290-92
astronomy facilities, 280-92
Atlanta University, 261
Atomic Energy Act, 32, 105, 234
Atomic Energy Commission (AEC):
  as model, 67, 68
  Condon on, 93
  and nuclear energy research, 105, 158
  and NSF, 142, 243
  and NSF fellowship program, 145, 161, 168
  grant policies, 163
  and NSF role, 188, 199, 200, 201
  fellowship program, 233-35
  and astronomy program, 283
  and accelerator development, 292-97
  and IGY, 298
  security policy, 331
  research support, 348
atomic scientists, 36, 59

Bacher, Robert F., 294, 418 n. 84
Barkley, Alben W., 46, 51
Barnard, Chester I.:
  NSB appointment, 119
  and Director's appointment, 123-24
  on NSF role, 186, 188, 197, 241, 326
  on social sciences, 267
  on government-university relations, 314-15
Barnard College, 260, 261
Barnes, Robert P., 119, 245
Baruch, Bernard M., 68
basic research. See research, basic; research, basic vs. applied
Basic Research—A National Resource, 343-45
Bates, Marston, 212
Baylor University, 220
Bayne-Jones, Stanhope, 329
Beckler, David Z., 201
Bell, Laird, 418 n. 84
Bell, Maurice E., 130
Bennett, Rawson, 295
Benson, William E., and geophysical institute, 308, 309
  on peer review, 357-62
Berkner, Lloyd V.:
  and NSF directorship, 124, 125, 126, 347
  and astronomy program, 281-85, 286-89

  and IGY, 297, 298, 303
  and geophysical institute, 307-08
Bernal, J. D., 36
Bestor, Arthur E., 240
"best science," 227, 245, 261, 276, 349
Bevis, Howard L., 252
"big science," 279, 307
Biological Abstracts, 175
Bio Sciences Information Exchange, 265
black colleges, 260-61
blacks, on NSB, 121
  and teachers' institutes, 246
Blinks, Lawrence R., 213, 214, 276
"Blue Book," and indirect costs, 322, 323, 324
Bok, Bart J., 283, 285
Borchardt, Kurt, 77
Bowdoin College, 260
Bowman, Isaiah:
  and Bush report, 13-16, 36-42
  at Magnuson and Kilgore bill hearings, 28-29
  on control issue, 29
  and Meyerhoff, 45, 62
  and Kilgore-Magnuson bill hearings, 49-53, 58-59
  and scientific unity effort, 62-65
  and Truman, 62
Bowman committee. See Committee Supporting the Bush Report
British University Grants Committee, 19, 161, 322
Brode, Robert B., 134, 153, 214
Bronk, Detlev W.:
  and science foundation legislation, 33
  and Kilgore-Magnuson bill hearings, 49
  and NSB nominations, 114
  NSB appointment, 119
  and Director's appointment, 122
  and Directorship, 124-26, 385 n. 47
  on Waterman, 131
  and NSF headquarters, 136, 139
  on military research, 143
  SAC appointment, 144
  and NSF budget, 153, 154, 159, 160, 218, 343
  abstention, 167
  and evaluation role, 181, 188, 326, 328
  on fellowship administration, 233
  and education program, 243
  and social sciences program, 273
  and astronomy program, 283-85, 288
  and IGY, 298, 300, 301, 303
  on international science role, 306-07
  on security issue, 330, 331, 333, 334, 335, 336
Brookhaven National Laboratory, 281,

283, 284, 286, 293, 314
Brooklyn College, 205, 206
Brown, Charles F., and science foundation legislation, 78, 86, 91-92, 97, 104, 105
Brown, Clarence J., 49
Brundage, Percival F., 218, 339-41, 342, 343
Bryn Mawr College, 205, 260, 261
Buchta, J. W., and institutes, 239
   and government-university relations report, 315-18, 321
Buckley, Oliver E., 144, 154, 159
Budget Bureau. *See* Bureau of the Budget
Bulletin of the Atomic Scientists, 87, 157
Bulwinkle, Alfred L., 58, 79
Bunting, Mary I., 216
bureaucracy:
   and scientists, 29, 213
   avoidance of, 161, 162, 349, 350
   growth, 256
   and university policies, 313
Bureau of Scientific Research, 26
Bureau of Standards, 87, 137, 259
Bureau of the Budget:
   social sciences support, 6
   and Bush report, 12
   Bush report on, 19
   on ONR, 63-64
   on control issue, 67-68
   on geographic distribution formula, 70
   and Smith bill, 81
   and compromise bill, 87, 89, 90-91
   and science foundation legislation, 92-95, 97
   on federal research expenditures, 99-100
   and NSB nominations, 115, 116, 117
   and NSF appropriation, 118
   and NSF role, 131, 141, 214, 228
   and medical research, 135, 327-28
   and fellowship program, 144-47, 233
   and NSF budget, 147-52, 159, 217
   and NSF evaluation and policy role, 181-201, 312, 337-43
   coordination role, 203, 348
   and scholarship program, 236, 238
   on teachers' institutes, 242
   and accelerator development, 293, 296
   and IGY funding, 298
   on international science role, 307
   and indirect costs issue, 320-25
Bush, Vannevar:
   NSF Founding Father, 3-7
   background and training, 4
   as NDRC chairman, 4
   as OSRD director, 4-5
   letter from FDR, 6, 9-10
   on patent policy, 6, 14, 22

   on Kilgore bill, 10-11, 368 n. 13
   and Kilgore, 10, 14, 40-43, 46
   and Carroll Wilson, 17
   and Jewett, 20
   on NSF Director, 21, 369 n. 54
   and science foundation legislation, 25, 97, 98
   and Harold D. Smith, 26-28
   on Magnuson and Kilgore bills, 27, 31
   and Truman, 31, 66-67, 82, 85, 86-87, 368 n. 19, 383 n. 5
   and Bowman committee, 40-42
   on Shapley, 46, 86
   and Kilgore-Magnuson bill, 46-54, 58-59
   and PSRB, 62-63
   and AAAS, 63, 65
   on military research, 63, 375 n. 10
   and Smith bill, 65-68, 69, 71-73, 74
   and Congress, 66-67
   on NSF control issue, 67-68, 72
   on NSF role, 72-73, 100
   and House Commerce Committee hearings, 76-79
   on Truman veto, 82
   and compromise bill, 86, 92
   and Teeter, 89
   on federal research expenditures, 98, 99
   letter on Smith amendment, 104-05
   on basic research, 109
   and NSB nominations, 114-15, 116-17
   on Waterman, 126, 127
   and NSF budget hearings, 155
   on NSF leadership, 216
   on social sciences, 267, 269
   on subsidies to universities, 313
   retirement, 314
   on security issue, 329, 334
   characteristics:
      management style, 12
      political awareness, 19
      self-confidence, 67, 85, 373 n. 6
Bush report. See *Science—The Endless Frontier*
Byrd, Harry F., 27, 51

California, 166, 174, 204, 207
California Institute of Technology:
   grants and fellowship, 166, 174-75, 198, 200, 205, 206, 231, 259
   and astronomy program, 281, 291
California Street office. *See* Potomac School (California Street)
Cannan, R. Keith, 135
Cannon, Clarence, 244
Carey, William D.:
   and Smith bill, 71, 81-82

and House Commerce Committee hearings, 77
and compromise bill, 90-91
and science foundation legislation, 93, 94, 95, 97, 104
on NSF role, 95
on federal research expenditures, 98-99
on NSB composition, 116
at first NSB meeting, 123
and NSF budget hearings, 159
and NSF policy and evaluation role, 183, 184, 185, 186, 187, 189, 192, 326, 338, 339, 340, 342
and universities, 199-200
and scientific manpower committee, 251
on accelerator development, 296
on IGY budget, 298, 300
and indirect costs issue, 323
on security issue, 332, 333
Carleton College, 260
Carnegie Corporation, 161
Carnegie Institute of Technology, 206
Carnegie Institution of Washington, 4, 281, 308
Carpenter, Edwin F., 291
Case, Clifford P., 84
Celler, Emanuel, 79, 373 n. 14
Central Intelligence Agency, 177
Central State College (Ohio), 260
Century Club, 4
Chalkley, Lyman, 11
Chapman, Sydney, 297
Chemical & Engineering News, 157
Chicago *Tribune,* 96
Childs, Marquis, 78
Cisler, Walker L., 396 n. 51
City College of New York, 205
Civil Rights Commission, 247
Civil Service Commission, 117
Civil Service regulations, 136, 387 n. 23
Clapp, Verner, 176
Clark, Robert L., 252
Classification Act, 136, 387 n. 23
Clifford, Clark, 115
Coggeshall, Lowell T., 124, 135, 328, 335
Cohen, Leon W., 257
Cold War:
 congressional concern, 90, 105
 effect on NSF, 212, 280
 regulations, 304
Cole, Fred C., 384 n. 23
College Entrance Examination Board, 236
College of Wooster, 205
colleges. *See* academic institutions
college teachers' institutes. *See* teachers' institutes
Colman, William G., 318, 340

Columbia University, 173, 204, 206, 231, 259
Commerce, Department of, 81, 298
Committee for a National Science Foundation, 38, 40, 61
Committee on Discovery and Development of Scientific Talent, 13
Committee on Medical Research, 5
Committee on Science and the Public Welfare, 13-16
Committee on Scientific Aids to Learning, 4
Committee Supporting the Bush Report, 36-42, 45, 47
Commoner, Barry, 32
communism, fear of, 38, 96-97, 101, 103, 176, 248, 252, 332, 337. *See also* security issue
compromise bill (80th Congress) (H.R. 6007), 90-92, 93
Compton, Karl T.:
 NDRC member, 4
 on Kilgore bill, 11
 on Magnuson bill, 34
 and Truman, 81
 and compromise bill, 85
 and NSB nominations, 115
 and Waterman, 129, 386 n. 1
computers, 343
Conant, James B.:
 founding role, 4
 NDRC member, 4
 and FDR letter to Bush, 10
 and science foundation legislation, 36, 97
 and Kilgore-Magnuson bill, 50, 51, 53
 and scientific unity effort, 62, 63, 64
 letter from Bush, 68
 and Smith bill, 69, 74
 and Truman, 81
 and compromise bill, 85, 87, 92
 on scholarships, 86
 NSB appointment, 119
 elected NSB chairman, 123
 on military research, 125, 143
 and NSF headquarters, 136, 137
 and fellowship program, 144, 145, 147
 SAC appointment, 144
 and NSF budget hearings, 154, 159, 160
 on evaluation role, 181
 on "best science," 227
Condon, Edward U.:
 on Mills bill, 49
 and Smith bill, 80
 on Bush, 87
 and compromise bill, 90
 on interagency rivalry, 93

and NSB nominations, 116
  on Waterman, 126, 127
conferences and symposia, 193, 263, 264
conflict of interest, 167
Congress:
  79th, 45, 61
  80th, 61, 62, 63, 68, 80, 82
  81st, 93
  and IGY, 298-99
  and geophysical institute, 307-10
  Waterman and, 348. *See also* House of Representatives; Senate
Congress of Industrial Organizations (CIO), 49
Connor, John T., 78, 92, 133, 171
Consolazio, William V., 276
contracts:
  vs. grants, 162, 163-64, 320
  procedures, 319
control of science policy:
  issue in science foundation legislation, 7, 12, 16, 36-39
  scientists' fear of, 16-17, 35
  Bush report on, 19
  Bowman on, 29, 37-39
  Harold D. Smith on, 30
  Kilgore on, 38-39
  by military, 63
  Washington Association of Scientists on, 87. *See also* National Science Foundation: control issue
Cooke, Morris L., 36
Cordon, Guy, 69, 156, 160
Cori, Gerty T., 119
Cornell, S. Douglas, 192
Cornell University, 205, 206, 231, 259
Cornwall-on-Hudson, N.Y., 130
Cosmos Club, 136, 138, 211
Cotton, Norris, 194
Cowen, Robert C., 329
Cox, Eugene E., 373 n. 18
Cox, Oscar S., 10, 11, 78
Crosser, Robert, 98, 101
Cutler, Lloyd N., 97, 105
Cutler, Robert:
  and science policy, 197
  on medical research support, 323, 324
  on NSF, 325
  and security issue, 332-33, 334

Darden, Colgate, 287
Davis, John W., 119
Davis, Watson, 48, 50
Dawson, Donald S., and NSF appointments, 118, 121, 122, 125, 126, 384 n. 17
Day, Edmund E.:
  on geographic distribution, 34
  and science foundation legislation, 38-39, 92, 94, 97
  and Kilgore-Magnuson bill hearings, 49
  on Mills bill, 62
  and scientific unity effort, 64, 65
  and House Commerce Committee hearings, 77
  and compromise bill, 91
  on NSF control issue, 94
Dees, Bowen C., 146, 233, 234, 235, 244
Defense, Department of:
  and Smith amendment, 105
  and NSF fellowship program, 144
  and NSF appropriation, 154-55
  and basic research, 182, 183, 184, 186
  and Executive Order, 200-01
  research budget, 222
  fellowships, 235
  and accelerator development, 293-96
  and IGY, 298, 299-300, 301
  research support role, 316
  indirect cost payments, 322
defense research. *See* military research
De Golyer, Everette L., 124
Delaware, 55
Dempster, Everett R., 166
Devitt School, 137
Dewey, Bradley, 42
DeWitt, Nicholas, 219, 241
directories, biographical, 177, 178
Dodds, Harold W., 315, 317, 382 n. 95
Dodge, Joseph M., 194-99, 201, 344
Dollard, Charles:
  NSB appointment, 119
  on NSF Director, 121
  on Waterman, 135
  and fellowship program, 145, 147, 168
  on social sciences, 269
  on military research, 388 n. 8
Dolley Madison House, 138, 211
Douglas, William O., 132, 133
Droessler, Earl G., 299-300
Dryden, Hugh L., 150, 197, 396-97 n. 53
DuBridge, Lee A.:
  on NSF appropriation, 118
  NSB appointment, 119, 121
  and Director's appointment, 122
  on military research, 143
  SAC appointment, 144
  on research sponsorship, 198-200, 202
  on Russian scientific strength, 253
  on indirect costs, 392 n. 6
  on evaluation role, 394-95 n. 18
Dumbarton Oaks, 387 n. 25
Dunning, John R., 124

Earlham College, 260

earth sciences program, 357-62
Eckhardt, E. A., 214, 296
Edmondson, Frank K., 286, 289, 291, 292
Edson, Peter, 50
education. *See* academic institutions; fellowships; National Science Foundation: education program; scholarships; science education; teachers' institutes
Education in the Sciences program, 239, 241, 243
Educational Testing Service, 169, 233
Educational Wastelands, 240
Einstein, Albert, 40
Eisenhart, Luther P., 85
Eisenhower, Dwight D.:
 and Taft, 196
 Executive Order Concerning Government Scientific Research, 201-02, 353-55
 on military-industrial complex, 212
 and NSF role, 217, 338, 340, 343
 and NSF budget, 218
 establishment of scientific manpower committee, 252
 and social sciences, 272
 on IGY, 298, 300
 and indirect costs issue, 323
 and security issue, 329
 on Waterman, 348
 on scientific morale, 416-17 n. 67
Emberson, Richard M., 289
Embrey, Lee Anna, 215
Embry, Lloyd, 131
Emmerich, Herbert, 34
employment, full, 10
engineering sciences, 35, 165, 223, 275, 347, 350
engineers, 254, 275. *See also* scientific manpower
Engineers Joint Council, 91, 381 n. 81
equipment funding. *See* facilities and equipment funding
equipment ownership, 320
Evans, Luther, 176
Ewell, Raymond H., 192
Ewing, Oscar R., 85
Executive Office of the President, 183
Executive Order 10521, issuance, 182, 201-02
 mentioned, 217, 250, 311, 312, 314, 319, 337, 339
 text, 353-55

facilities and equipment funding, 224-25, 279-80, 282, 290, 349
family allowances, 168

Federal Bureau of Investigation, 102, 103, 104, 105, 333
Federal Financial Support of Physical Facilities and Major Equipment for the Conduct of Scientific Research, 325
Federal Funds for Science, 193
Federal Security Agency (FSA), 86, 87, 147, 236
Federation of American Scientists (FAS):
 on NSF role, 94, 95
 office, 96
 Bush on, 108
Federation of American Societies for Experimental Biology and Medicine, 266
fellowships:
 Bush report proposals, 13
 Inter-Society Committee on, 65
 establishment of NSF program, 142, 144-47
 means test, 146
 administration, 167-71, 233
 applicants, 169, 170
 taxation, 169
 subject field distribution, 192, 229, 230
 awards, 205-07
 selection procedures, 228-30
 renewals, 230, 401 n. 6
 concentration and freedom of choice, 230-31
 senior postdoctoral, 231-32
 college faculty, 232
 social sciences, 232-33
 proliferation of programs, 233-35
Fenn, Wallace O., 418 n. 84
Fermi, Enrico, 32, 40
Field, John, II, 134, 166
Fisk University, 260
"Five Fundamentals," 19, 20, 27
Flemming, Arthur S., 154, 197, 199, 248, 249, 250, 251
Flood, Daniel J., 103
Fogarty, John, 324
Folk, George E., 48
Folsom, Marion B., 324, 328, 335
Ford, Henry, II, 119
Ford, Peyton, 105
Ford Foundation, 268, 271, 292, 403 n. 41
Forrestal, James, 85
Foster, Jackson W., 331
Foster, William C., 77
Fred, Edwin B., 64, 120, 121, 123, 134, 154
"frontier," 107-08
Fulbright, J. William:
 and science foundation legislation, 26, 28
 and revised Kilgore bill, 40
 and Bowman committee, 41

and Kilgore-Magnuson bill hearings, 51
and Smith bill, 69, 75
as leader, 83
Fulton, James G., 103
Fund for the Advancement of Education, 239, 240

Gant, Charles G., 162, 192, 193
Gardner, John W., 269
General Accounting Office (GAO), 22, 323
General Services Administration, 137-38
geographical distribution of research support:
 issue in NSF establishment, 5, 6, 350
 and Magnuson and Kilgore bills, 34
 Kilgore-Magnuson bill debates, 52-56
 Shapley on, 64
 Smith bill provisions, 69, 70, 75
 Wayne Morse on, 89-90
 Bush report on, 108
 role in proposal review, 174, 360-61
 grants and fellowships, 174, 204-07
 by region, 258-60
Glennan, T. Keith, 317
Goff, Abe McGregor, 79
Goldberg, Leo, 280, 284, 286, 289, 291
Golden, William T.:
 and Director's appointment, 122, 125, 126
 and Waterman, 130
 on military research, 141-44
 and fellowship program, 144
 on NSF budget, 157
Goodpasture, Ernest W., 119, 135
Goucher College, 261
Goudsmit, Samuel A., 104, 175
Gould, Laurence M., 298, 302, 303
Government and Science, 314
government control. *See* control of science policy; National Science Foundation: control issue
Government Printing Office, 21
government-university relationships, 311-20, 322-23
Government-University Relationships in Federally Sponsored Scientific Research and Development, 319
Graduate Record Examination, 169
Graham, Frank P., 80
 and NSF directorship, 121-23, 347
grants:
 vs. contracts, 162, 163-64, 198, 320
 awards, 166-67, 174, 203-07
 project vs. institutional, 191-92
 administration, 256, 319, 349, 402 n. 30
 typical budget breakdown, 257
 dollar value by academic field, 257-58

renewals, 263
 duration, 263, 319
 for departmental support, 274-75
 under IGY program, 302
 security issue, 330, 332, 335. *See also* institutional grants; project grants; travel grants
Grants for Scientific Research, 256
"grantsmanship," 311
Gray, Gordon, 334
Great Depression, 107
Green Bank, West Virginia, 282, 284, 286, 289, 290
Grinnell College, 260
Grobstein, Clifford, 87, 94, 337
Gross, Paul M., 120, 242, 243, 282, 291
Grundfest, Harry, 33
Gustavson, Reuben G., 115

Hafstad, Lawrence R., 90, 118
Hall, Clyde C., 271, 407 n. 43
Halleck, Charles A., 91, 92
Hancher, Virgil M., 313, 317, 321, 397 n. 62
Handler, Philip, 331
Harriman, Averell, 87
Harris, Oren, 101, 303
Hart, Thomas C., 51, 52, 54-55
Harvard University:
 Bush at, 4
 physics department telegram, 104
 and divisional committees, 173
 and review panels, 173
 grants and fellowships, 175, 198, 204, 205, 206, 259, 264
 NSF fellows, 231
 and astronomy program, 286, 291
 and accelerator development, 292
 proposal policy, 393 n. 35
Harwood, Wilson F., 136, 159, 162, 214
Hastings, A. Baird, 124, 125
Hauge, Gabriel:
 and science policy, 197, 200, 282
 and NSF budget, 218, 220
 on integration policy, 246
 and IGY, 300
 on security policy, 335
 and NSF role, 339, 340
Haverford College, 205, 260
Hawaii, geophysical institute, 307, 309-10
Haworth, Leland J., 294
Hays, Brooks, 153
Health, Education and Security, Department of, 85
Health, Education, and Welfare, Department of (HEW):
 medical research programs, 312, 325-29
 indirect cost payments, 324

security policy, 330-33, 335, 336
Herring, Pendleton, 269
Hershey, Lewis R., 125
Herter, Christian A., 92, 97
Hesburgh, Theodore M., 245, 272, 273, 301
Heselton, John W., 102, 153
Hess, Harry H., 308, 360
Hiatt, Robert W., 309
high school teachers' institutes. *See* teachers' institutes
Hilliard, John, 251
Hinshaw, Carl, 102
Hobby, Oveta Culp:
  and review of NIH, 325-27
  and security issue, 330, 331, 332
Hobson, Jesse E., 124
Hodgins, Eric, 19
Hoff, William J., 200, 241, 250, 330, 332, 333, 334
Hogg, Helen S., 283
Holifield, Chet, 103
Hoover, Herbert, 54
Hoover, Herbert, Jr., 306
Hoover Commission Report, 195
Hopkins, Harry, 4, 10
House of Representatives, U.S., 84, 264
  Military Affairs Committee, 26
  Commerce Committee, 76-79, 97, 303
  Rules Committee, 91-92, 97, 98
  Committee on Un-American Activities, 96
  Appropriations Committee, 152-54, 219-21, 291, 298-99
Houston, William V., 119, 282, 285, 321
Howard University, 260
Hubbert, King, 358, 361
Hughes, Emmet J., 197
Hughes, Rowland, and NSF evaluation and policy, 323, 325-27, 333, 339
Humphrey, George (Secretary of the Treasury), 196
Humphrey, George D. (National Science Board member), 120, 156
Humphrey, Hubert H., 271
Hunter College, 261
Hyman, O. W., 120
Hyman, Sidney, 342

Illinois, 175, 204
Independent Citizens Committee of the Arts, Sciences, and Professions, 46, 64
Indiana, 166, 175
Indiana University, 175, 204, 259, 280, 291
indirect costs:
  inclusion in grants, 162-63, 198, 257, 320-25
  NSF, AEC, and NIH policy, 392 n. 6
industrial establishment:
  and science foundation hearings, 29, 61-62
  research support, 344-45, 419 n. 123
Institute for Cancer Research, 166
institutional grants, 164, 261, 351
Interdepartmental Committee on Scientific Research and Development (ICSRD):
  establishment, 93
  and NSB nominations, 116
  Waterman and, 131
  and NSF, 151-52
  on scientific information exchange, 176
  coordination of research, 189
  evaluation of research and development, 196, 197
  on international science role, 307
  and indirect costs issue, 322
Interior, Department of the, 81
International Broadcasting Foundation, 71
International Council of Scientific Unions, 297
International Geophysical Year (IGY), 207, 211, 280, 297-304, 350
international science, 304-07
Inter-Society Committee for a National Science Foundation:
  establishment, 64-65
  and Smith bill, 70, 72, 80
  and House Commerce Committee hearings, 77
  Meyerhoff on, 84
  on compromise bill, 86
  and science foundation legislation, 92, 101
  Bush on, 108
Iowa State College, 206

Jewett, Frank B.:
  founding role, 4
  NDRC member, 4
  on Bush report, 15, 20
  and Bush report, 17
  opposition to science foundation, 35
  on Bowman committee, 38
  on socialization of science, 45-46
  and Kilgore-Magnuson bill hearings, 47, 59
  and Bush, 59
  and House Commerce Committee hearings, 76, 78
  on bureaucracy, 93
  and NSB nominations, 114
  on security issue, 381 n. 63
Johns Hopkins University:
  grants and fellowships, 166, 175, 204, 206, 207, 259, 264
  research support, 343
Johnson, Charles S., 119

Johnson, Edwin C., 40
Johnson, Thomas H., 294
Joint Research and Development Board, 63, 67
Jonas, Charles R., 299
Jones, A. R., 341
Joyce, J. Wallace, 307
Julian, Percy L., 119, 383 n. 9
Justice, Department of, 104, 333, 334

Kaempffert, Waldemar, 253
Kaplan, Joseph, 298, 301, 307
Keefe, Frank B., 102
Kefauver, Estes, 270, 271
Keller, Geoffrey, 291, 292
Kelly, Harry C.:
  background and training, 133-34
  and fellowship program, 146, 231-32
  and education programs, 214
  and social sciences, 231-32, 271
  on departmental support, 235
  on scholarships, 236-38
  and NSF budget, 242-43
  on racial discrimination, 245
  and scientific manpower committee, 250, 251

Kelly, Mervin J., 130
Kerr, Clark, 317, 406 n. 33
Kidd, Charles V., 183, 394 n. 6
Kilgore, Harley M.:
  founding role, 3, 5-7, 108
  patent policy view, 5-6
  and science foundation legislation, 10-11, 28, 32
  and Bush, 14, 155
  and Magnuson, 25, 28, 32, 370 n. 3
  on control issue, 38-39
  and Bowman committee, 41-42, 372 n. 74
  Bush on, 46
  and CIO, 49
  and Kilgore-Magnuson bill hearings, 46, 51-54
  on NAS, 52
  Homer Smith on, 69
  and Smith bill, 75
  as leader, 83
  and compromise bill, 89
  and NSB nominations, 119
  on social sciences, 370 n. 5
Kilgore bill (S. 1297), 25-26, 28-36
Kilgore bill, revised (S. 1720), 34, 39
Kilgore-Magnuson bill (S. 1850), 43, 46-56
Killian, James R., Jr., 129, 199, 238, 296, 397 n. 62
Kingsley, J. Donald, 67, 70-71, 90-91, 93, 377 n. 53, 383 n. 4

Kirner, Walter R., 257
Kitt Peak, 290
Klopsteg, Paul E.:
  staff appointment, 134
  background and training, 134-35
  and Albert Thomas, 220, 399-400 n. 27
  and teachers' institutes, 239
  and accelerator development, 294-95, 296
  on government-sponsored research, 313
  on indirect costs, 321
  and Waterman, 387 n. 19
Korean War, 118, 141
Krebs, William A. W., Jr., 133, 159, 162, 167
Kyes, Roger M., 198

Labor, Department of, 192
La Follette, Robert M., Jr., 53, 55, 56
land-grant colleges. *See* academic institutions
Langmuir, Irving, 29
Lanham, Fritz G., 91, 92, 96
Lea, Clarence F., 56, 57
Lear, John, 342
Lehman, Herbert H., 390 n. 56
Lerner, I. Michael, 166
Levin, Louis, 399-400 n. 27, 402 n. 22
Libby, Willard F., 234, 294
Library of Congress, 176
"little science," 255, 257
Loeb, Robert F., 120, 144, 326, 327, 334, 391 n. 70
Long, C. N. H., 328
Loomis, F. Wheeler, 122
Lovett, Robert A., 154-55
Loweth, Hugh F. 242, 323, 324, 339, 340
loyalty issue. *See* security issue
loyalty oaths, 101-02, 105, 169, 330, 332. *See also* security issue

Maclaurin, W. Rupert, 13, 15, 20
Magnuson, Warren G.:
  and Kilgore, 25, 28, 370 n. 3
  and science foundation legislation, 25, 28
  and Bowman committee, 40-41
  and Kilgore-Magnuson bill, 43, 46, 51-53, 54, 55
  and *Science,* 63
  and Smith bill, 69, 75-76
  as leader, 83
  and compromise bill, 89
  and social sciences program, 271
Magnuson bill (S. 1285):
  introduction, 25
  provisions, 25-26
  hearings, 28-36

and 1950 act, 109
Mahoney, Florence, 125
Maine, 132
Mallon, Mary. *See* Waterman, Mary Mallon
Martin, Joseph W., 91, 92
Massachusetts, 204
Massachusetts Institute of Technology (MIT):
  Bush at, 4
  solar energy research, 158
  and review panels, 173
  grants and fellowships, 198, 205, 206, 231, 259
  and accelerator development, 292
Mathematical Association of America, 239
Mather, Kirtley F., 65
Maverick, Maury, 29
McBride, Katharine, 173, 216, 232
McCann, Kevin, 272
McCarn, Doris, 130
McCarthy, Joseph R., 104, 329, 334
McCormack, John W., 50, 103, 104, 373 n. 18
McElroy, William D., 406 n. 12
McKellar, Kenneth D., 52, 154, 155, 159
McLaughlin, Donald H., 120
McMath, Robert R., 281, 286, 291, 292, 396 n. 51
McMillen, J. Howard, 293
Medical Advisory Committee, 16-18
medical research:
  Bush report on, 16-18
  Smith bill debate on, 76
  and NSF, 79, 147-48
  coordination and evaluation, 325-29
medical scientists, 16-17, 33
medical students, 264-65
Meharry Medical College, 260
Meinel, Aden B., 292
Menzel, Donald H., 284, 286-87, 289
Merck, George W., 69, 327
"meritorious proposal" formula, 223
Meyerhoff, Howard A.:
  on Kilgore and Magnuson bills, 30
  on revised Kilgore bill, 40
  and Bowman, 42, 45, 58-59
  and Kilgore-Magnuson bill hearings, 47, 48, 50, 57-59
  on Bowman committee, 62
  on Truman veto, 84
  and Teeter, 62, 88
  and NSF budget hearings, 157
  and NSB nominations, 383 n. 12
Middlebush, Frederick A., 120, 121, 244, 272, 318, 384 n. 17
Midwestern Universities Research Association (MURA), 292-97
military research, 5, 90
  and science foundation legislation, 27, 63
  and NSF, 125-26, 141-44
  expenditures, 212
Miller, Byron S., 56, 57
Miller, James G., 407 n. 45
Millikan, Robert A., 15
Mills, Thomas J., 253
Mills, Wilbur D., 25, 48, 63
Mills bill (H.R. 6448), 48, 49, 50, 56, 58, 61, 62
Mississippi, 259
Mitchell, James M., 344
Moe, Henry Allen, 13, 34
Moreland, Edward L., 120, 129
Morgan State College, 260
Morris, Joseph C., 120, 121, 282, 284, 285, 287, 288
Morse, Harold Marston, 120, 167
Morse, Wayne L.:
  and Kilgore-Magnuson bill debate, 56
  and Smith bill, 75, 80
  as leader, 83
  and compromise bill, 89-90
  and social sciences program, 271, 272
Mount Holyoke College, 205, 260, 261
Mundelein College, 261
Murphy, Charles, 80, 97
Murphy, Franklin D., 397 n. 62

National Academy of Sciences (NAS):
  and scientific information release, 12
  and Bush report, 14-15
  and NSB nominations, 16, 18, 70, 73, 114-15
  control of science foundation, 52
  Kilgore on, 52
  on Smith amendment, 104
  and NSF headquarters, 136, 139
  grants to, 166, 259
  Teeter on, 216
  and IGY, 300
  and security issue, 334-36
National Advisory Committee for Aeronautics (NACA), 4, 79
National Association of Manufacturers, 6, 47, 62
National Association of State Universities, 34
National Bureau of Standards. *See* Bureau of Standards
National Committee for the Development of Scientists and Engineers, 252
National Defense Research Committee

(NDRC), 4, 10
National Foundation for Infantile Paralysis, 79
National Foundation for Medical Research (proposed), 16-18
National Infantile Paralysis Foundation, 91
National Institutes of Health (NIH):
  budget growth, 76, 148
  NSF and, 102, 106, 109, 145, 402 n. 22
  grant policies, 163
  fellowship program, 233-35
  indirect cost payments, 322, 324
  peer review system, 358
  research support, 326-28, 348
National Merit Scholarship Program, 403 n. 41
National Patent Council, 96, 97, 101
National Register of Scientific and Technical Personnel, 151, 177-79, 253-54, 389 n. 34
National Research Council:
  research expenditure recommendations, 99
  and NSF headquarters, 136
  fellowship administration, 145, 146, 161, 167, 168
  fellowship applicant screening, 169, 170, 171, 229, 233
  and research review, 182
National Research Foundation, 16, 22, 25
National Resources Committee, 189
National Science Board (NSB):
  Bush report proposal, 16, 21, 22
  role of, 36-38
  approval of NSF awards, 105, 229
  establishment, 113
  first meeting, 123
  Director recommendation, 123
  on NSF role, 141, 184, 275-76
  on grant policy, 167
  on fellowship policies, 168
  and divisional committees, 171-72
  and social sciences program, 232, 269, 270, 272
  and scientific manpower committee, 250
  and education program, 264
  "big science" policy, 282
  and astronomy program, 282, 283-84, 291
  and accelerator development, 294
  and IGY, 298, 301
  government-university relations committee, 311
  and indirect costs issue, 324
  and security issue, 331, 333, 334, 336
  membership:
    qualifications, 113-14
    term of office, 114
    recommending institutions, 114
    nominations, 114-15, 383 n. 3
    selection criteria, 116-20, 384 nn. 15, 17
    political and personal considerations, 117, 119
    Truman appointments, 119-20
    balance, 120, 255
National Science Foundation (NSF):
  naming, 3, 11, 29
  issues in establishment, 5-7, 108, 350
  fear of political influence, 73
  Navy influence, 130
  office buildings, 136-39, 186, 211
  public relations, 156-58
  Executive Order on duties, 201-02, 353-55
  Board. See National Science Board; National Science Foundation: control issue
  budget, 185, 203
    Bush report estimates, 23
    appropriations, 118-19, 160, 194, 216-17
    hearings, 152-60
    growth, 211-12, 216-22
    obligations, 222
  control issue, 5, 7
    legislative history, 26
    Senate committee minority report on, 47-48
    in Kilgore-Magnuson bill debates, 52-56
    Inter-Society Committee on, 65
    Bureau of the Budget recommendations, 67-68
    Smith bill provisions, 69, 70-72, 74
    House Commerce Committee on, 79
    Truman and Bush on, 85
    compromise solution, 350
  coordination and evaluation role, 27, 30-31, 102, 109-10, 148-50, 181-202, 203, 216, 338-39
    Wolverton on, 77
    ICSRD on, 130
    medical research, 325-29
  Director:
    Bush report on, 21
    appointment by President, 27, 86, 109, 121, 122
    recommendation by Board, 113
    salary, 114
    term, 114
    qualifications, 123-24
    power, 347
    relationship with Board, 348. *See also*

National Science Foundation: control issue
divisional committees, 171-73, 222-25, 249-51
education programs, 225-26, 227, 350
staff appointments, 214
budget, 242-44, 247
leadership role, 195, 197, 275, 331, 339
legislative history, 3, 5-7, 25-106, 183
national science policy role, 150, 176, 181-202, 203, 312, 325, 337-45, 351
Waterman on, 193
security policy, 329-37
organization, 22-23, 132-36
  Division of Natural Sciences, 23
  Division of Medical Research, 23, 106, 109, 135
  Division of National Defense, 23, 109
  Division of Publications and Scientific Collaboration, 23
  Division of Scientific Personnel and Education (SPE), 23, 134
  Division of Biological and Medical Sciences (BMS), 106, 134, 212-14
  Division of Mathematical, Physical and Engineering Sciences (MPE), 134-35, 214
  Division of Defense Research, 143, 144
  Scientific Information Office, 175
  Program Analysis Office, 179, 188, 192, 195, 196, 267
  Office of Scientific Information, 211
  Office of Special Studies, 211
program directors:
  functions and status, 215, 261-66, 273, 358
  philosophy, 276-77
  and "big science," 279
  on indirect costs, 321
  academic values, 348-49
  competition among, 401 n. 35
research support role:
  military research, 141-44
  basic research, 147-48, 189, 217
  administrative policies and procedures, 161-67, 256-57, 261-66
  grants and fellowships awarded, 174-75, 203-07
  allocation of funds, 223
  staff attitudes, 274
  institutional programs, 310. *See also* geographical distribution of research support; grants; fellowships; research; scholarships
scientific information interchange role, 150-51, 175-77
staff:
  salaries, 136
  size, 138, 211
  appointments, 212-14
  rotation policy, 212-15
  morale, 273-74
National Science Foundation Act of 1950:
  signature, 106
  and Magnuson bill, 109
  amendments, 198, 228, 241

National Science Reserve, 13
National Scientific Register. *See* National Register of Scientific and Technical Personnel
National Security Council, 197, 300, 332, 340, 396 n. 52
Naval Research Laboratory, 284, 300
Navy influence, 130
Nevada, 170, 204
New Deal, 107, 108, 267
Newman, James R., 27, 28, 63, 371 n. 26, 372 n. 57
New York (state), 204
New York *Times,* 37, 84, 98, 129, 156, 328, 345
New York University, 206
1951 Constitution Avenue, 139
Nixon, Richard M., 271, 272
Nordhaus, William D., 389 n. 41
North Carolina, 244
Northrup, Eugene P., 240-41
Northwestern University, 205, 206
Nourse, Edwin G., 33
nuclear energy research, 292-97

Oak Ridge Institute of Nuclear Studies (ORINS), 285
Oberlin College, 205, 206, 260
observatories:
  national, 280-82
  optical astronomy, 281, 290-92
  radio astronomy, 282-90
O'Connor, Basil, 80
O'Daniel, W. Lee, 75
Odishaw, Hugh, 298, 301
O'Donnell, J. Hugh, 35, 49, 50-51, 372 n. 72
Office of Defense Mobilization (ODM):
  SAC under, 144
  and NSF budget, 154
  on scientific register, 178
  and interdepartmental scientific manpower committee, 248-53
  on IGY, 298
Office of Education, U.S.:
  and science foundation legislation, 35
  and scholarships, 86, 237-38

National Scientific Register, 151, 177
  and NSF, 187, 225, 228, 242, 395 n. 19
  and fellowships, 192
  role, 238
  and teachers' institutes, 240
Office of Naval Research (ONR):
  establishment, 62, 63-64
  Waterman at, 130, 131
  and NSF, 132, 142, 166
  and university research, 199
  and astronomy program, 284
  and accelerator development, 294
Office of Scientific Research and Development (OSRD):
  establishment, 4-5
  FDR on, 9
  Bush on, 11
  and Kilgore bill, 14
  as model, 31
  wind-up tasks, 47
  and industrial establishment, 62
Ogburn, William F., 33
Ogle Tayloe House, 138
O'Hara, Barratt, 103
Ohio State University, 206, 280, 291
O'Mahoney, Joseph C., 156, 159, 160
Oppenheimer, J. Robert:
  at Kilgore and Magnuson bill hearings, 32-33
  and Committee for a National Science Foundation, 40
  on staff appointments, 134
  and NSF budget hearings, 159
  security hearing, 329, 330, 334
Orlans, Harold, 318-19
overhead. *See* indirect costs

Pace, Frank, 98, 99
Pacific Science Board, 166-67
Paley Commission, 325
Palmer, Walter W., and Bush report, 16-18, 21
Panofsky, Wolfgang K. H., 296
Papago Indians, 290
Parsons, Talcott, 61, 67
patent policy issue:
  and establishment of NSF, 5-6, 350
  Bush on, 14
  legislative history, 26
  in Kilgore-Magnuson bill debates, 52-57
  Bush report on, 108
Patterson, Robert P., 32
Pauling, Linus, 16, 330, 417 n. 70
Payne, Fernandus, 212
peer review system, 165-66, 223, 330-31, 357-62
Pegram, George B., 11, 175

Pennsylvania State University, 204
Pepper, Claude D., 40, 76
Perkins, James A., 269
Pfeiffer, John E., 344
Philander Smith College, 260
Phillips, John, 153, 194, 299, 395 n. 43
Physical Review, 175
Piore, E. R., 198
Pisani, Joseph W., 328
"plank owners," 130
Platt, C. Spencer, 116
Plumb, Robert K., 156
Pocatello, Idaho, 106
Pollard, William G., 285, 286, 287
Pomona College, 205, 260
Porter, Charles O., 272
Potomac School (California Street), 137-38, 139, 161, 186
Potter, Andrey A., 120, 158, 159
President's Commission on Higher Education, 86
President's Committee on Scientists and Engineers, 211
President's Materials Policy Commission, 325
President's Scientific Research Board (PSRB), 62-63, 70, 85, 87, 375 n. 8
Price, Don K.:
  and Bush report, 19
  on Kilgore, 25
  and science foundation legislation, 27, 28, 94
  on control issue, 38
  and Bowman committee, 42
  and scientific information clearinghouse, 176
  on government-university relations, 314, 317
Priest, J. Percy:
  and Kilgore-Magnuson bill hearings, 49, 51, 56, 58
  and House Commerce Committee hearings, 79
  and science foundation legislation, 95-98, 101, 102
  introduction of H.R. 4846, 97
  and NSF budget, 153, 160
Princeton University:
  Waterman at, 130
  and review panels, 173
  grants and fellowships, 204, 206, 231
  and astronomy program, 291
  and accelerator development, 294
  and geophysical institute, 307-08
professional societies. *See* scientific societies
programmatic research, 190
project grants, 161-62, 164, 350, 392 n. 5

proposal pressure, 223
proposals:
  guide for submission, 165
  review of, 165-66, 173-75, 261-63, 357-62
  reasons for rejection, 174
public control. *See* control of science policy;
  National Science Foundation: control issue
Public Health Service (PHS), 17, 76, 79
  and medical research, 100
  and fellowship policies, 161, 168
  grant policies, 164
  and NSF, 182, 188
  indirect cost payments, 322, 324
  security policy, 330, 335
Purdue University, 175, 204, 206, 259
Putnam, Palmer, 9, 10

Quarles, Donald A., 201, 293, 299, 397 n. 68

Rabb, Maxwell M., 220, 342
Rabi, I. I., 371 n. 50, 389 n. 41
Rabinowitch, Eugene, 157
racial discrimination, 245-47, 404 n. 78
Radcliffe College, 261
Raleigh, North Carolina, 254
Randolph-Macon Woman's College, 261
Rankin, John E., 103
Rayburn, Sam, 103
Reed College, 205, 260, 264
regulatory biology program, 261-66
research:
  basic:
    definition, x, 6-7
    ONR funding, 62
    at universities, 100-01
    issue in founding, 109
    and military research, 142
    justification, 152, 312
    transfer to NSF, 182-83
    inventory of, 186
    NSF share, 217
    in social sciences, 267-68, 270-71
    in nuclear energy, 294, 296
    federal support, 311, 319, 341, 343, 344
    variety of patterns, 313-14
    self-coordination, 338
  basic vs. applied, 16, 33, 108, 270, 280, 326
  Bush report on, 16
  issue in NSF establishment, 5, 6-7, 350
  military domination of, 64
  funding, 78, 193
  federal expenditures, 98-100
  programmatic vs. nonprogrammatic, 190-91. *See also* medical research; military research; National Science Foundation: coordination and evaluation role; National Science Foundation: research support role; nuclear energy research; undergraduate research
Research and Development Board:
  coordination role, 90
  on Smith amendment, 104
  on NSF budget, 155
  on basic vs. applied research, 183
  and NSF evaluation role, 188, 189
Research Board for National Security, 27, 32
Research Corporation, 161
Research Education in the Sciences program, 239
research grants. *See* grants
research proposals. *See* proposals
research support:
  plurality of federal, 311, 319, 341, 348
  purpose of federal, 313, 319
  grant forms, 320. *See also* National Science Foundation: research support role
Revelle, Roger, 303
Revercomb, W. Chapman, 54, 69
Reyniers, James A., 120, 121
Reynolds, Edward, 285
Rhode Island, 170
Richards, A. Newton, 114-15
Robbins, William J., 11
Robertson, Charles R., 79
Robertson, Randal M., 214, 296, 360
Rockefeller, Nelson A.:
  on international science role, 304, 307
  and medical research, 325-26, 328
  and security issue, 333, 334, 335
Rockefeller Foundation, 161
Rogers, Dwight L., 102
Rollefson, Ragnar, 292
Roosevelt, Franklin D., 4, 9, 18, 107
Rosenman, Samuel I., 12, 21
Ross, Charles, 37, 384 n. 17
Rubinstein, Bertha W., 267, 268, 271
Ruebhausen, Oscar M.:
  and FDR letter to Bush, 10
  and Bush report, 18, 19
  and science foundation legislation, 25
  and House Commerce Committee hearings, 78
  and NSB nominations, 114
Russia. *See* USSR

Sabath, Adolph J., 97, 98

salaries:
  NSF staff, 136
  paid under grants, 316-17, 318, 319
Saltonstall, Leverett:
  and revised Kilgore bill, 40
  and Bowman committee, 41-42
  and Kilgore-Magnuson bill hearings, 51
  and scientific unity effort, 63
  and Smith bill, 69, 73, 74, 75
  as leader, 83
  and NSF budget hearings, 159
San Francisco *Chronicle*, 83
Sarah Lawrence College, 261
satellite program, 300-02
Saturday Review, 342
Scheele, Leonard, 135, 330, 335
Scherer, Paul A., 78
Schimmel, Herbert:
  on government, 3
  and science foundation legislation, 11, 28
  and Bowman committee, 39-42
  at Magnuson and Kilgore bill hearings, 28, 32
  and Kilgore-Magnuson bill, 57
  departure from government, 69
scholarships, undergraduate, 86, 147, 207, 235-38
  Bush report proposals, 13
  Inter-Society Committee on, 65
  Smith bill provisions, 69
Schuldt, Frederick C., Jr.:
  at first NSB meeting, 123
  and NSF director's nomination, 127
  on ONR, 133
  and fellowship program, 144, 145
  on NSF budget, 148, 149, 152, 159
  and NSF policy and evaluation role, 183, 184, 185
science:
  principle of unity, 27
  natural vs. social, 108
  government planning of, 108
  sociology of, 268
  internationalism, 304-07
Science, 40, 42, 48, 50, 57, 58, 63, 84, 87, 101, 157, 237, 335
science adviser to President, 142, 143, 144, 338, 339
Science Advisory Committee (SAC):
  establishment, 144
  and NSF, 149
  research coordination, 189
  and Executive Order, 200, 201
  and accelerator development, 296
  and basic research budget, 343

Science and Public Policy, 87, 187, 189
science attachés, 306, 412-13 n. 81, 413 nn. 83, 85
Science Clubs of America, 239
science education, 220, 227-28, 248-53
Science—The Endless Frontier:
  as seminal document, 3
  release of report, 21
  action recommended, 23
  mentioned as source, 54, 147, 189, 345
  budget estimates, 98
  Truman on, 106
  title, 107
scientific information interchange, 12, 150-51, 175-77
scientific journal subsidies, 175-76
scientific manpower:
  shortage, 13, 142, 144, 154, 167-68, 215, 219-20, 228, 248-49, 405 n. 103
  control of, 178
  register of, 177-79, 253-54
  committees on, 248-53
  NSF studies, 250, 253
Scientific Personnel Resources, 254
Scientific Research Agency, 143
scientific societies, 178, 179, 239, 263. See also individual societies
scientists:
  aversion to public control, 12
  division among, 45-48, 56-59, 61-65
  science policy role, 108, 292, 348, 349
  support of NSF, 157
  values, 212-13, 308
  statistical information on, 254
  independence of, 276, 345
  loyalty and security issue, 329-37
  morale, 329, 416-17 n. 67. See also scientific manpower
Scott, Hugh D., Jr., 78, 90
security issue, 93, 197, 207, 329-37
  congressional concern, 90, 102-05
  and grants, 102-05, 165, 381 n. 63, 382 n. 95
  and scientific information exchange, 176-77
  in HEW programs, 312
security regulations, 329, 388 n. 14
Seeger, Raymond J., 214, 223, 269, 276
  and astronomy program, 282-83, 286
  and accelerator development, 292
  and geophysical institute, 307
segregation, 245-47, 404 n. 78
Seitz, Frederick, 214, 297
Selective Service, 13
Senate, U.S.:
  Appropriations Committee, 154-56, 158-59, 219, 221

Commerce Committee, 26
Committee on Military Affairs, 43
Committee on Labor and Public Welfare, 89, 95
Shapley, Harlow:
  on Bush report, 20
  on Kilgore and Magnuson bills, 29
  and Committee for a National Science Foundation, 38-40
  Bush on, 46
  and Kilgore-Magnuson bill hearings, 51, 53
  and scientific unity effort, 64-65
  characteristics, 85-86
  and compromise bill, 85-86, 87, 91, 92
  and communism, 96
  on Waterman, 126
Shapley, Willis, 85, 182, 183, 184, 189
Sharp, Bob, 360
Sheppard, Franklin C., 233
Sherwood, Thomas K., 129
Sides, Virginia, 130, 139, 215
Sigma Xi, 46
Smith, H. Alexander:
  and Kilgore-Magnuson bill hearings, 48, 51-55
  and Smith bill, 69-76, 377 n. 64
  on NSF control issue, 73, 81
  on Truman veto, 82, 84
  as leader, 83
  and compromise bill, 85, 89
  and science foundation legislation, 92
  and NSB nominations, 117
  and NSF budget hearings, 159
  on research sponsorship, 198-99
  and security issue, 382 n. 95. *See also* Smith bill (S. 526)
Smith, Harold D.:
  and Bush, 26-28
  on government control, 30
  and Truman, 32
  on science foundation organization, 37-38
Smith, Homer W.:
  and Bush report, 17
  on Magnuson bill, 33
  and Bowman committee, 40-41
  and Kilgore-Magnuson bill hearings, 47, 48, 50, 51
  on Schimmel, 69
  on Teeter, 89
Smith, Howard W., 102, 103, 104
Smith, Margaret Chase, 156
Smith Act, 332
Smith amendment, 102-05
Smith bill (S. 526):
  drafting of, 65
  introduction of, 69
  provisions, 69-70, 72, 74
  debate, 75-76
  passage, 76
  Truman veto, 80
Smith College, 205, 260, 261
Smithsonian Institution, 93, 259
Smyth, Henry D., 73
Snyder, John W., 28, 32, 38
Social Function of Science, The, 36
socialism, fear of, 36
Social Science Research Council, 77
social sciences:
  inclusion in NSF, 5, 6, 61, 108, 266-73, 350
  Truman on, 26
  and science foundation legislation, 33-34
  in Kilgore-Magnuson bill debates, 50, 52-56
  and Inter-Society Committee, 65
  fellowships, 232-33
  NSF grants, 256
  research budget, 406 n. 28, 407 n. 41
  and Congress, 406 n. 20
Southern Methodist University, 220
Soviet Professional Manpower, 219, 241
Soviet Union. *See* USSR
Sparkman, John J., 373 n. 18
Sproul, Robert G., 252
Sputnik I:
  launch, 211
  and American education, 227
  and science scholarships, 237
  and NSF budget, 247-48
  and science policy, 338, 344
Staats, Elmer:
  on Smith bill, 82
  and science foundation legislation, 101
  and NSB nominations, 115, 116
  at first NSB meeting, 123
  and NSF's director's appointment, 126
  on military research, 143
  and fellowship program, 144
  and NSF budget hearings, 159
  on NSF policy and evaluation role, 184, 185, 186, 187, 188, 189
Stakman, Elvin C., 120
Stanford University, 173, 206, 231, 294, 295-96
State, Department of, 298, 300, 304, 306
Steelman, John R.:
  and Kilgore-Magnuson bill, 57
  PSRB chairman, 62
  on NSF control issue, 68

and Smith bill, 71, 80
Science and Public Policy, 87
and science foundation legislation, 92, 97, 101
on Smith amendment, 104
and NSB nominations, 115
at first NSB meeting, 123
on NSF role, 131
and NSF budget hearings, 154
Steelman report. See *Science and Public Policy*
Steinbach, H. Burr, 212, 213
Stephen F. Austin State College, 220, 246, 404 n. 77
Stephenson, H. Kirk, 307, 308, 358
Stevenson, Earl P., 302
Stewart, Irvin, 4, 10, 12-13, 285, 287
Stewart, John Q., 65
Stewart, M. A., 318
Stratton, Julius A.:
  and Waterman, 129
  and astronomy program, 287
  on science attachés, 306
  on subsidies to universities, 313, 315, 318
  and loyalty committee, 334-37
Strauss, Lewis L., 198, 200, 234, 243, 329
Street, J. Curry, 214
Struve, Otto, 280, 289
subversion. See security issue
Subversive Activities Control Act of 1950, 332
Suits, C. Guy, 130
summer institutes. See teachers' institutes
Sunderlin, Charles Eugene:
  and Waterman, 129-30
  background and training, 133
  on NSF budget hearings, 159
  and scientific information clearinghouse, 176
  and PHS, 182
  departure, 214
  and astronomy program, 290
  on international science role, 304, 306
  and geophysical institute, 309
  and indirect cost issue, 322
  on security issue, 330
Swarthmore College, 132, 205, 206, 260, 291
Swing, Raymond, 59
Switzer, Mary, 383 n. 7
symposia. See conferences and symposia
Szilard, Leo, 276

Taft, Robert A.:
  and Kilgore-Magnuson bill debate, 52, 54
  and Smith bill, 75, 76, 80
  on Truman veto, 83
  and House of Representatives, 84
  and compromise bill, 86
  and Eisenhower, 196
Tate, John T., 13
tax laws, 169, 313, 323, 344
Taylor, James H., 249, 250, 251
teachers' institutes, 220, 225, 227, 239-48
teachers of science, 228, 237, 240, 244, 247
Teeter, John H.:
  and Magnuson bill, 28
  at Kilgore and Magnuson bill hearings, 34
  and Kilgore-Magnuson bill, 47, 56, 58
  and Mills bill, 48-51, 373 n. 18
  and Meyerhoff, 62, 88
  on PSRB, 63
  and science foundation legislation, 68-69
  and Smith bill, 74
  and House Commerce Committee hearings, 77
  on Truman veto, 83
  and compromise bill, 88-89
  and Bush, 89
  on NSF director's appointment, 125
  on Waterman, 216
  and Smith bill, 376-77 n. 50
  Weaver and Waterman on, 398 n. 14
  on social sciences, 401-02 n. 16
Teller, Edward, 219
Tennessee Agricultural and Industrial State University, 261
Texas, 219-20, 246, 399-400 n. 27
Texas Southern University, 260
Thackrey, Russell I., 70, 75, 377 n. 51
Third International Congress for Biochemistry, 263
Thomas, Albert:
  and NSF budget, 118, 152-53, 160, 218-21, 241-44
  on research coordination, 194, 195
  use of influence for Texas projects, 219-20, 246, 399-400 n. 27
  on NSF role, 220-21
  and IGY, 298-99
Thomas, Elbert D.:
  and Bowman committee, 41
  and Kilgore-Magnuson bill, 54
  and Inter-Society Committee, 65
  Thomas bill introduction, 69
  and Smith bill, 70
  as leader, 83
  introduction of S. 247, 94
Thomas bill (S. 525), 69
Thomson, Vernon W., 295

Time, 386 n. 4
"Toward a National Science Policy?," 87
travel grants, 177, 224, 263, 264
Treasury, Department of, 323
Trefethen, Lloyd M., 133
Truman, Harry S.:
  support of social sciences, 6, 26
  and Bush report, 12, 17, 21
  patent law study, 14
  and science foundation legislation, 26, 28, 92, 97-98, 101
  and Bush, 31, 66-67, 82, 85, 86-87, 368 n. 19, 383 n. 5
  on control issue, 37-38
  and Kilgore-Magnuson bill, 56, 57
  and Bowman, 62
  and Smith bill, 74, 75, 80-82, 378 n. 90
  signs NSF act of 1950, 106
  NSB appointments, 114-18
  and NSF appropriation, 118-19
  and Graham, 121-23
  on Bronk, 124
  and military research, 141
  on NSF role, 217
  on servicemen's education, 368 n. 19
Trytten, M. H., 145
Tufts College, 4
Tumbleson, Robert C., 175
Turner, Frederick Jackson, 107
Tuskegee Institute, 260
Tuve, Merle A., and astronomy program, 281-87

undergraduate research, 264, 266
universities. *See* academic institutions
University of Arizona, 280, 291
University of California, Berkeley:
  grants and fellowships, 166, 204, 206, 231, 259
  and review panels, 173
  and astronomy program, 291
University of California, Los Angeles, 206
University of Chicago:
  and review panels, 173
  grants and fellowships, 198, 204, 205, 206, 231, 259
  and astronomy program, 291
University of Colorado, 239
University of Hawaii, 309-10
University of Illinois, 173, 175, 204, 206, 231, 259
University of Kansas, 166
University of Michigan, 206, 231, 259, 291
University of Minnesota, 166, 204, 206, 239, 240, 259, 264
University of Mississippi, 166
University of North Carolina, 245
University of Pennsylvania, 173, 175, 204, 206, 259
University of Texas, 220
University of Virginia, 287, 288
University of Washington, 205, 206, 240
University of Wisconsin, 204, 206, 231, 259, 264, 291
Urey, Harold C., 38, 39, 40, 46, 51, 64
"user participation" fees, 291, 410 n. 36
USSR:
  scientific information and, 176, 177, 264
  impact of scientific advances, 211, 217, 218, 219, 228, 248, 253, 280
  and IGY, 299, 301. *See also* Sputnik I
  scientific progress and U.S. security, 345

Van Allen, James A., 297
van de Kamp, Peter, 290
Vanderbilt University, 291
Vassar College, 261
veterans, 12-13
veto of science foundation legislation, 80-82, 83
Viault, George, 136
von Neumann, John, 308

Wabash College, 166, 205
Wadsworth, James W., 92
  asks spending limit, 97-101
Wald, George, 331
Wallace, Henry A., 14, 31, 49
Washington Association of Scientists, 87
Washington Merry-Go-Round column, 86
Washington Post, 65, 156-57
Washington Post and Times Herald, 330
Washington Star, 83
Washington University, 204, 264
Waterman, Alan Tower:
  and NSF directorship, 122, 124, 126-27, 129-30
  on military research, 126, 143
  background and training, 130-31
  first moves, 130-40
  on NSF evaluation and policy role, 131, 181-89, 192-95, 197-202, 326-27, 337-43
  staff appointments, 132-36, 212-14
  Board relationship, 135-36
  SAC appointment, 144
  on NSF role, 147-52
  on research support role, 162, 275
  and fellowship program, 145-47, 168, 169-70, 229, 230, 231, 233
  on ICSRD, 151-52
  and NSF budget, 152-60, 217-20, 342
  and divisional committees, 171, 222
  on review system, 173-74

on scientific information exchange, 176-77
and scientific register, 177, 178
on women in science, 216
and Teeter, 216, 398 n. 14
and NSF charter, 228
and AEC, 234
on departmental support, 235
on scholarship program, 236-38
on education programs, 242-44
on segregation, 245
on interdepartmental scientific manpower committee, 248-49, 251-52
and social sciences program, 269, 270
and astronomy program, 279, 281-91
and accelerator development, 294-96
and IGY, 298-303
international science role, 304, 306-07
and geophysical institutes, 307-10
and government-university relations, 314, 318
and indirect costs issue, 321-25
on security issue, 329, 330, 331-35
NSF policy statement, 340-41
science policy statement, 343-45
and Albert Thomas, 399-400 n. 27
characteristics:
    shown in portrait, 131, 386 n. 8
    outdoor recreation, 132
    musical ability, 132, 386 n. 9
    prose style, 139
    administrative style, 139-40
    caution, 347-48
    avoidance of politics, 348
    academic values, 350-51
Waterman, Mary Mallon, 127, 130, 132
Weaver, Warren, 117, 122, 275-76, 301, 309, 398 n. 14
Webb, James E.:
Bush letter to, 66, 67
and Smith bill, 71, 72-73, 74, 75, 81
and compromise bill, 85, 86, 89
Webster, Bethuel M.:
founding role, 4
and Bush report, 18
and Bowman committee, 41
on Truman veto, 84
and compromise bill, 88, 92
and NSB nominations, 117
Webster, Daniel, 238
Wellesley College, 261
Wesleyan University, 205, 260
West Virginia, 283, 288,
West Virginia University, 286, 287
Wherry, Kenneth S., 160

Whitaker, Douglas M., 393 n. 31
White, Philip R., 33
White, Wallace, 51
White House Conference on Education, 242
Wiesner, Jerome B., 284, 285
Williams, Clyde E., 124
Willis, Raymond E., 42, 52
Wilson, Carroll:
on FDR letter to Bush, 9-10
on Kilgore bill, 11
and Bush report, 17, 18, 19
and science foundation legislation, 25
Wilson, Charles Edward, 120, 123
Wilson, Charles Erwin, 198, 301
Wilson, E. Bright, Jr., 418 n. 84
Wilson, John T.:
staff appointment, 192, 214
and evaluation role, 193, 194, 195, 196
and social science program, 267
on retrenchment, 273, 274, 277
Winchell, Walter, 157
Winder Building, 138, 211
Wolfle, Dael:
and scientific unity effort, 65
and compromise bill, 91
and science foundation legislation, 94, 101, 103-04
and scientific register, 177-78, 179
and Program Analysis Office, 192
on scholarships, 237
on NSF fact book, 254
on security policy, 335
Wolman, Abel, 34
Wolverton, Charles A.:
and House Commerce Committee hearings, 77-79
and compromise bill, 86, 89, 90-91
and science foundation legislation, 103
women, on NSB, 121
on NSF staff, 215-16
Wood, Richardson, 19
Wriston, Henry M., 418 n. 84

Xavier University of Louisiana, 260

Yale University:
Waterman at, 130-31, 132
and divisional committees, 173
and review panels, 173
grants and fellowships, 166, 175, 204, 206, 231, 259
and astronomy program, 291
Yancey, Patrick H., 120
Yates, Sidney R., 153